MW00576649

CHAOS IN NATURE

2nd Edition

WORLD SCIENTIFIC SERIES ON NONLINEAR SCIENCE

Editor: Leon O. Chua
University of California, Berkeley

Series A. MONOGRAPHS AND TREATISES*

Volume 77: Mathematical Mechanics: From Particle to Muscle
E. D. Cooper

Volume 78: Qualitative and Asymptotic Analysis of Differential Equations with Random Perturbations
A. M. Samoilenko & O. Stanzhytskyi

Volume 79: Robust Chaos and Its Applications
Z. Elhadj & J. C. Sprott

Volume 80: A Nonlinear Dynamics Perspective of Wolfram's New Kind of Science (Volume V)
L. O. Chua

Volume 81: Chaos in Nature
C. Letellier

Volume 82: Development of Memristor Based Circuits
H. H.-C. Iu & A. L. Fitch

Volume 83: Advances in Wave Turbulence
V. Shrira & S. Nazarenko

Volume 84: Topology and Dynamics of Chaos: In Celebration of Robert Gilmore's 70th Birthday
C. Letellier & R. Gilmore

Volume 85: A Nonlinear Dynamics Perspective of Wolfram's New Kind of Science (Volume VI)
L. O. Chua

Volume 86: Elements of Mathematical Theory of Evolutionary Equations in Banach Spaces
A. M. Samoilenko & Y. V. Teplinsky

Volume 87: Integral Dynamical Models: Singularities, Signals and Control
D. Sidorov

Volume 88: Wave Momentum and Quasi-Particles in Physical Acoustics
G. A. Maugin & M. Rousseau

Volume 89: Modeling Love Dynamics
S. Rinaldi, F. D. Rossa, F. Dercole, A. Gragnani & P. Landi

Volume 90: Deterministic Chaos in One-Dimensional Continuous Systems
J. Awrejcewicz, V. A. Krysko, I. V. Papkova & A. V. Krysko

Volume 91: Control of Imperfect Nonlinear Electromechanical Large Scale Systems: From Dynamics to Hardware Implementation
L. Fortuna, A. Buscarino, M. Frasca & C. Famoso

Volume 92: Modeling, Analysis and Control of Dynamical Systems with Friction and Impacts
P. Olejnik, J. Awrejcewicz & M. Fečkan

Volume 93: Coupled Phase Locked Loops: Stability, Synchronization, Chaos and Communication with Chaos
V. V. Matrosov & V. D. Shalfeev

Volume 94: Chaos in Nature (2nd Edition)
C. Letellier

*To view the complete list of the published volumes in the series, please visit:
http://www.worldscientific.com/series/wssnsa

WORLD SCIENTIFIC SERIES ON NONLINEAR SCIENCE Series A Vol. 94

Series Editor: Leon O. Chua

CHAOS IN NATURE

2nd Edition

Christophe Letellier

CORIA, Normandy University, France

NEW JERSEY • LONDON • SINGAPORE • BEIJING • SHANGHAI • HONG KONG • TAIPEI • CHENNAI • TOKYO

Published by

World Scientific Publishing Co. Pte. Ltd.
5 Toh Tuck Link, Singapore 596224
USA office: 27 Warren Street, Suite 401-402, Hackensack, NJ 07601
UK office: 57 Shelton Street, Covent Garden, London WC2H 9HE

Library of Congress Cataloging-in-Publication Data
Names: Letellier, Christophe, author.
Title: Chaos in nature / Christophe Letellier (Normandie Universite - CORIA, France).
Other titles: World Scientific series on nonlinear science. Series A, Monographs and treatises ; v. 94.
Description: Second edition. | Singapore ; Hackensack, NJ : World Scientific Publishing Co. Pte. Ltd., [2019] | Series: World Scientific series on nonlinear science. Series A, Monographs and treatises ; vol. 94 | Includes bibliographical references and index.
Identifiers: LCCN 2019000259| ISBN 9789811201196 (hardcover ; alk. paper) | ISBN 9811201196 (hardcover ; alk. paper)
Subjects: LCSH: Chaotic behavior in systems. | Mechanics, Analytic. | Nonlinear theories. | Celestial mechanics.
Classification: LCC Q172.5.C45 L478 2019 | DDC 003/.857--dc23
LC record available at https://lccn.loc.gov/2019000259

British Library Cataloguing-in-Publication Data
A catalogue record for this book is available from the British Library.

For any available supplementary material, please visit
https://www.worldscientific.com/worldscibooks/10.1142/11305#t=suppl

Preface

Chaos. An ambiguous word designating a deterministic dynamics which is often misinterpreted as synonymous for a random behavior. Unveiling the hidden determinism behind the apparent complexity of the world always stimulates me. I am among those who consider the real world governed by deterministic rules, including human beings. I also like to be at the interface between different disciplines, and chaos theory was a dreamed approach to delve into those issues.

With this book I also enjoyed exploring the history of the different fields related to Chaos. Whenever I could, I went back to the primary sources, a key point in the methodology of History of Science. Therefore, in this second edition, I included some missing sources I noticed and corrected few points. I did my best to take the facts as they are and not as I wanted to see them. Nevertheless, I realize that my view on some of the topics discussed in the book is biased by my own history, my sensitivity, and my, possibly, limited understanding.

Chaos is not a topic in itself but a paradigm to deal with nonlinear dynamical systems ranging from pure abstract systems to systems from the real world. The tools developed to characterize chaotic behaviors may be adequate to investigate experimental or observational data. Practical applications often arise when one uses them, adapts them and transforms them to answer questions posed by specialists in the corresponding domain. For instance, clinicians are not too much concerned by knowing whether a physiological state is chaotic or not: they mainly want to be helped to understand the disease, to characterize it and to develop a better treatment.

Throughout my scientific journey, I had the chance to meet Otto E. Rössler, thanks to René Thomas. This was an extraordinary opportunity to exchange with an open mind, always flowing between different winds, and to learn a lot about the history of Chaos Theory. Otto wrote the preface to the French edition of this book that was published in 2006. I should also mention Robert Gilmore with whom I worked for nearly 20 years. He nourished me with not only physics and mathematics but also with history and arts (Bach, Millet...). French food (cheese) and wines were never far away! Bob wrote the preface to the first English edition of this book. I must mention that he made a major contribution in translating the French edition during a long stay at the hospital: this is how Bob may have rest! There are two other close friends with whom I traveled a lot: Luis A. Aguirre and Claudia Lainscsek. Twenty years later, we are still working together with the beginner's view, enjoying understanding new things. Later, I met Sylvain Mangiarotti: he is special since he started where more or less I left the topological characterization and global modelling. Like all the friends mentioned above, he has his own way of thinking and the interaction with him is very stimulating. The last to enter this "scientific family" are Irene Sendiña-Nadal, who introduced me into the network world, and Fabrice Denis, with whom pluri-disciplinary studies actually mean sharing knowledge... All of them contributed to the spirit of this second English edition.

Normandy, September 19, 2018

Foreword

For the first French edition

It is a great honor to be invited to present a foreword to this book. The author is a gentle hardworking person. He introduced a new instrument into chaos called the Gilmore's template which allows even short time series from the heart or the sunspot cycle to be identified as chaotic. So he can bend his mind along folded strips in 3D space, a type of dancing not many people can follow actively.

This book is very scholarly. The author goes back to the beginnings. No other book in the field is based on history like this one, the history of ideas, be it variable stars in old Babylon or the famous three-body problem of the heavens. The book does not shy away from giving the whole history, with verbatim quotes and the, as it turns out easy to read, underlying "equations". So it will probably become the Bible in the field.

But this is not yet enough reason why you should read it, you may feel. "What is chaos and why should we be mindful about it?", as Joe Ford put it. Chaos was but a word for fate and for understanding without opening one's eyes, to the old Chinese. In the Bible it participates in creation, and an old Greek saw in it the ultimate complexity that only the mind can understand and control (Anaxagores).

When the early phase of rationalism spread across the world from its two centers in Greece and Nepal, with old Babylon in between, humanism was born. The second wave of rationalism was triggered by the Renaissance and erupted to full bloom in France, with its beneficial effects like human rights and democracy. The gentle mind of Descartes, aided by Bruno and, perhaps, Kepler, enabled celestial mechanics. Can three heavenly bodies like sun, earth and moon, remain together stable for millions or billions of year?

After centuries, Henri Poincaré found the solution — No. The complexity of their entanglement is not only infinite, it is transfinite. The homoclinic point in a cross section through the flow (these literal terms are allowed as you will see) is mind-boggling. Infinitely many alternating closed paths of differing winding numbers are infinitely close together in every neighborhood of a single one. Poincaré cringed away in horror from the complexity himself and turned his mind to other riddles like the speed of light. Or so is the folklore.

The book brings together many other sources that independently rediscovered chaos in different contexts. So after a while you realize that the weather and the cosmos and the heart and the concentration movements in your cells indeed follow one baton, the sound of chaos. This has never before been made so palpable as in the living examples brought forward out of their history, in this book.

Some people like to think in terms of deterministic strings — flow lines that are like braids, close together but each chosen with an infinite delicatesse. Chaos is the science that caters to those minds. There is no hair falling from your head... There is method to this conception. The puppetee pulls the strings. The butterfly effect, discovered by the second major figure covered in this book, Ed Lorenz exemplified the infinite sensitivity and delicacy of chaos. Even a simple butterfly's wing-flap, if added or subtracted to the weather, changes the course of a hurricane half a year later. Conversely, the sensitivity of hearts to microparticles — nanoparticles — suspended in the breathing air of automobilists could not have been discovered by Letellier outside this loving haircombing paradigm. A renaissance of chaos is a consequence of this author's works, and now perhaps of this book.

Let me close with an almost dangerous remark. If it is true that this historical account of one of the most influential undercurrents in the mental life of the planet reaches its audience — as I predict —, the future course of the planet might be changed. Not because of the chaos-butterfly effect but because of the chaos-book effect. For everybody would start thinking differently. The discrete charm of chaos, revealed by Letellier, reflects the discrete charm of rationalism in a way which has not been observed since Poincaré's writings. There is an optimism in this book that is contagious. Maybe, the world is rational, after all? Why is this so important in our present world? There are two reasons for that. The one is the future of the planet. The young people are on the look-out for a guiding science and for decent scientists who give them hope. The rationalist idea to put all reliable knowledge free of charge on the Internet is an expression of the same optimism. But if flowing with what everybody is thinking is a modern wave, the book's flowing along with this rationalistic hope and giving it a voice could still be put in doubt.

This leads me finally to a topic not covered in this book, quantum mechanics. Chaos is the theory of chance. Quantum theory is a theory of chance. Pauli called it "primary chance". Poincaré could not have dissented more sharply. Maybe that is why he turned his attention to light? However, the fact that this question is not taken up in this book is not a weakness but another strength. Nothing is more imposing than not being imposed oneself. For the first time after a century, the full charm of rationalism is re-exposed in this book in the tradition into which it belongs. There is a different air in France. Poincaré's long shadow is at last continued. It is a shadow of pure light.

Otto E. Rössler, September 6, 2004.

For the first English edition

> Into this Universe, and How not knowing,
> Nor Whence, like Water willy-nilly flowing:

Who can deny that this couplet describes the subject of this book? Who will not appreciate trodding in the footsteps of our author and our storyteller as he walks through history, bringing to light the hints of chaos and the confused reactions of the lucky souls who first encountered them? Did Fitzgerald learn from Navier and Stokes that willy-nillyness could be encoded by equations and that even so........ it was impossible to predict?

We are reminded forcefully by Prof. Letellier that the seeds of Chaos lie in Astronomy and that the more we learned (Kepler, Newton, Laplace, ...), the less we knew how to describe these unpredictable motions. Until ...

> There was the Door to which I found no Key:
> There was the Veil through which I could not see:

... Poincaré ran into the Door with no Key. Bouncing off this Door, his greatest mathematical mistake, he created a new field of mathematics designed to provide the theater in which these new tools would confront these old tribulations. In the process he was given the gift of understanding that the Veil had a Keyhole through which he might see.... And what might he see?

> And many Knots unravel'd by the Flow:
> But not the Master-Knot the Planets Rode.

In a little less than one hundred years, Poincare's insights are guiding us to a fuller understanding of motion that is simultaneously predictable and not predictable.

This book is a delight to read. In part because of its historical sweep. It begins at the beginning of the main branches of Nature in which Chaos has been encountered and brings us up to date in a step by step, savant by savant description of the short steps forward, shorter steps backward, and sometimes giant steps forward, that have occurred. As we come to the present we encounter equations introduced to describe particular experiments or created to understand particular phenomena. We encounter the most significant constructions currently available for the description, possibly even the classification, of physical systems that may behave chaotically. We are also led to the Edge, the Door, the Veil: even the Keyhole that, like Alice, we can barely squeeze through. Prof. Letellier at last points us in the direction of the future and shows us that there is no bridge to carry us from our present to this future ... Yet.

Robert Gilmore, Rouen, July 5th, 2012.

Acknowledgments

The data measured in the thermionic diode were provided by Thomas Klinger (University of Greifswald, Germany).

The data measured in the electrodissolutions were provided by Zihao Fei and Jack Hudson (University of Virginia).

The data measused in the Belousov-Zhabotinskii reaction were provided by Françoise Argoul and Alain Arnéodo (University of Bordeaux, France).

The data measured in noninvasive ventilation were collected by Linda Achour when she was my Ph.D. student and working in collaboration with the hospital unit directed by Jean-François Muir (Rouen Universitary Hospital, France). A part of their analysis was also performed with Herinaina Rabarimanantsoa when she was a Ph.D. student under my supervision. The corresponding global models were obtained by Giovani Rodriguez under the supervision of Luis A. Aguirre (Universidade Federal de Minas Gerais, Brazil).

The ECG measured in rats were provided by Jean-Paul Morin (INSERM-Rouen Universitary Hospital, France) and analyzed with Élise Roulin.

The ECG measured in newborn were collected by Emad Yacoub during his Ph.D. thesis, in collaboration with the pediatric unit directed by Éric Mallet (Rouen Universitary Hospital, France). They were analyzed with Emeline Fresnel during her master thesis.

Manel Luján Torne (Universitat Autònoma de Barcelona, Spain) is thanked for stimulating discussions about analyzing ventilation data in patients with chronic respiratory failure.

The data produced by the model of the W Vir were provided by Robert Buchler (University of Florida, Gainesville).

The work related to cancer was mainly performed with Fabrice Denis who co-supervised Louise Viger and Clément Draghi for their Ph.D. thesis.

Among these last years, I am very grateful to those who helped me in various manners.

Luis A. Aguirre (Universidade Federal de Minas Gerais, Brazil), Alain Arnéodo (University of Bordeaux, France), Jean-Pierre Barbot (ENSEA, Cergy-Pontoise, France), Arnaud Bultel (Normandie University, France), Fabrice Denis (Centre

Inter-régional de Cancérologie, Le Mans, France), Robert Gilmore (Drexel University, Philadelphia), Claudia Lainscsek (University of San Diego, California), René Lozi (University of Nice, France), François Lusseyran (LIMSI, Orsay, France), Jean-Marc Malasoma (ENTPE, Lyon, France), Sylvain Mangiarotti (IRD, CESBIO, Toulouse, France), Thibaut Ménard (Normandie University, France), Valérie Messager (Normandie University, France), Fabrice Onofri (IUSTI-CNRS, Marseille, France), Otto E. Rössler (University of Tübingen, Germany), Irene Sendiña-Nadal (Juan Carlos University, Madrid, Spain), Luc Valentin (University Paris-Diderot, France).

Contents

PART 1

From Celestial Mechanics to Chaos

Chapter 1

The Laws of Dynamics

1.1 Kepler's Empirical Laws

In order to show the importance of the three-body problem for the emergence of the idea of chaos, we begin by looking at the set of conceptual problems surrounding celestial mechanics at the time when Nicholas Kopernik (1473–1543) published his *De Revolutionibus* in 1543. He had the magnificent idea to place the sun near the center of the planetary orbits, following in the footsteps of his Greek predecessors Philolaus the Pythagorian (5th century BC), who argued that the earth revolved around a central fire, or Aristarchus of Samos (-310: -230). In spite of this Kopernik assumed that the only role that the Sun played was to provide light for the Earth. As did his predecessors, Kopernik was content simply to describe the motions of the planets, without any real understanding of the causes. Johannes Kepler (1571–1630) was one of the first to claim that the Sun was responsible for the movement of the planets. In fact, in his *Mysterium Cosmographicum* of 1596, he attributed a real dynamical role to the sun by arguing that it was the source of an attracting force on all planets, and that this force decreased with increasing distance of the planets from the sun.

In spite of this insight, Kepler's name is forever associated with the description of planetary motion in terms of elliptical orbits. Up to then, planetary orbits had always been described by uniform circular motions or combinations of uniform circular motions as had been taught by Aristotle (-384: -322), following Plato's lead (-428: -348). The idea that circular motion was fundamental to the description of celestial motion goes back at least as far as Plato's *Timeus*. Aristotle justified this by stating that circular motion was the only perfect type of motion that stars could design to follow. It was only after failing to describe planetary motion in this way over a period of five long years that Kepler became convinced that planetary motions could only be described by ellipses. He once wrote:[1]

> My first mistake was to assume that the planetary orbits were perfect circles. This error cost me so much time because it had been propagated

[1] J. Kepler, *Astronomia Nova* (1609), Chap. XL.

> by the authority of all the philosophers, and further was metaphysically very reasonable.

Aware of the criticism that his contradiction of Aristotelian physics would incite, Kepler divided his *Astronomia Nova* (1609) into seventy chapters where he attempted to show that any other description of planetary motion contradicted the very precise measurements of Tycho Brahe (1546–1601), in which he had absolute confidence.

Already persuaded of the dynamical role played by the sun, Kepler naturally placed the sun at one of the foci of an ellipse (Figure 1.1). For Kepler, the elliptic shape of planetary orbits was explained by two different contributions. The first one corresponds to a force emanating from the sun and influencing each planet. Propagated within the ecliptic plane — the mean plane in which planets' orbits were inscribed — this force depends on the inverse of the distance between the sun and each planet. For Kepler, this force shall induce a circular motion around the sun. A second — magnetic — force emanating from each planet was responsible for varying the distance between each planet and the sun. In other words, the magnetic force was responsible for the ellipticity and only emanates from each planet, just because ellipticity was planet dependent. Despite the imperfections of his system, this was a description of Nature that reduced the role of God to that of a creator: having given us the laws according to which the world evolves, He no longer needs to intervene. This view is presented in a letter dated 10 February 1605 as follows.[2]

> My aim is to show that the heavenly machine is not a kind of divine, living being, but a kind of clockwork [...], insofar as nearly all the manifold motions are caused by a most simple, magnetic, and material force, just as all motions of the clock are caused by a simple weight. And I show how these physical causes are to be given numerical and geometrical expression.

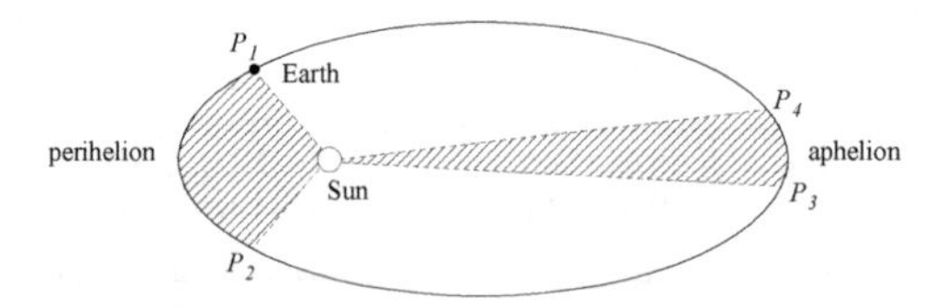

Figure 1.1 Kepler's system. Elliptical trajectory of the Earth around the Sun, which is placed at one of the foci of the ellipse. The point on the trajectory closest to the Sun is called the perihelion and the furthest point is called the aphelion. The variation in the distance between the Earth and the Sun was driven by a magnetic force emanating from the Earth.

Kepler believed that the motions of the planets were completely determined,

[2]J. Kepler, Letter dated on February 10, 1605, quoted in I. Peterson, *Newton's clock: Chaos in the Solar system*, Freeman, 1993.

governed by unchanging laws and evolving like clockwork. He succeeded in describing planetary motion, within the limits of Tycho Brahe's observations, by three laws that were stated as follows:

- the path of the planets about the sun are elliptical in shape, with the center of the sun being located at one focus;
- an imaginary line drawn from the center of the sun to the center of the planet will sweep out equal areas in equal intervals; areas delimited by $\widehat{P_1P_2}$ and $\widehat{P_3P_4}$ are described in equal intervals; thus, the planet moves at the perihelion faster than at the aphelion (Figure 1.1);
- the ratio of the squares of the mean motions[3] n is equal to the inverse of the ratio of the cubes of the semi-major axe a of their ellipses, that is, the product $n^2a^3 =$ is constant. This law expresses the fact that, the more distant from the Sun the planet is, the slower its motion is. It was published in Kepler's book *Harmonices Mundi* (1619).

Despite this, if Kepler obtained very good agreement with the observations of planetary motion, and if his *Tables Rudolphines* were incontestably the best of the time, he had more difficulty with the problem of the moon's motions, which is particularly sensitive to the motions of the other planets:[4]

> how adding or substracting the "small" lunar orbit, which could not extend very much beyond the thinness of the Earth's orbit by very much, could influence the increase or decrease of all the other spheres.

He stated, as had Kopernik before him, that he was often faced with large deviations caused by small errors in either the planetary masses or the diameters of their orbits:[5]

> we are constrained to determine large orbital changes from very small and almost imperceptible [elements], and from which, due to a departure by a few minutes, this is 5 or 6 degrees which are lost, and thus a small error can be immensely propagated.

This rapid growth of small errors in the description of the trajectories of heavenly bodies is a phenomenon that we run into throughout this work.

---

[3]The mean motion is defined as the mean speed the planet would have if its motion was uniform circular.

[4]J. Kepler, *Le Secret du Monde* (1596), Transl. A. Segonds, Gallimard, 1993, p. 150.

[5]N. Kopernik, *Des Révolutions des orbes célestes*, Book III, Chap. 20 quoted by J. Kepler, *Le secret du Monde* (1596), *Ibid.*

1.2 The Law of Gravitation

Kepler's elliptical trajectories involve only two bodies, the more massive being placed at a focus of the ellipse. Combinations of the ellipse with additional motions are used to take into account the influence of other bodies. Before defining the three-body problem we should describe the interactions among several bodies. The law of gravitation is expressed in this way.

Towards the middle of the 17th century several scientists attempted to find an expression according to which the force exerted by the sun decreases as a function of the distance r which separates the interacting bodies. Kepler imagined a law depending on the inverse square of the distance as he got for the propagation of light in his *Optica* (1604), but he abandoned this idea when he realized the force seemed to only propagate within the ecliptic plane, that is, according to a circle perimeter. The force should therefore depend on the inverse law of the distance since varying according to a circle and not to a sphere. Jeremiah Horrocks (1617–1641) was one of the earliest to take up Kepler's works. While he was a student at Cambridge University he did this himself because, at that time, there was no course in astronomy, much less courses describing the works of Kopernik, Tycho Brahe, or Kepler. Horrocks discovered Kepler's works by reading the work of Philips van Lansberge[6] in which this Belgian astronomer defended Kopernik against Tycho Brahe but argued against Kepler's ellipses. Horrocks convinced himself very quickly that Kepler's ellipses were more accurate than uniform circular motion. Horrocks applied Kepler's ideas to the interactions between the sun and the planets:[7]

> I, on the contrary, make the planet naturally to be averse from the Sun and desirous to rest in his own place, caused by a material dullness naturally opposite to motion and averse to the Sun without either power or the will to move to the Sun of itself. But then, the Sun by its own rays attracts and by its circumferential revolution carries about the unwilling planet, conquering that natural self-rest that is in it; yet not so far, but that the planet doth much abate and weaken this force of the Sun, as is largely disputed afore.

Reviewing Kepler's ideas that the Sun is the source of planetary motion, he proposed a mathematical law describing the decrease in the force with distance between the sun and planets. In his theory of the moon, Horrocks observed that although the Moon is between the Earth and the Sun, the ellipse described by the Moon — with the Earth at one of its foci — is elongated: this is because the eccentricity and apogee vary in time. He also studied cometary motion — which he found to be

[6] P. van Lansberge, *Tabulae motuum caelestium perpetuae: ex omnium temporarum observationibus consentientes*, 1632.

[7] J. Horrocks, *Philosophical exercices*, Part 1, para 26, (1661), quoted by Robert Brickel, *A Chapter of Romance in Science 1639–1874: In Memoriam Horroccii* and as mentioned by V. Barocas, A country Curate, *Quaterly Journal of the Royal Astronomical Society*, **12**, 179–182, 1971.

almost elliptical — and the tides. All these ideas found their way into Newton's *Principia*. In fact, among Horrock's contemporaries at Cambridge was John Wallis (1616–1703), whose works were read attentively by Newton, and Ralph Cadworth, who influenced Newton's mechanistic philosophy. We point out that Wallis, who directed Newton to the calculus of changes, was charged by the Royal Society of London with the publication[8] of Horrock's works in 1666, the year during which Newton declared that he began his studies of planetary motions. Newton held a very high opinion of Horrocks:[9]

> More inequalities in the Moon's motion have not hitherto been taken notice of by astronomers. But all these follow from our principles, and are known really to exist in the heavens. And this may be seen in that most ingenious, and, if I mistake not, of all the most accurate, hypothesis of Mr. Horrox, which Mr. Flamsteed has fitted to the heavens.

and in the first edition of *Principia*[10]

> Our Countryman Horrox [who] was the first who advanced the theory of the moon's moving in an ellipse about the Earth placed at its lower focus.

Horrocks was an important bridge between the works of Kepler and those of Newton.

Christiaan Huygens (1629–1695) had studied uniform circular motion and established that the centrifugal force followed a $1/r^2$ law. In addition, Robert Hooke (1635–1703) and Christopher Wren (1632–1723) tried to establish a relation between the $1/r^2$ law and the elliptical trajectories of celestial bodies. Specifically, Hooke developed a qualitative model based on the *principle of inertia*, correctly stated by Descartes:[11]

> Each particular part of matter continues always to be in the same state unless collision with others constrains it to change that state.

He coupled this principle with the equilibrium between the centrifugal force and the force due to the Sun. If he found motion qualitatively in agreement to observations, he was not able to obtain results quantitatively in agreement to Kepler's laws. Nevertheless, he claimed that the force was not only between the sun and the planets, as it was in Kepler's *Astronomia*, but between any massive bodies:[12]

---

[8] Horrocks' *Opera* were published in 1672.

[9] I. Newton, *A treatise of the system of the world*, London, p. 56, 1728.

[10] I. Newton, *Principia Mathematica*, Book III, Scholium 475, 1687.

[11] R. Descartes, *Le Monde : ou Traité de la lumière*, in Oeuvres de Descartes, ed. AM-Tannery (Paris: L. Cerf, 1897–1913), **11**, p. 435 (1677 pagination), translated by M. S. Mahoney, New York, p. 61, 1979.

[12] R. Hooke, *An attempt to prove the Motion of the Earth from Observations*, 1674.

> all Coelestial Bodies whatsoever, have an attraction or graviting power towards their own Centers, whereby they attract or not only their own parts, and keep them from flying from them, as we may observe the Earth to do, but that they do also attract all the other Coelestial Bodies that are within the sphere of their activity; and consequently that not only the Sun and Moon have an influence upon the body and motion of the Earth, and the Earth upon them, but that also, and by their attractive powers, have a considerable influence upon its motion as in the same manner the corresponding attractive power of the Earth has a considerable influence upon every one of their motions also.

It was Isaac Newton (1642–1727) who reaped the honor of showing that a $1/r^2$ force leads directly to Kepler's laws. To do this he resorted to very subtle geometric arguments that related motion to infinitely small displacements. He studied different laws of the form $1/r^n$ and stated, in Book III of his *Principia Mathematica* (1687) that gravity follows a law in which it decreases like the inverse square of the distances:[9]

> Proposition II: That the forces by which the primary planets are continually drawn off from rectilinear motions, and retained in their proper orbits, tend to the sun; and are reciprocally as the squares of the distances of the places of those planets from the sun's centre.

and is universal:

> Proposition VII: That there is a power of gravity tending to all bodies proportional to the several quantities of matter which they contain.

With these two propositions, Newton unified celestial mechanics with the empirical laws of Kepler and the terrestial mechanics of falling bodies studied by Galilei (1564–1642): he shows that a single force was responsible for all these phenomena. To show that Kepler's laws result from a $1/r^2$ force law Newton used, among other arguments, the idea of an accelerating force introduced in Book I of the *Principia* as follows.

> Lemma X: Spaces which a body describes by any finite force urging it, whether that force is determined and immuable, or is continually augmented or continually diminished, are in the very beginning of the motion one to the other in the duplicate ratio of the times.

It was in this form that the *fundamental principle of dynamics* was presented by Newton. We had to await the development of differential calculus, independently discovered by Newton and the "school" of Gottfried Leibniz (1646–1716) for a modern formulation of this principle, stated by Leonard Euler in 1747:[13] the product of the mass and the acceleration of a body is equal to the sum of the forces on the body.

Using this fundamental dynamical principle, the *geometries*, as it was called, were able to show the relation between changes in motion and the forces that caused them. Any system in which motion results from applied forces is a *dynamical system*, in the sense that its behavior evolves in time. Since this fundamental principle of dynamics establishes a relation between an acceleration and the applied forces, it is expressed by a *differential equation* which involves the second derivative of the position — the acceleration — and the position evolving under the influence of the forces on which it depends.[14]

In the meantime, the first differential form of Newton's equation describing the problem of two massive bodies under gravitational interaction were first written in 1710 by Jacob Hermann (1678–1733),[15] one pupil of Johann Bernoulli (1667–1748).[16] Both of them opened the door for Euler's principle. They solved the differential equations and confirmed Newton's result that the laws of motion are, in this case, exactly Kepler's laws. Thus, when a single planet orbits the sun, it moves exactly according to the laws found by Kepler. The planet follows an elliptical trajectory that repeats itself forever: this is a *periodic solution*. Kepler's third law gives us the period of this solution as a function of the distance from the sun as measured by the semi-major axis a of the ellipse (in astronomical units):

	Mercury	Venus	Earth	Mars	Jupiter	Saturn
a	0.38	0.72	1.00	1.52	5.2	9.5
$1/n$	88	224	365	687	4307	10767
n^2a^3	7.09	7.44	7.50	7.44	7.58	7.39

where $1/n$ corresponds to the inverse of the average motion, that is, to the period of revolution, given in Earth days. Only the planets known to Kepler are presented in this Table but the near constant value of the product n^2a^3 is satisfied for all the planets (major and minor) known today. As a result, we can consider the two body problem as solved, and that Kepler's Laws describe their solutions.

---

[13] L. Euler, Découverte d'un nouveau principe de mécanique, *Mémoires de l'Académie des Sciences de Berlin* (1750), **6**, 185–217, 1752. The modern writing of this principle has the form of a vectorial equation $m\vec{a} = \sum \vec{F}$ where m is the mass of the body, $\vec{a}$ the acceleration vector and $\sum \vec{F}$ is the sum of the forces applied on the body.

[14] Writing this in a differential form came after the contribution by Pierre Varignon (1654–1722) who associated the concept of acceleration with the first time derivative of the velocity, $\vec{a} = \frac{d\vec{v}}{dt}$, or to the second time derivative of the position, $\vec{a} = \frac{d^2\vec{OM}}{dt^2}$. The fundamental principle of dynamics is written as the differential equation $\frac{\mathrm{d}^2x}{\mathrm{d}t^2} = F(x)$ which is a second-order differential equation since involving a second time derivative.

[15] J. Hermann, Letter to J. Bernoulli, July 12, 1710, in J. Bernoulli, *Opera*, **85**.

[16] D. Speiser, The Kepler problem from Newton to Johann Bernoulli, *Archive for History of Exact Sciences*, **50**, (2), 103–116, 1996.

1.3 Theory of the Moon

Newton had already been interested in the problem where three bodies interacted gravitationally. This configuration occurs when the action of a second body on a third cannot reasonably be neglected compared to the action of the first body. In our solar system there are two systems where this type of interaction is particularly important. These are the Sun-Earth-Moon system, because of the close proximity of the Moon to the Earth, and the Sun-Jupiter-Saturn system, due to Jupiter's large mass. Nevertheless, Newton treated the Sun-Earth-Moon system as a perturbation of the two-body Earth-Moon system:[17]

> The area which the moon describes by a radius drawn to the earth is proportional to the time of description, excepting in so far as the moon's motion is disturbed by the action of the sun, and here we propose to investigate the inequality of the moment, or horary increment of that area or motion so disturbed.

He specifically stated that the plane of the orbit oscillates and that the eccentricity also varies. Even so, the theory of the Moon that he published in his *Principia* was "very imperfect", as he himself stated in the preface to this work. In order to produce a better theory, Newton undertook a more general study of the three-body problem but immediately ran into major difficulties. As a result he adopted a simplified form of this problem either by choosing a $1/r$ form of the gravitational law in order to simplify the computations, or else by assuming a very massive central body whose motion was almost unaffected by the motion of the two other bodies, or else taking one of the three bodies very far away from the other two. The general problem was treated in a not very clear way in 22 corollaries in which he proposed a semi qualitative evolution of the motion. Even though Newton's mechanics had already explained tidal phenomena and the flattening of the Earth at its poles, it was unable to solve the problem of describing the motion of three bodies under their mutual gravitational interaction.

Because it is very simple to state but also because it is at the heart of the theory of the Moon, the three-body problem has been at the center of mathematical and mechanical studies for close to two centuries.

---

[17] I. Newton, *The mathematical principles of natural philosophy* (1687), Translated by A. Motte, Book III, Proposition XXVI, 1846.

Chapter 2

The Three-Body Problem

2.1 Imperfections in Newton's Theory

In order to outline the various difficulties that need to be solved in order to understand the three-body problem, we elaborate a little on one of the major problems that Newton's successors had to face. This problem deals with the Moon.

The Sun's influence on Lunar motion is of the same order of magnitude as the Earth's: as a result, neither one can be neglected and the problem cannot be reduced to a two body problem, for which a solution is known. In his preface, Newton admitted this problem in the case of Lunar motion. In fact, he was never able to find the correct value for the motion of the apogee. We focus on the apogee because, while there is no doubt that the Earth revolves around the Sun, Newton described the Moon's motion relative to the Earth, from which all measurements were made. It is much simpler to compare earth-based observations with a theory of the Moon based on a geocentric coordinate system (Figure 2.1): in such a coordinate system the Sun undergoes an apparent motion about the Earth (in conformity with our earliest intuitions), as does the Moon.

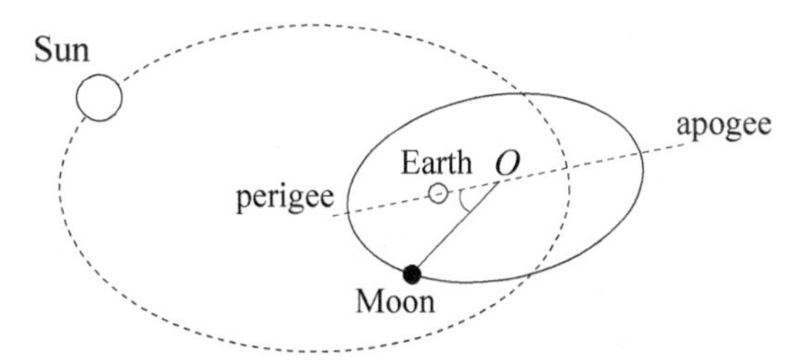

Figure 2.1 Description of the Moon's motion in a geocentric coordinate system: the furthest point on the elliptical trajectory is the apogee and the nearest point is the perigee.

Because of the $1/r^2$ law and its interactions with the Earth and the Sun, the Moon undergoes, in second approximation, elliptical motion in which the apogee slowly rotates (Figure 2.2). The speed with which the apogee moves depends sensitively on the interactions of the Moon with the Earth and the Sun; in fact, an estimate of this speed cannot be made if the Sun's influence is neglected. Using this hybrid geometry and his earliest results for the three-body problem, Newton found a motion of the apogee that was too slow by a factor of two: in particular, he computed that the apogee rotated around the earth in 18 years, rather than 8.9 years, which is observed. This disagreement between the theory and the observations had the result that Newton's successors were not convinced of the correctness of Newtonian mechanics.

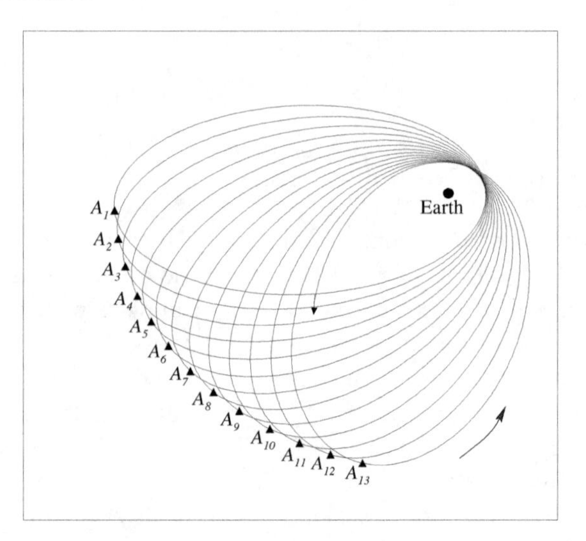

Figure 2.2 Motion of the Moon's apogee. Because of its interactions with the Sun, the Moon's elliptical motion undergoes a precession around one of the foci that is shown by the successive apogees $A_1, A_2, A_3, \ldots$, which rotate through 360° in about 9 years.

2.2 Challenges to the Law of Gravitation

At the beginning of the 18th century the best mathematical physicists (those who applied differential calculus to the problems of physics) little by little rewrote Newton's theorems in the language of differential calculus. Among the problems that resisted their efforts: the three-body problem and the problem of the advance of the Moon's apogee, which are intimately related. Pierre Simon de Laplace (1749–1827) summarized the state of the theories left by Newton:[1]

> In the large number of perturbations of celestial motions, he only considered those of lunar motion, whose the largest, the evection,[2] escaped to his researches. He well established the existence of the principle that he discovered; but developments of its consequences and its advantages

[1]Pierre Simon de Laplace, *Exposition du système du monde* (1796), pp. 524–525, Fayard, 1984.
[2]The evection is a periodic alteration in moon's orbit caused by solar attraction.

> was due to the work of this important geometre's successors. Imperfection of inifinitesimal calculus at its birth did not allow him to completely solve the difficult problems offered by the theory to the system of the world.

The infinitesimal calculus once again reproduced the great difficulties previously encountered in the study of the three-body problem: predictions of the advance of the apogee were still too large by a factor of two. This explains why, in 1745, Alexis-Claude Clairaut (1713–1765) wound up by questioning Newton's law of gravity:[3]

> Based now on my lunar theory, I am only fighting with the weakness of the law of squared distances.

He proposed to add a small supplementary force of the form $1/r^n$ (n being larger than 2). The effects of such a force are smaller for more distant bodies than closer bodies. As such, this additional term would only have an effect on the Earth-Moon interaction, the Sun being too far away. The presence of such a force would be indicated by the motion of the apogee. This idea already occurs in Newton's work, since he studied planetary motion under the combined forces of the form $1/r^2$ and $1/r^3$. Clairaut began with $n = 3$ but was not able to find a good estimate for n due to the lack of precise observational data, including estimates of the masses of these bodies.

This problem of the motion of the apogee was the occasion of extended scientific arguments between Clairaut, Jean le Rond d'Alembert (1717–1783), and Euler. The latter two were unable to resolve the disagreement between the computed value ($\simeq$ 18 years) and the observations ($\simeq$ 9 years). As did Clairaut at the beginning of his work, both rederived Newton's results, that is, half the actual value. At this time all three identified the three-body problem as the fundamental problem to solve. In this vein, in 1745 Clairaut wrote[4]

> After a long examination of M. Newton's theory without the conviction that I was expecting, I convinced myself to no longer borrow anything from him, and to directly research for the determination of celestial motions from the assumption of mutual attraction. To succeed in this I needed to start with the following problem: *Given three bodies with their positions, their masses and their velocities, find the curves which they must describe by their mutual attraction, according to the inverse squared distances.* Many geometres felt that nothing satisfactory and general was reached in the system of the world, without having determined before these curves; but nobody, to my knowledge, got them...

[3]A. Clairaut, Du système du monde dans les principes de la gravitation universelle, *Histoire de l'Académie Royale des Sciences*, (1745), 329–364, 1745.
[4]Ibid.

These three scientists used three different methods to arrive at their results. Their common result pointed to a problem, not with the computational methods, but rather with the Law of Gravitation itself.

Following Clairaut's example, Euler did not have much confidence in an action-at-a-distance law, which was difficult to justify. Instead, he developed a description of planetary motion based on a theory of turbulence in an ether, one of Descartes pet beliefs, according to which the planets are carried around their orbits entrained by turbulent vortices. This type of theory could not explain much else. Euler devoted himself to the problem of the Moon as well as the other three-body problem, the Sun-Jupiter-Saturn system. He also confessed to the difficulties that he encountered in the context of the three-body problem:[5]

> It must be confessed that this Problem is one of the most difficult in mechanics, and from which a perfect solution could be hoped, without considerable progresses in the analysis.

After having exhausted all the guesses that could justify the irregularities observed in Saturn's motion, he also proposed an argument, more or less reasonable, to justify a modification in the law of gravitation:[6]

> Having rigorously compared all Moon observations with the theory, I found that the distance between the Moon and the Earth is not as large as it should be according to the theory: hence it follows that the gravity of the Moon toward the Earth is slightly less than according to the inverse squared distance law: and few small irregularities in the Moon motion, which could not be explained according to this theory, confirmed me in this feeling.

Emboldened by frustration, he blamed the shapes of the planets, which are flattened spheres: this departure from sphericity, very noticeable for Saturn, could be responsible for the observed irregularities, which renders likely "*that the forces that govern the motion of Saturn differ considerably from the general law, because of its flattened shape.*"

D'Alembert was always more circumspect when reviewing the validity of the $1/r^2$ law of gravitation. He noted that the center of gravity of the Moon (a useful abstraction) was diverted towards the Earth by another small force because of the form of the gravitational law. This force, of the form $1/r^n$ could come either from the ether or from perturbations due to the non spherical nature and the heterogeneity of the Earth. He wound up by rejecting these hypotheses and adopting a force, specific to the Earth-Moon pair, whose origin was magnetic, more or less, as Kepler did to explain the departure from circular orbits he observed in planetary motions. In addition to that, it seemed to him that the variation in the eccentricity of the

[5] L. Euler, Prix de l'Académie des Sciences de Paris (1748), *Opera*, **2**, 28, 45–157.
[6] *Ibid.*

elliptical trajectory was not sufficiently taken into account. He remarked "*that a very small error in the value of* [the distance] *could produce a much larger error in the motion of the apsides.*"[7] By then, the computations of d'Alembert were generally in agreement with the Lunar Tables of Newton, which lead him to write "*that Newton's system is absolutely correct except for a small correction which leads to the movement of the apogee and for which he had nothing to say. Finally, he doubted that it would ever be possible to overthrow Newton's system.*"

Only Comte de Buffon (1707–1788) forcefully defended the law of universal gravitation. His main argument was the simplicity of this law and the many successes of this law, such as the flattening of the Earth and the explanations of the tides. He was moved to write[8]

> M. Clairaut proposes a difficulty against Newton's system; but this is not more than a difficulty which cannot nor must become a principle; it is necessary to search for solving it, and not to turn it into a theory whose consequences are only founded on a computation...

D'Alembert, who never found the correct solutions for the motion of the Moon's apogee, shared Buffon's position:

> I believe that it is quite difficult to metaphysically show that the attraction cannot be only expressed by a single term but I am very ready to believe that this is exactly according to the square distances, because this laws seems simple to me.

Clairaut resolved this stand off in 1748 by taking into account the second-order terms.[9] The complexity and the length of the calculations made it easy to

[7]In astronomy, an apsis (plural apsides) is the point of greatest or least distance of the elliptical orbit of a celestial body from its center of attraction (the center of mass of the system).

[8]Buffon, Réflexions sur la loi de l'attraction, *Mémoire de l'Académie Royale des Sciences* (Paris), p. 500, 1745.

[9]The concept of "*terms of the second order*" is related to a relevant result, stated by Brook Taylor (1685–1731) in his work *Methodus incrementorum directa et inversa* (1715) and which is written today as

$$f(x_0+\xi) \approx \sum_{n=0}^{p} \frac{f^{(n)}(x_0)}{n!}\xi^n \approx f(x_0) + f^{(1)}(x_0)\xi + \frac{f^{(2)}(x_0)}{2}\xi^2 + \dots + \frac{f^{(p)}(x_0)}{p!}\xi^p$$

where $f^{(n)}(x)$ is the nth derivative of the function $f(x)$ and p the order of the expansion. The right member is the called *Taylor expansion in series*. For instance, if one investigates the function $f(x) = e^{-x}$ that he would like to estimate in the neighborhood of $x = 0$, he obtains

$$e^{-\xi} = 1 - \xi + \frac{\xi^2}{2!} - \frac{\xi^3}{3!} + \frac{\xi^4}{4!} - \dots$$

If one only retains $1 - \xi$, he has an expansion at the first order of the function e^{-x} en $x = 0$; if the term $\frac{\xi^2}{2}$ is added, one obtains an expansion up to the second order; and so on. In the case of the lunar theory, the function f is unknown and it is required to determine, step by step, using successive approximations, each of the terms.

understand why both Newton and his successors were content to consider only the first-order corrections. It was only through study of the second order terms that Clairaut found a solution that he published in January 1748 in a memoir entitled *On the Moons' orbit, not neglecting squares of the quantities having the same order as the perturbing functions.*[10] The second-order introduced a correction almost half the total value observed. As a result, he corrected the value for the motion of the apogee computed by Newton in such a way that there resulted a good agreement between observation and Newton's universal law of gravitation.

2.3 Problem of the Convergence of Series

Clairaut's discovery initiated a rapid development in this field. To resolve a three-body problem such as the Lunar problem, it was necessary to start from Kepler's laws and add to them perturbations that describe the evolution in terms of more and more complex series. Leonard Euler quickly reproduced Clairaut's results, once Clairaut had announced them. Somewhat bitter, D'Alembert raised the ante by posing the problem of convergence of series for the first time:[11]

> the first term of the Serie only gives the apogee about half of the actual motion which is found by observations. It was natural to think that the other terms of this Serie, taken altogether, were much smaller than the first one, as it commonly arises and as one assumes how it may happen in problems solved by approximations, neglecting small quantities [...] M. Clairaut, in calculating more exactly the Serie describing the motion of the Apogee, was the first to realize that it was not sufficient to only consider the first term. To this important remark, I add another one which does not seem to me less relevant, it is not enough to only take into account the second term of this Serie, it is required to increase the computation accuracy up to the third and to the fourth term, because it is the sole way to be ensured that the Serie is convergent enough after the second term, so that the terms beyond this first four or five terms can be neglected without worry.

[10] A. C. Clairaut, De l'orbite de la lune, en ne négligeant pas les quarrés des quantités de même ordre que les fonctions perturbatrices, *Histoire de l'Académie Royale des Sciences* (Paris, 1748), 421–440, 1752.
[11] J. le Rond d'Alembert, *Recherches sur différents points important du système du monde*, 1751.

Thus, it does not suffice that the second term was small to conclude that all the remaining were negligible. It was necessary to prove that the series converged.[12]

Further, d'Alembert asked whether it was possible "*to find several terms of the fifth or even higher order that gave a similar or even greater result?*" In fact, at that time, the "Géomètres"[13] treated the problem of the convergence of a series from the point of view of how slowly the terms in the series decrease. Beyond some rare exceptions such as the Marquis de Condorcet (1743–1794), they rarely asked if a series was convergent and if the limit existed and was a solution of some

[12]Let us take an example. Let us assume that the series

$$S_p(x) = \sum_{k=0}^{p} \frac{1}{2k+1} \sin[(2k+1)x]$$

corresponds to an expansion in serie up to the order p. When the series is taken at the first order ($p = 0$), it is reduced to a single term, that is, $S_1(x) = \sin x$. When the expansion is continued, for instance up to order 3, the series becomes

$$S_3(x) = \sin x + \frac{1}{3} \sin 3x + \frac{1}{5} \sin 5x \,,$$

and so on. One can show that higher the order p is, closer to an asymptotic function the series is. In the present case of the difference between two Heaviside functions (Example (a)): it is said that the series converges because higher the order is, smaller the contribution of the pth order is and, consequently, closer to the target function the series $S_p(x)$ is. Let us consider now a series as

$$S'_p(x) = \sum_{k=0}^{p} (2k+1) \sin[(2k+1)x] \,.$$

When the order of the expansion is increased, the function associated with the series $S'_p(x)$ describes solutions whose the amplitude increases up to infinity. Indeed, each term has a contribution with the same order of magnitude than the previous ones: the series is no longer convergent (Example (b)).

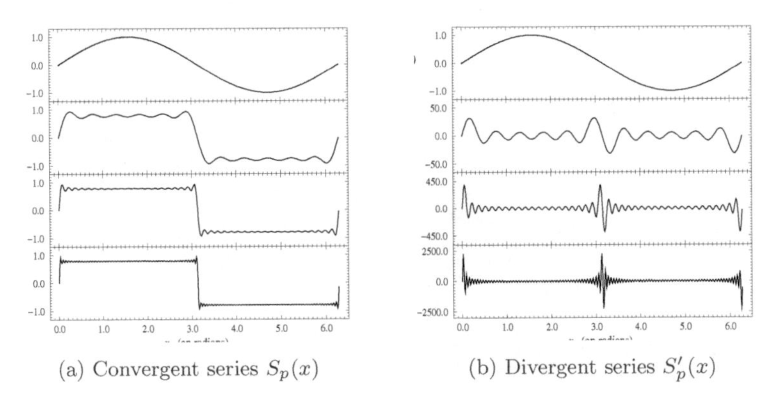

(a) Convergent series $S_p(x)$ (b) Divergent series $S'_p(x)$

Two examples of series with different converging properties; the series $S_p(x)$ is convergent but the series $S'(x)$ is not since the amplitude of the oscillations increases with the number of terms involved in the series (pay attention to the evolution of range over which each series S'_p evolves).

[13]This name was used to designate the scientists working with differential equations at the 18th century.

differential equation. In his work *The Three-Body Problem* (1767), Condorcet stated the conditions that should be satisfied for a method of successive approximations to be valid:[14]

> i) it is necessary that the Serie given by the method of approximation [...] can be pushed up to infinity without being able to stop at any term and to change either its form or its nature, and the more terms taken, the less the sum of the Serie differs [from what it should be];
>
> ii) the identity between the sum of the entire Serie and the actual value, or a value slightly equal to the true one, must be rigorously proven.

Celestial mechanics had now become a study of approximations by series. Disagreements between observations and simple calculations resulted in approximations by series that were ever more complicated. The universal Law of Gravitation, because of its inverse quadratic form, is not simple to work with, and each of its successes should be treated as yet another confirmation of this law. As d'Alembert has pointed out:[15]

> It is true that the need to include all those terms leads to long and difficult calculations. But we are compensated by the results, which are very satisfying and should be considered as confirming the universal law of gravitation.

Celestial mechanics seems condemned to long and difficult computations to obtain ever more accurate results that agree with ever more precise observations. The problem of gravitational motion was not yet resolved by laws "*à la Kepler.*"

[14]N. de Condorcet, *Du problème des trois corps*, 1767.
[15]The computations performed by d'Alembert by this time can be seen in the recent French edition of this Moon theory published in 1748, *in* D'Alembert, *Oeuvres complètes*, I/6, with footnotes by M. Chapront-Touzé, CNRS Editions, 2002.

Chapter 3

Simplification of the Three-Body Problem

3.1 Simplification of the Geometry

The problem of the motion of the Moon's apogee helped Geometers to realize that they must use higher-order terms to obtain results that were quantitatively in agreement with the observations. Methods of computation depending on the differential calculus allowed scientists to push the precision of their computations far beyond that which was available through purely geometric methods, such as those used by Newton. In spite of this, the difficulties associated with the three-body problem remained insurmountable. As a result, at the beginning of the 17th century Geometers treated only the three-body problem, as d'Alembert confessed:[1]

> The question reduces to determining the orbit that the Moon follows under the influence of the Sun and the Earth; and even though this question is very simplified in this formulation, it still contains enough difficulties to prevent anybody to add new ones.

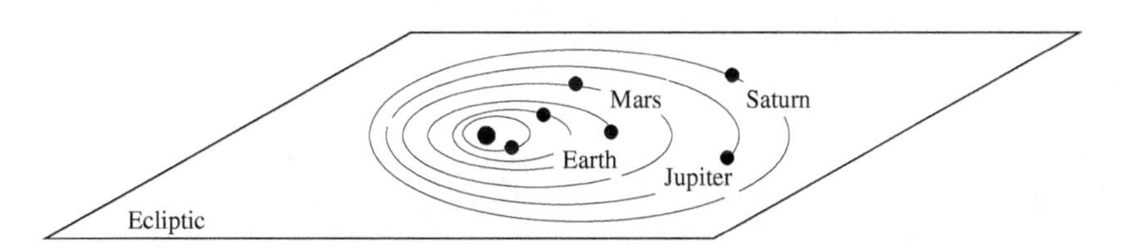

Figure 3.1 On average, the planets can be treated as if they all moved in the same plane, the one containing the orbits of the Earth, Sun, and Moon. This plane is called the Ecliptic.

In this treatment the interactions with the other planets are neglected. Yet another difficulty comes from the inclination of the planetary trajectories with respect to the *plane of the Ecliptic*. This plane, so-called because the eclipses of the Sun and the Moon on the Earth occur when all three are in this plane, corresponds, on average, to the plane that contains all the planets, including the Sun and the Moon

[1] J. le Rond d'Alembert, *Recherches sur différents points important du système du monde*, 1751.

(Figure 3.1). Nevertheless, if we look more closely at the elliptical orbits, we see a slight *inclination* i that adds an additional direction (degree of freedom) to the motion of the planets. This is called the *precession of the nodes.* The nodes are the lines of intersection of the elliptical orbits with the Ecliptic (Figure 3.2). The nodes precess in the plane of the Ecliptic as the elliptical orbit turns around itself. From the viewpoint of the equations, taking account of the precession of the nodes greatly complicates the computations. The inclinations of the various planetary orbits are:

	Mercury	Venus	Earth	Mars	Jupiter	Saturn
Inclination i	7.0^o	3.4^o	0.0^o	1.85^o	1.3^o	2.5^o

The Earth's orbit defines the plane of the Ecliptic since the inclination of the Earth's ellipse is zero degrees with respect to it.

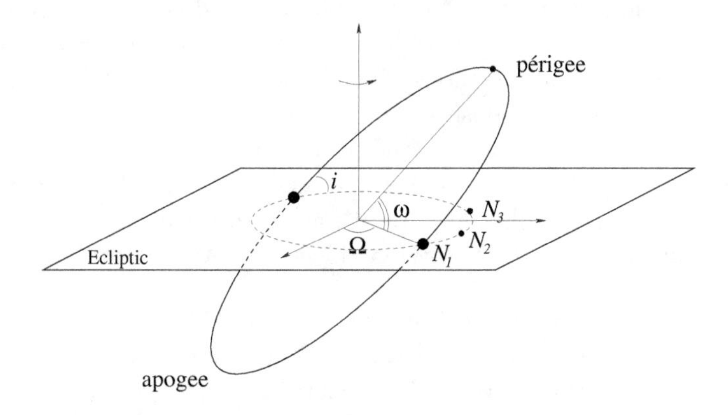

Figure 3.2 The inclination i of a planetary orbit introduces an additional degree of freedom with which to describe the motion of the planet. This leads to the precession of the nodes $N_1, N_2, N_3, \ldots$ which contributes, among other effects, to the motion of the apogee while the trajectory rotates around an axis.

In a search for simplicity, astronomers often simplify the three-body problem by assuming all three bodies move in the same plane, as Johann Euler (son of Leonhard Euler) explained:[2]

> The large number of equations which must be used to determined the location of the Moon to one minute of accuracy, provides a quite evident proof, because it obviously follows that, if one wants to improve this accuracy, the number of equations would become so large, that one could not use it in practice. While one is not successful in the general solution of the three-body problem, The surest way to improve the Lunar theory will be to simplify the question as much as possible,

[2] J. Euler, Réflexions sur la variation de la Lune, *Mémoires de l'Académie de Berlin*, **22**, 334–353, 1768.

> forgetting some circumstances which contribute to increase the number of inequalities. [...] it is therefore allowed to start these researches in assuming that the Moon's motion takes place in the Ecliptic, and that the Sun moves uniformly in a circle around the Earth...

He guessed that most of the major difficulties were still present in the simplified problem and that, if a solution to this problem were to be found, it would not be too difficult to extend this solution to the problem of the Moon's motion:[3]

> although this equation may appear quixotic, I dare to ensure that, if one would succeed to find a perfect solution, one would find almost no further difficulty in determining the actual motion of the real Moon. This equation is thus of the last importance, and it will be always good to go into details about all its difficulties, before one can expect a complete solution.

3.2 Simplification of the General Equations

At the present time the two most commonly encountered simplifying assumptions for the three-body problem are that the planets all move in the same plane, and that the Sun rotates uniformly around the Earth in this plane. Once these assumptions are made, the differential equations governing the motion are known and the principal remaining problem is one of integrating these equations.

In 1759 Clairaut determined the most general equations for three bodies moving in a plane. Starting from the fundamental principle of dynamics established by Euler twelve years earlier, and using the inverse square law of gravitational attraction, he wrote down six equations to describe the motion of three bodies under their mutual gravitational attraction. These equations, using modern notations, are

$$\left\{\begin{array}{ll}\ddot{x}_1 = \dfrac{m_2(x_2 - x_1)}{r_{12}^3} + \dfrac{m_3(x_3 - x_1)}{r_{13}^3} & \ddot{y}_1 = \dfrac{m_2(y_2 - y_1)}{r_{12}^3} + \dfrac{m_3(y_3 - y_1)}{r_{13}^3} \\ \ddot{x}_2 = \dfrac{m_3(x_3 - x_2)}{r_{23}^3} + \dfrac{m_1(x_1 - x_2)}{r_{21}^3} & \ddot{y}_2 = \dfrac{m_3(y_3 - y_2)}{r_{23}^3} + \dfrac{m_1(y_1 - y_2)}{r_{21}^3} \\ \ddot{x}_3 = \dfrac{m_1(x_1 - x_3)}{r_{31}^3} + \dfrac{m_2(x_2 - x_3)}{r_{32}^3} & \ddot{y}_3 = \dfrac{m_1(y_1 - y_3)}{r_{31}^3} + \dfrac{m_2(y_2 - y_3)}{r_{32}^3}\end{array}\right.$$

where (x_i, y_i) designate the coordinates of the three bodies and r_{ij} designate the distances between the ith and the jth body (Figure 3.3). The three bodies have masses m_1, m_2 and m_3, respectively. There are six second-order differential equations involving second derivatives of the position coordinates, that is, accelerations $\ddot{x}_i$ and $\ddot{y}_i$.

Clairaut stated that this problem could be simplified. In particular, the description of the motion of these bodies could be made with respect to the center of mass

[3] *Ibid.*

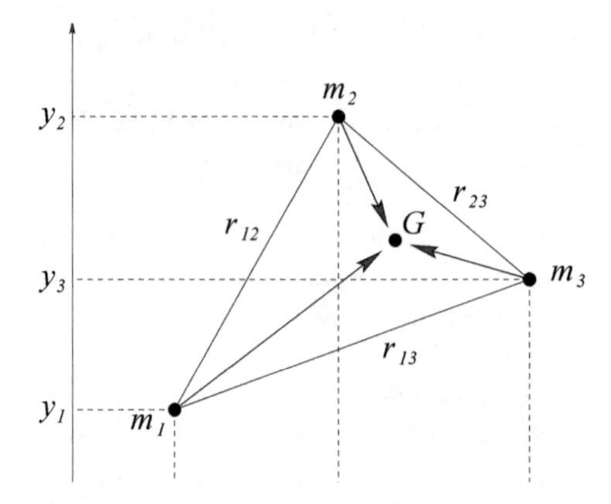

Figure 3.3 Configuration studied by Clairaut. The three masses m_1, m_2, m_3 move in a plane. The motion can be described with respect to the center of mass G of the three bodies.

of the Earth-Moon system (Figure 3.3). This reduces the number of second order equations to be studied from six to four. To illustrate this simplification, suppose the Moon moves on a perfect ellipse around the Earth, which itself moves on an elliptical orbit around a stationary Sun. Now look at the Earth-Moon system. In the reference frame of the fixed Sun, our Moon follows a somewhat complicated trajectory (Figure 3.4(a)). Since the mass of the Moon is about 100 times smaller than the mass of the Earth, their common center of mass can be identified, to a first approximation, with that of the Earth. The description of Moon's trajectory with respect to this center of mass is then an ellipse (Figure 3.4(b)). This trajectory is far simpler than its trajectory with respect to the fixed Sun. Perturbations with respect to this simplified trajectory are then treated in order to account for the interactions of the Earth-Moon system with the Sun.

Clairaut further observed that Kepler's law of equal areas could be used to further simplify this problem. Finally, he used an extension of Huygens' principle of "living forces" to write down a conservation equation, known today as the law of conservation of energy. The conservation of equal areas and the conservation of energy provide two *constants of motion.* Of the original six second-order differential equations, there remain only two to integrate, in addition to two first-order differential equations. In spite of this tremendous simplification, Clairaut never really devoted himself to the solution of these equations:[4]

> I never put much effort into resolving these things, because they always seemed very difficult. Maybe they work better than other methods. In any case, I abandoned this approach to use the method of approximations.

[4] A. Clairaut, Réflexions sur le problème des trois corps, avec les équations différentielles qui expriment les conditions de ce problème, *Journal des Savans*, 563–566, 1759.

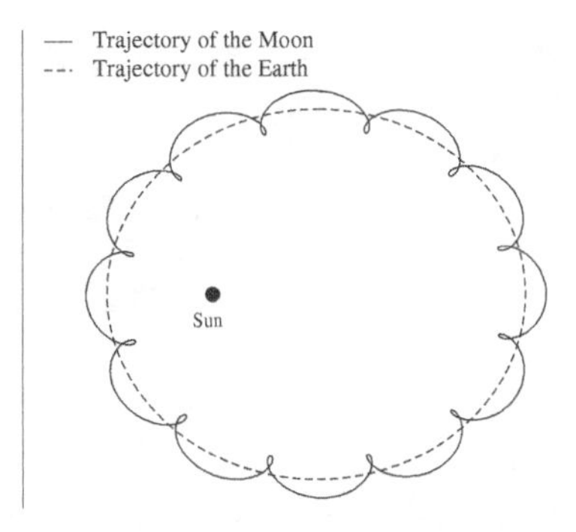

(a) In the absolute frame

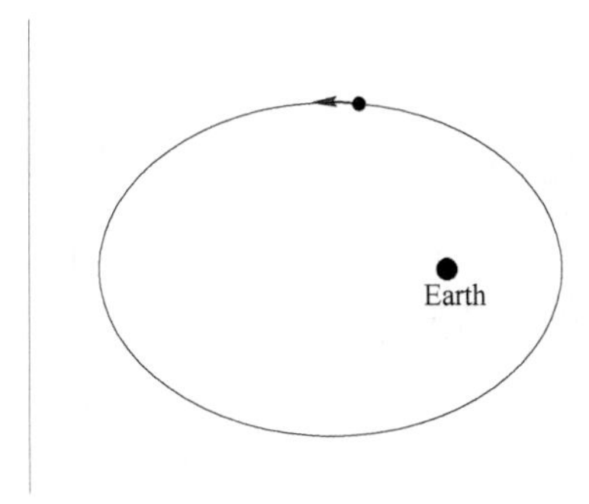

(b) In the frame of the center of mass of the Earth-Moon system (approximately the Earth)

Figure 3.4 Study of the Earth-Moon system under the influence of the Sun. The description of the trajectory of the Moon is simplified when it is treated in the reference frame of the Earth-Moon center of mass, which can be approximately identified with the center of the Earth, since the mass of the Moon is only about 1% that of the Earth.

and he contented himself with the ironic challenge "*Let him integrate who can.*"[5]

[5]Two examples can be provided to explain what "integrating differential equations" means. For instance, the second-order differential equation

$$\ddot{x} = -\omega^2 x$$

which involves a second-order time derivative has for solution

$$x(t) = A \sin(\omega t + \varphi).$$

It can be easily checked that $A \sin(\omega t + \varphi)$, once it is derived twice with respect to the time, is solution to the previous equation. When the solution is described under such a form, one can say that the equation is "*integrated*" or that it is "*resolved*".

Let us take now the first-order differential equation

$$\dot{x} = kx \tag{3.1}$$

where x is a function depending on time t. In order to solve this equation, one start to assume that its solution x can be rewritten as a power series in time t as

$$x = a_0 + a_1 t + a_2 t^2 + a_3 t^3 + ... + a_n t^n + ...$$

He summarized his position:[6]

> it might even be possible that if the problem is solved with geometric rigor, it will not be as useful for astronomical calculations. [In addition, the difficulty] is light when you consider the art of finding the required [differential] equations, but it is very considerable as for finding solutions to these equations.

Clairaut also claimed that his methods can be "*applied with the same ease*" when the motions of the three bodies were not confined to a single plane, so that they move in space. These methods were developed by the Marquis de Condorcet in 1770 in his *Memoire on the differential equations for the three-body problem* and later by Joseph-Louis Lagrange (1736–1813) in 1772 in his *Essay on the three-body problem.*[7] Lagrange described the motion of the three-bodies with respect to their common center of mass, which allowed him to reduce the set of nine second-order differential equations to six. Using the equal-area laws and the conservation of living forces, he reduced these twelve first-order differential equations to eight. Toward the end of the 19th century Heinrich Bruns[8] (1848–1919) and Henri Poincaré[9] (1854–1912) showed that no additional constants of motion could exist, that is, quantities that are conserved during the motion, so that these equations could not be simplified any further. Consequently, they are not integrable, meaning that there is no general analytical solution to them. A yet more general proof for the non-integrability of

---

Deriving this solution with respect to time, we obtain

$$\dot{x} = a_1 + 2a_2 t + 3a_3 t^2 + \dots + n a_n t^{n-1} + \dots$$

Identifying the powers in t in each side of the equation (3.1), we obtain

$$\begin{cases} a_1 &= k a_0 \\ 2a_2 &= k a_1 \quad \Rightarrow a_2 = \frac{k^2}{2} a_0 \\ 3a_3 &= k a_2 \quad \Rightarrow a_3 = \frac{k^3}{2\times 3} a_0 \\ \vdots & \\ n a_n &= k a_{n-1} \Rightarrow a_n = \frac{k^n}{n!} a_0 \\ \vdots & \end{cases}$$

Each coefficient a_n of solution x is determined by recurrence. The accuracy of the approximated solution depends on the number of terms taken into account. In favourable cases, few terms are sufficient to obtain a good approximation. Unfortunately, most of time, solving the differential equations for the three-body problem with such a method presents great difficulties related to the lack of convergence in the series.

[6] *Ibid.*

[7] J. L. Lagrange, *Essai sur le problème des trois corps*, Prix de l'Académie Royale des Sciences de Paris, tome IX, 1772. *Oeuvres* **6**, 229–331.

[8] H. Bruns, Über die Integrale des Vielkörper-Problems, *Acta Mathematica*, **11**, 25–96, 1887.

[9] H. Poincaré, Sur le problème des trois corps et les équations de la dynamique (1889), Memoire awarded by the King Oscar II from Sweden, published after corrections, *Acta Mathematica*, **13**, 1–270, 1890.

the three-body problem was quite recently provided by Alexei Tsygvintsev.[10]

3.3 The First Exact Solutions

Lagrange understood the difficulty of the three-body problem, and decided to "*learn as much as possible from the theory of the Moon so that he could learn what was left to analyze.*" As a result, he was content to study the simplest cases of the three-body problem, which could be solved exactly. Even though these cases did not correspond to any real physical situations, he believed these cases merited the consideration of Geometers because they could shed light on more general solutions of the three-body problem.

Lagrange assumed that the distances r_{ij} (Figure 3.3) between the three bodies remained constant, so that the three bodies assumed the shape of a triangle that remained unchanged in shape as the bodies moved. He observed that when the triangle was equilateral, the three bodies always had the same velocity and their shape remained that of an equilateral triangle; in addition, the bodies moved in a single plane. The equilateral triangle formed by the three bodies rotated with an angular velocity that remained constant about their common center of mass. As Leonard Euler had previously mentioned in 1730,[11] each of the bodies was placed at a point where the forces balanced out: as a result no relative motion can occur. The three-body problem is exactly solvable in this simple case. Lagrange found yet another exact solution that corresponds to the three bodies aligned in a straight line, as Johann Euler had pointed out in 1768. Lagrange concluded:[12]

> There are only two cases when the orbit of the Moon could be a circle; one when the Moon is constantly in conjunction with the Sun and the other when it is always diametrically opposite with the Sun. In both cases the motion is uniform and equal to that of the Sun.

In the context of the latter configuration, in 1795 Pierre Simon de Laplace calculated that:[13]

> if, at the beginning, the Earth and the Moon had been placed on the same line with the Sun with distances of 1 and $1 + \frac{1}{100}$, respectively: if, in addition, one had given them parallel velocities proportional to these distances, the Moon would always be in opposition with the sun;

---

[10]A. Tsygvintsev, La non-intégrabilité méromorphe du problème plan des trois corps, *Comptes-Rendus de l'Académie des Sciences* (Paris), **331**, 241–244, 2000.

[11]L. Euler, *De Trium Corporum mutua attractione*, Proposition 1, Corollary 4, 1730:

> If the triangle is equilateral, one isolated body is attracted toward the centre of mass of the two others. Thus, if the three bodies are isolated, they tend toward their common centre of mass.

[12]Lagrange, 1772, *Ibid.*

[13]P. Simon de Laplace, *Exposition du système du Monde*, Ibid.

> these two bodies would follow each other on the horizon; and if, at that distance from the Earth the Moon would not be eclipsed, its light would be replaced, during these nights, by the light of the Sun.

Lagrange called these solutions "*pure curiosities*"... Even so, that corresponding to three bodies forming a finite equilateral triangle does in fact describe a real physical system. On 22 February 1906 Maximilian Wolf (1863–1932) discovered Achilles,[14] an asteroid that forms an equilateral triangle with the Sun and Jupiter. Following this, more than a dozen other asteroids, the Trojans and the Greeks, were discovered to be oscillating around what are now known as the Lagrange points (Figure 3.5). A second such system was subsequently discovered. Pierre Lacques, Raymond Despiau (Pic du Midi Observatory) and Jean Lecacheux (Meudon Observatory) discovered a satellite of Saturn named Helene,[15] and Dione, discovered in 1684 by Cassini (1625–1712), form an equilateral triangle with Saturn and this triangle rotates rigidly around the common center of mass.

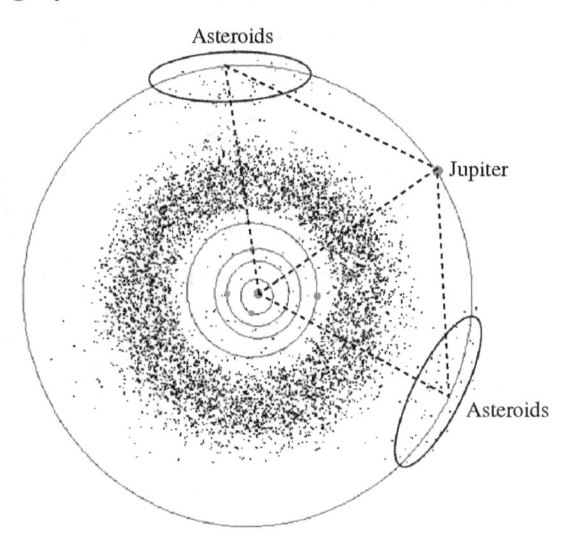

Figure 3.5 Locations of the asteroids that are known today. One sees that on both sides of Jupiter the asteroids cluster around the Lagrange points to form, with the Sun, two equilateral triangles that rotate rigidly around the Sun, which is very close to the center of mass of this system.

Since 14 February 1996 the SOHO satellite — the *SOlar and Heliospheric Observatory* — has been parked in a way that takes advantage of the Lagrange point L_1 (this lies on a straight line connecting the Earth and the Sun, between the two), about 1.5 million kilometers from the Earth (Figure 3.6). There, the satellite takes advantage of a position fixed between the Sun and the Earth to remain at rest

[14] M. Wolf is credited for the discovery of more than 200 asteroids by using astro-photography. He worked at Heidelberg.

[15] J. Lecacheux, P. Lacques, L. Vapillon, A. Auge & R. Despiau, A new satellite of Saturn: Dione B, *Icarus*, **43**, 111–115, 1980.

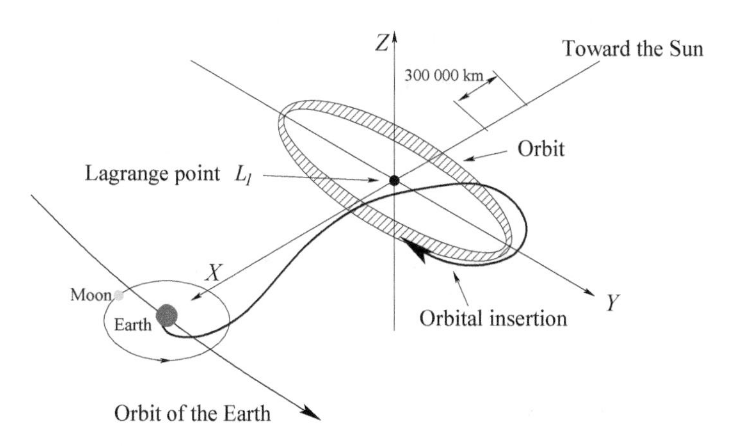

Figure 3.6 Diagram for the orbital insertion of the SOHO satellite, launched 14 February 1996. SOHO follows an elliptical orbit with a long axis of 666 672 km and a short axis of 206 448 km.

between the two without using any energy, or almost any energy, because the point L_1 is unstable and it is necessary to make small corrections in SOHO's position from time to time.[16] The energy required to keep the satellite parked at this location is much less than required at any other site.

In 1896, Henri Poincaré showed that every class of non-colliding orbits contains at least one periodic solution[17] but did not provide any explicit solution. In 1909, Karl Sundman showed that there exists some convergent series which, consequently, correspond to periodic solutions to the three-body problem.[18] But none of them is explicited. Thus, there were only two exact explicit solutions to the three-body problem up until 1993, that is, when Christopher Moore addressed the problem to classify periodic orbits by braids and found the figure-8 periodic orbit for the three-body problem.[19] Then this orbit was independently discovered by Alain Chenciner (Bureau of Longitudes) and Richard Montgomery (University of California, Santa Cruz). When the three bodies have equal masses, they can chase each other around a figure-eight curve[20] (Figure 3.7). The three bodies are aligned in an Eulerian (linear) configuration periodically. Carlos Simó, from Barcelona, showed that this solution remains stable when the masses are slightly unequal.[21] These three astronomers wonder if there are three stars which follow a figure eight trajectory and if their solution could be anything more than just a curiosity!

[16] V. Domingo & D. Wyn-Roberts, The L_1 Lagrangian point orbit as a suitable site for helioseismologic measurements, *Memoire della Societa Astronomica Italiana*, **55** (1–2), 375–381, 1984.

[17] H. Poincaré, Sur les solutions périodiques et le principe de moindre action, *Comptes-Rendus de l'Académie des Sciences* (Paris), **123**, 815–818, 1896.

[18] K. F. Sundman, Nouvelles recherches sur le problème des trois corps, *Acta Societatis Scientiarium Fennicae*, **35** (9), 3–27, 1909.

[19] C. Moore, Braids in classical gravity, *Physical Review Letters*, **70**, 3675–3679, 1993.

[20] A. Chenciner & R. Montgomery, A remarkable periodic solution of the three-body problems in the case of equal masses, *Annals of Mathematics*, **152** (3), 881–901, 2000.

[21] C. Simó, New families of solutions in N-body problem, *3rd European Congress of Mathematics*, 10–14 July 2000.

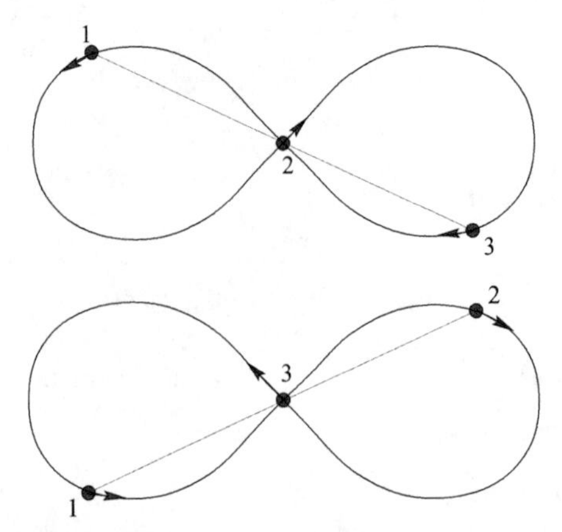

Figure 3.7 Periodic trajectory followed by three equal masses found by Alain Chenciner and Richard Montgomery in 1999.

Despite all the simplifications made on the three-body problem, only three exact solutions are known today, and these have very particular configurations. This result could be considered as an early indication that simple systems can produce complicated behavior, which we will identify as chaos later in this book.

Chapter 4

The Success of Celestial Mechanics

Despite the absence of exact general solutions, the magicians who practice celestial mechanics have obtained remarkable results using perturbation theory. In this setting, when the differential equations are expanded in series, a particular class of terms is singled out as particularly problematic: the *secular terms.* They have very little effect over the short term but as time evolves, their contributions grow continually and, in the long run, these terms make preponderant contributions. This property means it is impossible to make long term predictions of planetary trajectories. Worse, these trajectories are extremely sensitive to initial conditions. These are the two most important properties of chaotic motion.

4.1 Perturbation Theory

The search for exact solutions of the three-body problem leads to a very difficult question. Geometers have been humbled by this question, in spite of Lagrange's successes. For instance, Leonhard Euler wrote:[1]

> everything we have done up to this point rests on the very particular case in which the motion of each of the three bodies follows very closely Kepler's laws, and in this case one is forced to determine the motion by approximation methods. In all other cases we are embarrassed to admit that the problem of three-body motion remains as much of a mystery now as if we had never even thought about this problem.

Lagrange seconded his colleague:[2]

> the problem has become so complicated that the various efforts of the geometers during the last thirty years to solve it has hardly succeeded in getting some more or less approximated solutions.

[1] L. Euler, *Considérations sur le problème des trois corps*, 1768.

[2] J. L. Lagrange, Remarques générales sur le mouvement de plusieurs corps qui s'attirent mutuellement en raison inverse des carrés des distances, *Nouveaux Mémoires de l'Académie Royale des Sciences et Belles-lettres de Berlin*, 401–418, 1777 — *Oeuvres complètes*, IV, 401–418.

In addition, following in the footsteps of his predecessors, Laplace continued to use the methods of perturbation theory to construct his tables:[3]

> The simplest way to analyzed these various perturbations is to imagine that a planet moves according to the elliptical laws of motion, along an ellipse whose elements vary slightly, and to conceive at the same time that the true planet oscillates around the position of this imaginary planet, in a very small orbit whose nature depends on periodic perturbations.

He considered the motion of the Moon, as treated by Clairaut, Euler, and d'Alembert, to be the *principal problem* of celestial mechanics. In this problem, the three bodies — the Sun, the Earth, and the Moon — are treated as point particles. Perturbations due to the extended nature of these bodies, their deformation, and the actions of the other planets, were not taken into account. The orbit of the Earth around the Sun is assumed to be elliptical, with a slight precession of the perihelion. The starting point of perturbation theory was the assumption that the Moon's orbit was nearly elliptical, with a small eccentricity and with the Earth at one focus. The influence of the Sun was treated as a perturbation.

Independent of the approach used, the principal problem of the Moon's motion depends on the values of several constants that must be determined observationally. Of these, six are integration constants (the mean motion of the Moon, its average eccentricity, the average inclination, the initial values of its average longitude and that of its node and perigee), four are constants describing the Earth's orbit around the Sun (the average motion, eccentricity, the longitude of the Earth and its perihelion). These quantities are the *initial conditions* of the problem. Add to these the masses of the bodies, which were not very well known at that time, and the value of the Gravitational constant. In some cases the results of calculations were particularly sensitive to values determined from observations and injected directly into the equations: this occurred especially in the approaches of Clairaut and Euler. One of Laplace's objectives was the elimination of empirical terms. In addition, he often attempted to eliminate some time-dependent terms.

As he had done for the Moon and other three-body problems, Laplace began by considering only two planets and neglecting interactions with all other planets. Not surprisingly, the motion he found obeyed Kepler's laws. This motion was perturbed by interactions with other planets. Variations from idealized elliptical motion resulted from correcting terms that he called *inequalities*. Laplace distinguished two types:[4]

---

[3]P. Simon de Laplace, *Exposition du système du Monde*, p. 254, *Ibid.*

[4]P. Simon de Laplace, Mémoire sur la figure de la Terre, *Mémoires de l'Académie Royale des Sciences de Paris* (1783), 3–32, 1786 — *Oeuvres complètes*, XI, p. 7.

> Some are periodic and depend on the positions of the bodies, either with respect to each other or with respect to their aphelia; these are relatively small with respect to the equation for the center [of gravity], and wash out themselves after a small number of years; the others change the elements of the orbits by very tiny amounts at each revolution of the planets; but these alterations accumulate without end, and in the long run completely change the nature of the orbit and the position of the planets; as after centuries these changes can be quite large, so we call them *secular inequalities.*

Periodic inequalities could be treated as very small periodic perturbations around the elliptical trajectory established by motion in the presence of only the Sun (Figure 4.1(a)). By contrast, secular inequalities are proportional to time. The proportionality factor is typically very small, so that these terms are generally negligible when the calculations are carried out for only a short time (for example, a dozen years). When the calculations extend over longer periods, these contributions cumulate without averaging out, opposite what happens for the periodic perturbations. Ultimately, the secular terms have a preponderant influence on planetary motion (Figure 4.1(b)). The secular terms prevent the convergence of series expansions: as a result, it is impossible to guarantee that an almost negligible term will not eventually dominate the motion. Because of this Laplace, following in the footsteps of his predecessors, always searched for solutions without secular terms since otherwise solutions would be accurate only for short times. The major question was always the same, to know whether these terms would lead to predictions that the planets would evolve to positions far from their current positions: this is the problem of the stability of the solar system.

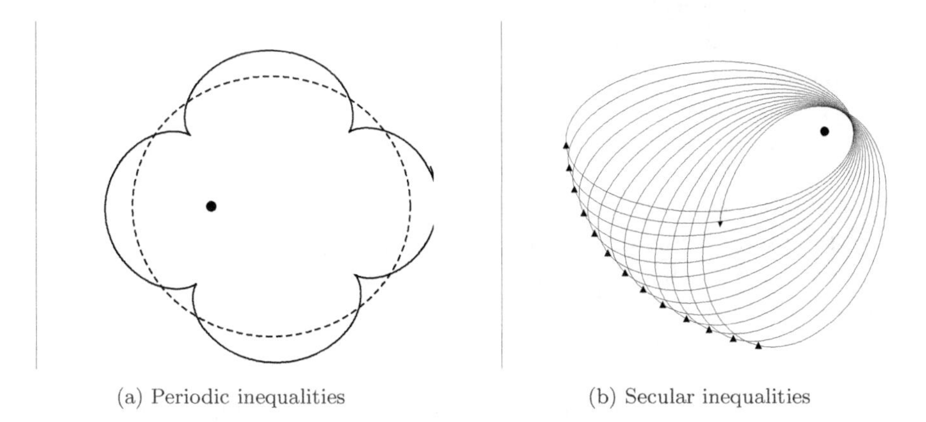

(a) Periodic inequalities

(b) Secular inequalities

Figure 4.1 Mutual interactions of two planets under two types of inequalities. There are periodic inequalities that seem, at first glance, to make major perturbations on the elliptical motion but that, because of their periodic nature, ultimately average out. Secular inequalities, directly proportional to time or some power of time, are initially negligible. Because they add up relentlessly, they wind up by making significant contributions to the elliptical motion.

4.2 The Theory of Jupiter and Saturn

When Laplace approached the theory of Jupiter and Saturn, quite a number of secular terms appeared in the equations of motion of these planets when their mutual gravitational interaction was taken into account. These could greatly affect the form and location of the planetary orbits, as well as their average motion. Since the secular terms are not periodic, their influence could seriously affect the motion of the planets and as a result, call into question the stability of the solar system. In particular, for Laplace, a system is stable if, when the motion is weakly perturbed, the system undergoes only small oscillations about its original orbit. In other words, it is subject only to periodic inequalities. Thus, to draw conclusions about the stability of the solar system, he tried to eliminate all the secular terms that appeared in the planetary equations of motion.

Laplace's first achievement was the elimination of the secular terms from the equations describing the motion of Jupiter and Saturn. These terms had been introduced by Edmund Halley (1656–1742) who, comparing his observations with those of the Chaldeans in 228 BC (recorded by Ptolemy), determined that Jupiter's motion accelerated while that of Saturn slowed down. This behavior was described by two secular terms that grew with the square of the elapsed time, one adding to the motion of Jupiter, the other substracting from the motion of Saturn. After ruling out the possibility that this could be due to the effects of comets, Laplace realized that the the conservation of energy in the Sun-Jupiter-Saturn system required that if the average speed of one of the planets increased, the other would have to decrease.[5]

> One general property of the action of the planets among themselves is that, at least for very long period properties, the sum of the masses of each planet, divided respectively by the long axis of their orbits, remains approximately constant, from which follows that the squares of the average motion is inversely proportional to the cubes of the axes, if the motion of Saturn is slowed down by Jupiter's action, that of Jupiter is accelerated by the pull of Saturn, which is consistent with what we observe.

The ratio of the deceleration of Saturn to the acceleration of Jupiter was very close to the rational number 7/3. Laplace had previously shown that up to third order in the small parameters e (eccentricity) and i (inclination of the orbits), there was no secular term in the mean motion and the mean distances of the planets to the Sun. In fact, he remarked:[6]

> examining the details of the motion of Jupiter and Saturn, one sees

[5] P. Simon de Laplace, Mémoire sur les inégalités séculaires des planètes et des satellites, *Mémoires de l'Académie Royale des Sciences de Paris* (1784), 49–92, 1787 — *Oeuvres complètes*, XI, p. 50.

[6] P. Simon de Laplace, Théorie de Jupiter et de Saturne, *Mémoires de l'Académie Royale des Sciences de Paris* (1785), 95–207, 1788 — *Oeuvres complètes*, XI, p. 97.

> readily that their average motions are quite commensurable, and that five times the mean motion of Saturn is approximately equal to twice that of Jupiter; from which I concluded that, in the differential equations describing the motion of these two planets, those terms which have for their argument five times the average longitude of Saturn, minus twice that of Jupiter, could become large when integrated, though multiplied by the cubes and products of three dimensions of the eccentricities and inclinations of the orbits.

In this way Laplace showed that terms depending on five times the mean motion of Saturn, minus twice the mean motion of Jupiter, lead to the observed variations of the two planets. These terms have a period of about 910 years. As a result, Laplace's calculations related the inequalities describing the motions of Jupiter and Saturn with a very long period term. There was no need for any secular terms in this theory and Laplace could make comparisons between observations made during very different epochs. In particular, he found good agreement between the observations of the Chaldeans during the second century BC and those of Tycho Brahe at the end of the 15th century. Showing great confidence in his calculations, Laplace used his theory to estimate the date of even more ancient observations. He found that the Indians had observed the mean motions of the two planets when the apparent motion of Saturn was very slow and that of Jupiter was very fast:[7]

> The motions that the Astronomers of these people have attributed to Jupiter and Saturn could help to determine the time when these observations were made; I have found, in this way, that the Indians have determined the mean motions of these two planets ... during which the apparent motion of Saturn was very slow and that of Jupiter very fast. Two astronomic epochs fulfill this condition, one goes back to the year 3102 before our era and the other occurs in 1491.

He also concluded that "*the observations combined with the theory have been able to show that there is no need for secular terms in the equations for Saturn which, of all the planets, had seemed to astronomers to show the largest secular motion.*"

4.3 The Theory of the Moon

Flushed with his successes of 1785–1786, Laplace attacked the Lunar problem, for which the observations of the Chaldeans, the Arabs (eclipses of the Sun observed in Cairo in 977 and 978) and contemporary observations left no doubt for Edmund Halley: the Moon's motion is uniformly accelerating due to a secular equation.[8]

[7] *Ibid.*

[8] E. Halley, Some account of the ancient state of the city of Palmyra, *Philosophical Transactions of the Royal Society*, **19**, 160–175, 1695.

Because of Kepler's harmonic law, when the period of the Moon's revolution around the Earth decreases, its distance from the Earth also decreases. This could pose a risk of collision with the Earth. To study this possibility, the Academy of Paris organized a competition on this subject. Euler won it: he concluded that "*the secular irregularities in the Lunar motion could not come from gravitational effects alone: they arise from a resistance to motion.*"[9] In other words, friction slows the Moon down. However, Laplace was convinced that this variation in the Moon's motion could be explained by the law of gravitation in terms of a secular contribution to the motion, as he had already found for the motion of Jupiter and Saturn:[10]

> the agreement of all the other celestial phenomena with the theory of gravity is so perfect and so satisfying that one can regard only with regret that the secular equation of the moon falls outside this theory and is the only exception to a law that is so simple, whose discovery, and whose range is so broad, that it brings honor to the human spirit.

Laplace was able to convince himself that the secular inequality describing the Moon's motion was periodic on a scale of several millions of years. With this Lunar theory, Laplace believed that he had solved the major problems of the solar system and that he had formulated a theory that was accurate for periods much longer than the age of the Earth, estimated to be several thousands of years at that time.

4.4 Laplacian Determinism

The major remaining uncertainties in the determination of planetary motions depended on their masses, most particularly on the uncertainties of the masses of Venus and Mars, then not well known. In spite of this, Laplace thought he showed that, no matter what the masses of these planets and their satellites were, their secular inequalities were in fact periodic. For Laplace as for Lagrange, the secular terms were not divergent but rather of very long period. Thinking that he had extended the agreement between the theory of gravitation and solar system observations from a century to several thousands of years, or even several millions of years, Laplace concluded that the solar system was stable:[11]

> The system of the world only oscillates around an average state from which it never deviates by very much. Because of its constitution and

[9] L. Euler, *Theoria motuum lunae, nova methodo pertractata una cum tabulis astronomicis, unde ad quodvis tempus loca lunae expedite computari possunt incredibili studio atque indefesso labore trium academicorum: Johannis Alberti Euler, Wolffgangi Ludovici Krafft, Johannis Andreae Lexell. Opus dirigente Leonhardo Eulero acad. scient. Borussicae directore vicennali et socio acad. Petrop. Parisin. et Lond. Petropoli, typis academiae imperialis scientiarum*, 1772.
[10] P. Simon de Laplace, Sur l'équation séculaire de la lune, *Mémoires de l'Académie Royale des Sciences de Paris* (1786), 243–271, 1788 — *Oeuvres complètes*, XI, p. 244.
[11] *Ibid.*

> the law of gravity, it possesses a stability that cannot be overcome except by foreign causes.

Nevertheless, Laplace's results were not complete because he was unable to calculate eccentricities beyond the first order. A complete proof of the stability of the solar system depended on a demonstration that no secular terms existed *to any order*. Joseph-Louis Lagrange had studied the stability of the solar system since 1774. He carried out his computations using a method of perturbation theory that depended on only three small quantities: the eccentricities, the inclinations of the orbits, and the ratios of the masses of the planets to that of the Sun. In 1776 he was able to show that no secular terms occurred in the description of planetary motion up to any order in the eccentricities of the planetary orbits, any order in the sines of the inclinations, and the first order in the mass ratios.[12] Although only the first order of the mass ratios was included, Laplace believed that the stability of the solar system had been proven since "*M. de la Grange had been able to show, using simple but ingenious arguments, that the mean distances of the planets from the sun remained unchanged forever.*" Laplace expressed an incomparable confidence in the universal law of gravitation which[13]

> has this inestimable advantage, that it may be reduced to calculation, and by a comparison of its results with observation, it presents the most certain method of verifying its existence. We shall see that this great law of nature represents all the celestial phenomena even in their minutest details, that there is not one single inequality of their motions which is not derived from it, with the most admirable precision, and that it explains the cause of several singular motions, just perceived by astronomers, and which were either too complicated or too slow for them to recognize their law. Thus, so far from having to fear that new observations will disprove this theory, we may be assured before-hand, that they will only confirm it more and more; and we may be assured that its consequences are equally certain as if they actually had been observed.

Thus, when Laplace began his *Philosophical Essay on Probabilities* in 1825, he could not help but write:[14]

> We ought then to regard the present state of the universe as the effect of its anterior state and the cause of the one which is to follow. Given for one instant an intelligence which could comprehend all the forces by which nature is animated and the respective situation of the

[12] J. L. Lagrange, Sur l'altération des moyens mouvements des planètes, *Nouveaux Mémoires de l'Académie Royale des Sciences et Belles-lettres de Berlin*, 255–271, 1776.
[13] P. Simon de Laplace, *Exposition du système du monde*, p. 239 — *The system of the world*, II, translated by J. Pond, London, 1809.
[14] Pierre Simon de Laplace, *Essai philosophique sur les probabilités* (1825), I, p. 3, Gauthier-Villars, Paris, 1921 — Translated by Henry H. Harte, Dublin University Press, 1830.

> beings who compose it — an intelligence sufficiently vast to submit this data to analysis — it would embrace in the same formula the movements of the greatest bodies of the universe and those of the lightest atom; for it, nothing would be uncertain and the future, as the past, would be present in its eyes. The human mind offers, in the perfection which it has been able to give to astronomy, a feeble idea of this intelligence. Its discoveries in mechanics and geometry, added to that of universal gravity, have enabled it to comprehend in the same analytic expressions the past and future states of the system of the world. Applying the same method to some other objects of its knowledge, it has succeeded in referring to general laws observed phenomena and in foreseeing those which given circumstances ought to produce. All these efforts in the search for truth tend to lead it back continually to the vast intelligence which we have just mentioned, but from which it will always remain infinitely removed. This tendency, peculiar to the human race, is that which renders it superior to animals; and their progress in this respect distinguishes nations and ages and constitutes their true glory.

Here Laplace combined the notions of absolute determinism and prediction: "*chance does not exist in and of itself: it is only a term to attribute to our ignorance.*" Scientists can no longer be content to only describe and understand, they must also predict. Laplace hoped to estimate confidence intervals in which his predictions would fall, so that he could insulate himself from eventual errors. This was one of the motivations that encouraged Laplace to formulate a theory of probabilities: to quantitatively estimate differences between computational predictions and a perfect knowledge of phenomena. Laplace was vague in the sense that he implicitly meant that he would extend his predictions infinitely far into the future; this is how this Laplace's quotation was understood.

In spite of this, Laplace's confidence was based on yet another incomplete demonstration of the stability of the solar system. In 1809 Siméon Denis Poisson (1781–1840) compounded this confidence by showing that the large axes of the planets did not exhibit any purely secular terms up to second order perturbations in the planetary masses.[15] However, the idea of stability was slightly different for Poisson: while for Laplace and Lagrange stability is attained if the large axes remained within certain limits, Poisson considered a system to be stable if the planets return to a position previously visited, again and again. Solar system stability seemed finally to be proven.

[15] S. D. Poisson, Sur la variation des constantes arbitraires dans les questions de mécanique, *Journal de l'Ecole Polytechnique*, VIII, 266–344, 1809.

4.5 The Discovery of Neptune

The great confidence in the powers of celestial mechanics was reinforced in the middle of the 19th century by the works of Urbain Jean Joseph Le Verrier (1811–1877) and of John Couch Adams (1819–1892) on the perturbations of Uranus, discovered in 1781 by William Herschel[16] (1738–1822). Laplace realized very quickly that the inequalities that this new planet obey were easy to discover: he spoke then of unknown influences. In 1821 Alexis Bouvard (1767–1843) suggested that the variations observed in the motion of Uranus could be due to some unknown action.[17] His nephew, Eugène Bouvard presented, after Alexis' death, his own tables on September 1st 1845 at the Academy of Science and remarked that[18]

> The departure between the observations and the theory lead me to believe that there is a lot of plausibility in the idea emitted by my uncle on the existence of a planet disturbing Uranus.

Eugène Bouvard had mentioned this problem in his letter to George Airy (1801–1892), director of the Greenwich Observatory.

Friedrich Bessel (1784–1846) also proposed this solution in his exchanges with Herschel but died before completing his calculations. Le Verrier plotted the difference between the computed and observed longitudes between 1690 and 1845 (Figure 4.2 as reported by André Danjon[19]). The curve so obtained (from Bouvard's tables corrected by Le Verrier) allows to draw a continuous curve passing by all the points with less than a few seconds of error: these departures were too systematic to be attributed to observational noise, and shall result either from an unknown perturbation (a planet) or from a lack of accuracy of the gravitation law. The latter hypothesis was not very likely after the success obtained by Laplace. Consequently, the remaining solution was to identify a cause perturbing Uranus' motion; one of the simplest ideas was then to assume the existence of an unknown planet in the neighborhood of Uranus.

It was not until September 1845 that John Couch Adams sent Airy the elements of the orbit of the hypothetical planet that could account for the unexplained motions of Uranus. In November of the same year. Le Verrier wrote a preliminary report containing similar results. British astronomers did not pay attention to the work of the young Adams, who became discouraged and abandoned this project while Le Verrier, then a more established astronomer, persisted and published his

[16]W. Herschel, Account of a comet, *Philosophical Transactions of the Royal Society of London*, **71**, 492–501, 1781 — W. Herschel, On the proper motion of the Sun and solar system: with an account of several changes that have appeared among the fixed stars since the time of Mr. Flamstead, *Philosophical Transactions of the Royal Society of London*, **73**, 247–283, 1783.

[17]A. Bouvard, *Tables astronomiques publiées par le bureau des longitudes de France contenant les tables de Jupiter, de Saturne et d'Uranus construites d'après la mécanique céleste*, Bachelier & Hanzard, Paris, 1821.

[18]Quoted by J. Lequeux, La découverte de Neptune par Le Verrier (1846), *BibNum*, 2010.

[19]A. Danjon, Le centenaire de la découverte de Neptune, *Ciel et Terre*, **62**, 369–383, 1946.

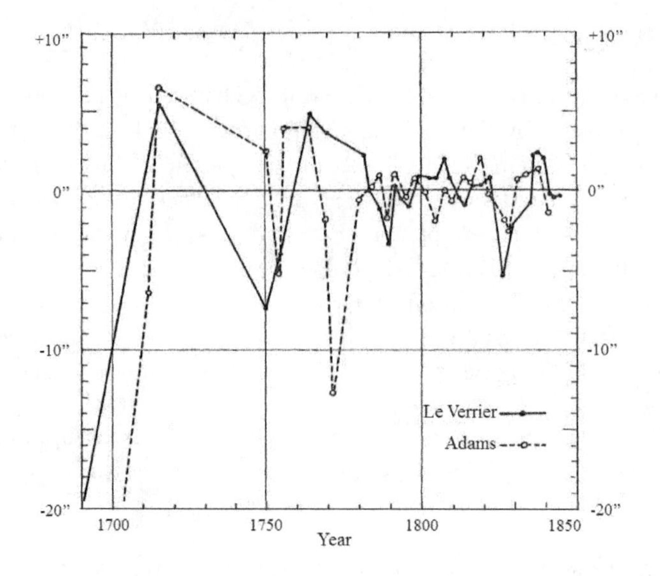

Figure 4.2 Departures between the computed (using corrected Bouvard's table) and observed longitudes of Uranus between 1690 and 1845. Values are those reported by Le Verrier. Note that data before 1781 result from observations of Uranus considered as a star.

results. On 31 August 1846 he wrote:[20]

> I have proved that it is impossible to account for the observations of this body using the universal gravitational law, assuming that it is subject to the forces of the sun and the known planets. All of the observed anomalies are explained, down to the smallest details, by the influence of a new planet located beyond Uranus and which follows an orbit that I have determined.

But to guarantee that the planet in question had really been seen, an astronomer who directed his telescope in the direction predicted by Le Verrier had to compare what he had seen with a detailed chart of the same region of the sky, to verify that the body was really on the chart and, if it had a proper motion, whether it was a planet or a comet. In fact, a detailed map of the region of the sky where Uranus was expected had just been published in Berlin by the publisher Bremicker, and had not yet reached Paris. Therefore Le Verrier sent a letter to the young astronomer, John Gottfried Galle (1812–1910), in Berlin on 18 September 1846, asking for his help. Galle, with Heinrich d'Ariest, observed this planet on the 23 September, on the same day that he received the letter from Le Verrier. It was $0°52'$ distant from the

[20] U. J. J. Le Verrier, Sur la planète qui produit les anomalies observées dans le mouvement d'Uranus: détermination de sa masse, de son orbite et de sa position actuelle, *Comptes-Rendus de l'Académie des Sciences* (Paris), **23**, 428–438, 1846.

predicted longitude. Galle could write to Le Verrier on the 25 September that:[21]

> The planet whose position you sent to me really exists. The very day that I received your letter I observed a star of eighth magnitude that was not inscribed in the excellent *Hora* XXI chart (compiled by Dr. Bremiker), in the collection of celestial charts published by the Royal Academy of Berlin. Observation the following day confirmed that this was the searched planet.

Le Verrier was overtaken by Laplace's enthusiasm:[22]

> The position was predicted within a degree. We find this error incredibly small when one recalls the perturbations of this body are so tiny. This success allows us to hope that after thirty or forty years of observing this new planet one could use the observations, in turn, for the discovery of yet more planets even further from the sun. Following this route, unfortunately, we will surely be lead to bodies whose orbits could be traced with great exactitude over the centuries using the theory of secular inequalities, but that cannot be seen due to their great distance from the sun.

The orbits computed by Le Verrier and Adams were reported by Danjon in Figure 4.3 for comparison with the actual orbit of Neptune. The departure between computed and observed orbits mainly results in errors in the estimation of the mass and the distance from the Sun, both made by Le Verrier and Adams.

This discovery was greeted with a great deal of enthusiasm, as documented by Francois Arago (1786–1853) (truth in praise: a friend of Le Verrier):[23]

> M. Le Verrier has discovered a new star without need to peer through a telescope: he saw it using his pencil; using the power of computation he determined both its mass and its location, situated well beyond the known limits of our solar system, at a distance of 1200 millions of "lieues", and which hardly appears as a disk, even in our most powerful telescopes. In summary, the discovery of M. Le Verrier is one of the most brilliant manifestations of the exactness of modern astronomy; it will encourage our best astronomers to search, with renewed ardor, for the eternal truths that remain hidden, according to a phrase of Pliny, in the majesty of theories.

---

[21] F. Arago, Planète de M. Le Verrier, *Comptes-Rendus de l'Académie des Sciences*, **23** (14), 659–662, 1846.

[22] U. J. J. Le Verrier, Sur la planète qui produit les anomalies observées dans le mouvement d'Uranus. Cinquième et dernière partie, relative à la détermination de la position du plan de l'orbite, *Comptes-Rendus de l'Académie des Sciences* (Paris), **23** (14), 657–659, 1846.

[23] F. Arago, Planète de M. Le Verrier, *Comptes-Rendus de l'Académie des Sciences* (Paris), **23** (14), 659–662, 1846.

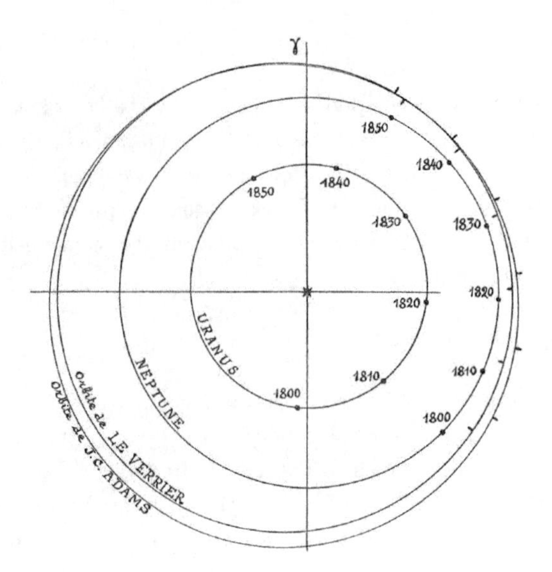

Figure 4.3 Representation (due to Danjon) of the orbits of planets computed by Le Verrier and Adams compared to the actual orbit of Neptune. Note the closeness of predicted positions and actual positions in the neighborhood of the conjunction of Uranus and Neptune (1821).

The German astronomer Johann Encke (1791–1865), the head of Galle's observatory, wrote to Le Verrier that "*his name would forever be associated with the most astonishing proof imaginable of the correctness of the universal law of gravitational attraction.*"[24]

4.6 The Development of Perturbation Theory

This enthusiasm encouraged Geometers to improve their calculations of lunar and planetary tables, particularly those of the Moon. During the second half of the 19th century, Charles-Eugene Delaunay (1816–1872) redid the calculations of Laplace and Le Verrier. In order to derive a more precise theory of the Moon using sines and cosines, he began by considering a simplified problem in which the Earth and the Moon follow elliptical orbits that are not in the same plane. He then computed the perturbations produced by the Sun and the other planets, including perturbations in the radius up to seventh order. He presented his method in 1846 in a proceedings of the Academy of Sciences of Paris[25] but these calculations were very long, more than 478 terms for which even the coefficients were polynomials that had to be computed,

[24] J. Encke, Letter to Le Verrier, September 25, 1846, quoted by J. Lequeux, *Le Verrier: savant magnifique et detesté*, p. 33, EDP Sciences, 2009.

[25] C.-E. Delaunay, Nouvelle théorie analytique du mouvement de la Lune, *Comptes-Rendus de l'Académie des Sciences* (Paris), **23**, 968–970, 1946.

one by one. The results were published in two volumes, in 1860 and 1867.[26] In this work he completely eliminated the secular terms in the theory of Lunar motion. The Lunar tables computed by Delaunay were far better than all previous Lunar tables. Other theories supplanted this. Ernst Brown (1866–1938) constructed the next improvement between 1891[27] and 1909[28] and published his tables in 1911. This theory includes planetary perturbations calculated by Rodolphe Radau (1835–1911) in 1895[29] and those due to the flattening of the Earth calculated by George Hill in 1891.[30] This lead to the discovery that the Earth's rotation was variable. This theory included 818 terms, of which 396 addressed the principal problem and 422 described the perturbations. The major effects of the attraction of the Sun on the Moon were the regression of the line of nodes with a period of 18.6 years and the precession of the apogee with a period of 8.9 years. Other small contributions, such as the attraction of the smaller planets and the perturbations induced by the oblate shape of the Earth and the Moon were also taken into account. More accurate solutions did not become available until the development of computers.

In 1939 Spencer Jones[31] (1890–1960) showed that solar time was not uniform and also that the secular acceleration of the Moon's motion was due to tides, which dissipate some Lunar energy. This showed at last that Laplace's explanation was incorrect and that the apparent agreement between his (incomplete) calculations and the ancient observations was due to our failure to understand the sources of irregularities in solar timekeeping on which these ancient observations depended.

More recently Jean Chapront and Michelle Chapront-Touzé, of the Bureau of Longitudes, developed a lunar theory depending on 35,000 terms.[32] Calculations involving such a huge number of terms can only be done thanks to computer software allowing symbolic computations. For example, the calculations done by Delaunay during the course of 20 years can now be done on a small computer in a little more than a day.[33] The current objective of Lunar theories is to provide a description of Lunar motion that is as accurate as the available measurements. The intrinsic precision of Lunar observations, made with the aid of laser beams, is currently a few centimeters over an average distance of about 400,000 km. Currently, the

[26]C.-E. Delaunay, Théorie du mouvement de la lune I, *Mémoire de l'Académie des Sciences* (Paris), **28**, 1–883, 1860 and II, *Mémoire de l'Académie des Sciences* (Paris), **29**, 1–931, 1867.
[27]E. W. Brown, On the Determination of a certain class of inequalities in the Moon's motion, *Monthly Notices of the Royal Astronomical Society*, **52**, 71–80, 1891.
[28]E. W. Brown, On the plans for new tables of the Moon's motion, *Monthly Notices of the Royal Astronomical Society*, **70**, 148–175, 1909.
[29]R. Radau, Recherches concernant les inegalités planétaires du mouvement de la Lune, *Annales de l'Observatoire de Paris*, **21**, 1–114, 1895.
[30]G. W. Hill, Determination of the inequalities of the moon's motion which are produced by the figure of the earth. A supplement to Delaunay's lunar theory, *Astronomical Papers of the American Ephemeris*, **3** (2), 201–344, 1891.
[31]S. Jones, The Rotation of the Earth, and the secular accelerations of the Sun, Moon and Planets, *Monthly Notices of the Royal Astronomical Society*, **99**, 541–558, 1939.
[32]M. Chapront-Touzé et J. Chapront, *Lunar Tables and programs from 4000 B.C. to A.D. 8000*, Richmond, 1991, p. 80.
[33]Once the algorithm achieved!

precision of the best solutions is about 20 meters for the center of gravity of the Moon. The theory of Jean and Michelle Chapront is semi-analytic in the sense that certain coefficients are determined by observations and injected into the equations as Laplace had done: this allows more accurate predictions. This theory provides, at every instant of time, the position of a point attached to the Lunar surface with respect to the center of gravity of the Earth. This requires a knowledge of the motion of the Moon's center of gravity with respect to the Earth as well as the motion of the Moon around its own center of gravity. The predictions of this theory are valid for several thousand years. Beyond that, the precision falls off and becomes comparable to what can be found with an analytic method, that is, without introducing values of coefficients determined from observations. This limit on the precision of Lunar theories is due essentially to the proliferation of terms which introduces both a propagation and a cumulation of numerical errors that are introduced in the computations that are done numerically with limited precision (only dozens of significant figures). As a result, these methods cannot be used to make statements about the stability of the solar system, which Laplace and Lagrange thought they had shown.

Chapter 5

Birth of the Global Analysis

The development of computational methods depending on perturbation theory improved the quality of predictions and the time intervals over which they were valid. Nevertheless, for very long times these predictions always contained large errors. The source of these errors was only understood through an entirely new approach, now known as the *global* analysis. The global nature comes from treating the evolution of an entire ensemble of trajectories, not a single isolated trajectory.

5.1 The Restricted Three-Body Problem

The power of the method of successive approximations (perturbation theory) for solving differential equations was demonstrated by the successes of Laplace, Lagrange, and Le Verrier. Nevertheless, Le Verrier observed that the solutions were very dependent on the initial conditions. He began by believing that this property depended on the presence of nonlinear terms (terms whose power exceeded 1) in the differential equations. This sensitivity to initial conditions was particularly troublesome because it prohibited general statements about the convergence of the perturbation series. This required a specific treatment of these series from a mathematical point of view. That is, it was not sufficient to show that the series converged only up to a certain order but necessary to pay attention to the limit of an infinite number of terms, as recommended by d'Alembert.

Since the convergence problem was very important, it was necessary to come up with an explanation for the source of these difficulties. The three-body problem was an ideal context for the search for solutions to this problem. In 1836 Carl Gustav Jacobi (1804–1851) conceived the idea for treating the three-body problem as follows:[1]

> We consider the motion of a massless point around the sun and perturbed by a planet whose orbit is assumed circular. [...] In the theory of the moon, it is useful to replace the sun by the earth and take the sun for the perturbing body.

[1]C. G. Jacobi, Lettre, *Compte-Rendu de l'Académie des Sciences* (Paris), **3**, 59–61, 1836.

Jacobi showed that in this simplified form of the three-body problem there existed a new integral equation (constant of motion) that existed "*between the terms that are independent of the eccentricity of the perturbing planet, and that held rigorously to all powers of the mass of the perturbing planet.*" This restricted form of the three-body problem was taken up by George William Hill (1838–1914), whose contributions to the global analysis were absolutely fundamental. Having worked on the theory of the Moon starting with Delaunay's works, he observed that the convergence of terms depending on the ratio of the Lunar's motion to that of the Sun was slower than convergence of other terms in this series. Thus, rather than starting from the two-body problem relating the Moon and the Earth, he started from the Sun-Moon two-body problem, which is perturbed by the Earth. He carried out his perturbation theory in cartesian rather than polar coordinates to obtain purely algebraic expressions rather than trigonometric expressions. These innovations allowed Hill to greatly improve the convergence properties of his series and, as a result, to find a better description of this problem by taking account of the non spherical shape of the Earth.

Despite this, Hill was not satisfied by these results, because they showed that terms formerly considered as negligible, could still make major contributions in perturbation theory. He did not hesitate to break with the traditional approach of finding better solutions by making successive approximations to previous solutions. Rather, he became interested in studying the properties of the differential equations governing planetary motions:[2]

> When we consider how we may best contribute to the advancement of this much-treated subject, we cannot fail to notice that the great majority of writers on it have had before them, as their ultimate aim, the construction of Tables: that is they have viewed the problem from the stand-point of practical astronomy rather than of mathematics. [...] their object compelling them to go over the whole field, they have neglected to notice minor points of great interest to the mathematician, simply because the knowledge of them was unnecessary for the formation of Tables.

To focus his attention on the mathematical origins of these difficulties, he returned to the simplified version of the three-body problem already studied by Jacobi. He studied the problem of three point particles moving in a plane under their mutual gravitational interactions. For this case he found four ordinary differential equations. Up to this time the problem was very complicated and remained insoluble. For this reason, Hill used the version of this problem simplified by Jacobi who assumed that the two primary massive bodies were not perturbed by the third body (of very small mass) which remained sufficiently far from them. In addition, the two primaries were assumed to follow a circular, rather than an elliptical, orbit. They

[2]G. W. Hill, Researches on the Lunar theory, *American Journal of Mathematics*, **1**, 5–26, 1878.

moved along circles about their common center of mass with a constant angular velocity. These assumptions allowed to describe the motion of the third body in a plane corotating with the primary bodies. This plane rotates with the angular velocity of the two primaries, which are therefore at rest in the plane. The Ox axis in this plane passes through the two primary masses: the x-y plane is the *synodic plane* (Figure 5.1).

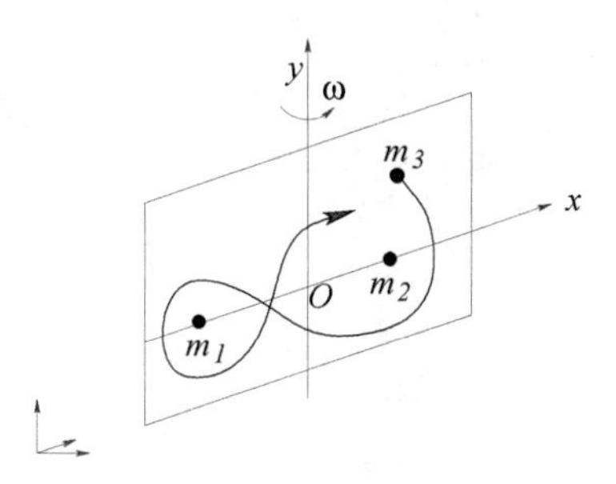

Figure 5.1 Synodic plane turns with angular velocity $\omega = \dot{\theta}$ around the Oy axis. The two primaries m_1 and m_2 are at rest in this plane. Hill chose a coordinate system in which the two masses determine the Ox axis.

To simplify these equations even further, Hill chose a system of units for which $m_1 + m_2 = 1$ and in which the constant distance between these two masses is also equal 1. He set the strength of the gravitational attraction equal to one and also the angular velocity $\omega = 1$. He thus found the set of four first-order dimensionless differential equations

$$\begin{cases} \dot{x} = u \\ \dot{y} = v \\ \dot{u} = x + 2v - \dfrac{(1-\mu)(\mu + x)}{\rho_1^3} + \dfrac{\mu(1-\mu-x)}{\rho_2^3} \\ \dot{v} = y - 2u - \dfrac{(1-\mu)y}{\rho_1^3} + \dfrac{\mu y}{\rho_2^3} \end{cases}$$

that describes the motion of the massless third body.[3]

These equations define what is now called the *restricted three-body problem*. These equations can be numerically integrated (using a computer). Two trajectories arising from slightly different initial conditions are shown in Figure 5.2. One sees that these two trajectories rapidly separate from each other. This is a signature of sensitivity to initial conditions which arises from the secular terms in the equations

[3]Masses of the two bodies are chosen such as $m_1 = 1 - \mu$ and $m_2 = \mu$. This condition satisfies $m_1 + m_2 = 1$. Both bodies are located on the axis Ox at $x_1 = -\mu$ and $x_2 = 1 - \mu$. In the four equations, we have $\rho_1 = \sqrt{(x+\mu)^2 + y^2}$ and $\rho_2 = \sqrt{(x+\mu-1)^2 + y^2}$. Numerical computations that are displayed in Figure 5.2, were performed as follows. The first trajectory starts from the point $(x_0, y_0, u_0, v_0) = (0.45; 0; 0; 1; -0.1)$, the second trajectory is issued from a point differing from y_1 by a small displacement $\delta y = 0.025$. Parameter μ is equal to 0.2.

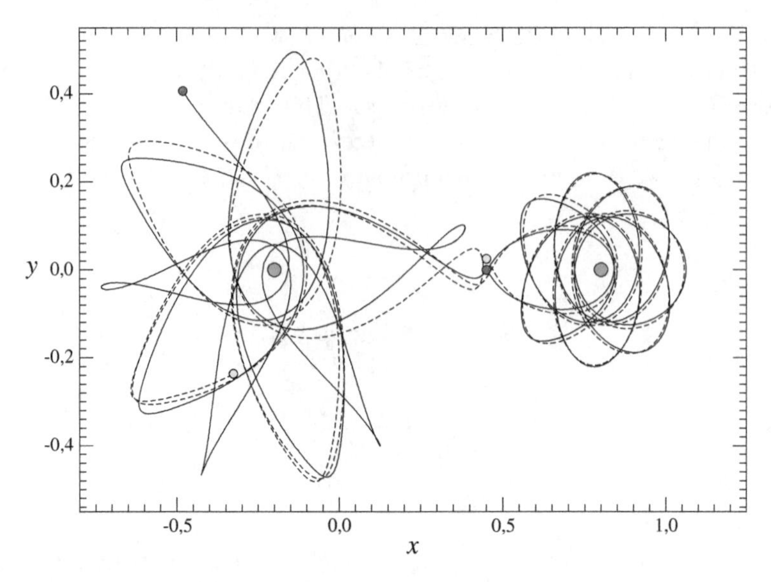

Figure 5.2 Two solutions of the restricted three-body problem obtained by numerical integration. The two solutions show that the solutions are very sensitive to the initial conditions.

and which plays a very important role. This explains why the convergence of the perturbation series depends strongly on the initial conditions, as Le Verrier had remarked much earlier.

5.2 A Qualitative Analysis

George Hill was not really interested in finding a particular solution, neither was he interested in making *quantitative* predictions. Rather, he was interested in understanding how the solutions were *qualitatively* organized in the synodic plane. For example, he looked for the points in the synodic plane where the speed of the third body was zero. More remarkable still, he was not content to find solutions with a fixed value of the constants of motion (for example, the energy of the third body); instead, he studied how the solution curves changed as these parameters were changed. In doing so, he found a series of curves shown in Figure 5.3. One can see that these curves are arranged around five remarkable points as well as the locations of the two primary masses, P_1 and P_2.

Of these, three, identified as E_1, E_2 and E_3, are aligned with the two primaries: if the third body is placed at one of these points E_i, it remains there, no matter what the values of the parameters. These three points correspond precisely to the exact solution found by Johann Euler: when the three bodies are arranged in one of these three configurations, they rotate rigidly with a common angular velocity ω. The two points L_1 and L_2 correspond to Lagrange points: when the third body is placed at either of these two points, it forms an equilateral triangle with the

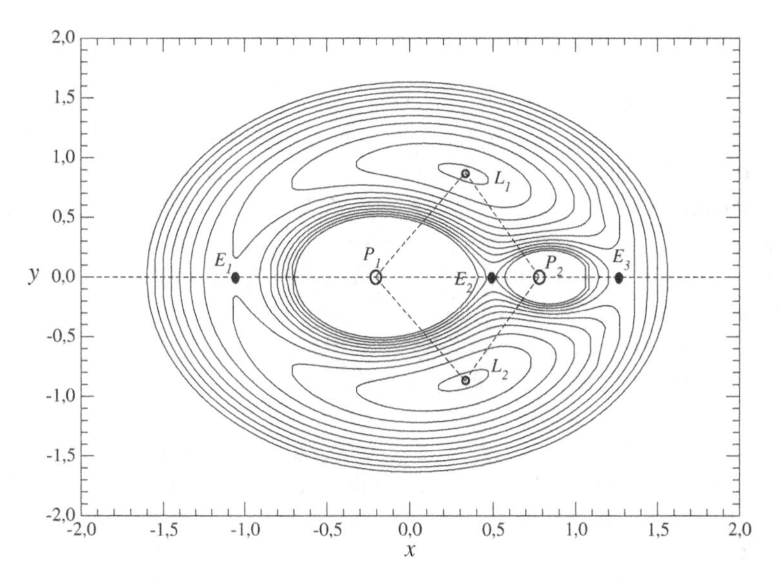

Figure 5.3 Curve of zero speed in the synodic plane when one of the system parameters is varied (in this case, the energy). For each value of the energy there is a curve (or a symmetric pair of curves) corresponding to a zero speed for the small body. The three points E_1, E_2, and E_3 correspond to a configuration similar to Johann Euler's configuration: the bodies P_1, P_2 and the three points E_i ($i = 1, 2$ or 3) fall along a straight line and turn together around the center of mass with angular velocity ω. Points L_1 and L_2 correspond to Lagrange points: the three bodies P_1, P_2 and L_i (i=1 or 2) form an equilateral triangle.

two primaries and this triangle rotates rigidly around its center of mass. Hill found curves corresponding to the Sun-Earth-Moon system: he discovered curves on which the third body had zero speed enclosed each of the two primary masses. As a result, he concluded that the Moon, if it was initially in the vicinity of the Earth (one of the primaries), could never escape from the Earth because it would have to cross a null curve that encloses it.[4] This result was the very first result in Astronomy coming from a global approach to the study of differential equations. Hill found this result without knowing an exact solution for the motion. From the point of view of methodology, this approach was really new: it was not necessary to know an exact trajectory followed by the system to determine stability properties that characterize the dynamics. A global view of the architecture of all the solutions offered a simple, direct understanding of many of the essential properties of the dynamics (the curves corresponding to zero speed are much simpler to determine than a single trajectory!).

[4] G. W. Hill, 1978. *Ibid.*

5.3 Studies of Sets of Solutions

Henri Poincaré (1854–1912) provided major advances in our understanding about the source of difficulties encountered in the study of the three-body problem. He introduced a large number of new methods into the study of differential equations. His 1881 memoir *On the curves defined by a differential equation* gave birth to the field that we now call the *theory of nonlinear dynamical systems.* Earlier he had presented his thesis[5] devoted to the study of partial differential equations depending on an arbitrary number of independent variables. Unfortunately, such equations are very often difficult (that is, impossible) to integrate. As a result, Poincaré quickly redirected his attention to a simpler program:[6]

> Searching what are the properties of differential equations is thus a question of the greatest interest. One has already taken a first step along this road by studying the proposed function *in the neighborhood of a point in the plane.* Today we hope to go further by studying this function *in the entire plane.*

To do this he insisted on the need for a qualitative, rather than a quantitative analysis:[7]

> In the past, one did not consider an equation as solved except when one had expressed its solution using a finite number of known functions: but this is not even possible one time in a hundred. What we can always do, or what we should always try to do is to study the problem qualitatively, that is, to try to understand the general form of the curve that represents the unknown function.

A qualitative analysis involves, for example, showing the range of possibilities of some function without previously finding a quantitative solution — that is to say, a plot of the function. To do this, he followed a path opened up by Evariste Galois (1811–1832). While Niels Abel (1802–1829) showed that it was not possible to solve a general algebraic equation of degree greater than four,[8] Galois looked at the ensemble of solutions of such equations. Since it was not possible to extract roots one by one, he studied the relations that the roots had among themselves and showed the importance of permutations of these roots. By considering the entire set

[5] H. Poincaré, *Sur les propriétés des fonctions définies par les équations aux différences partielles*, Ph.D. thesis, Université de Paris, 1879.

[6] H. Poincaré, Mémoire sur les courbes définies par une équation différentielle, *Journal de Mathématiques*, III, **7**, 375–422, 1881.

[7] Henri Poincaré, *Science et Méthode*, Flammarion, p. 33, 1908.

[8] N. Abel, Démonstration de l'impossibilité de la résolution algébrique des équations générales qui passent le quatrième degré, *Journal für die reine und augewandte Mathematik, herausgegeben von Crell* (Berlin), **1**, 1826. Reproduced in *Oeuvres complètes*, **1**, 66–94, Gabay (Paris), 1992.

of roots, he was able to determine the conditions under which an algebraic equation could be solved by radicals.

For second order linear differential equations, Charles Sturm (1803–1855) provided one of the first examples of global qualitative analyses:[9]

> We do not know how to integrate these except in a very small number of particular cases, beyond which we cannot obtain even a first integral; and even when we have an expression for a function that satisfies such an equation, [...] it is very often difficult to recognize in this expression the characteristic properties of this function. Thus, for example, one cannot see if this expression becomes zero or infinite in an interval, if it changes sign, if it has a maximum or a minimum. Nevertheless, the knowledge of such properties allows one to make remarkable predictions about physical or dynamical properties of systems governed by such differential equations. To determine the value of such a function at an isolated value of the variable on which it depends, it is only necessary [...] to examine the form and the sinuosity of the curve for which the function is the ordinate and the independent variable is the abscissa. One can realize this goal only by studying only the differential equations themselves, without need for their integration.

Sturm was forced into this global qualitative analysis in part because he had difficulties finding explicit solutions, but also because he was no longer satisfied with quantitative results: he also wished to explain the qualitative behavior of these solutions.

In this program Augustin-Louis Cauchy (1789–1857) proposed, between 1820 and 1830, the first results that showed the existence and uniqueness of solutions of differential equations: starting from a given initial condition, there exists exactly one solution.[10] In other words, starting from a given state of the system, a single future is possible. One of his objectives was to develop series solutions around singular points (points where the system is at rest). Charles Briot (1817–1882) and Jean-Claude Bouquet (1819–1885) followed up on Cauchy's work by studying the theory of the solutions of differential equations that could be expanded in power series; they were among the first to study singularities of solutions, the first problem studied by Poincaré.

---

[9]C. Sturm, Mémoire sur les équations différentielles linéaires du second ordre, *Journal de Mathématiques Pures and Appliquées*, **1**, 106–186, 1836.

[10]A.-L. Cauchy, Mémoire sur l'emploi du calcul des limites dans l'intégration des équations aux dérivées partielles, *Comptes rendus de l'Académie des Sciences* (Paris), **15**, 85–101, 1842.

5.4 Dynamical Systems

Henri Poincaré began by studying the set of two ordinary differential equations in the plane

$$\begin{cases} \dot{x} = f_1(x, y) \\ \dot{y} = f_2(x, y) \end{cases} \tag{5.1}$$

where f_1 and f_2 are arbitrary functions that depend only on x and y. $\dot{x}$ and $\dot{y}$ designate the derivatives of x and y with respect to time, respectively (that is, $\dot{x} = dx/dt$). These are the components of the velocity vector with respect to the axes Ox and Oy. Rather than searching for algebraic solutions of this system, he treated x and y as the coordinates of a point moving in time, for which the components of the velocity vector are given as a function of the coordinates x and y by the functions f_1 and f_2.

The system (5.1) in fact defines a *dynamical system*, that is, it describes the motion of a physical system as a function of time starting from the initial condition (x_0, y_0). The system depends on two *variables* x and y, in terms of which a representation of the solution is based: this is called the *state space*. This space had been introduced by William Rowan Hamilton (1805–1865). Equations (5.1) define the velocity vector $\vec{V} = (\dot{x}, \dot{y})$ at every point of the state space: one calls this a *vector field*. Thus, to every point (x, y) is associated a velocity vector $\vec{V}$ which, by definition, is tangent to the trajectory. Knowledge of a trajectory describing the motion of the system occurs naturally by following the velocity vector. It is possible to construct a large number of trajectories that differ in their *initial conditions* from a given velocity vector field.

The initial conditions are only defined according to the accuracy of the observations. Since each initial condition defines a trajectory determined from the vector field according to Eq. (5.1), it is not possible to know exactly the trajectory that an experiments will follow.

5.5 The Ideal Pendulum

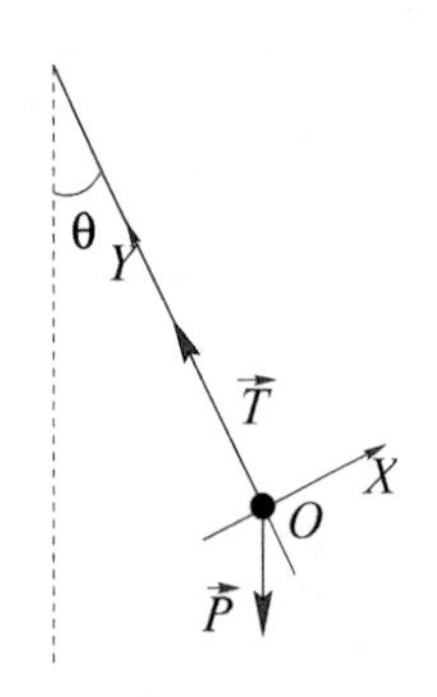

In order to make these ideas a little more palpable, let us start with the case of the ideal pendulum. An ideal pendulum (no friction) is subject to a gravitational force $\vec{P}$ and a tension $\vec{T}$ due to a support of length L. The fundamental principle of dynamics leads to

$$m\vec{a} = \vec{P} + \vec{T}$$

where $\vec{a}$ is the acceleration vector acting on the constant mass at the end of its rod. At any instant t the two forces can be decomposed along the axes XOY as follows

$$\begin{cases} ma_X &= -mg\sin\theta \\ ma_Y &= T - mg\cos\theta \end{cases}$$

where m is the mass of the pendulum, θ the angle that the pendulum makes with the vertical and g is the gravitational constant. Along the OX axis we find

$$a_X = -g \sin\theta \,. \tag{5.2}$$

In this case the radial velocity V_R is given by $L\dot{\theta}$ where $\dot{\theta}$ designates the first derivative $\frac{d\theta}{dt}$. The acceleration of the pendulum is given by the differential equation

$$\ddot{\theta} = -\frac{g}{L} \sin\theta \,. \tag{5.3}$$

This differential equation describes the dynamical system that is the ideal pendulum. This means that the motion of the system is described in terms of the forces acting on the system by the differential equation (5.3). It now remains to integrate this equation to learn how the pendulum moves. The differential equation (5.3) directly results from the fundamental principle of dynamics while the *laws of motion* correspond to the solutions of these equations. It is thus of greatest importance to find a solution to this differential equation. This is sometimes a very delicate step, as Clairaut had already indicated.

The differential equation (5.3) is second order: it involves the second derivative of the angle θ with respect to time. It can be reduced to the pair of first-order differential equations

$$\begin{cases} \dot{x} = y \\ \dot{y} = -\dfrac{g}{L} \sin x \end{cases} \tag{5.4}$$

(simpler to study) with the aid of this important change of variables ($x = \theta, y = \dot{\theta}$). It seems that *two state variables* are needed for a complete description of the pendulum: we must know simultaneously the angle $x = \theta$ that the rod makes with the vertical and the angular velocity $y = \dot{\theta}$. In other words the motion is not the same if we start the pendulum at an angle of 100° with an initial velocity of zero (point B in Figure 5.4) as it is if the initial angle is 100° but the initial velocity is 40° per second in one direction (point A in Figure 5.4) or the other (point C in Figure 5.4). In the two latter cases the pendulum rotates completely around its axis rather than performing oscillations about the vertical. The parameters g and L are constant during this experiment: they are called *parameters*.

For these reasons, we have more information if we represent its evolution in the plane defined by the coordinates x and y. In this case at each point in the trajectory we know the value of the angle $x = \theta$ and the value of the angular velocity $y = \dot{\theta}$. The trajectory obtained in this way completely describes the motion of the pendulum. We must never forget that the space, called the *state space*, is by nature very different from the physical space (the *configuration space*) in which displacements occur.

Depending on the initial conditions, various trajectories representing the motion of the pendulum can be obtained, all of them solutions to equation (5.3). In fact, for a conservative system such as the pendulum there is no loss of energy due

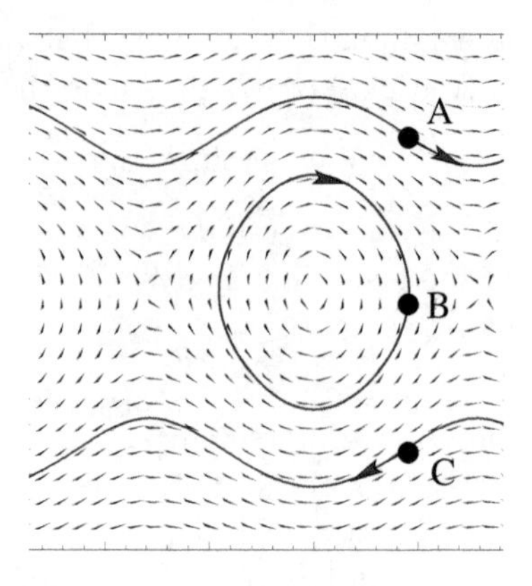

Figure 5.4 Vector field defined by equation (5.3). Any trajectory that describes the motion is naturally tangent to these vectors. The motion of the pendulum is represented here by solid curves through initial conditions (x_0, y_0), represented by the points A, B and C.

to friction. To each initial condition there corresponds a trajectory that is distinct from all other trajectories. Three such solutions in the (x, y) plane are shown for the pendulum in Figure 5.4. The set of all possible trajectories is called the pendulum's *state portrait.*

One of the essential points found by Poincaré is that the trajectories are organized around the singular points of the system (5.1). These are the points of the dynamical system (5.1) where the "velocity vector" is zero, that is, for which

$$\begin{cases} \dot{x} = 0 = f_1(x, y) \\ \dot{y} = 0 = f_2(x, y) \,. \end{cases}$$

In fact, the state portrait (Figure 5.5) is structured around the *singular points.* These correspond to the equilibrium states, or the states of rest, of the pendulum. The singular points found at $\ldots, -360^\circ, 0^\circ, +360^\circ \ldots$ are physically indistinguishable: they correspond to the (stable) rest state of the pendulum. The two indistinguishable points located at $\pm 180^\circ$ correspond to the unstable equilibrium state (the pendulum is inverted).

The singular points alternate in type: the centers located at $\ldots, -360^\circ, 0^\circ, +360^\circ, \ldots,$ around which the trajectories describe ellipses, and the saddles located at $\pm 180^\circ, \pm 540^\circ, \ldots,$ and the intersection of convergent and divergent directions (identified by arrows in Figure 5.5). The centers correspond to the rest state of the pendulum $x = \theta = 0$ (Figure 5.6(a)) and are associated with marginal stability (the circles in Figure 5.5). In other words, any perturbation that is applied in the neighborhood of these states results in elliptical motion around this point. This is due to the conservation of energy. The saddles, because of their divergent directions, correspond to an unstable rest state (Figure 5.6(b)). They appear at an angle of 180° (mod 360°): the slightest perturbation in the neighborhood of this unstable equilibrium point results in very large amplitude motions.

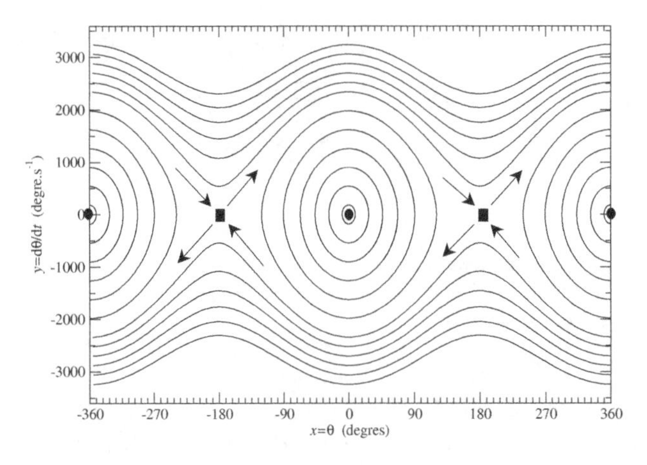

Figure 5.5 Trajectories emerging from various initial conditions in the state space of the ideal pendulum. The singular points are represented by the black points (stable state, on the bottom) and the black squares (unstable states, at the top).

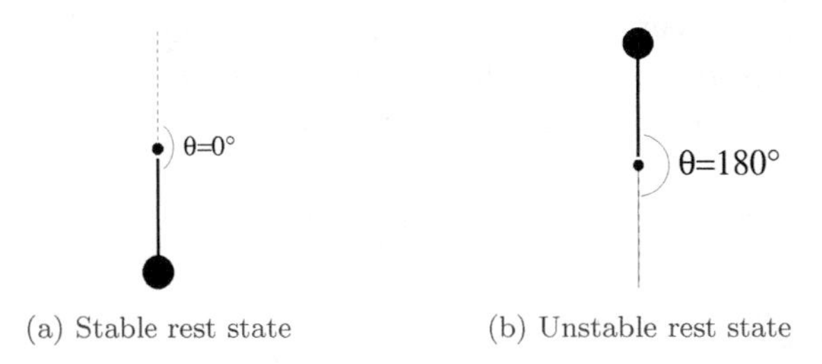

(a) Stable rest state (b) Unstable rest state

Figure 5.6 Two rest states of an ideal pendulum: the line from which the angle θ is measured is directed down. The positions $0°, 360°, 720°, \ldots$ that describe the pendulum at rest (stable equilibrium) are not physically distinguishable.

5.6 The Poincaré-Bendixon Theorem

Not only did Poincaré show that the trajectories that describe motion are organized around the singular points, but he also showed that in two dimensions there are exactly four different types of singular points: saddles, foci, nodes, and centers[11] (Figure 5.7). In addition, Poincaré stated a theorem,[12] later proved by Ivar Bendixon (1861–1935), according to which, in two dimensions, only two types of bounded asymptotic behavior can exist: limit cycles and singular points. Thus, in two dimensions a system that can be completely described by only two variables must eventually either be at rest or exhibit periodic motion.[13]

[11]These four types of singular points were in fact described by Nikolaï Joukavsky (1847–1921): N. E. Joukovsky, Kinemtaika jidkgo tela (kinematics of fluid bodies), *Mathematisch Sbornik* (Moscou), **8** 1–79 & 163–238, 1876. This was discussed in A. Dobrovlsky, Sur l'histoire des points singuliers des équations différentielles, *Revue d'Histoire des Sciences*, **25** (1), 3–11, 1972.
[12]H. Poincaré, Sur les courbes définies par les équations différentielles, *Journal de Mathématiques Pures et Appliquées*, IV, **1**, 167–244, 1885.
[13]I. Bendixson, Sur les courbes définies par des équations différentielles, *Acta Mathematica*, **24**, 1–88, 1901.

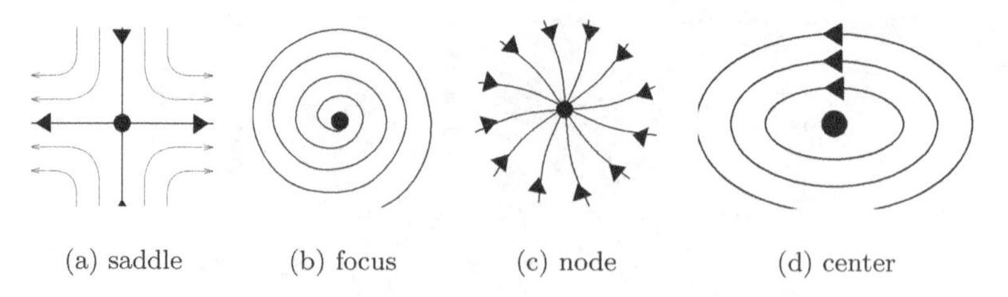

Figure 5.7 The four types of singular points in two dimensions. The foci and nodes can be either stable or unstable, depending on whether a small perturbation is damped or amplified. Oscillations occur around foci and centers.

In fact, systems that can be described in a two-dimensional state space are *integrable*. The idea of integrability is related to the number of *degrees of freedom* and the number of *constants of motion*. A degree of freedom is a direction along which the system can move. For example, when the pendulum is mounted on an axis as in the case of a classic grandfather clock, there is only one degree of freedom: the angle $x = \theta$ is sufficient to describe the position of the pendulum. However, we have seen that it is also necessary to know the angular velocity $y = \dot{\theta}$ to completely determine the state of the pendulum. More generally, a system with N degrees of freedom will be in a completely determined state only if the N position variables are known *as well as* the N variables related to the velocities (for example, the momentum is equal to the product of the mass with the components of the velocity vector associated with the position vector). In the case of a pendulum fixed to a rigid rod, there is one degree of freedom associated with the angular position $x = \theta$ the second variable associated with that degree of freedom is angular velocity $y = \dot{\theta}$. This set of two variables spans the state space for the system.

A system with N degrees of freedom is described by N second-order differential equations that relate positions and velocities with accelerations. The set of N second-order differential equations is equivalent to a set of $2N$ first-order differential equations. This is analogous to what we have done when we reduced the second-order equation (5.3) (depending on a second derivative) to a pair of first-order differential equations (5.4) (depending on first derivatives). The system is said to be integrable when the set of N second-order differential equations can be reduced to a set of N *first*-order differential equations relating the positions to the velocities. To do this, it is necessary to find N constants of motion to reduce the $2N$ first-order equations to N first-order equations.

In fact, there is always one constant of motion for conservative systems since the energy is constant. Due to this the motion of a system with N degrees of freedom can always be described as taking place in a space of dimension at most $2N - 1$. As a result, a system with one degree of freedom is always integrable and only the simple behavior described by the Poincaré-Bendixon theorem can be observed.

When the system under consideration consists of two bodies moving in a plane, it possesses four degrees of freedom: two for each body because each is described by a point in the plane with coordinates x and y. To these four position variables, there are necessarily four variables related to the velocity. The state space therefore has dimension eight! Nevertheless, we have seen that when the problem is treated in the center of mass coordinate system the problem simplifies: in fact the number of degrees of freedom is now only two and the state space has only dimension four. When the conservation of energy is satisfied (thus providing a first constant of motion), the second constant of motion is given by the conservation of areas (Kepler's second law). These two constants of motion guarantee that this system is integrable. Under these conditions only two ordinary first order equations remain to describe the motion of the system. The two-body problem is therefore integrable and elliptical orbits are obtained as solutions to these equations. These satisfy Kepler's laws.

When the problem of three bodies moving in a plane is considered, there are six degrees of freedom (two position variables for each of the three bodies). By describing the problem in the center of mass coordinate system we introduce two constants of motion. The state space is now eight-dimensional. The conservation of energy and of angular momentum (conservation of areas) provide two additional constants of motion. Heinrich Bruns[14] and Henri Poincaré[15] have shown that there are no other constants of motion for this problem. As a result the three-body problem is not integrable because that would require two additional constants of motion. In other words there are no exact analytic solutions to the planar three-body problem: it is impossible to find laws "*à la Kepler*" for the three-body problem. The origin of the difficulties surrounding this problem is at least understood.

5.7 Doubly Asymptotic Orbits

In 1885 Gösta Mittag-Leffler (1846–1927) of Stockholm University decided to organize a competition to honor the sixtieth birthday of the King of Sweden on 21 January 1891. The prize would honor an important discovery in some area of mathematical analysis. He asked Karl Weierstrass (1815–1897) to propose several different subject areas for this competition. Weierstrass took seriously remarks (without proof) by Gustav Lejeune-Dirichlet (1805–1859) that he had discovered an approximation method for solving the n-body problem. Dirichlet was famous for proving convergence conditions for Fourier series expansions of a function.[16] Always impressed by the powers of convergent series expansions, Weierstrass took advantage of the proposed prize to draw the attention of mathematicians to the n body problem with the ultimate goal of investigating the stability of the solar

[14]H. Bruns, Über die Integrale des Vielkörper-Problems, *Acta Mathematica*, **11**, 25–96, 1887.

[15]H. Poincaré, Sur le Problème des trois corps et les équations de la dynamique, *Acta Mathematica*, **13**, 1–279, 1890.

[16]G. Lejeune-Dirichlet, Sur la Convergence des séries trigonométriques qui servent à représenter une fonction arbitraire entre des limites données, *Journal für die reine und angewandte Mathematiks*, **4**, 157–169, 1829.

system. In response to this challenge, Henri Poincaré submitted a thick manuscript of more than 200 pages which did not touch the n body problem because Poincaré knew that "*the difficulty begins as soon as the number n of bodies is equal to three.*" He thus wrote

> the three-body problem has resisted all the efforts of analysts up to now, its complete and rigorous solution is clearly not possible.

Further, he concentrated on the restricted three-body problem. The approach of Poincaré is new in the sense that he started with the periodic orbits, which he assumed played a relevant role in this problem. Following Hill, who had the honor of being the first to fully understand their importance, Poincaré pointed out that the periodic solutions were easy to find and he understood that their study lead to an understanding of all possible solutions. He justified this point of view in the *New methods of celestial mechanics*:[17]

> ...the three-body problem includes an infinite number of periodic solutions. [...] At first it seems that this fact could be of no practical interest. In fact, there is zero probability for an initial condition to be such that the motion would be exactly periodic. But things could be viewed from a different perspective very easily, in a way that the older methods remain applicable. For example, one could choose a periodic solution as a first approximation. [...]
>
> There is even more: here is something that I cannot prove rigorously, but which nevertheless seems very reasonable. Given the equations [...] and an arbitrary particular solution of the equations, one could always find a periodic solution (whose period, in truth, might be arbitrarily long), such that the difference between the two solutions is as small as you wish. Moreover, what makes these periodic solutions so precious, is that they are the sole breach, so to speak, that we can try to penetrate into a place reputed unaffordable.

In order to study the stability of the periodic orbits, Poincaré resorted to a new approach. Rather than studying the evolution of a state space trajectory governed by the continuous differential equations, he introduced a plane, transverse to the trajectory. He studied the motion in the neighborhood of a periodic orbit (Figure 5.8). A trajectory intersects this plane in a succession of points $I_0, I_1, \ldots, I_n, \ldots$ The stability of a periodic orbit is determined by studying the law describing the passage from I_n to the next intersection I_{n+1}. This leads to a recurrence map, simpler to study than a set of differential equations.

Thanks to this insight, the study of the stability of periodic orbits reduces to a study analogous to the study of singular points. In short, Poincaré studied the relation between periodic orbits and periodic points of maps. He found different

[17]H. Poincaré, *Les Méthodes Nouvelles de la mécanique céleste*, Tome I, Gauthier-Vilars, Paris, pp. 81–82, 1892.

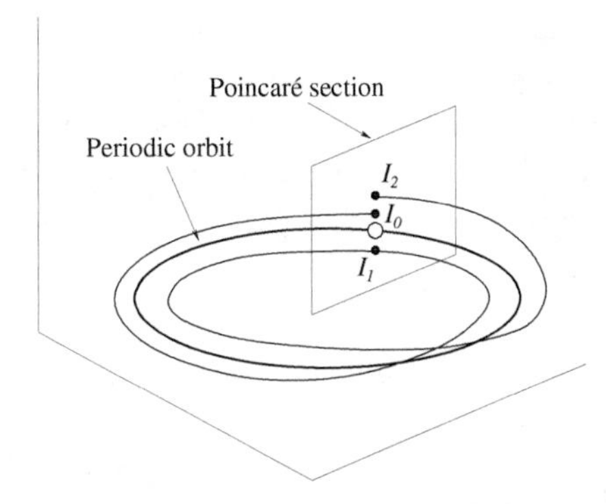

Figure 5.8 Study of the stability of a periodic orbit with the aid of a return map in a transverse plane, now called a "Poincaré section."

types of periodic orbits analogous to the different types of singular points (Figure 5.9). Thanks to this type of analysis, Poincaré found that there are periodic orbits, solutions to the three-body problem, of different types:[18]

> To better understand what I mean by that, let me introduce a simple example. First, imagine an earth and a sun isolated in space, moving under Kepler's laws. Suppose, to further simplify, that their motion is circular. Now suppose that the earth has two satellites, L_1 and L_2, whose masses are negligible, so that they do not perturb the orbits of either the sun or the earth, or even each other — each one moves as if it were alone. Choose an initial position of L_1 in such a way that this moon follows a periodic orbit; we could then choose an initial condition for moon L_2 in such a way that it follows what is called an asymptotic orbit. Initially sufficiently far from L_1, it approaches and then remains very close to L_1 for an infinitely long time. Now imagine an observed placed on the earth and turning slowly in such a way as to face the sun constantly. To him the sun seems stationary and the moon, L_1, whose movement is periodic, appears to him to follow a closed orbit $\mathcal{C}$. For him the moon L_2 appears to follow a curve that gets closer and closer to the closed curve $\mathcal{C}$. There is an infinite number of similar asymptotic orbits. The ensemble of these asymptotic orbits forms a continuous surface S which passes by the closed curve $\mathcal{C}$ and on which exist the trajectories of which I have just spoken.
>
> But there is yet another category of asymptotic solutions. It could happen, if one chooses the initial condition of L_2 appropriately, that this moon becomes very distant from L_1, but that in the distant past if remained very close to L_1. For our observer this satellite also describes a spiral curve, but one which gradually becomes further and further from the curve $\mathcal{C}$. The ensemble of this new class of asymptotic orbits forms yet a second surface S' which also passes close to the curve $\mathcal{C}$.
>
> Finally, there is a doubly asymptotic set of solutions; *this is the point that I am having difficulty to establish rigorously.* It could happen that

[18]H. Poincaré, Le Problème des trois corps, *Revue Générale des Sciences*, **2**, 1–5, 1891.

the satellite L_2, initially very near the orbit of L_1, departs from it and eventually returns anew to it. In the very distant past this moon finds itself on the surface S' and follows a trajectory that departs from the curve $\mathcal{C}$; eventually it is very far from $\mathcal{C}$; yet after another very long time it returns to the surface S and follows a trajectory that spirals down to the curve $\mathcal{C}$ again.

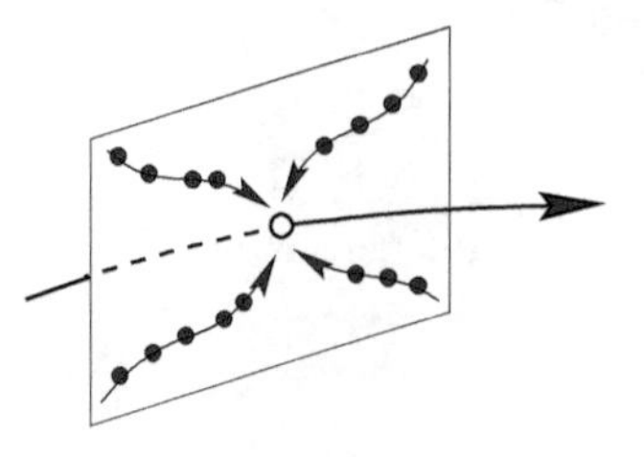

(a) All orbits tend toward the periodic solution (node)

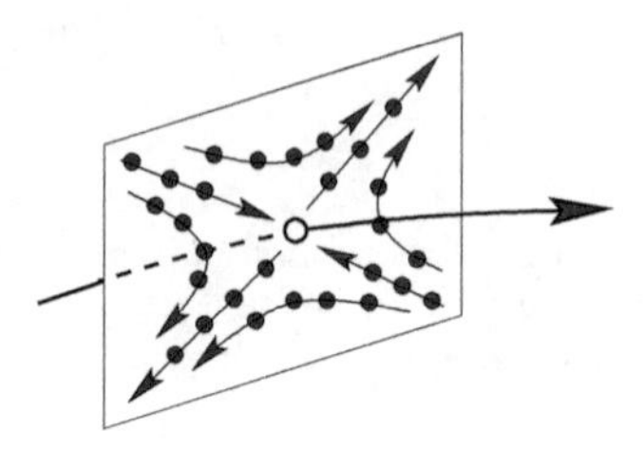

(b) Most of the orbits start to converge toward the periodic solution before going far away (saddle)

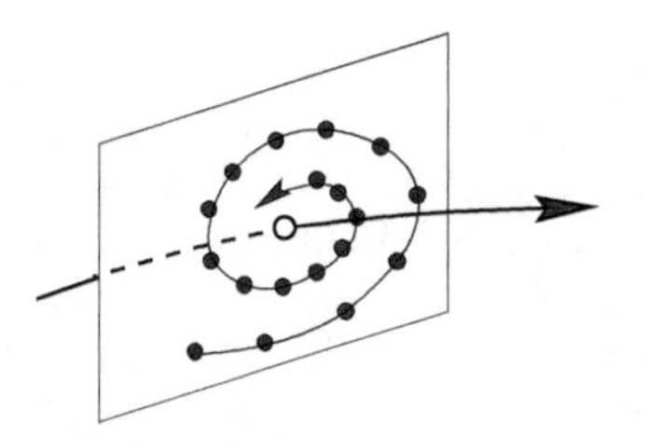

(c) All close orbits tend toward the periodic solution in spiralling around (focus)

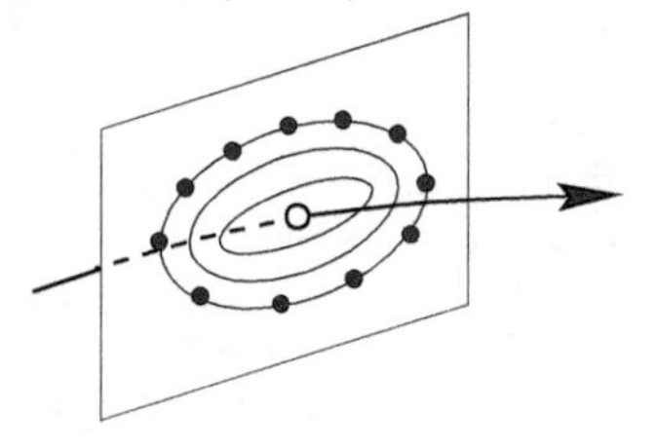

(d) Close solutions spiral around the periodic solution but never reach it (center)

Figure 5.9 Different types of periodic orbits: these figures bear a strong resemblance to figures describing the different types of singular points.

By doing this, Poincaré showed that there is a double infinity of asymptotic curves because there is an infinite number of periodic solutions, that can be grouped into two categories (Figure 5.10(a) and 5.10(b)). He concluded that "*if two curves in the same category could not intersect*" than, on the contrary, "*there is no reason that two asymptotic curves from different categories could not intersect*".[19] He then described how complicated the organization of the doubly periodic solutions could be (Figure 5.10(c)). To do this he showed that the two asymptotic surfaces S and S' passing through the same closed trajectory $\mathcal{C}$ must always intersect outside this trajectory. The asymptotic curves of the first category, which end at the points on a periodic orbit, always intersect the curves of the second category which approach the same points. In other words, on each asymptotic surface there is at least one

[19]H. Poincaré, Les Méthodes Nouvelles de la mécanique céleste, tome III, p. 383, 1899.

doubly periodic solution. In fact, he concluded in his *New methods in celestial mechanics* that "*there is an infinity of doubly periodic solutions*". He called these *homoclinic orbits*. Then, a little further on, he added:[20]

> On an arbitrary asymptotic surface, between any two doubly asymptotic solutions there is an infinity of other doubly asymptotic solutions.

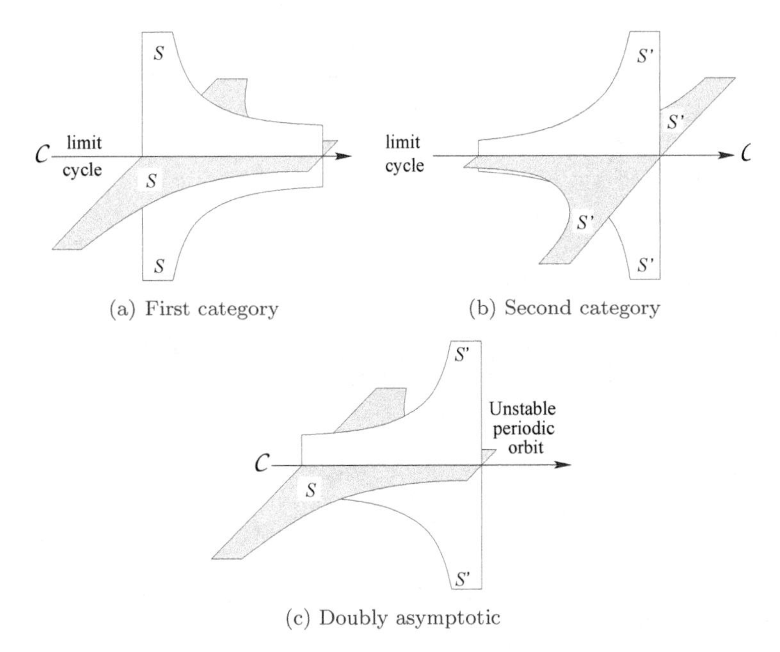

Figure 5.10 Sketch of the convergent surfaces S and divergent surfaces S' around a curve $\mathcal{C}$. Trajectories within the surfaces S evolve asymptotically to the curve $\mathcal{C}$ while those in the surfaces S' progressively depart from the curve $\mathcal{C}$, which is a doubly asymptotic orbit. The solutions of the first and second categories correspond to the type shown in Figure 5.9(a) while those of the third category correspond to orbits like those shown in Figure 5.9(b).

In fact, he gave a clear demonstration of what we now call *chaos*. Nowadays, chaotic behavior is perceived as occurring around a skeleton of unstable periodic orbits.[21] The presence of a homoclinic orbit assures the existence of an infinite number of unstable periodic orbits and as a result, the possibility of having a chaotic trajectory. Because of the existence of such orbits, Poincaré was able to show that no additional constant of motion could exist in the restricted three-body problem. To do this, he showed almost all series could not be convergent and, as a result, were inadequate to describe motion over an infinite duration.

[20] *Ibid.*
[21] P. Cvitanović, Periodic Orbits as the skeleton of classical and quantum chaos, *Physica D*, **51**, 138–151, 1991.

Poincaré attempted to describe the complex structure of these solutions. The surfaces S and S' could be drawn as shown in Figure 5.10 in the neighborhood of the curve $\mathcal{C}$. In the case of the restricted three-body problem, he proved that the surfaces S and S' intersect each other an infinite number of times in curves that approach $\mathcal{C}$. Poincaré described the curves that occur at the intersections of the surfaces S and S' (Figure 5.11):[22]

> If one tries to describe the figure formed by these two curves and their infinite number of intersections, each of which corresponds to a doubly asymptotic solution, these intersections form a sort of trellis, a woven cloth, a network of threads infinitely close together; each of these curves can never intersect itself, but each must fold itself in a very complicated way so that it can cut the other an infinite number of times.

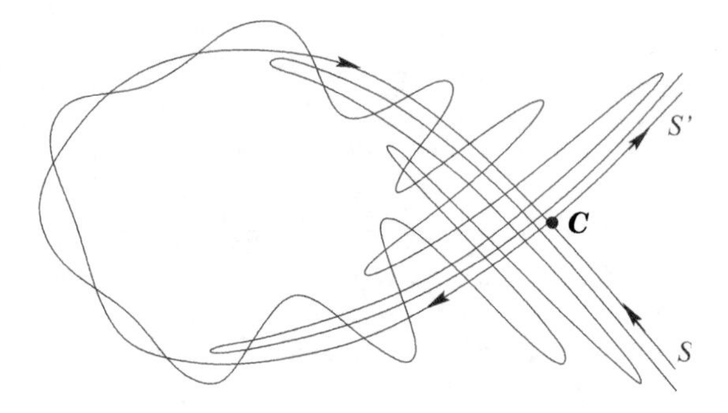

Figure 5.11 Illustration of the trellis formed by the intersections of a plane transverse to the curve $\mathcal{C}$ and the two surfaces S and S'.

The computational techniques available to Poincaré were not powerful enough to allow him to plot this trellis, as he states in his "*New Methods in Celestial Mechanics*:[23]

> One will be flabbergasted by the complexity of this figure, that I cannot even begin to sketch it. There is nothing better suited to given an inkling of the complexity of the three-body problem.

He next considered the order in which successive points intersected along the two curves. He showed that the order along one axis was not at all related to the order along the other axis. For this he considered several doubly asymptotic solutions; in the far distant past they were both very near the periodic solution and they appeared in a particular order, certain among them being closer to the periodic orbit while others were less so. Eventually all left the neighborhood of the periodic

[22]Henri Poincaré, *Les Méthodes Nouvelles de la Mécanique Céleste*, Tome III, 1899, p. 389.
[23]*Ibid.*

orbit; later, in a far distant future, they were once again near the periodic orbit; "*but they then evolved in a completely different way.*" If there are two solutions, the first being closer to the periodic orbit than the second in a far distant past, it could happen that, in the future the first could be further from the periodic orbit than the second. But the opposite could also happen. In other words, he described a situation in which a small error in initial conditions leads to a very large long term error, despite the fact that both trajectories are organized about the same periodic orbit.

Poincaré explained the long and unsuccessful quest for a general solution of the three-body problem as follows:

> The more I think about the properties that I have just described, the better I understand these unbelievable difficulties, the more I sense the failure of my effort, the more I feel the nature and the grandeur of this problem.

5.8 Deterministic but Unpredictable

In fact, Poincaré was also faced with the problem of entangled solutions that were, in addition, burdened with the additional problem of *sensitivity to initial conditions.* The problem of the rapid growth of small errors raised its ugly head again for Poincaré, as it had previously for Kopernik, Kepler, and all their successors. Only this time, for Poincaré, the growth of small errors was no longer a result of the methods of computation but rather a property that was *intrinsic* to a certain class of systems:[24]

> A very small cause which escapes our notice determines a considerable effect that we cannot fail to see, and then we say that that effect is due to chance. If we knew exactly the laws of nature and the situation of the universe at the initial moment, we could predict exactly the situation of that same universe at a succeeding moment. But, even if it was the case that the natural laws had no longer any secret for us, we could still only know the initial situation *approximately.* If that enabled us to predict the succeeding situation *with the same approximation*, that is all we require, and we should say that the phenomenon had been predicted, that it is governed by laws. But it is not always so; it may happen that small differences in the initial conditions produce very great ones in the final phenomena. A small error in the former will produce an enormous error in the latter. Prediction becomes impossible, and we have the fortuitous phenomenon.

[24]Henri Poincaré, *Science and Méthode*, Flammarion, Paris, pp. 68–69, 1908. Translated by F. Maitland, Thomas Nelson & Sons, p. 67, 1914.

Poincaré developed many fundamental insights while studying the three-body problem. In particular, even though a dynamical system may be determinist, it can produce behavior that is unpredictable in the long run because of the rapid growth in errors due to imprecision in the initial conditions. To offset this problem, Poincaré placed the unstable periodic orbits that underly the state portrait at the heart of his analysis, since these are the orbits that organize the entire state portrait. The ideas of the Poincaré section and of the first return map, which allow passage from continuous flows to discrete maps and studies of how one intersection follows from the previous intersection, are now central and powerful tools for the characterization of chaotic attractors.

Chapter 6

The Stability of the Solar System

Urbain Jean-Joseph Le Verrier repeated Laplace's calculations on planetary motions taking into account higher order terms. As far as Le Verrier was concerned, Laplace had shown that Newtonian mechanics is basically correct; he was not interested in testing whether the gravitation law was exact but rather was interested in constructing as precise a theory as possible. For this reason he took account of the perturbations due to all the planets and expanded perturbing functions between planet pairs up to sixth order with respect to inclinations, and up to seventh order with respect to eccentricities.

At that time expansions of series in powers of small quantities (eccentricity, the ratio of masses with respect to the Sun's mass, inclinations, etc.) were used without worrying about the convergence of these series. Thus, astronomers assumed that the more terms were used in a series, the more accurately they could compute the true orbit of a planet. The discovery of the new planet Neptune by these methods did nothing but reinforce this attitude. Nevertheless, Le Verrier showed that Laplace's conclusions about the stability of the solar system were ill-founded:[1]

> We have integrated the differential equations on which the secular inequalities of the orbits depend, neglecting terms of third-order with respect to the eccentricities and the inclinations. We can now consider these terms, to recognize if, by successive approximations, the integrals can be developed in series sufficiently converging to let us conclude to the stability of the solar system.

By doing this, Le Verrier proposed a new formulation of the problem of solar system stability: the existence of quasi-periodic motions was no longer a guarantee of stability and it became necessary to determine that the amplitudes of perturbations was not too large. He suggested that the problem of convergence of series ought to be studied as mathematicians would study such a problem, by studying *all* the terms of the series, and not in the way astronomers would study the problem, who would retain only the leading terms in the series. He exhibited large corrections

[1] U. Le Verrier, Recherches astronomiques, *Annales de l'Observatoire Impérial de Paris*, **II**, Mallet Bachelet, Paris, p. 165, 1856.

due to nonlinear terms that Laplace had considered to be negligible in lowest order. Nevertheless, these computational methods did not allow him to establish systematic results on the importance of perturbing terms because the convergence of these approximations also depended on initial conditions, as Jacques Laskar mentioned:[2]

> Le Verrier's comments on possible secular resonances clearly show that he believes that the convergence of the series is not guaranteed for all possible initial conditions, and that in certain cases one can find instabilities due to secular resonances where Laplace's approximation may not give an accurate idea of the solution...

6.1 The Problem of Small Divisors

If Lagrange and Laplace had tried to demonstrate the stability of the solar system, their calculations were valid for only two or three thousand years, depending on the order of the approximations used. In 1878, Spiru Haretu (1854–1915) showed that when the series approximations up to third-order in the relative masses were used, secular terms appeared in the motion of the principal axes of the planets.[3] For this reason it is not possible to reach conclusions about the stability of the solar system using perturbation theory. It is partly for this reason that the global analysis was introduced.

Poincaré's works showed that the three-body problem was not integrable. From this work the conclusion that there was no stable solution (characterized by the absence of a convergent series) for the three-body problem seemed reasonable to mathematicians. The solutions were inextricably intertwined and, as a result, extremely sensitive to initial conditions. All this left little room to hope that it would be possible to find general results based on series whose convergence was sufficient for a satisfying description of planetary motion. The question of the stability of the solar system, considered as one of the most important questions since the time of Laplace, still remained open and one of the most important questions for Poincaré.

Jean-Baptiste Biot (1774–1862), who had helped Laplace to publish his *Celestial Mechanics*, thought that a very small perturbation of Saturn's orbit would be sufficient to eject Saturn from the solar system because of the 2/5 resonance that existed between Jupiter and Saturn.[4] As he pointed out to Laplace, the two planets return to the same position once every 900 years. Biot expected that the perturbations would add up and in the long run modify these orbits significantly. Karl Weierstrass, who believed that convergent power series expansions could always be found to describe planetary motions, objected that the stability of planetary orbits

[2] J. Laskar, *La Stabilité du système solaire*, *in* Chaos et déterminisme, p. 188, Points Seuil, Paris, 1992.

[3] Spiru Haretu, *On the invariability of the major axes of the orbits described by the planets*, Thesis defended on 30 January 1878, Université de la Sorbonne, Paris.

[4] J.-B. Biot, Précis de l'histoire de l'astronomie planétaire écrit à l'occasion de la découverte de M. Le Verrier, Imprimerie Royale, Paris, 1847.

could not depend on the rationality or the irrationality of their periods:

> How can one possibly measure the orbits with sufficient precision to distinguish between rationality and irrationality?

At the beginning of the 19th century Joseph Fourier (1768–1830) had shown that a function could be represented by a sum of trigonometric functions.[5] Weierstrass, in a letter to Sofia Kovalevskaya wrote that[6]

> I have been less fortunate with the initial investigations on the solution of dynamical problems by series development, which correspond to the peculiarity of the differential equations to be integrated. I reached a certain point. For instance, I express the differential equations for the n-bodies problem in such a way that they formally allow an integration in the form of an arbitrarily long series, but my attempts to prove the convergence of that development fail due to an obstacle that I am not able to cope.

He was convinced that the series obtained would be convergent, although he was aware of the underlying difficulty to prove it. Indeed, he found some coefficients that were ratios of a numerator by a very small denominator. Such coefficients assume very large values, calling into question the convergence of the series. This is the small denominator problem of celestial mechanics. It was not until 1942 that Carl Siegel (1896–1981) offered the first example of the convergence of a series with small denominators.[7] This example seemed to renew hope that this problem could be solved, despite Poincaré's incomplete demonstration that had seemed to destroy this hope.

6.2 The KAM Theorem

The problem of the convergence of series was raised by Andreï Nilolaevich Kolmogorov (1903–1983) during the International Congress of Mathematicians in 1954: he treated a nonintegrable system with two degrees of freedom.[8] Each degree of freedom had an associated characteristic frequency. In this case motion occurs on a two-dimensional torus (a tire tube) and is characterized by the frequencies f_1 and f_2, related to the inverse of the periods T_1 and T_2 (Figure 6.1). This figure describes two cases:

---

[5] In his *Théorie de la Chaleur*, Fourier used the fact that a function $f(x)$ can be decomposed in a trigonometric series as $f(x) = a_0 + \sum_{n=1}^{+\infty} (a_n \cos nx + b_n \sin nx)$. The problem is then to determine coefficients a_n and b_n.

[6] K. Weierstrass, Letter to S. Kovavleskaya, August 15, 1878, in G. Mittag-Leffler, Zur Biographie von Weierstrass, *Acta Mathematica*, **35**, 29–65, 1912.

[7] C. Siegel, Iterations of analytic functions, *Annals of Mathematics*, **43**, 607–612, 1942.

[8] A. N. Kolmogorov, On the Conservation of conditionally periodic motions under small perturbations of the Hamiltonian, *Doklady Akademii nauk SSSR*, **98**, 527–530, 1954.

- the ratio f_1/f_2 is irrational, the motion is described as *quasi-periodic*, and the trajectory covers the surface of the torus;
- the ratio f_1/f_2 is rational and one expects that the motion is periodic (we will see that this is not necessarily the case).

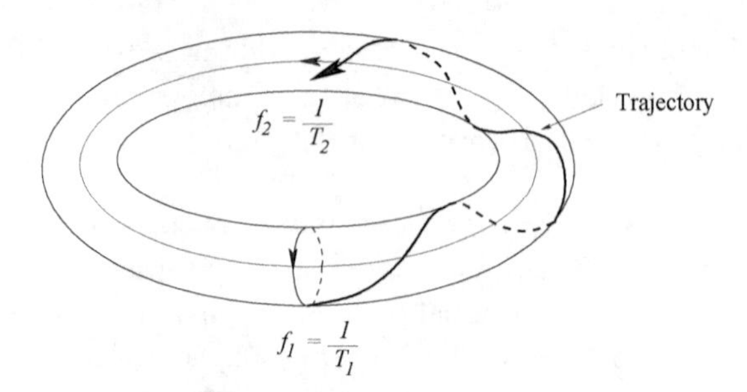

Figure 6.1 Torus on which trajectories representing the motion occur. The structure of the torus comes from the combination of the two frequencies f_1 and f_2.

In the first case a typical trajectory covers almost the entire surface of the torus without ever closing on itself. One says that the trajectory is *dense* on the torus. This means that it comes arbitrarily close to every point on the torus. In fact, a quasi periodic orbit fails to be periodic: it returns infinitely close to any point that it has previously visited without exactly returning to that point. If a system with two degrees of freedom is integrable the trajectories describing the motion in the state space are contained in a family of tori which enclose each other (Figure 6.2). Any given trajectory evolves along a torus "chosen" by its initial conditions.

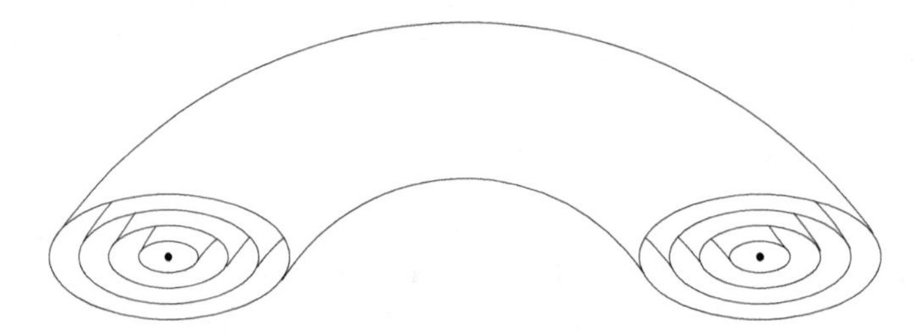

Figure 6.2 Organization of the tori on which typical trajectories occur in the state space. They correspond to initial conditions with different energies. At the center of this series of tori is a trajectory that differs very little from a periodic trajectory. Such a trajectory is treated as a periodic orbit. It is very likely that the motion of Saturn and Jupiter are associated with a configuration of this type.

When the ratio f_1/f_2 is rational one could expect that the trajectory would be periodic because, in this case, the trajectory would seem to be close on itself. Nevertheless, when the calculations are carried out using perturbation theory, some coefficients occur that force the series to diverge.[9] This is the *small divisor problem*

[9]These cœfficients take the form $\beta_n = \frac{\alpha_n}{1 - e^{-2i\pi n f_1/f_2}}$. When nf_1/f_2 is very close to an integer,

of celestial mechanics. When f_1/f_2 is rational, certain terms diverge at order n which can be very large. For this reason it is difficult to obtain results that are valid for long times: there is a *resonance*. In this case the trajectory does not follow a periodic orbit but rather a more complicated trajectory that results in a very sensitive dependence on the initial conditions: this problem is related to the presence of small divisors and not to the convergence of the series. In this case the trajectory visits a part of the state space contained between two tori labeled by two irrationals that bound the rational fraction f_1/f_2. In fact, for the real numbers each rational number is contained between two nearby irrationals, and *vice versa*.

Earlier, Georg Cantor (1845–1918) had shown that the irrational numbers are infinitely more numerous than the rationals; in other words, it is infinitely more likely to find an irrational than a rational number.[10] It is therefore infinitely more probable to find a trajectory that evolves on a torus than one that evolves between two different tori in the same family. Not only is it possible for stable orbits (convergent series) to exist in the absence of an additional constant of motion, but most orbits share this property under certain conditions. This was provided in 1954 by Kolmogorov as follows:[11] "*an analytical dynamical system with an integral invariant on a torus, appears as having only quasi-periodic solutions.*" The existence of quasi-periodic motion as well as more complicated trajectories, now called *chaotic*, is related to the rationality or irrationality of the ratio of the characteristic frequencies. In fact, periodicity is found for a rational ratio only when the corresponding trajectory occurs at the center of the family of tori in which it is emprisoned (Figure 6.2). The existence of such trajectories is very likely the explanation for the stability of the motion of Saturn and Jupiter.

When the ratio f_1/f_2 is irrational, the existence of tori on which typical trajectories evolve, acts almost like a constant of motion: under these conditions the system is almost integrable. Further, Kolmogorov raised the following fundamental problem: "*what happens to the quasi-periodic motion of a conservative system when the equations of motion are perturbed by terms that preserve the conservative structure of the system?*" This perturbation could appear, for example, as a modification of the energy of the system. Kolmogorov answered this question in the form of a theorem in the case where the ratio of frequencies f_1/f_2 is continuously varied when the energy E is continuously varied:

> Let be a conservative system, then for a hamiltonian perturbation sufficiently small, most of the invariant tori will persist, although slightly deformed, so that most of the state space is filled with invariant tori rather than chaotic behaviors.

term $e^{-2i\pi n f_1/f_2}$ is slightly different from $e^{-2i\pi} = 1$: the denominator thus becomes very small, implying a divergence in the series.

[10] G. Cantor, Über eine Eigenschaft des Inbegriffes aller reellen algebraichen Zahlen, *Journal de Crelle*, **77**, 258–262, 1874.

[11] A. Kolmogorov, Théorie générale des systèmes dynamiques de la mécanique classique, In Séminaire Janet, *Mécanique analytique et mécanique céleste*, **1**, exposé n° 6, pp. 1–20, 1957–1958.

In fact, as the perturbation is increased, the tori — initially present in the state space — disappear one after the other. Their resistance to the perturbation is related to the ability of the ratio f_1/f_2 to be approximated by a rational number. In particular, the most persistent tori (the last to disappear) are characterized by a *diophantine* ratio.[12] As a result of this, the nonintegrability of a system does not necessarily indicate that its motion is chaotic, as long as most of the irrationals are poorly approximated by rationals. If a perturbation of an integrable system is sufficiently small, the resulting motion is equally likely to be regular (quasi-periodic) as chaotic. While Kolmogorov laid the basis for this theory, it was Jürgen Moser (1928–1999) and Vladimir Arnol'd (1937–2010) who provided a complete proof of this theorem in 1962.[13] This theorem is now known as the KAM theorem.

To summarize, when the ratio of the frequencies is irrational the motion is quasi-periodic and lies on an *invariant torus*. The term *invariant* means that a trajectory which goes through a point on the torus remains on that torus. These tori enclose each other, forming a family of tori. Chaotic behavior occurs when the motion takes place between two of these tori, as a rational is bounded by two irrationals. In fact, not only can quasi-periodic orbits exist in the absence of a conservation law but in addition, under certain conditions, most of the orbits are quasi-periodic. As the strength of the perturbation is increased, quasi-periodic and chaotic motions coexist in the state space, the latter becoming increasingly probable as the strength of the perturbation increases.

6.3 A Model for the KAM Theorem

In this section we show what can happen to the tori when a perturbation is applied to an almost integrable system. In 1964 Michel Hénon and Carl Heiles tried to find a third constant of motion in addition to the conservation of energy and areas (angular momentum) in the case of galactic motion.[14] They thought that under certain conditions such a constant of motion could be found. To simplify their problem, they considered a system with two degrees of freedom associated with coordinates in a plane. The state of the system is defined by these two variables as well as the two components of the velocity vector, V_x and V_y. The state space is defined by the variables (x, y, V_x, V_y). The motion of the system is determined by

---

[12]Diophantine numbers α were discover by Joseph Liouville (1809–1882): numbers α were distant from a rational number p/q by a quantity ϵ such as

$$\epsilon = \left|\alpha - \frac{p}{q}\right| > \frac{c}{q^\delta}$$

where c is an integer and δ is the diophantine exponent. Smaller exponent δ is, greater the departure between the irrational number α and its closest rational number is, and more robust to a perturbation it is.

[13]V. Arnold, The classical theory of perturbations and the problem of stability of the solar system, *Soviet Mathematics Doklady*, **3**, 1008–1012, 1963.

[14]M. Hénon and C. Heiles, The Applicability of the third integral of motion: some numerical experiments, *Astrophysical Journal*, **69**, 73–79, 1964.

the four first-order differential equations

$$\begin{cases} \dot{x} = V_x \\ \dot{y} = V_y \\ \dot{V}_x = -x - 2xy \\ \dot{V}_y = -y - x^2 + y^2 \end{cases}$$

for which the energy

$$E = \frac{1}{2}\left[\left(V_x^2 + V_y^2\right) + \left(x^2 + y^2 + 2x^2y - \frac{2}{3}y^3\right)\right] \tag{6.1}$$

is a constant of motion. Angular momentum (area) is not conserved for this system. As a result, the integrability of this system cannot be guaranteed unless a second constant of motion can be found. An example of a trajectory in their configuration (coordinate) space is shown in Figure 6.3.[15]

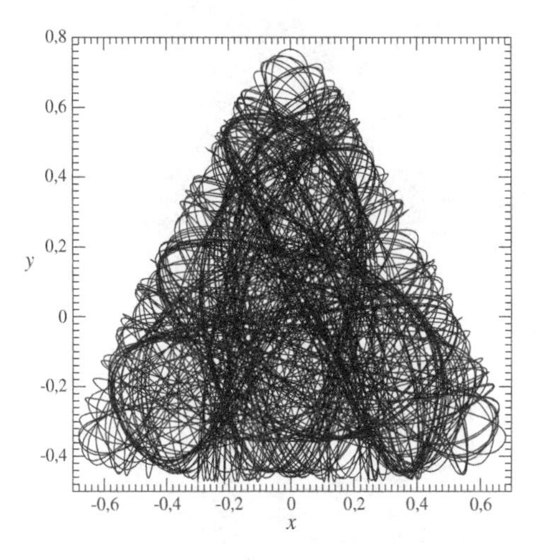

Figure 6.3 Typical trajectory for the Hénon-Heiles system in the coordinate space, for energy $E = 0.148189336$. Initial conditions: $y_0 = 0$, $V_x = 0$ and $V_y = 9$.

Since the trajectories are entangled in the state space in a very complicated way, it is simpler to view them in the *Poincaré section*. We will see that we recover results in agreement to the KAM theorem using the Poincaré section. When the energy is small ($E < \frac{1}{2}$) the system behaves almost as if there is another constant of motion. This is shown in the Poincaré section for several initial conditions, each with energy $E = 0.08353$ (Figure 6.4).[16] The set of behaviors shown here are quasi-periodic and

[15]The initial conditions were: $x(0) = 0$, $y(0)$ and $V_y(0)$ being chosen in an appropriate way to represent the different types of solution. The last initial condition is then provided by

$$V_x(0) = \sqrt{2E - V_y^2(0) - y^2(0)\left(1 - \frac{2y(0)}{3}\right)}.$$

[16]Values of energy result from specific initial conditions and from the equations used by Hénon and Heiles.

the intersections of these different orbits with the Poincaré section define closed curves, one for each set of initial conditions. These behaviors are characterized by two incommensurable (irrational) frequencies. We point out that one of these surfaces is somewhat more complex than the others, as it exhibits self-intersections. This property recalls the behavior of Poincaré's homoclinic orbits and, as a result, is a hint of the complexities to come.

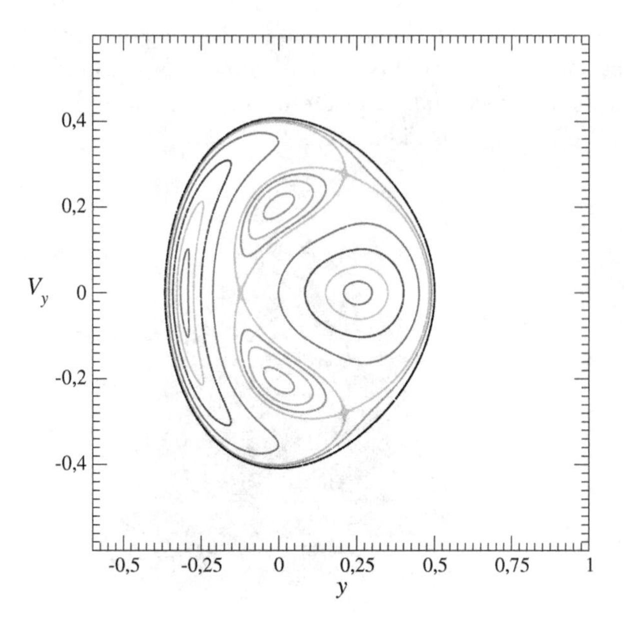

Figure 6.4 Intersections with a Poincaré section of typical trajectories solution to the Hénon-Heiles system for small values of the energy ($E = 0.08353$).

As the energy is increased, the behavior becomes more complicated and a *chaotic sea* forms when the energy reaches $E \approx 1/9$ (Figure 6.5(a)). At this energy there are still invariant tori, that is, motion that occurs with two irrational frequencies, but for certain initial conditions the ratio f_1/f_2 is rational and a trajectory that represents the evolution visits a large fraction of the state space (Figure 6.5(a)). This chaotic sea is bounded by tori associated with the irrationals that bound the rational ratio f_1/f_2 describing the chaotic sea. This entanglement of chaotic and quasi-periodic behaviors is compatible with the KAM theorem. The presence of the chaotic sea shows clearly that the system does not have an additional constant of the motion, otherwise the behavior would be regular. Nevertheless, regions of state space in which motion remains regular appear as "remnants" of the kind of behavior seen at low energies.

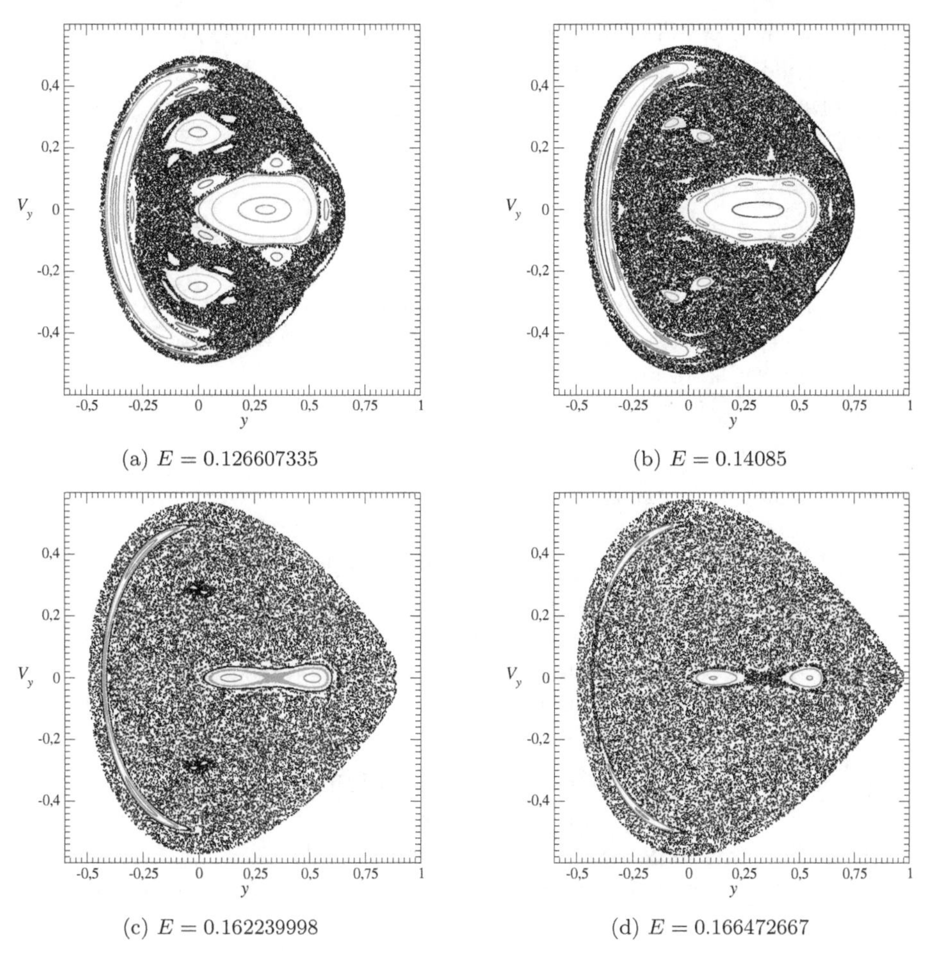

(a) $E = 0.126607335$ (b) $E = 0.14085$

(c) $E = 0.162239998$ (d) $E = 0.166472667$

Figure 6.5 Evolution of invariant tori as a function of energy. As the energy increases, the invariant tori are destroyed, leaving behind a chaotic sea that becomes larger and larger.

As the energy increases new types of regular behavior appear in the form of islands immersed in the chaotic sea (Figure 6.5(b)). These islands can themselves be surrounded by smaller islands. Their sizes decrease rapidly as their number increases. Beyond $E = 0.125$ the area of the Poincaré section occupied by islands, that is, describing quasi-periodic motion, decreases very quickly until $E = 1/6$, when the chaotic sea occupies all the space available, excepting for the trajectories that escape to infinity.

The Hénon-Heiles system offers a perfect example of how are working the theorem of Kolomogorov and the KAM theorem. From this study we learn that, despite the nonintegrability of this system, a great deal of quasi-periodic behavior can occur. The very complicated intertwined structure of the orbits announced by Poincaré is hinted at by the results (Figure 6.5). However, Michel Hénon showed, in 1966, that the planetary mass ratios required for an application of the KAM theorem must be extremely small:[17] as a result, the KAM theorem could not be used directly to deduce information about the stability of the solar system and a numerical approach is required.

6.4 Numerical Approach

Differential equations are simpler to write down than to integrate. These equations define relations that exist between variables and their derivatives over an infinitely small time interval. As Poincaré has written:

> Instead of trying to consider in its globality the progressive development of a phenomenon, one searches simply to relate the current instant to the immediately preceding instant; one assumes that the current state of the universe depends only on the state immediately preceding, without being directly influenced, so to speak, by the memory of the far distant past. Thanks to this assumption, rather than directly studying the global evolution of a phenomenon one can limit oneself to writing down its differential equations.

The problem becomes one of integrating the infinitesimal segments in order to determine the relations describing the evolution starting from some particular initial condition. This is exactly what we ask a computer to do.

In 1988 Gerald Jay Sussman and Jack Wisdom of Cambridge University used a computer to integrate the trajectories of the outer planets (Jupiter, Saturn, Uranus, Neptune and Pluto) forward in time for 845 million years in order to study the stability of the solar system.[18] In their model Pluto was considered as a planet without mass, since its mass is so much smaller than the masses of the other outer planets (more than 7500 times smaller than the mass of Uranus, the lightest of the outer planets). In addition, they neglected the masses of the four inner planets (Mercury, Venus, Earth and Mars) and the asteroid belt, which represent 2/1000 of the mass of the exterior planets, as well as the mass loss of the sun due to the solar wind. These simplifications are negligible compared to the uncertainties due both to the masses and initial conditions of the exterior planets. As a result, Sussman and Wisdom believed that their calculations correctly reflected the future of the solar system.

---

[17] M. Hénon, Exploration Numérique du problème restreint, *Bulletin Astronomique*, **1**, 49–66, 1966.

[18] G. J. Sussman and J. Wisdom, Numerical evidence that the motion of Pluto is chaotic, *Science*, **241**, 433–437, 1988.

Pluto is special for several reasons. First, its orbit is very eccentric ($\epsilon \approx 0.25$) and it is highly inclined to the ecliptic ($i = 17.2^o$).[19] In addition, the trajectories of Neptune and Pluto cross because of a 3/2 resonance between their periods of revolution. This resonance, whose period is about 20,000 years,[20] guarantees that Pluto is far from its perihelion when Pluto and Neptune are in conjunction (aligned with the Sun). Pluto is also involved in a resonance between the motion of its ascendent node and that of its perihelion, which oscillates around $\pi/2$ with a period of the order of 3.8 million years.[21] This resonance guarantees that Pluto's perihelion remains far from the line of intersection of the orbital planes of Pluto and Neptune, thereby preventing an eventual collision between them. Sussman and Wisdom computed that Pluto moves with significant changes over long times (34 million years for variations in the location of its perihelion and 134 million years for a commensurability between its ascendent node and a secular frequency for a massive planet). They showed that these motions are chaotic in the sense that an uncertainty in the initial conditions of Pluto is multiplied by a factor of three every 20 million years: an exponential growth of errors occurs over the course of time. For example, after 400 million years the position of Pluto can greatly change.

In 1989 Jacques Laskar of the Bureau of Longitudes, repeated these calculations taking into account the solar system's interior planets.[22] To do this he used perturbation theory, developed by Laplace and Lagrange, in order to only take into account of the variations in the planetary orbits. He used an expansion to second-order in the planetary masses and to fifth-order in the eccentricities ϵ and the inclinations i. The secular equation of the Moon and relativistic corrections, neglected by Sussman and Wisdom, were also taken into account. The final system of equations involved more than 150,000 terms.[23] He found several long-period resonances for the interior planets. This suggests that the interior of the solar system may not be stable. He also found that the exterior planets, with the exception of Pluto, were stable. For the interior planets the error increases by a factor of three every five million years. An error of 15 meters in the position of one of the interior planets grows to an error of 150 million kilometers after 100 million years. Any prediction about the state of the solar system is impossible beyond that time; in other words, it is possible to answer questions about the stability of the solar system only by studying properties of trajectories emerging from initial conditions near to the estimated current initial conditions.

[19]The very small mass and the large orbital inclination of Pluto led astronomers to remove it from the planets of the solar system.

[20]C. J. Cohen and E. C. Hubbard, Libration of the close approaches of Pluto and Neptune, *Astronomical Journal*, **70**, 10–13, 1965.

[21]J. G. Williams and G. S. Benson, Resonances in the Neptune-Pluto system, *Astronomical Journal*, **76**, 167–176, 1971.

[22]J. Laskar, A numerical experiment on the chaotic behavior of the Solar system, *Nature*, **338**, 237–238, 1989.

[23]J. Laskar, Accurate methods in general planetary theory, *Astronomy & Astrophysics*, **144**, 133–146, 1985 — Secular terms of classical planetary theories using the results of general theory, *Astronomy & Astrophysics*, **157**, 59–70, 1986.

The stability of the solar system cannot be understood without a global analysis of a set of solutions. The origins of the behaviors exhibited might result from resonances between the slow precessions of the orbits of the Earth and Mars on the one hand, and between those of the orbits of Mercury, Venus, and Jupiter, on the other. One is always faced with the small divisor problem and the impossibility of representing the motions of the planets by quasi-periodic formulas for more than a few tens of millions of years.

PART 2

Chaos in Nature: Properties and Examples

Chapter 1

Periodic and Chaotic Oscillators

Chaotic behavior is intimately intertwined with the three-body problem. In celestial mechanics we treat the energy as a conserved quantity because dissipation is negligible since the planets move in a very high vacuum. This is very rarely observed for phenomena that occur on the earth (there is always friction somewhere): systems dissipate energy through heat. The trajectories of such systems are "attracted" to certain regions in their state spaces: these regions correspond to the existence of *attractors* of the type that we will encounter with the damped pendulum. In this case the attractor is a simple point in the state space that defines a **stable** state of rest (zero angle, zero angular velocity). There exist *much more interesting* situations in which the attractor is more complicated (chaotic, for example).

The purpose of this chapter is to describe the fundamental differences between conservative and dissipative dynamical systems. In addition, the manner in which periodic behavior can be understood as superposition of sinusoidal oscillations of different frequencies — Fourier spectrum — will be illustrated with simple examples before we introduce the history of the discoveries that paved the way for the development of the chaos theory.

We will show that sensitivity to initial conditions for dissipative systems is not of the same nature as that encountered for conservative systems, such as the Hénon-Heiles system. In fact, for conservative systems evolving under the same parameter values the motion can be either periodic, quasi-periodic or chaotic, depending on the initial conditions. For a dissipative system the trajectories are organized somewhat differently. Because of energy dissipation there is often a set of initial conditions for which the asymptotic behavior is *globally* the same. That is, the object in the state space (attractor) towards which typical trajectories evolve is always the same. In other words, for a large number of initial conditions, trajectories converge to the same attractor which they never leave. In fact, as we will see in the case of the damped pendulum, there is a transient regime between the initial conditions and the attractor: this is of little interest for physicists and only the asymptotic behavior will be considered. Under time evolution the attractor for a dissipative system is invariant in the same sense that the torus associated with quasi-periodic motion for a conservative system is invariant: a trajectory in the attractor never leaves it.

1.1 Oscillators and Degrees of Freedom

Each mechanical system with n degrees of freedom is associated with a system of n oscillators. The idea of degree of freedom is related to the possible directions of motion. For example, an ideal pendulum oscillating in a plane is a system with one degree of freedom. If the pendulum is now fixed at a point it can move in two directions: this system has two degrees of freedom. In fact, a system consisting of a single body at the end of a rigid rod moving on an axis has a single degree of freedom, if moving on a surface has two degrees of freedom, more complicated pendulum, as double pendulum (two rods and two rotation axes), can move in a volume or a hypervolume, having a large number of degrees of freedom. One can look at other types of systems. For example, two bodies interacting gravitationally (such as the Sun and a planet) has $2 \times 2 = 4$ degrees of freedom if each body moves in a plane. According to the classical approach, the number of degrees of freedom depends on the number of oscillators needed to describe the system's motion. For example, an ideal pendulum fixed on a rigid axis is a system with a single degree of freedom, and consequently can be described by a single oscillator.

Let us consider a simple case. According to Equation (5.2), the differential equation that describes an ideal pendulum is

$$\ddot{\theta} = -\frac{g}{L}\sin\theta\,. \tag{1.1}$$

The presence of the (*nonlinear*) sine function complicates the solution of this equation. If we restrict ourselves to small amplitude oscillations, the (nonlinear) term $\sin\theta$ can be well approximated by the (linear) term θ; then

$$\ddot{\theta} = -\frac{g}{L}\theta\,. \tag{1.2}$$

This equation has for solution

$$\theta(t) = A_0 \sin(\omega t + \varphi)$$

where $\omega = \sqrt{\frac{g}{L}}$ is the angular frequency of the pendulum and φ is the phase. The phase permits us to distinguish different trajectories obtained by releasing or pushing on the pendulum from different positions. Thus, small oscillations of the pendulum are correctly described by the term $A_0 \sin(\omega t + \varphi)$. The evolution of the pendulum is periodic, that is, it repeats regularly with period $T = \frac{2\pi}{\omega}$, since $\sin(\omega t + \varphi) = \sin(\omega t + \varphi + 2\pi)$. Under this small amplitude approximation, the period of the oscillation does not depend on the amplitude. More precisely, the amplitude of the oscillation at any time t depends only on the amplitude A_0 at $t = 0$. In Figure 1.1 we show the time evolution of the pendulum for several values of the initial amplitude A_0.

There is a way to determine the period directly from the time evolution of the angle θ as shown, for example, in Figure 1.1: this is from its *Fourier spectrum.* A Fourier spectrum consists of the set of frequencies that describe the motion: in other words, the time evolution of the angle θ can be decomposed into a sum of

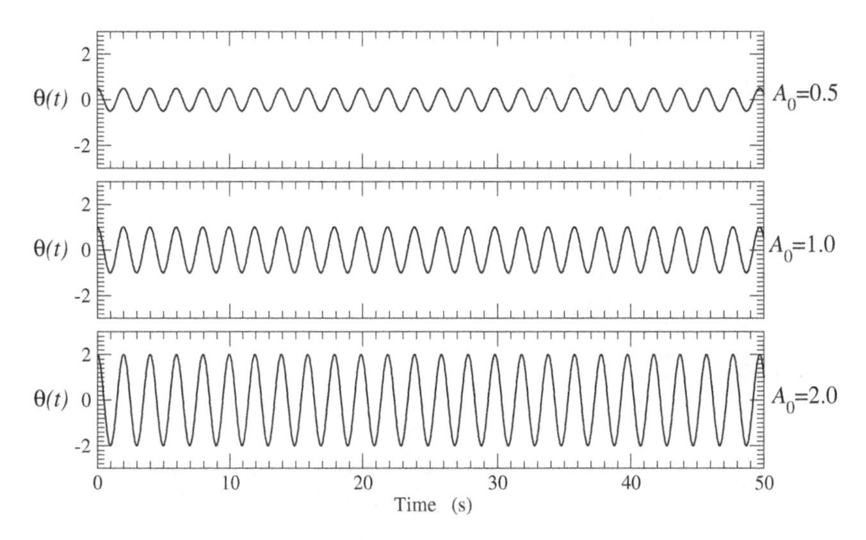

Figure 1.1 Evolution of the angle θ that the pendulum makes with the vertical as a function of time for different initial amplitudes A_0 (the pendulum is released at $t = 0$, thus $\varphi = +\pi/2$). Within the framework of the approximation made for Eq. (1.1) the time period is independent of the initial amplitude.

oscillating sinusoids with amplitudes A_i, pulsation ω_i[1] and phase φ_i.[2] There are numerical techniques to estimate parameters A_i, ω_i and φ_i. Fourier spectra provide a representation of amplitude A_i (or of its squared value) versus to the frequency $f_i = \frac{\omega_i}{2\pi}$. In our pendulum example, when approximation (1.2) is used the motion is exactly sinusoidal at the frequency $f_0 = 0.5$ Hz: the Fourier spectrum contains just a single frequency (Figure 1.2(a)).

When the approximation of $\sin\theta$ by θ — replacement of Eq. (1.1) by Eq. (1.2) — cannot be made, the pendulum is described by Eq. (5.3) and the evolution of the angle θ is no longer exactly sinusoidal: two other components with significant amplitudes appear in the Fourier spectrum (Figure 1.2(b)). The time evolution of the pendulum is still periodic but it can be expressed as the sum of three sinusoids:

$$\theta(t) \approx A_1 \sin\omega_1 t + A_2 \sin\omega_2 t + A_3 \sin\omega_3 t \tag{1.3}$$

[1]The pulsation is equal to the frequency multiplied by 2π; it is thus expressed in radians per second and not in Hertz as the frequency.

[2]The sum is mathematically written as:

$$\theta(t) = \sum_{i=1}^{n} A_i \sin(\omega_i t + \varphi_i)$$

where A_i designates amplitude of ith mode, ω_i its pulsation and φ_i its phase.

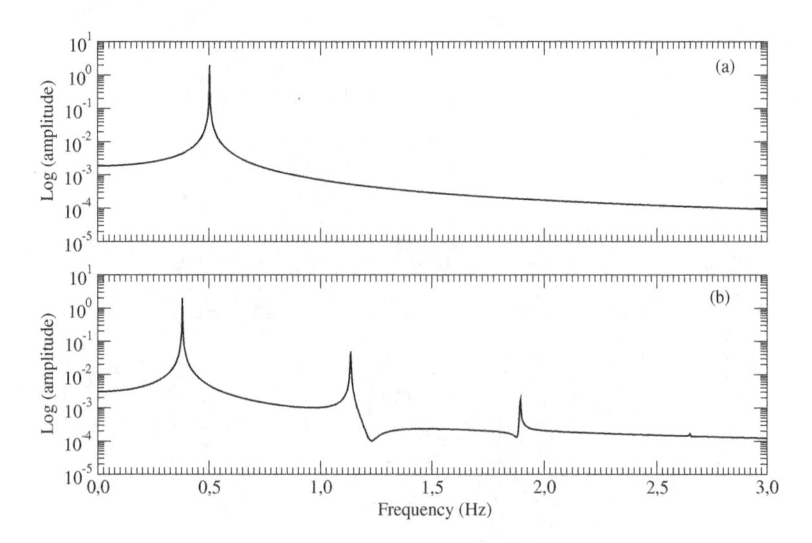

Figure 1.2 Fourier spectra when the time series is (a) a sinusoide and (b) slightly non sinusoidal. Note that in the case where the linear approximation of the sine is no longer used (b), the main frequency ($f_1 = 0,37$ Hz) is slightly less than in the case where the approximation is used. (A semi-logarithmic plot is used to better exhibit the various frequencies involved.)

where the angular frequencies ω_i are related to the frequencies f_i by $f_i = \frac{\omega_i}{2\pi}$ (here all the phases are zero). The three frequencies are

$$
\begin{aligned}
f_1 &= 0.37 \text{ Hz} \\
f_2 &= 1.13 \text{ Hz} \approx 3f_1 \\
f_3 &= 1.89 \text{ Hz} \approx 5f_1
\end{aligned}
$$

The amplitudes A_i of the different frequencies decrease very quickly (notice that the plot in Figure 1.2 is semi-logarithmic). This is due to Fourier who showed that every periodic signal could be decomposed into a sum of sinusoids[3] in the manner shown in Eq. (1.3).

1.2 Damped Pendulum

The pendulum that we have just described is an idealization of a real pendulum. In particular, we have ignored all types of friction, such as friction at the suspension point as well as friction due to motion through the air. Experimentally, motion decreases and eventually ceases due to dissipation of energy in the form of heat. For this reason we now treat the damped pendulum, a dissipative system, by taking account of friction. The differential equation that describes the damped pendulum is

$$\ddot{\theta} = \frac{k}{m}\dot{\theta} - \frac{g}{L}\sin\theta \tag{1.4}$$

[3] J. Fourier, *Théorie analytique de la chaleur*, Firmin Didot (Paris), 1822.

where k is a constant describing frictional losses. All trajectories now converge to the origin in state space (zero angle, zero angular frequency) corresponding to the rest state of the pendulum. The amplitude of oscillations decreases inexorably in time and the state space trajectory winds down in a spiral towards the origin, where it remains forever (Figure 1.3(b)).

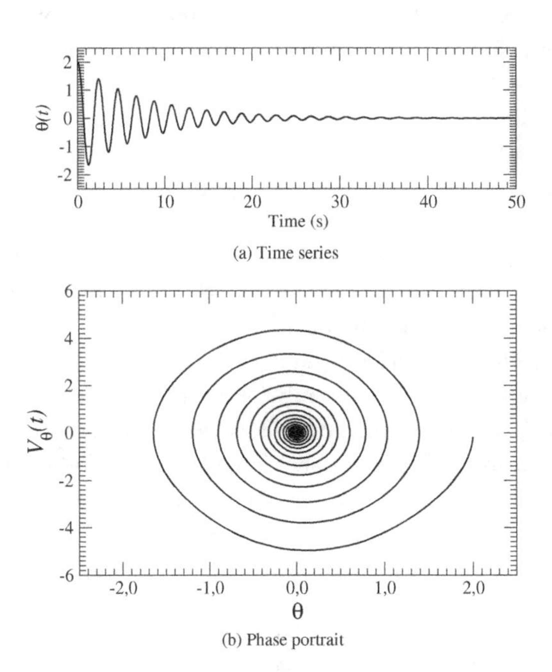

Figure 1.3 State space trajectory of a damped pendulum. After a transient regime the motion stops at the origin ($\theta = 0, \dot{\theta} = 0$) corresponding to the rest state of the pendulum. (The friction constant k is chosen as 0.05 kg.s^{-1} and the mass m is chosen as 20 g.)

Two ideas have been introduced above. The first is the idea of a transient regime: starting from an initial condition the system evolves asymptotically towards a state of rest at $(\theta, \dot{\theta}) = (0, 0)$. As physicists, we are usually not interested in the transient regime. Basically, the objective of our science is to describe reproducible phenomena: the initial conditions of an experiment are usually not well known, therefore one is interested in the stationary regime which is easily reproducible. For example in the class of experiments involving heated fluids, physicists wait until an appropriate temperature is attained before making measurements. The second idea implicitly introduced above is that of an *attractor*. The rest state of the pendulum at $(\theta, \dot{\theta}) = (0, 0)$ is such that, in the state space, trajectories from arbitrary initial conditions evolve towards the origin: this point is the *attractor* because it attracts to itself all trajectories in the state space that describe the evolution of the pendulum.

1.3 Linear System of Two Oscillators

We now consider a system of two oscillators for which the time evolution is

$$\theta(t) = \theta_1(t) + \theta_2(t) = A_1 \sin \omega_1 t + A_2 \sin \omega_2 t$$

where θ_1 describes the evolution of the first oscillator and θ_2 that of the second. One says that the two oscillators are linearly coupled (by simple addition): in other words, the angle θ is directly proportional to the sum of the angles assumed by the two oscillators. If one plots $\theta(t)$ as a function of $\theta_1(t)$ (θ_2 being held constant) one obtains a straight line. This holds also if θ_1 is held constant and $\theta(t)$ is plotted as a function of $\theta_2(t)$. The evolution of this system depends on the ratio of the angular frequencies ω_1 and ω_2. If ω_1/ω_2 is rational the behavior is periodic and two frequencies are observed in the Fourier spectrum (Figure 1.4(a)). On the other hand, if the ratio ω_1/ω_2 is irrational the Fourier spectrum still has two frequencies (Figure 1.4(b)) but the time evolution of the angle θ is no longer periodic; it is quasi-periodic. The time evolution of the angle $\theta(t)$ never exactly repeats itself. In fact, in the state space defined by the coordinates $(\theta_1, \dot{\theta}_1, \theta_2, \dot{\theta}_2)$ (a space of dimension 4!) the trajectory evolves on a torus resembling a tire tube: the trajectory will cover the entire torus without ever returning to a point previously visited. One says that it is *dense* on the torus. In this way the behavior is aperiodic (the negative prefix "a" indicates that there is no period). Nevertheless, it differs from chaotic behavior in the sense that there is no sensitivity to initial conditions: small errors propagate without amplification. The adjective aperiodic is not sufficiently strong to indicate chaotic behavior.

In the case of quasi-periodic behavior, classical analysis using Fourier spectra remains useful because it allows us to determine the two characteristic frequencies and, by doing so, to provide a precise signature of the dynamics. Further, even in the quasi-periodic case where the evolution of the angle never repeats itself, the classical approach allows us to describe the motion in terms of linear combinations of the frequencies related to the two oscillators. As a result it is possible to isolate the contribution of each of the oscillators to understand each of their roles: the system is linear.

1.4 Non-linear System of Two Oscillators

We can improve our system of two oscillators by taking a pendulum and providing a mechanism for driving its motion. In this way we compensate for its dissipation of energy by supplying energy from the outside. This is the principle of the grandfather clock: friction around its suspension points is compensated for by the work of the falling weights.

In this case the pendulum is described as two coupled oscillators. One is associated with the damped pendulum and the other with the periodic drive. One such system, thoroughly studied in the chaos theory, corresponds to the system studied

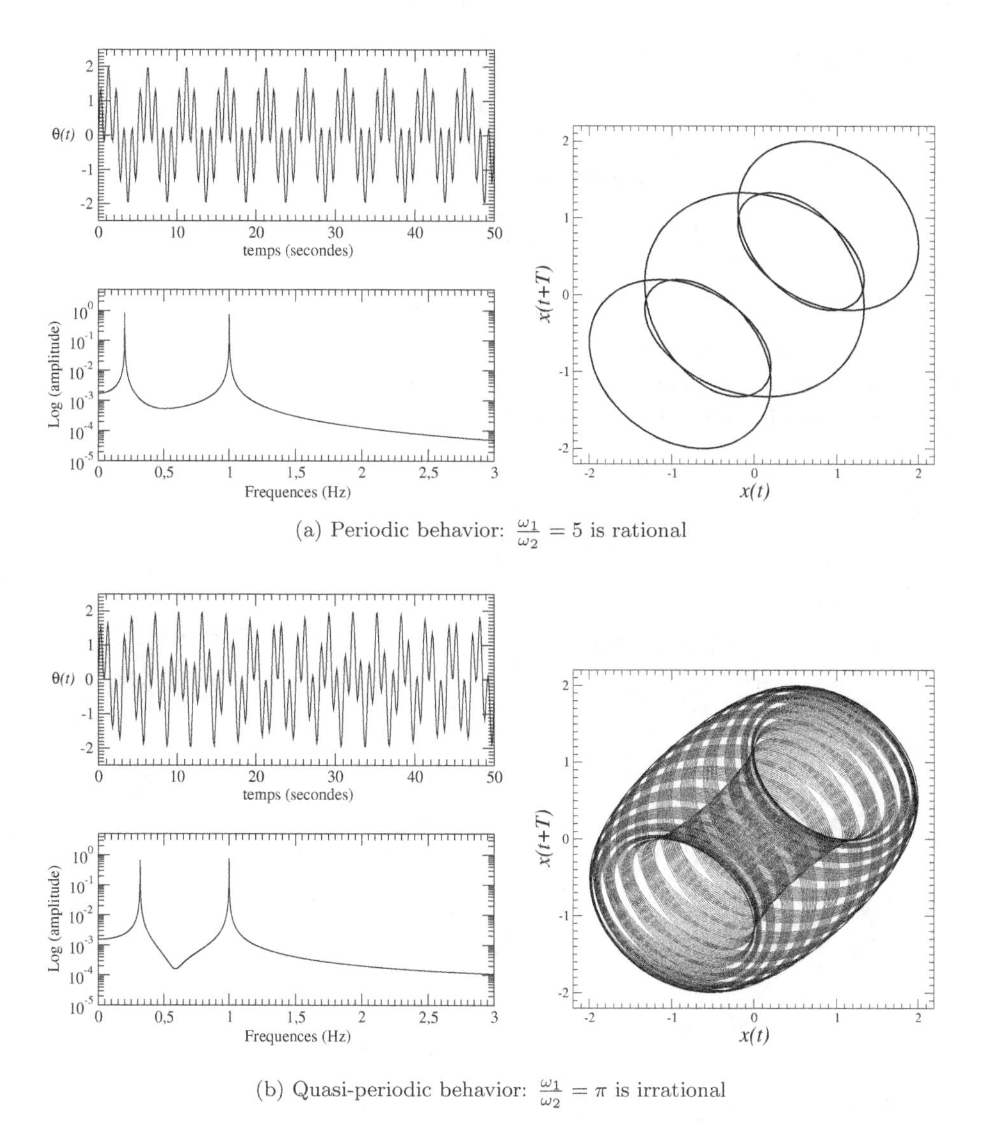

(a) Periodic behavior: $\frac{\omega_1}{\omega_2} = 5$ is rational

(b) Quasi-periodic behavior: $\frac{\omega_1}{\omega_2} = \pi$ is irrational

Figure 1.4 Evolution of two linearly coupled oscillators: the Fourier spectrum consists of a finite number of frequencies. The state portraits clearly reveal the principal differences between the two types of behavior.

by Georg Duffing (1861–1944) in 1918:[4] it consists of a pendulum whose sketch is shown in Figure 1.5. The equation of motion of this driven damped pendulum is

$$\ddot{x} + \alpha x - \beta x^2 - \gamma x^3 = A \sin \omega t \,, \tag{1.5}$$

[4]G. Duffing, *Erzwungene Schwingungen bei veründerlicher Eigenfrequenz und ihre technische Bedeutung*, Vieweg, Braunschweig, 1918, p. 134. Excerpt available at `http://www.atomosyd.net/spip.php?article97`

where $x = L(\Psi - \Psi_0)$ and

$$\begin{cases} \alpha = \dfrac{gS}{J}\cos\Psi_0 + \dfrac{c^2}{K}(\kappa_1+\kappa_2+\kappa_3)\,, \\ \beta = \frac{1}{2L}\frac{gS}{J}\sin\Psi_0\,, \\ \gamma = \frac{1}{6L^2}\frac{gS}{J}\cos\Psi_0\,, \\ k = \frac{cf_1L}{J}a\,, \end{cases}$$

κ_1, κ_2 and κ_3 being the constant of the three springs, a is a constant that is given by the respective maximal excursion of pendulum β, gS the static momentum of the pendulum's body (with drum and weights), c is the radius of the driving drum, and J the moment of inertia of the mass of the pendulum relative to the axis of rotation.

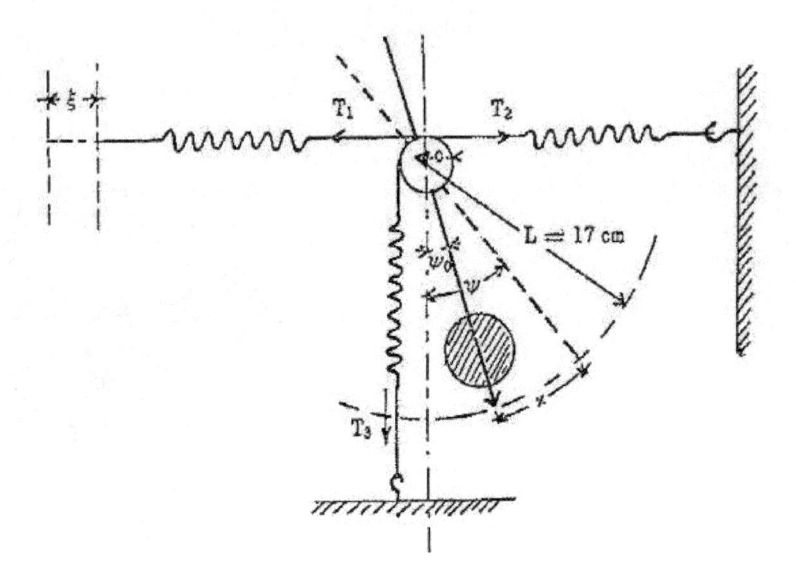

Figure 1.5 Sketch of the double pendulum investigated by Georg Duffing in 1918.

In order to be able to perform quantitative calculations, Duffing only considered forced symmetric pseudo-harmonic vibrations (parameter β is therefore set to 0) whose equation of motion is

$$\ddot{x} + \rho\dot{x} + \alpha x - \gamma x^3 = A\sin\omega t \tag{1.6}$$

where A is the amplitude of the periodic forcing term and ω is its angular frequency. This equation describes the balance between energy losses ($\alpha\dot{x}$ and $-\gamma x^3$) and energy input ($A\sin\omega t$). Following the classical approach, this system possesses two degrees of freedom and one could expect that only two frequencies are observed in its Fourier spectrum. Surprisingly, for the parameter values studied by Yoshisuke

Ueda[5] of the University of Tokyo (Japan) in the 60s[6] the behavior of the Duffing equation is somewhat complicated (Figure 1.6(a)) and its Fourier spectrum consists of an infinite number of characteristic frequencies (Figure 1.6(b)).

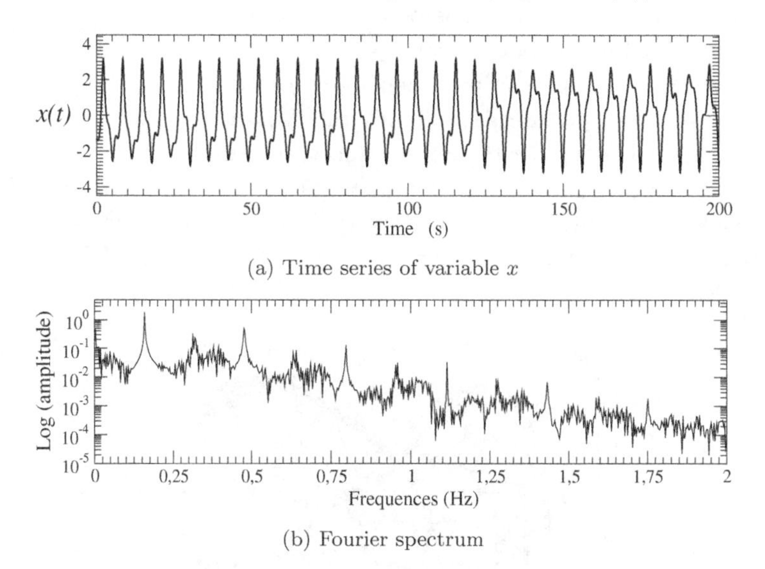

(a) Time series of variable x

(b) Fourier spectrum

Figure 1.6 Dynamic behavior produced by the Duffing equation (1.6). The time evolution of the angle x is complicated and seems to vary in a random manner: the amplitude varies at each oscillation as in quasi-periodic motion but in this case the Fourier spectrum contains an infinite number of frequencies. Parameter values: $\rho = 0.25$, $\alpha = 0$, $\gamma = -1$, $A = 7.8$ and $\omega = 1.0$. Initial conditions: $x_0 = 0.1$ and $y_0 = 0.1$.

Since the system consists of only two oscillators and the Fourier spectrum contains an infinite number of frequencies the classical interpretation fails: it is not possible to isolate the contributions of each of the two oscillators. This is a direct consequence of the nature of the coupling between the two oscillators. The contribution of the oscillator associated with the periodic drive is injected directly into the oscillator associated with the damped pendulum: the behaviors of the two oscillators are inextricably bound and it is impossible to isolate the contribution of one with respect to the other. This is seen directly in the Fourier spectrum, which shows that it is no longer possible to provide an interpretation in terms of frequencies. This is a consequence of the nonlinear coupling between the oscillators: the evolution of the exterior drive directly influences the evolution of the damped oscillator and we no longer obtain a straight line when we plot variable x as a function of the driving term $A \sin \omega t$. Since the system has only two degrees of freedom, the nonlinear coupling is necessary and may be sufficient to obtain an infinity of characteristic frequencies.

[5] See Section 2.4, p. 122 for details.

[6] Y. Ueda, *Some Problems in the theory of nonlinear oscillations*, Ph.D. Thesis (1965) reproduced in *The Road to chaos*, Aerial Press, Inc. 1992.

This is crucial because we can no longer consider a system as composed of two parts whose contributions simply add. It is necessary to study the system as a whole, indivisible, which is not equal to the sum of its parts. This is one of the reasons for which the term *chaos* has been used since the 1970s: nonlinear systems cannot be described using classical concepts, they were not descriptible.

Henri Poincaré has told us that we should perform a global analysis. The best approach for studying dynamics is to study the evolution of a set of trajectories in the state space. While neither the Fourier spectrum nor the time evolution of variable x reveals regular structures that describe the behavior of the Duffing equation, the state space trajectories show a certain regularity (Figure 1.7): trajectories do not evolve in an arbitrary way but seem to respond to laws which we must attempt to determine.

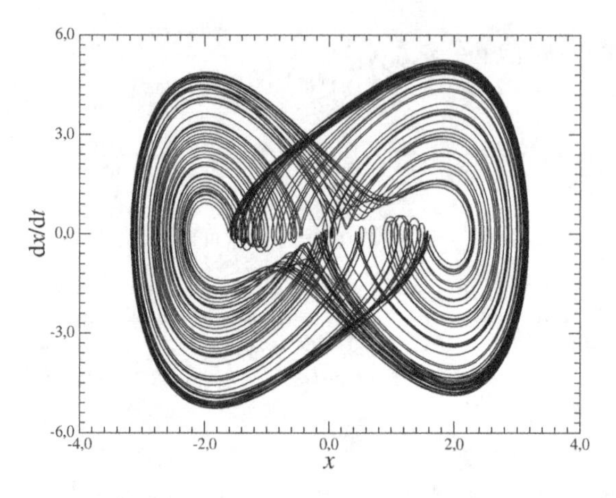

Figure 1.7 Evolution of the Duffing system in its state space. A particular structure for the attractor is outlined. The trajectory never passes exactly through a point that it has already visited. This behavior is chaotic, characterized by aperiodicity and associated with sensitivity to initial conditions.

A second dogma in classical physics has been brought into question by nonlinear systems: that is the relationship between determinism and long-term prediction. Following the work of Laplace, scientists believed that the evolution of all systems was determined (predictable) "forever" since the equations describing them were known. Nevertheless, even though we know the equations for the Duffing equation, it is not possible to predict its long term behavior. In fact, suppose we take two slightly different initial conditions: according to the classical scheme of science, a small difference in initial conditions induces only a small change in the final state. This is not exactly what happens for nonlinear systems: in fact, the two trajectories begin by following very similar trajectories, according to classical ideas, but the distance between the two trajectories grows to the point that they evolve in a completely different way (Figure 1.8). This is what we call *sensitivity to initial conditions.* It becomes very expensive to predict the long term evolution of a system because it requires a ridiculously precise knowledge of the present state of the system. Further, perturbations, inevitable in any experimental system, are very quickly amplified by the system, preventing realistic long term predictions.

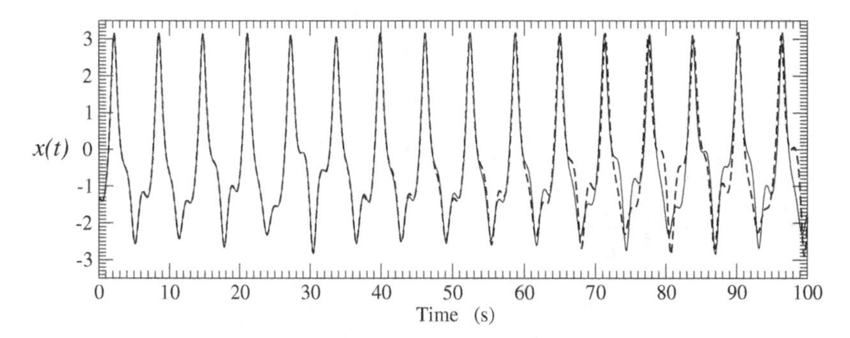

Figure 1.8 Two trajectories produced by the Duffing equation (1.6) with nearby initial conditions; the two trajectories very quickly evolve in a very different way.

Chapter 2

From Mathematics to Electronic Circuits

Close behind celestial mechanics with its three-body problem, radio-engineering created a class of models leading directly to the study of chaotic behavior. These physical and mathematical problems appeared at the beginning of the 20th century in connection with the earliest vacuum tubes (diodes, triodes, ...). The corresponding paradigm is designated under the name *Theory of Oscillators*, the title of the fundamental book on the subject by the founding members of the Russian school, namely Aleksandr Aleksandrovich Andronov, Aleksandr Aadol'fovich Witt and Semen Emmanuilovich Khaikin. The first edition appeared in 1937. The very practical context under which these studies were undertaken provided a central role for the differential equations that described these systems. The general problem is correctly and precisely presented in the introduction to the *Theory of Oscillators*.[1]

> A certain idealization of the problem can never be avoided; in order to construct a mathematical model of the physical system (that is, in order to write down a set of equations) we must take into account the basic factors governing just those features of the behaviour of the system which are of interest to us at a given time. It is quite unnecessary to try to take into account all its properties without exception. The latter process is not usually feasible and, even if we should succeed in taking into account a substantial part of these properties, we would obtain such a complicated system that its solution would be extremely cumbersome, if not altogether impossible.
>
> Since an idealization of the problem is in any case inevitable, the question arises, first of all, of how far we can go in this direction, that is, to what extent can we idealize the properties of the system and still obtain satisfactory results? The answer to this question can only be given in the end by experiment. Only the comparison of the answers provided by analysis of our model with the results of the experiment will enable us to judge whether the idealization is legitimate.

[1]A. A. Andronov, A. A. Witt & S. E. Khaikin, *Theory of Oscillators* (1937), Translated and revised by N. A. Sjelstov (1966), Dover, 1987.

Andronov and his colleagues make clear that a rigorous theory will not necessarily give us precise *quantitative* answers, but it can give us quantitative results that allow us to reach precise *qualitative* conclusions (for example, on the existence of periodic solutions). Such an approach makes it possible to determine what is important and what is not. The theory of oscillators deals only with *dynamical models* of real oscillators — fluctuations and all other statistical processes are neglected. The differential equations studied are anchored in real world applications.

> When we speak about idealizations of real physical systems in the form of dynamic models, then these idealizations are connected in the first place with the number of quantities, determining the state of the system (for example, coordinates and velocities) and, in the second place, with the choice of the laws, connecting these states or the velocities of variation of the states and establishing the relations between them. In these relations, which, in the majority of the cases considered, can be expressed in the form of one or other differential equations, there usually occur a certain number of constant parameters, characterizing the system. For example, for an ordinary electric circuit, in the simplest case the charge and current will serve as the quantities defining the state of the system; the inductance, capacitance and resistance are the constant parameters.

The study of real physical systems leads directly to the study of differential equations and their solutions. Andronov and his colleagues worked as electrical engineers and attempted to apply the concepts that were inherited from Poincaré, Birkhoff, and van der Pol to concrete examples, among which the *Audion* was the most important.

2.1 From Vacuum Tubes to Oscillating Circuits

Diodes are current converters, that is, devices that convert alternating current to direct current. The diode itself was not a new device. In its original form it was a vacuum tube. The precise designation was "*vacuum discharge tube*:" a sealed glass tube containing electrodes from which the air has been removed using a vacuum pump. Vacuum tubes date back to Francis Hauksbee (1666–1713).[2] Their study began as a pure curiosity because the technology for creating vacuums was not highly developed.

Vacuum technology actually started with Heinrich Geissler (1815–1879), a master glassblower, who was recruited to the University of Bonn as much for his ability to teach mechanics as to manipulate glass. There he established a laboratory in

[2]F. Hauksbee, *Physico-Mechanics experiments on various subjects. Containing an account of several surprising phenomena touching light and electricity, producible on the attrition of bodies*, R. Brugis (London), 1709. Figure 2.1 corresponds to plate VII and was presented in L. Figuier, *Les Merveilles de la Science – Machines électriques*, Fig. 226, p. 436, Ed. Jouvet et Cie, 1867–1869.

Figure 2.1 Francis Hauksbee's vacuum tube.

which he made instruments for physics and chemistry experiments and refined mercury vacuum pumps to obtain very high vacuums (1/100 mm of mercury). In 1858 Julius Plücker (1801–1868) took advantage of his ability to investigate a series of low pressure gas tubes,[3] which he called Geissler tubes. Geissler also developed a method for soldering glass to metal before inserting electrodes into the tubes in order to study electrical discharges in rarified gasses. By 1856, William Crookes (1832–1919) studied glass tubes containing low pressure gas and provided with electrodes at their ends.[4] He observed light coming from inside the tubes that could be influenced by magnetic fields outside the tubes. At the same time Johann Hittorf (1824–1914), student of Plücker, showed that particles were emitted by the cathode; these particles could be stopped by screens and bent by magnetic fields. He showed that two types of ions with opposite signs and various charges were produced. This work foreshadowed not only the discovery of X-rays by Wilhelm Röntgen,[5] but also the discovery of electrons. In fact, following a series of experiments undertaken between 1895 and 1897, John Joseph Thompson (1856–1950) proposed the hypothesis that a very light charged particle moved in the interior of the tube. These particles could be manipulated by electromagnetic fields. In 1899, Thompson measured the mass to charge ratio of these *electrons*[6] whose existence was announced by George Stoney (1826–1911).[7]

[3] J. Plücker, Mémoire sur la constitution des spectres électriques des vapeurs des gaz, *Annales de Chimie et de Physique*, **57**, 497–505, 1859.

[4] W. Crookes, On the illumination of lines of molecular pressure, and the trajectory of molecules, *Philosophical Transactions of the Royal Society A*, **170**, 135–164, 1879 — W. Crookes, Electricity in transit — From plenum to vacuum, *Scientific American* (Supplement), **31**, 795, 1891.

[5] W. C. Röntgen, On a new kind of rays, *Nature*, **53**, 274, 1896.

[6] J. J. Thomson, On the masses of the ions in gases at low pressures, *Philosophical Magazine*, Series 5, **48** (295), 547–567, 1899.

[7] G. J. Stoney, On the physical units of nature, *Philosophical Magazine*, V, **11**, 381–390, 1881.

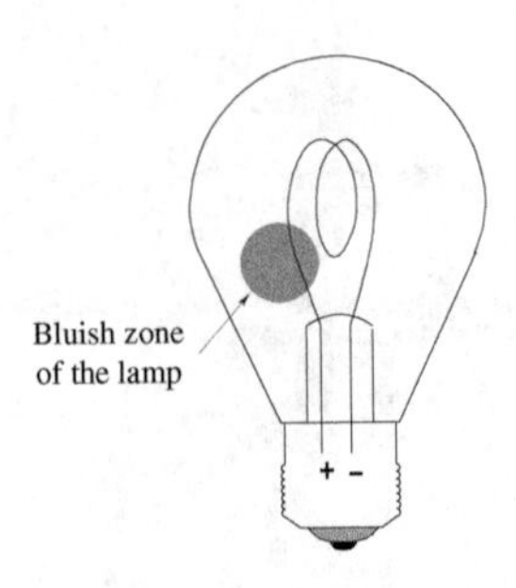

Figure 2.2 Edison Effect: electrons represented by the darkened zone move from the negative to the positive contact. Due to the imperfect vacuum, they collide with air molecules and are scattered towards the glass, causing darkening.

During this period electric lighting began to attract public attention. Thomas Edison developed bulbs with incandescent filaments in 1878. In February 1879, Edison and his colleague Francis Upton (1852–1921), who was hired to put Edison's ideas into mathematical form, observed that a blue glow always surrounded the positive pole and the filament always darkened at the negative pole: this is the *Edison Effect* (Figure 2.2). In 1883 Edison placed a plate between the carbon filament and the glass surface to reduce the darkening of the glass near the negative contact. During these experiments he connected the plate to the positive contact in the circuit and observe a weak current passing through the plate.

The resulting device was further investigated by John Ambrose Fleming (1849–1945). In October 1877 he started to study electricity and magnetism with James Clerk Maxwell (1831–1879) at Saint-John College (Cambridge). He obtained his doctorate of Science under the supervision of Frederick Guthrie (1833–1886) who discovered that a iron wire heated by an electric current was emitting some charged particles.[8] After completing his doctorate, in the Spring of 1882, Fleming was appointed Scientific Advisor to the Edison Electric Light Company of London while being a professor of electrical engineering at Imperial College, London. He carried out a series of experiments to investigated the Edison effect.[9] In 1884, he took up the Chair of Technology at the University College of London.

In fact while attempting to solve the eponym effect, Edison found in 1883 that[10]

> ... if a conducting substance is interposed anywhere in the vacuous space within the globe of an incandescent electric lamp, and said conducting substance is connected outside of the lamp with one terminal, preferably the positive one, of the incandescent conductor, a portion of the current will, when the lamp is in operation, pass through the shunt-

[8]F. Guthrie, *Electricity and magnetism*, W. Collins (London), pp. 83–84, 1876.
[9]J. A. Fleming, On a phenomenon of molecular radiation in incandescence lamps, *Proceedings of the Physical Society of London*, **5**, 283–284, 1882.
[10]T. Edison, *Electrical indicator*, Patent No. 307,031 (November 1883), Patented October 21, 1884.

> circuit thus formed, which shunt includes a portion of the vacuous space within the lamp. This current I have found to be proportional to the degree of incandescence of the conductor or candle-power of the lamp.

The phenomenon remained to explain. Fleming noted — as Edison had also remarked — that no current passed through the plate when it was connected to the negative contact. He showed the tripolar lamp at the Electricity Exposition in Philadelphia in 1884 (Figure 2.3). The tubes used included the two electrodes to which is connected the heated filament and a plate for collecting the emitted current. Fleming called these tubes *diodes*, but did not explain the phenomenon until 1890.[11] In 1896, Fleming wrote[12]

> The whole of the experiments which are detailed here seem to be capable of consistent interpretation if we may justifiably make the hypothesis that these carbon molecules or atoms so projected from the conductor when intensely heated by the current flowing through it are all negatively charged. Some of the observed facts seem to point to the conclusion that the molecules projected from the incandescent conductor, whether they are portions of the conductor itself or molecules of the residual gases, respectively carry away negative charges proportional in magnitude to the potential of the conductor at the point from which they are thrown off. They may, therefore, be looked upon as condensers of small but definite electrostatic capacity charged to the potential (negative) of that part of the incandescent conductor at which they separate from it. [...] There is much to lead to the conclusion that from all parts of the incandescent carbon conductor there is a constant radiation of matter carrying a negative electric charge.

In fact, as he later recognized himself,[13] Fleming was observing a current of electrons which were discovered a few years later by Thomson.[14]

In 1899, Fleming became associated with Gulielmo Marconi (1874–1937) as "*an adviser of his Wireless Telegraph Company, and assisted him in the transformation of his physical laboratory apparatus for creating space electric waves of long-wave length into engineering plant suitable for sending wireless telegraphic signals across the Atlantic.*"[15] At this time, the single practical method for detecting wireless waves was a modified "*radio-conducteur*" discovered by Edouard Branly

[11] J. A. Fleming, On electric discharge between electrodes at different temperatures in air and high vacua, *Proceedings of the Royal Society of London*, **47**, 118–126, 1890.
[12] J. A. Fleming, A further examination of the Edison effect in glow lamps, *Proceedings of the Physical Society of London*, **14**, 187–242, 1895.
[13] J. A. Fleming, On the history and development of the thermionic valve, *Journal of Scientific Instruments*, **11** (2), 44–49, 1934.
[14] J. J. Thomson, Cathode rays, *Philosophical Magazine*, V, **44**, 293–316, 1897.
[15] J. A. Fleming, 1934. *Ibid.*

(1833–1940) in 1890,[16] and later named "*coherer*" by Oliver Lodge (1851–1940).[17] After some further improvements of the coherer,[18] Alexandr Popov (1858–1905) demonstrated at a meeting of the Russian Physical Chemical Society in Saint Petersburg held on 7 May 1895 that he had constructed a Hertzian wave receiver. As he concluded in 1896, he was still hoping to be able to transmit a message with such a device.[19]

> In conclusion, I can express my hope that my apparatus [when further perfected] will be applied for signaling on great distances by electric vibrations of high frequency, as soon as there will be invented a more powerful generator of such vibrations.

Some improvements were remaining to perform. With the help of Fleming, Marconi who became the great promoter of wireless telegraphy managed in 1901 the first transmission of a message across the Atlantic Ocean.

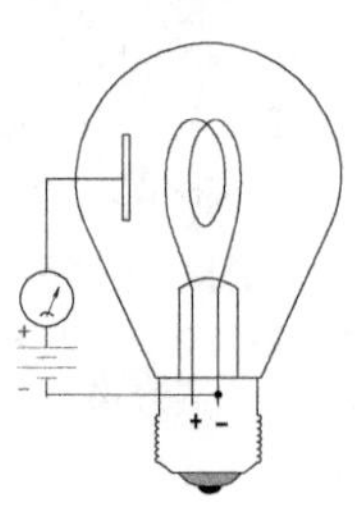

Figure 2.3 Edison tripolar lamp.

At this time Fleming also observed that while the "lamp" was driven by an alternating current, only a direct current was output.[20] However, it was not until 1904 that he observed that the direct current that passed through the plate depended on the power of the radio frequency that was applied. He recounted this observation as follows.[21]

[16]E. Branly, Variations de conductibilité sous diverses influences électriques, *Comptes-Rendus de l'Académie des Sciences*, **111**, 785–787, 1890.

[17]O. J. Lodge, On the sudden acquisition of conducting-power by a series of discrete metallic particles, *Philosophical Magazine*, **37**, 94–95, 1894.

[18]A. S. Popov, On the relation of metallic powders to electrical oscillations (in Russian), *Zhurnal Russkago Khimicheskago Obshchestva i Fizicheskago Obshchestva*, **27**, 259–260, 1895.

[19]This excerpt is quoted by O. Vendik, Significant contribution to the development of wireless communication by professor Alexander Popov, *IEEE Communications Magazine*, **48** (10), 20–26, October 2010 at the end of the paper: A. S. Popov, Apparatus for the detection and recording of electrical oscillations, (in Russian), *Zhurnal Russkago Khimicheskago Obshchestva i Fizicheskago Obshchestva*, **28**, 1–14, 1896 which was translated in English in A. S. Popov, Letter to the editor, *The Electrician*, **40**, p. 235, 1897.

[20]J. A. Fleming, The construction and use of oscillation valves for rectifying high-frequency electric currents, *Proceedings of the Physical Society of London*, **20**, 177–185, 1906.

[21]O. E. Dunlap, *Radio's one hundred men of science: biographical narratives of pathfinders in electronics and television*, Harper & Brothers, 1944.

> It was about 5 o'clock in the evening when the apparatus was completed. I was, of course, most anxious to test it without further loss of time. We set the two circuits some distance apart in the laboratory, and I started the oscillations in the primary circuit. To my delight I saw that the needle of the galvanometer indicated a steady direct current passing through, and found that we had in this peculiar kind of electric lamp a solution of the problem of rectifying high-frequency wireless currents. The missing link in wireless telegraphy was "found" and it was an electric lamp!
>
> I saw at once that the metal plate should be replaced by a metal cylinder enclosing the whole filament, so as to collect all the electrons projected from it. I accordingly had many carbon filament lamps made with metal cylinders and used them for rectifying the high-frequency currents of wireless telegraphy.
>
> This instrument I named an oscillation valve. It was at once found to be of value in wireless telegraphy, the mirror galvanometer that I used being replaced by an ordinary telephone, a replacement that could be made with advantage in those days when the spark system of wireless telegraphy was employed. In this form my valve was somewhat extensively used by Marconi's Telegraph Company as a detector of wireless waves. I applied for a patent in Great Britain on November 16, 1904.[22]

In order to show this he used an oscillation circuit (Figure 2.4) by connecting a Leyden jar in series with a square coil of wire of a few turns, and join the tunable condenser — to select frequencies — and inductance across a spark-ball discharger connected to the secondary terminals of an induction-coil. At a certain distance the square coil of wire of a secondary oscillation circuit — at the same frequency — in series with a galvanometer and an oscillation valve. He found that when oscillations are produced by the primary circuit, a steady deviation of the galvanometer indicates that the second coils receives a series of discharges.

With these tubes he thus obtained receivers that were more sensitive than Branly-Lodge's coherers which were difficult to use. In Fleming's diode, electrons were emitted by a heated filament, the cathode, and received by a "cold" plate, the anode: the name *thermionic diode* was finally retained. In 1906 Lee de Forest (1873–1961) improved Fleming's diode by adding a control grid between the filament and the plate: this grid allowed a second method to control over the current, in addition to varying the voltage between the filament and the anode (Figure 2.5). This new design allowed amplification of the signal. In 1907 De Forest patented this new tube,[23] which he called the "*Audion*."[24] The Audion is a triode — there are three electrodes – the two electrodes and the grid. It was used as a radio signal

[22] J. A. Fleming, *Improvements in instruments for detecting and measuring alternating electric currents*, British Patent No. 24850, granted on the 21st September, 1905.

[23] L. de Forest, Space telegraphy, US Patent No. 879,532 filed January 29, 1907 and granted February 18, 1908.

[24] L. de Forest, The Audion — a new receiver for wireless telegraphy, part I and II, *Scientific American Supplement*, **1665**, 348–350 and **1666**, 354–356, 1907.

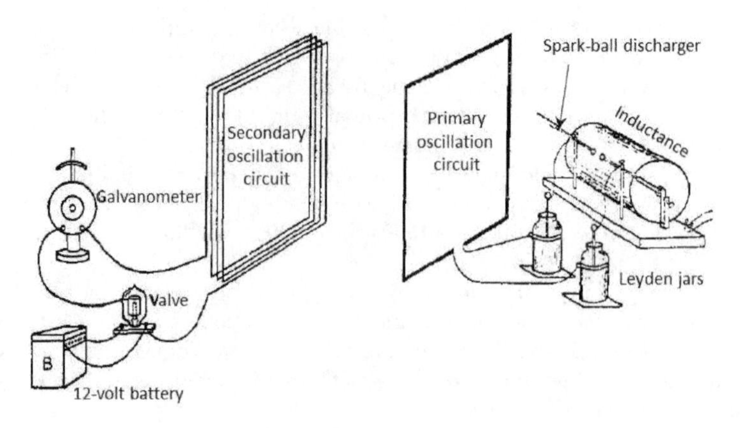

Figure 2.4 Scheme of the experiment conducted by Fleming for showing how his valve can transform oscillations into a constant current. Adapted from Fleming, 1906.

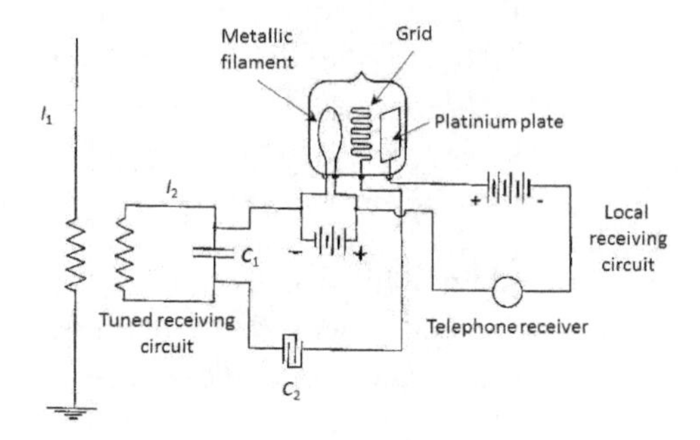

Figure 2.5 The wireless telegraph receiving system designed by Lee de Forest. The filament is heated preferably to incandescence. Adapted from de Forest, 1907.

detector, an audio amplifier, and an oscillator.[25] The Audion represented a significant advance for the development of radios, but its performance remained inadequate.

During this work de Forest realized that the effect of these diodes was not observed unless some residual gas was present in the tube. In 1913 Edwin Armstrong (1890–1954) observed that the gain of the triode could be enormously increased by reinjecting the output of the tube back into its input, that is, by creating a positive feedback loop.[26] With sufficient reinjection, the amplifier became stable and an excellent oscillator, perfect for the development of radio transmitters. With somewhat less reinjection, the amplifier became a radio-receiver more sensitive than any other at that time. Other engineers had this idea also, but it was Armstrong who characterized its properties and understood its behavior and potential sufficiently well to provide practical applications. Armstrong's triode was adopted by telephone

[25] L. de Forest sold in three parts his patent at the AT&T company for an amount of 390 000 $.
[26] E. H. Armstrong, Operating feature of the Audion — Explanation of its action as an amplifier, as a detector of high-frequency and as a valve, *Electrical World*, **64** (24), 1149, 1914.

systems in 1914: it allowed the development of intercontinental telephone networks. The improvement of vacuum tubes continued.

2.2 Dynamics of Various Oscillators

2.2.1 *The Colpitts Oscillation Circuit*

Edwin Colpitts (1872–1949), while he was a research branch chief for the Western Electric, was working to improve emitter-receiver for wireless telegraphy. He thus patented an oscillation circuit.[27] The improvement provided by Colpitts was related to the "*effectiveness of the apparatus required for the production of the modulated oscillations*" as used to encode the transmitted messages. He was thus able to use a single device not only for producing the sustained high-frequency electromagnetic waves but also to modulate them. Based on an Audion whose output was connected to the input, the potential in the input circuit was varied by connecting a transmitter with the grid (Figure 2.6). As a result, the sustained oscillations were modulated according to the message to be sent.

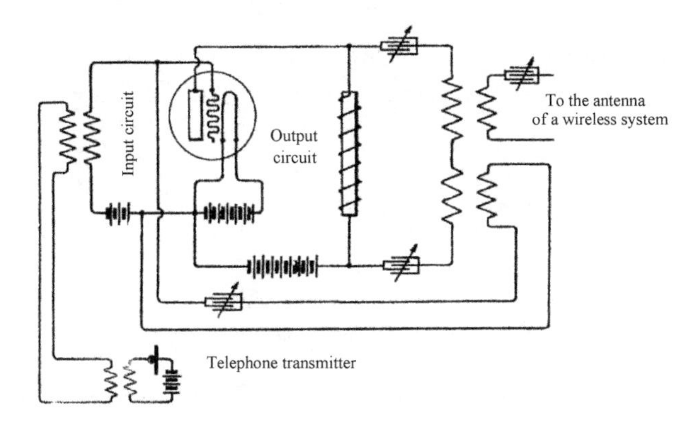

Figure 2.6 Oscillation circuit patented by Edwin Colpitts in 1915 for producing modulated high-frequency elelctromagnetic waves for wireless telegraphy. Adapted from Colpitts, 1915.

Few years later, he developed an "*oscillation generator*" based on an Audion to be able to produce oscillations of "*any desired frequency by providing a tuned circuit* (the input) *suitably associated with the tube circuit*" (the output).[28] Compared to the other types of oscillation circuits, the coupling between the input circuit (the "*oscillation circuit*") and the output circuit was electrostatic and not electromagnetic (Figure 2.7). One of the advantages is that the produced oscillations are actually at the frequency determined by the tuned circuit. This patent for the now so-called "Colpitts oscillator" was granted on February 1918 but only published on April 1927.

[27]E. H. Colpitts, System for the transmission intelligence, *US Patent* 1,137,384, April 27, 1915.
[28]E. H. Colpitts, Oscillation generator, *US Patent*, 1,624,537, April 12, 1927.

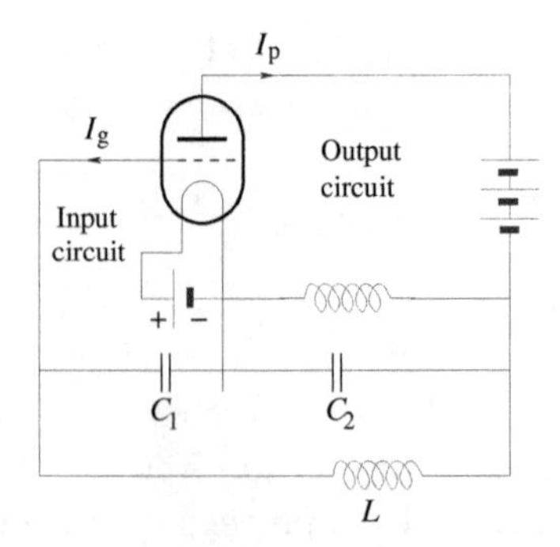

Figure 2.7 The Colpitts circuit (as patented in 1927) based on an Audion. The inductance L cooperates with condensers C_1 and C_2 to form an oscillation circuit.

The oscillation frequency for a Colpitts oscillator corresponds to the resonant frequency of the LC tank circuit, that is, to

$$f_C = \frac{1}{2\pi\sqrt{L\dfrac{C_1 C_2}{C_1 + C_2}}} .$$

This oscillation generator is typically used for frequencies such as 20 kHz $< f <$ 300 MHz. The behavior of this oscillation circuit can be described by the set of three differential equations[29]

$$\begin{cases} \dot{x} = \dfrac{g(z + 1 - e^{-y})}{Q(1-\kappa)} \\ \dot{y} = \dfrac{g}{Q\kappa} z \\ \dot{z} = -\dfrac{Q\kappa(1-\kappa)(x+y)}{g} - \dfrac{z}{Q} \end{cases} \tag{2.1}$$

governing the dimensionless current $z = I_L$ across the inductance L and the voltage $x = V_{C_1}$ and $y = V_{C_2}$ at condensers C_1 and C_2, respectively. In these equations, parameters are such as

$$\begin{cases} \kappa = \dfrac{C_2}{C_1 + C_2} \\ Q = \dfrac{\omega_0 L}{R} \end{cases}$$

where $\omega_0 = 2\pi f_C$. Typical sinusoidal oscillations produced by the model for a Colpitts oscillator are shown in Figure 2.8.

In 1919, John H. Morecroft and H. Trap Friis showed that non-sinusoidal oscillations can be produced with a Colpitts circuit: the plate current remains nearly null during about the half of a complete cycle[30] as shown in Figure 2.9. Morecroft and

[29] G. M. Maggio, O. De Feo & M. P. Kennedy, Nonlinear analysis of the Colpitts oscillator and applications to design, *IEEE Transactions on Circuits and Systems*, **46** (9), 1118–1130, 1999.
[30] J. H. Morecroft & H. Trap Friis, The vacuum tube as a generator of alternating-current power, *Transactions of the American Institute of Electrical Engineers*, **38** (2), 1415–1444, 1919.

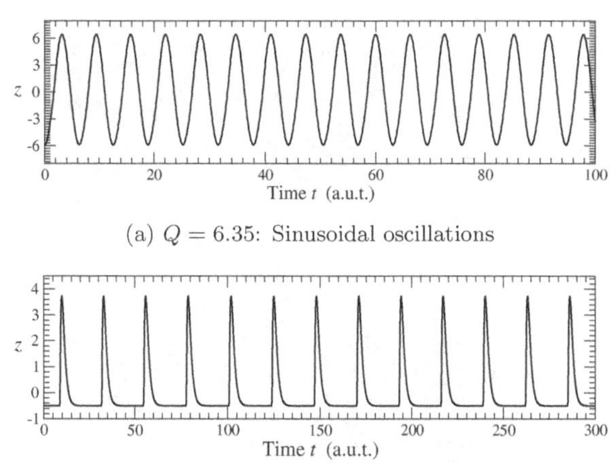

(a) $Q = 6.35$: Sinusoidal oscillations

(b) $Q = 0.5$: Nonsinusoidal oscillations

Figure 2.8 Typical time series of the dimensionless current z across the inductance L by the model (2.1). Parameter values: $\kappa = 0.5$, $y = 10^{0.88}$ and $Q = 6.35$.

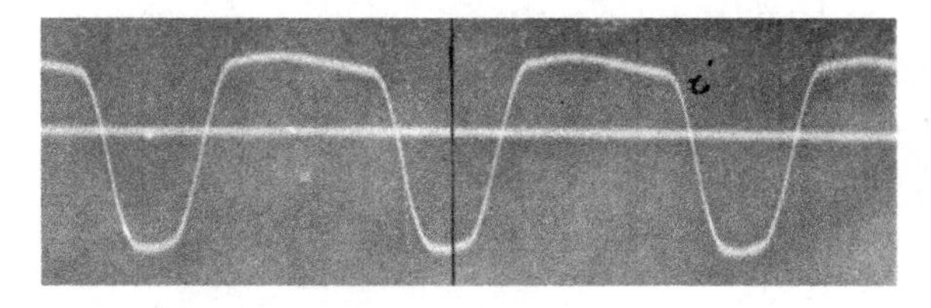

Figure 2.9 Nonsinusoidal oscillations of the current produced by a Colpitts circuit. (Adapted from Morecroft and Friis, 1919.)

Friis' works deserve attention since devoted to "*the forms and phases of voltages and currents in the different parts of the circuit.*" From that respect, they were able to show that various waveforms can be obtained with an oscillation circuit as the Colpitts circuit.

As explained by Hendrick van der Bjil (1887–1948), these particular oscillations were obtained when the current in the oscillation circuit is "90° *out of phase with the plate current* I_p".[31] The grid current I_g is in phase with the plate current and the grid potential. The grid potential and the plate current are nearly 180° out of phase with the plate potential (Figure 2.10). These nonsinusoidal oscillations are well-reproduced by the model (2.1) for the Colpitt circuit as shown in Figure 2.8(b).

2.2.2 *Synchronization between Distant Circuits*

While they were using many oscillation circuits, radio-engineers were quickly confronted with an unexpected interplay observed between distant electronic circuits (without any wire connecting them). This is for instance described by J. H. Vincent from the Paddington Technical Institute (Westminster, London) who investigated

[31] H. J. van der Bijl, *The thermionic vaccum tube and its applications*, McGray-Hill, 1920.

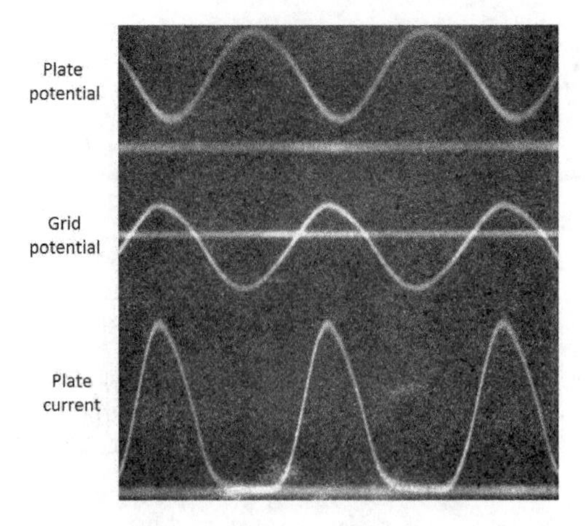

Figure 2.10 Nonsinusoidal oscillations produced by a Colpitts circuit. Adapted from van der Bjil's book, 1920.

how two oscillation circuits sufficiently distant one from the other for having no influence on each other can interact with a resonating circuit (Figure 2.11). He showed in particular that the combined effect on the resonating circuit was the sum of the effects of the oscillation circuits taken separately.[32]

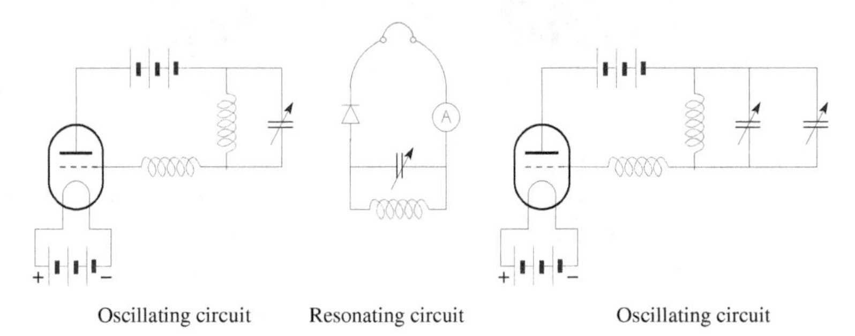

Figure 2.11 Scheme of the experimental device conducted by Vincent for showing that the effects of the two oscillation circuits on a resonating circuit are summed. Redrawn from Vincent, 1919.

Edward Appleton (1892–1965) reproduced Vincent's experiments and confirmed that "*when the difference of the frequencies of two interacting triodes is less than a certain amount, automatic synchronization takes place, and the two oscillators vibrate with one frequency.*"[33] He investigated experimentally bidirectional couplings and theoretically unidirectional couplings, the latter case being easier to treat mathematically. With an unidirectional coupling, only one oscillator is affected by the other one, the former (latter) being designated by Appleton as the weaker (stronger)

[32] J. H. Vincent, On some experiments in which two neighbouring maintained oscillatory circuits affect a resonating circuit, *Proceedings of the Physical Society of London*, **32** (1), 84–91, 1919.
[33] E. V. Appleton, The automatic synchronization of triode oscillators, *Proceedings of the Cambridge Philosophical Society*, **21**, 231–248, 1922–1923.

oscillator. Appleton proposed to approximate this problem by the equation

$$\ddot{V} + \left(\frac{R}{L} + \frac{-\alpha + 2\beta V + 3\gamma V^2}{C}\right) + \dot{V} + \omega_0^2 V = E_0 \omega_0^2 \sin \omega_1 t \tag{2.2}$$

where the action of the stronger oscillator on the weaker one is described by the driving term $E_0 \sin \omega_1 t$. In order to detect the synchronization range, Appleton used a "*cathode-ray oscillograph*", thus plotting the output of one oscillator *versus* the output of the other one. In his problem, this is equivalent to plot $E_0 \sin \omega_1 t$ *versus* the voltage V (Figure 2.12). Appleton defined the *range of synchronization* as the range of ω_1 values for which "*there is definite phase relation between the voltages of the two oscillators.*"

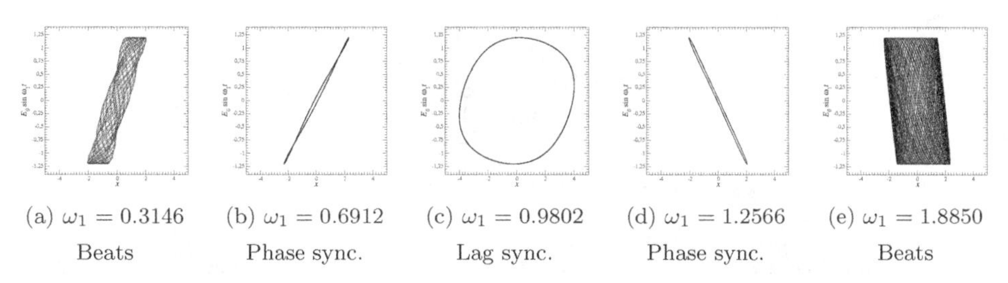

(a) $\omega_1 = 0.3146$ Beats
(b) $\omega_1 = 0.6912$ Phase sync.
(c) $\omega_1 = 0.9802$ Lag sync.
(d) $\omega_1 = 1.2566$ Phase sync.
(e) $\omega_1 = 1.8850$ Beats

Figure 2.12 "Lissajous' figures" as used by Appleton for detecting synchronization and here produced by numerical simulations using the equation (2.3). The values of the angular velocity (pulsation) are chosen to reproduce a sequence of pictures similar to those presented by Appleton in his original paper. Parameter values: $\mu = 0.1$, and $E_0 = 1.2$. Initial conditions: $x_0 = 0.5$ and $\dot{x}_0 = 0.5$.

"Lissajous curve," as developed by Jules Lissajous (1822–1880) for comparing vibrating motions of two bodies and determining the exact ratio between the numbers of their respective vibrations and characterizing the relative motion,[34] were used by Appleton for characterizing the relative motions between his two oscillators. As explained by Lissajous, the oscillators are in phase when the curve is a straight line with $\theta = \frac{\pi}{4}$ (Figure 2.12(b)). This is the case when the two oscillators (which are not identical) vibrate with the same phase but with different amplitudes (Figure 2.13(b)): this corresponds to what is called today *phase synchronization*. The numerical simulations here discussed were produced by the dimensionless equation

$$\ddot{x} + \mu(1 - x^2)\dot{x} + x = E_0 \sin \omega_1 t \tag{2.3}$$

which was considered as an approximation of the equation used in Appleton's paper.

In the middle of the "*synchronization range*" as designated by Appleton, there is a roughly circular curve (Figure 2.12(c)): the two oscillators are in "*quadrature*", that is, they are vibrating with a phase-lag equal to $\Delta\varphi = \frac{\pi}{2}$ (Figure 2.13(c)). This is what Appleton called "*resonance*". Increasing the frequency ω_1 of the stronger oscillator increases the phase lag $\Delta\varphi$ up to π (Figure 2.12(d)): the two oscillators are anti-phase synchronized (Figure 2.13(d)). Appleton showed explicitly that these

[34] J. Lissajous, Mémoire sur l'étude optique des mouvements vibratoires, *Annales de Chimie et de Physique* III, **51**, 146–231, 1857.

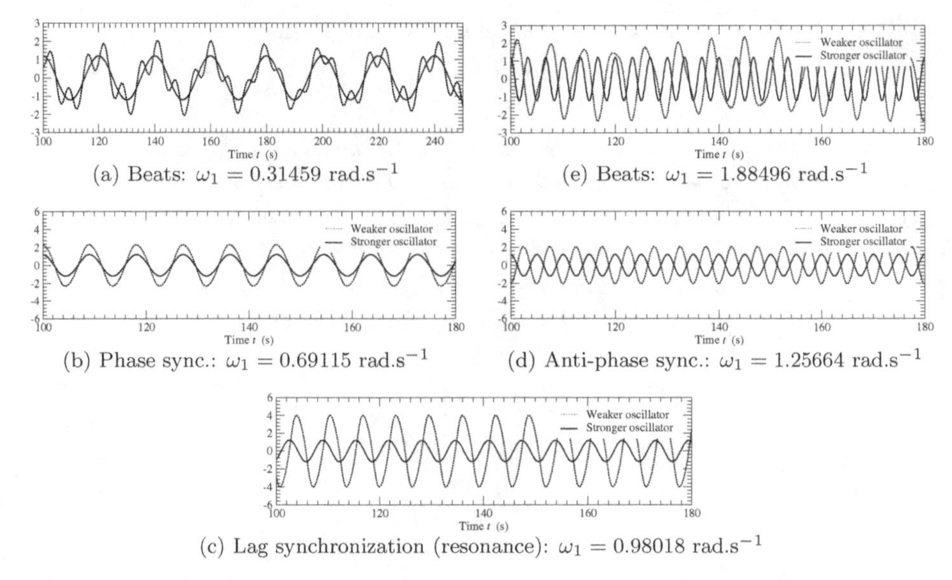

Figure 2.13 Simulated time series of the voltages of the two oscillators in the synchronization problem as investigated by Appleton. Parameter values and initial conditions as in Figure 2.12.

three cases belong to the "silent zone", meaning that there is no beats (no "noise") between the two oscillators. Out of the synchronization range, beats are observed and the dynamics is quasi-periodic (Figure 2.12(a) and 2.12(e)) as clearly shown by the time series of the voltages of the two oscillators (Figure 2.13(a) and 2.13(e)). Beats between the two oscillators can induce some "noise".

Another series of experiments was conducted by Jean Mercier who spent his Ph.D. thesis under the supervision of Henri Abraham (1868–1943) and then became professor at the faculty of Bordeaux (France). He investigated the mutual effects of two oscillation circuits when they are at a sufficiently small distance. He thus observed the possibility to synchronize two nearly identical bidirectionally coupled oscillation circuits tuned at close frequencies.[35] When he progressively varied the frequency of one of the two circuits, there is a value at which there is a sudden extinction of the beats between the two oscillation circuits which are thus *synchronized* (Figure 2.14).[36] He also showed that there is a *synchronization range* over which the two circuits have the same frequency which depends on the characteristics of the two circuits. For instance, if the value of a capacitance of one circuit is slightly varied, the frequency at which oscillate the two circuits is slightly changed too.

Mercier also showed that it was possible to synchronize one circuit oscillating at a frequency f with a second one oscillating at nf where n is an integer. These

[35] J. Mercier, Sur la synchronisation harmonique des oscillateurs électriques, *Comptes-Rendus de l'Académie des Sciences*, **174**, 448–450, 1922.

[36] J. Mercier, De la synchronisation harmonique et multiple, *Journal de Physique et du Radium*, **5** (6), 168–179, 1924.

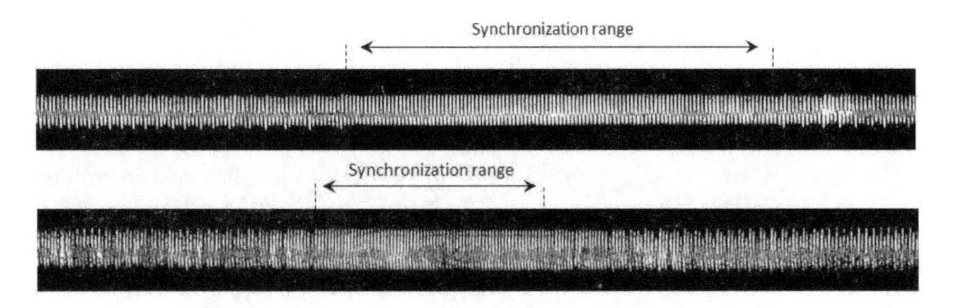

Figure 2.14 Current across one coil of one oscillating circuit while one condenser is slightly varied. Beats are progressively removed up to the synchronization range (middle of the time series) and appears again beyond that range.

synchronization ranges can be simulated with two bidirectionally coupled Colpitts oscillators (Figure 2.15). In fact, when oscillators are linear the synchronization can only occur when the two frequencies are exactly the same. The existence of a synchronization range requires nonlinear oscillation circuits.[37]

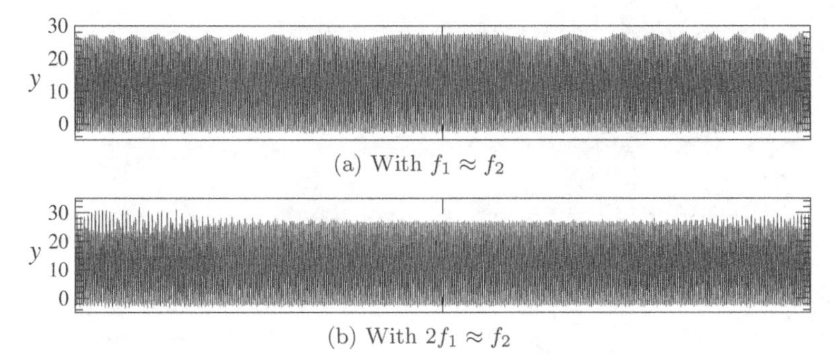

Figure 2.15 Synchronization range for two bidirectionally coupled Colpitts oscillators. (Our simulations)

2.2.3 *The van der Pol Equation*

Crucial for the development of the wireless telegraphy, oscillation circuits were extensively investigated in the early 1900's. We already discussed some of them with the Colpitts oscillator. A major contribution was also developed by Balthazar van der Pol (1889–1959) who investigated a triode oscillator whose resistance depends on the current,[38] that is, whose characteristic is nonlinear. Van der Pol studied experimental physics under Fleming and John Joseph Thomson in England, and

[37]N. Minorsky, *Introduction to non-linear mechanics*, Edwards Brothers (Ann Arbor, Michigan), p. 284, 1947.

[38]B. van der Pol, A Theory of the amplitude and forced triode vibrations, *Radio Review*, **1**, 701–710 and 754–762, 1920.

with Hendrick-Antoon Lorentz (1853–1928) in Holland.[39] As a result he had a solid foundation in electric circuits, vacuum tubes and electromagnetism. During the 1920s van der Pol worked for the Philipps Research Laboratories in Eindhoven. He began his study of the dynamics underlying electrical oscillation circuits including triodes. His approach was strongly based on analytical studies of the differential equations governing the oscillating dynamics produced by these circuits, an approach he reinforced with Appleton when he came to the Cavendish Laboratory in the early 1920's for working with John Joseph Thomson. Appleton and van der Pol started by investigating a "simple" self-excited oscillation circuit (Figure 2.16(a)) in which they recorded time series of the current (Figure 2.16(b)) through the coil L_1. They justified their interest for these times series due to the "*departure from the ordinary sinusoidal form.*"[40] They studied the stability of the solution of the differential equation

$$\ddot{x} + \frac{\mathrm{d}}{\mathrm{d}t}\left[\frac{Rx}{L} + \frac{\Psi(x)}{C}\right] + \omega_0^2 x = 0$$

where x is the anode potential, $\omega = \frac{1}{\sqrt{LC}}$ and $\Psi(x)$ is the characteristic of the circuit that they expressed as a polynomial expansion.

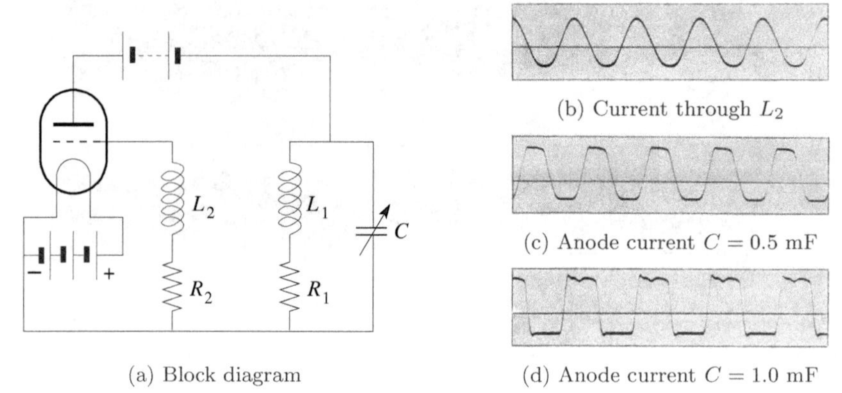

(a) Block diagram (b) Current through L_2 (c) Anode current $C = 0.5$ mF (d) Anode current $C = 1.0$ mF

Figure 2.16 Self-excited oscillating circuit including a triode as investigated by Appleton and van der Pol (1921). $L_1 = L_2 = 0.1$ H, $R_1 = R_2 = 20\,\Omega$. Oscillations frequency is 450 Hz for (c) and 660 Hz for (d).

Appleton further developed the study of this equation with William Greaves (1897–1955).[41] Also under the supervision of Appleton, Alfred Robb (1873–1936) initiated a study of the differential equation

$$\ddot{x} - f(x)\,\dot{x} + \omega x = 0 \tag{2.4}$$

[39] H. Brummer, the scientific work of Balthazar van der Pol, *Philips Technical Review*, **22**, 36–52, 1960.

[40] E. V. Appleton & B. van der Pol, On the form of free triode vibrations, *Philosophical Magazine*, VI, **42**, 201–220, 1921.

[41] E. V. Appleton & W. M. H. Greaves, On the solution of the representative differential equation of the triode oscillator, *Philosophical Magazine*, VI, **45**, 401–414, 1923.

governing the "*production of sustained electrical oscillations by various types of generators, such as the Poulsen and Duddell arcs, and the Dynatron, or the ordinary type of three-electrode thermionic tube.*"[42] This equation was also investigated with a forcing term, that is, under the form

$$\ddot{x} - f(x)\,\dot{x} + \omega x = a \sin \omega t\,.$$

At the end of Robb's paper, Appleton added a small note insisting on the rather generic character of Robb's equation.

This is only in 1926 that van der Pol introduced the dimensionless equation[43]

$$\ddot{x} - \mu(1 - x^2)\dot{x} + x = 0\,. \tag{2.5}$$

which is the simplest nonlinear form that Robb's equation (2.4) can take. Variable x did not received any physical meaning to exhibit the generic character of this differential equation which was first introduced without any corresponding electrical circuit. In this work, van der Pol investigated only a mathematical equation for producing oscillations: triode oscillations were only considered as a particular example of it. With a single parameter, van der Pol was able to provide ordinary sinusoidal oscillations (Figure 2.17(a)) as well as oscillations with a "*marked departure from the sinusoidal form*" (Figure 2.17(b)). In fact, van der Pol was able to reproduce the time series he recorded five years earlier with Appleton (Figure 2.17(c)).

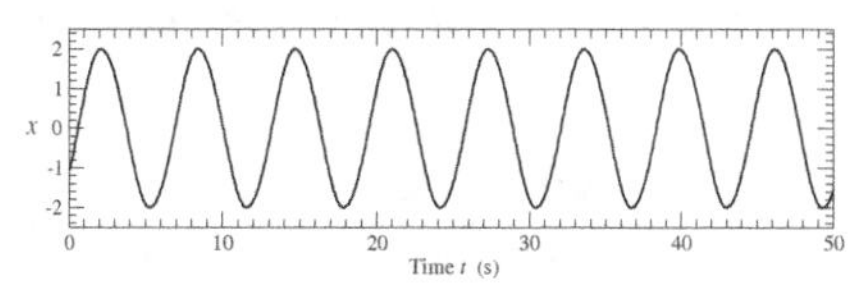

(a) $\mu = 0.1$: sinusoidal oscillations

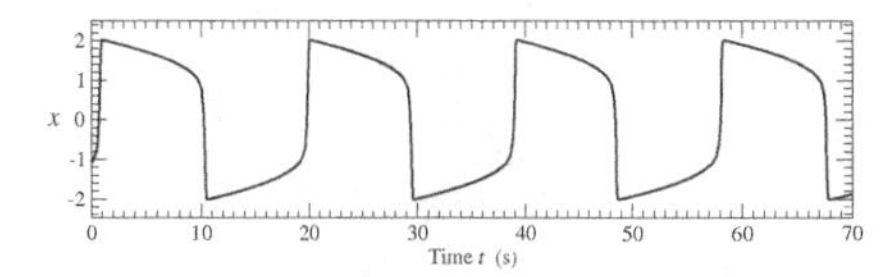

(b) $\mu = 10$: nonsinusoidal oscillations

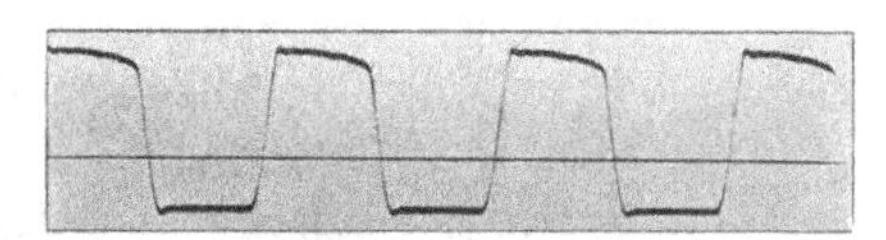

(c) Time series recorded in 1921

Figure 2.17 Sinusoidal and relaxation oscillations produced by the generic "van der Pol" equation (2.5) for two different μ-values. The time series measured with Appleton in 1921 (c) corresponds to the sum of the anode and the grid current (from Appleton and van der Pol, 1921).

Van der Pol also showed a state portrait of these different types of oscillations (Figure 2.18) where he evidenced that different initial conditions lead to the same sustained oscillations, which were named *limit cycle* by Poincaré.

Van der Pol was wise to name these oscillations by the specific "*relaxation oscillation,*" a name related to the relaxation associated with the discharge of a condenser. This is only at the end of his paper that he proposed a possible electrical circuit

[42]A. A. Robb & E. V. Appleton, On a graphical solution of a class of differential equations occurring in wireless telegraphy, *Philosophical Magazine*, VI, **43**, 206–215, 1922.
[43]B. van der Pol, On "relaxation oscillations", *Philosophical Magazine*, **2**, 978–992, 1926.

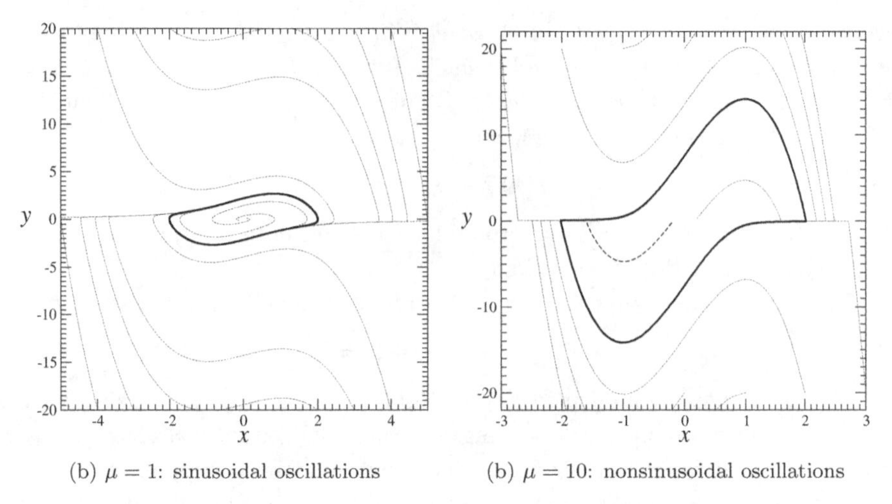

(b) $\mu = 1$: sinusoidal oscillations (b) $\mu = 10$: nonsinusoidal oscillations

Figure 2.18 State portraits produced by the generic "van der Pol" equation (2.5) for two different μ-values.

made of a tetrode, two resistances r and R, a condenser C and an inductance L between the condenser and the outer grid (Figure 2.19). He also noted that when resistance r is replaced by a telephone receiver, "*the oscillations become audible and the change of frequency by changing R and C is easily demonstrated.*" He concluded his paper as follows.

> Finally it seems quite likely that, when the total characteristic (including the parts with a negative slope) is taken into account, the well-known vibration of a neon-tube connected to a resistance and condenser in shunt may be similarly treated under the heading of relaxation-oscillations.
>
> Similarly, (though no detailed investigation has been carried out) it is likely that the oscillation of a "Wehnelt" interrupter belong to the general class of relaxation-oscillations and perhaps also heart-beats.

He investigated heart-beats with Jan van der Mark (1893–1961) two years later.[44]

The problem of automatic synchronization — as investigated by Appleton or Mercier — was investigated in 1927 by van der Pol and van der Mark by using a circuit (Figure 2.20(a)) made of a neon glow lamp, a resistance R of few megaohm, a variable condenser C and a battery E of about 200 volts.[45] According to Mary Lucy Cartwright (1900–1998),[46] this circuit is well described by the differential equation

$$\ddot{x} - \mu(1 - x^2)\dot{x} + x = E_0 \sin(\omega t)\,, \tag{2.6}$$

[44]B. Van der Pol & J. Van der Mark, Le battement du cœur considéré comme oscillation de relaxation et un modèle électrique du cœur, *L'Onde Électrique*, **7**, 365–392, 1928.

[45]B. van der Pol & J. van der Mark, Frequency demultiplication, *Nature*, **120**, 363–364, 1927.

[46]M. L. Cartwright, On non-linear differential equations of the second-order. III. The equation $\ddot{x} - k(1 - x^2)\dot{x} + x = p \cdot k\lambda \cos(\lambda t + \alpha)$, k small and λ near 1, *Mathematical Proceedings of the Cambridge Philosophical Society*, **45** (4), 495–501, 1948.

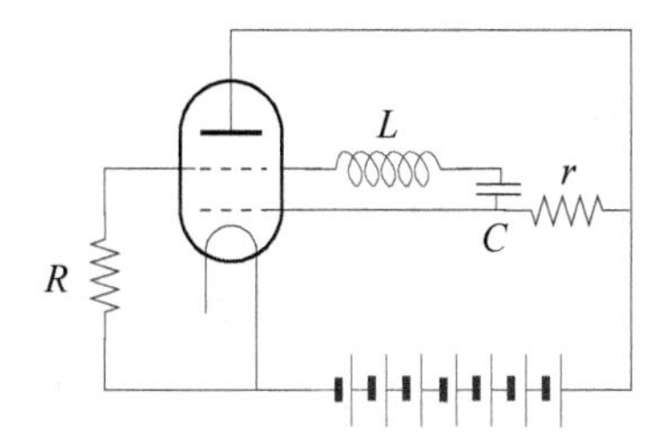

Figure 2.19 Electric circuit with a tetrode corresponding to Eq. (2.5) proposed by van der Pol (1926). The coil L represents a residual inductance that cannot be neglected due to its role in the production of the observed oscillations.

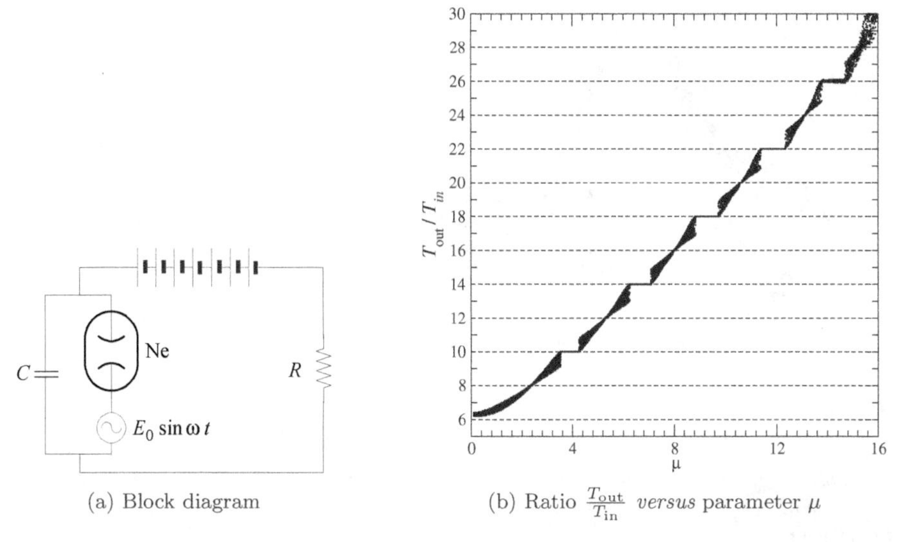

(a) Block diagram

(b) Ratio $\frac{T_{\text{out}}}{T_{\text{in}}}$ *versus* parameter μ

Figure 2.20 Oscillating circuit made of a neon glow lamp used by van der Pol and van den Mark in their study of frequency demultiplication. The output frequency (expressed in terms of the input frequency) is plotted versus parameter μ directly acting on the natural frequency of the oscillating circuit (our simulations). Parameter values: $E_0 = 1.2$ and $\omega = 0.318$ rad.s^{-1}. Initial conditions: $x_0 = 0.2$ and $\dot{x}_0 = 0.2$.

that is, the so-called van der Pol equation forced by a periodic term. While varying the ratio between the frequencies of the telephone receivers, van der Pol and van der Mark observed values for which an "*irregular noise is heard in the telephone receivers before the frequency jumps to the next lower value.*"

This can be reproduced using the driven van der Pol equation (2.6) by varying parameter μ as shown in Figure 2.20(b) where the ratio between the period T_{out} of the driven circuit is divided by the period T_{in} of the driving term (we have thus $\omega = \frac{2\pi}{T_{\text{in}}}$). For some ranges of the parameter μ, the driven circuit oscillates with "*discrete frequencies, these being determined by whole submultiples of the applied frequency.*" There are thus some "*synchronization ranges for which there is a frequency demultiplication*" (up to $\frac{1}{26}$ in Figure 2.20(b)). Between each "plateau" observed for $\frac{T_{\rm out}}{T_{\rm in}} = 2n$, the synchronization is lost and then observed for a very narrowed range of μ-values when $\frac{T_{\rm out}}{T_{\rm in}} = 2n+1$. This lack of synchronization corresponds to the irregular noise heard by Appleton in 1921 and by van der Pol and van der Mark in 1927. Nevertheless, most likely, this noise did not correspond to chaos since, in the present simulations, the lack of synchronization is associated with a quasi-periodic behavior, that is, with a trajectory in a toroidal surface governed by the natural frequency of the oscillation circuit and the frequency associated with the driving term. This is for instance illustrated in Figure 2.21 where a first-return map to a Poincaré section (see details in Section 4.2, p. 213) has clearly an annular shape, the very characteristic signature of a quasi-periodic behavior.

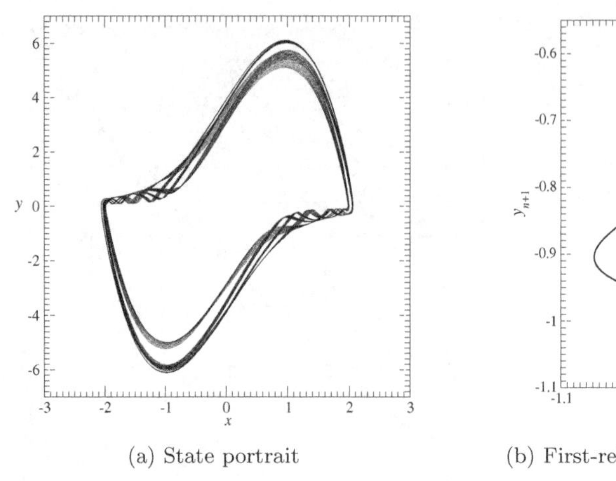

(a) State portrait

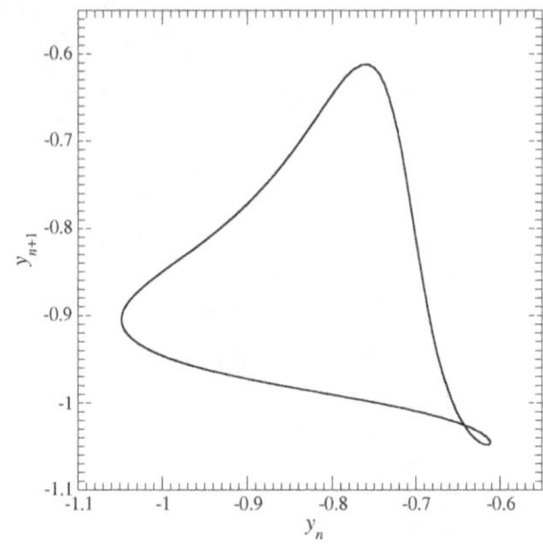

(b) First-return map to a Poincaré section

Figure 2.21 Quasi-periodic behavior produced by the driven van der Pol equation (2.5) as observed on both sides of the synchronization range between the driven oscillation circuit and the driving oscillator.

2.2.4 *From Limit Cycle to more Complex Solutions*

During the 1920s a great deal of work, using more or less explicitly the ideas introduced by Poincaré, were devoted to systems governed by two first-order differential equations, that is, associated with two-dimensional state spaces. Most of these studies belong to the field of electrical engineering. They included works not only by van der Pol but also those by Alfred-Marie Liénard (1869–1953),[47] Philippe Le Corbellier (1891–1980),[48] and those produced by the Russian school under the direction of Andronov, who created the Institute of Radiophysics at Gorki in 1931.

One of the examples investigated by Andronov and co-workers is made of an Audion with an oscillation circuit in the anode loop and an inductive feedback loop

[47] A. Liénard, Etude des oscillations auto-entretenues, *Revue Générale de l'Electricité*, **23**, 901–912 and 946–946, 1928.

[48] Ph. Le Corbeiller, The Nonlinear Theory of the maintenance of oscillations, *Journal of the Institution of Electrical Engineers*, **79**, 361–378, 1936.

(Figure 2.22). The equation[49]

$$\ddot{x} + 2\mu\dot{x} + \omega_0^2 x = \begin{vmatrix} 0 & \text{for } \ddot{x} < 0 \\ \omega_0^2 & \text{for } \ddot{x} > 0, \end{vmatrix} \tag{2.9}$$

where

$$x = \frac{I}{I_s}, \quad \omega_0^2 = \frac{1}{LC} \quad \text{and} \quad 2\mu = \frac{R}{L},$$

governs the current in the Audion.

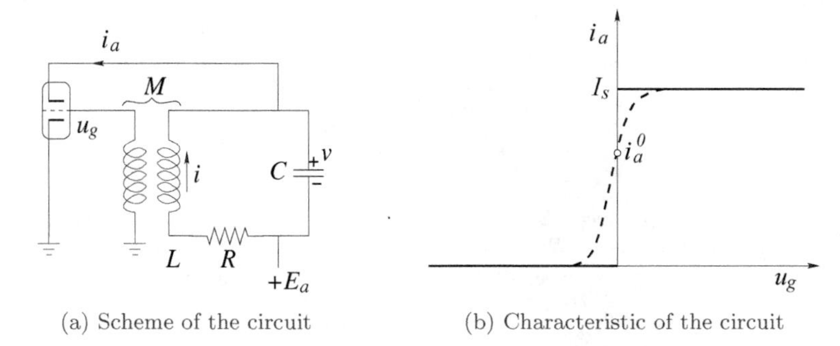

(a) Scheme of the circuit (b) Characteristic of the circuit

Figure 2.22 Oscillation circuit with an oscillation circuit in the anode loop of the Audion as investigated by Andronov's school. Redrawn from Andronov *et al.*, Dover, 1987.

The dynamics produced by the equation (2.9) leads to the state portrait shown in Figure 2.23. Independent from initial conditions — not well controlled in this type of experiments — the asymptotic behavior of the oscillation circuit is a limit cycle, that is, corresponds to sustained periodic oscillations. Initial conditions chosen inside or outside of the limit cycle outside lead to the limit cycle after a transient regime. Note that a similar state portrait was obtained with the van der Pol equation (2.5),

[49]Neglecting the grid current and using notations of Figure. 2.22, we have

$$RI = -U - L\dot{I}, \qquad I = I_a + C + \dot{U}$$

After eliminating U, it comes that

$$LC\ddot{I} + RC\dot{I} + I = I_a \tag{2.7}$$

where $I_a = I_a(U_g)$ is the anode current only depending on the potential $U_\text{g} = -M\dot{I}$ applied to the grid. Let us assume that the characteristic curve of the valve $I_\text{a} = I_\text{a}(U_\text{g})$ (Figure 2.22(b)) has a saturation current I_s and reaches this values according to a squared peak. The working point is located at I_a^0. When amplitude of oscillations of the grid potential are sufficiently large to ensure that the anode current is most of the time neither null (the valve is off) nor equal to the saturation value I_s, then we can correctly represent properties of the Audion by the idealized characteristic curve

$$I_\text{a} = \begin{vmatrix} 0 & \text{for } U_\text{g} < 0 \\ 1 & \text{for } U_\text{g} > 0 \end{vmatrix} \tag{2.8}$$

corresponding to the continuous line in Figure 2.22(b). It is required to assume that for $U_\text{g} = 0$, the condition $I_\text{a} = I_\text{a}^0$ is satisfied. This approximation is sufficient when the damping R is sufficiently small in the oscillation circuit and that a strong coupling exists with the grid. Coils are such as $M < 0$, in order to allow oscillations. Equation (2.7) for the current in the oscillation circuit can thus be reduced to the second-order differential equation (2.9).

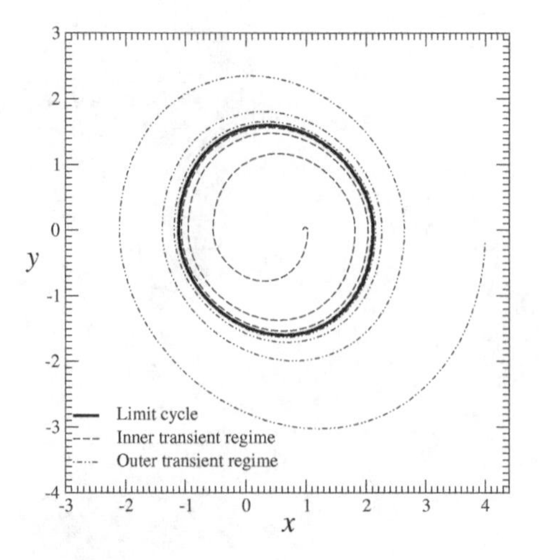

Figure 2.23 Limit cycle produced by equation (2.9) describing the oscillation circuit with an Audion as studied by Andronov, Witt and Khaikin. Parameter values: $\mu = 0.2$ and $\omega_0 = 1$. Initial conditions: $(x_0; y_0) = (0.95; 0)$ (inside the limit cycle), and $(x_0; y_0) = (4; 0)$ (outside).

meaning that, qualitatively, its dynamics is equivalent to the one governed by the equation (2.9). The sustained periodic oscillations announced by Armstrong are clearly evidenced in this state portrait.

The Russian school was not content to stop at state portraits of the systems they studied. They followed this with analyses "*à la Poincaré*" by using ideas such as *Poincaré section*, as well as *stability analyses* based on methods developed by Aleksandr Lyapunov (1857–1918).[50] Singular points, their type of stability, topological invariants and homoclinic orbits were also used. The chapter of the book by Andronov and his colleagues titled "*Fundamentals of the qualitative theory of differential equations of second order*" summarized Andronov's research program: "*application of Poincaré's theory of bifurcation points and changes in stability to self-oscillating systems.*"[51] If electrical circuits occupied an important place in this work, other real physical systems were also included, such as clock mechanisms, hydrofoils, electric motors, autopilots for aircraft and ships... It is remarkable that theory and real problems alternate in this volume. For all of the systems studied motion occurs in two-dimensional spaces, so that the most complex behavior that can be seen is a limit cycle.

[50] A. M. Liapounoff, Problème général de la stabilité du mouvement, (Traduit de l'original en russe — 1892 — par Édouard Davaux), *Annales de la Faculté des Sciences de Toulouse: Mathématiques*, II, **9**, 203–474, 1907 — Translated in English from the French version by A. T. Fuller, The general problem of the stability of motion *International Journal of Control*, **55** (3), 531–773, 1992.
[51] A. A. Andronov & A. G. Lyubiana, Application of Poincaré's therory on "bifurcation points" and on the "change of stability" to simple self-oscillating systems, *Zhurnal Éksperimental'nori i Teoreticheskoi Fiziki*, **5**, 3–4, 1935.

Two-dimensional dynamical models remained at the center of such studies until after the Second World War.[52] Shortly before this tragic event, the development of powerful amplifiers remained a critical problem because soldiers blamed builders for their erratic behavior. Further, in 1938, just before the war, the *Department of Scientific and Industrial Research* issued a memorandum to the *London Mathematical Society* inviting the assistance of pure mathematicians to study the differential equations that occur in radio engineering, laying emphasis on the need to know how the frequencies of the periodic solutions depend on the parameters of the equation. In the early 1940s, the van der Pol equation (2.5) thus arose as a model for the oscillations of the potential in the cavity magnetron discovered at the end of 1939.[53] Such a device was used to produce the high-frequency oscillations required to develop powerful radar. By then, the 1934 paper by van der Pol[54] had a strong impact on radio-engineers.[55] Electronic experiments then showed that the driven van der Pol equation has periodic solution with a period which can be many times the period of the driving term. Moreover, for some values of the amplitude of the driving term, the driven van der Pol equation can present two solutions with different periods, depending on the initial conditions.

Responding to this call, Mary Lucy Cartwright (1900–1998) and John Edensor Littlewood (1885–1977) undertook a study of the driven van der Pol equation. They showed that this equation could have two stable regimes, as previously observed by van der Pol and van der Mark. They also showed that the existence of two periodic solutions implies the existence of "*bad*" solution which was "*very difficult to rule out.*"[56] These non-periodic orbits described as a "*discontinuously recurrent*" motion that would be likely called *quasi-periodic* or *chaotic* today. From the practical point of view, radio builders were not to blame for erratic behavior because when the gain is increased the solutions to the equation — the van der Pol equation describing a radio amplifier driven by sinusoidal oscillations — become more and more irregular.[57] At low power the solutions have the same period as the driving signal but as the power increases, their periods could be doubled, tripled ... or be infinite!

Norman Levinson (1912–1975) also investigated the sinusoidally driven van der Pol equation (2.6) but he replaced the nonlinear characteristic of the circuit by a

[52]H. T. Davis, *Introduction to nonlinear differential and integral equations*, Dover, 1962.
[53]H. A. Boot & J. T. Randall, Historical notes on the cavity magnetron, *IEEE Transactions on electron devices*, **23** (7), 724–729, 1976.
[54]B. van der Pol, The nonlinear theory of electric oscillations, *Proceedings of the Institute of Radio Engineers*, **22** (9), 1051–1086, 1934.
[55]For instance, M. L. Cartwright, Nonlinear vibrations: a chapter in mathematical history, *The Mathematical Gazette*, **36** (316), 81–88, 1952 — D. G. Tucker, Forced oscillations in oscillator circuits and the synchronization of oscillators, *Journal of the Institute of Electrical Engineers*, **93** (1), 57–58, 1945 — R. Adler, A study of locking phenomena in oscillators, *Proceedings of the Institute of Radio Engineers*, **34** (6), 351–357, 1946.
[56]Ibid. Cartwright, 1945.
[57]M. L. Cartwright & J. E. Littlewood, On non-linear differential equations of the second-order, *Annals of Mathematics*, **48** (2), 472–494, 1947.

piecewise linear function. Then converting its solutions into symbolic sequences (see next chapter), he was able to conclude that "*most of the solutions are not periodic since the symbolic sequences are not periodic.*"[58] He associated these solutions to the *discontinuous recurrent motions* introduced by Birkhoff[59] whose examples are the geodesics on certain surfaces of negative curvatures as discussed by Jacques Hadamard[60] and Birkhoff,[61] as well as certain systems like the restricted three-body problem.[62] Levinson also investigated periodic solutions using rotation numbers, a fundamental aspect that will be relevant in the topological analysis. The approach for investigating aperiodic motion was emerging, opening a new way of thinking.

2.3 Biological Systems as Electrical Circuits

2.3.1 *Simulations with Complex Electrical Circuits*

In the early 1940s, Albrecht Bethe (1872–1954) — Hans Bethe's father, the physicist (1906–2005) who received the Nobel prize for his work on stellar nucleosynthesis — published a series of papers in which he developed an analogy between "*discharge switching systems*" and spontaneous or stimulated oscillations in living systems.[63] Bethe started by proposing a rather complex electrical model for the heart electrical activity (Figure 2.24).[64] Contrary to van der Pol and van der Mark who tried to reproduce accurately an electrocardiogram with its different waveforms,[65] Bethe was more interested by reproducing arrhythmias as, among others, extrasystoles, Wenckebach's periodic rhythm, alternans as when the delay between the P-wave and the QRS complex increases up to the lack of the latter complex, preventing from a heart contraction. Starting from the fact that during systole and the beginning of diastole the heart is refractory to stimuli and only gradually recovers its full excitability, Bethe designed electrical switching systems (conveniently prevented from being self-oscillating) in such a way that if the stimuli are sufficiently separated

[58] N. Levinson, Second-order differential equation with singular solutions, *The Annals of Mathematics*, **II**, **50** (1) 127–153, 1949.

[59] G. D. Birkhoff, Surface transformation and their dynamical applications, *Acta Mathematica*, **43**, 1–119, 1922.

[60] J. Hadamard, Les surfaces à courbures opposées et leurs lignes géodésiques, *Journal de Mathématiques Pures et Appliquées*, V, **4**, 27–75, 1898.

[61] G. D. Birkhoff, Nouvelles recherches sur les systèmes dynamiques, *Memorie della Pontificia Academia della Scienze Nuovi Lincei*, **4**, 1, 1934.

[62] G. D. Birkhoff, Sur le problème restreint des trois corps, *Annali della Scuela Normale Superiore di Pisa*, **4**, 267–306, 1935 and **5**, 9–50, 1936.

[63] A. Bethe, Die biologischen Rhythmus-Phänomene als selbständige bzw. erzwungene Kippvorgänge betrachtet, *Pflüger's Archiv für die gesamte Physiologie des Menschen und der Tiere*, **244** (1) 1–42, 1940 — A. Bethe, Teilrhythmus, Alternans, Amplitude und die Grenzen des Alles-oder-Nichts-Gesetzes, *Pflüger's Archiv für die gesamte Physiologie des Menschen und der Tiere*, **244** (1), 43–49, 1940.

[64] A. Bethe, Analogien zwischen Rhytmusstörungen des Herzens und Vorgängen in konstlichen Kippschwingungsystemen, *Klinische Wochenschrift*, **20** (2), 33–36, 1941.

[65] B. van der Pol & J. van der Mark, The heartbeat considered as a relaxation oscillation, and an electrical model of the heart, *Philosophical Magazine*, VI, **38**, 763–775, 1928.

one from the other and, provided that the stimuli are not too weak, the electrical system responds always with the same discharge. The electrical circuit used by Bethe was rather complex as shown in Figure 2.24. He was thus able to correctly reproduce — from the rhythm point of view — these arrhythmias (Figure 2.25).

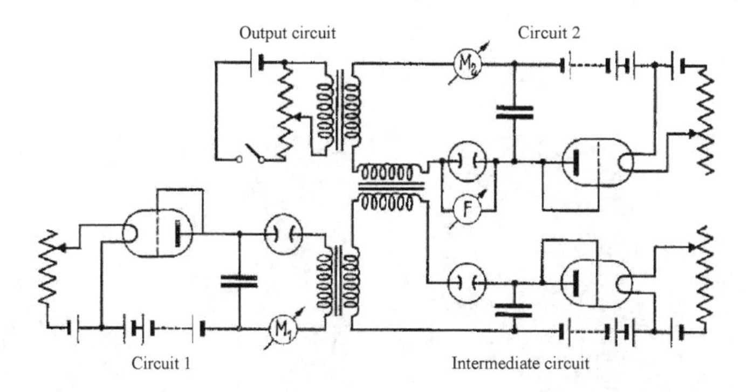

Figure 2.24 Schematic diagram of a two-component electrical switching model with an intermediate circuit and an output circuit. Adapted from Bethe, 1941.

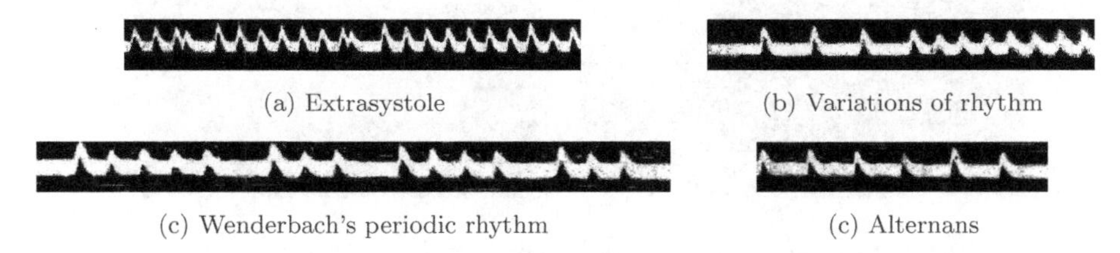

(a) Extrasystole

(b) Variations of rhythm

(c) Wenderbach's periodic rhythm

(c) Alternans

Figure 2.25 Examples of cardiac rhythms reproduced by Bethe's switching circuit. "Alternans" result as the manifestation of concomittant alternations of end-diastolic pressure and volume. Adapted from Bethe, 1941.

Bethe became convinced that these relaxation oscillations were observed in living systems much more frequently than sinusoidal oscillations. These oscillation processes result from more or less sudden discharges of accumulated energy that occur when certain conditions hold; they are latent otherwise. He was thus motivated for investigating these phenomena with the help of oscillation circuit.[66]

> If the charge, which is presumably of chemical origin, reaches the magnitude of firing voltage, spontaneous rhythmic discharges occur; if the charge remains below the firing voltage, discharges can only be induced by an external energy supply *via* nerve or muscles. It was necessary to investigate the extent to which the "excitement laws" found in nerve and in transverse muscles under electrical stimulus correspond to switching electrical circuit under firing voltage.

Bethe also investigated the breathing rhythms in common lizards (*Lacerta*

[66] A. Bethe, Modellversuche zur Theorie der Erregung biologischer Objekte, *Naturwissenschaften*, **31** (23), 276–277, 1943.

vivipara or *Lacerta agilis*) from the measurements performed by Konrad Herter (1891–1980), a German zoologist. It is quite interesting to describe a little bit these latter results. Lizards were placed on a plate whose temperature was varied with a Bunsen burner. He recorded the breathing of his animals by measuring their thorax oscillations.[67] While varying the temperature, he observed the evolution of the breathing movement as shown in Figure 2.26. Clearly, nonlinear processes are underlying such evolution of the breathing dynamics.

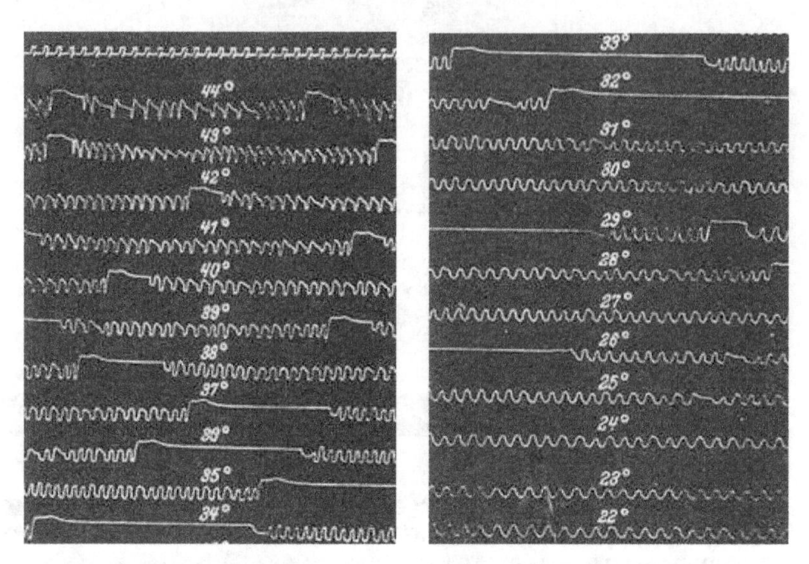

Figure 2.26 Respiratory movement of a lizard (*Lacerba agilis*) in anesthesia when the temperature is decreased from 44 to 22°C: the breathing patterns are clearly nonsinusoidal at very high temperature (44°C) and progressively become sinusoidal at lower temperature (22°C). There is a kind of intermittencies at the intermediate temperature, for which long pauses are observed (the longer full "apnea" has a duration of 22 s and was observed at $T = 33$°C, top of the right panel). Each time series corresponds to a duration of 30 s. From Herter, 1940.

Bethe was particularly interested into Cheyne-Stokes-like breathing patterns that Herter also observed in his lizards (Figure 2.27) or Paul Uhlenbruck (1887–1969) in humans.[68] Cheyne-Stokes breathing is commonly observed when breathing is interrupted by apneas, leaving the impression that breathing occurs by bursts. Again, Herter showed that the higher the temperature, the more frequent the apneas (Figure 2.27).

Bethe was able to reproduce these very particular breathing patterns with a switching electric circuit (Figure 2.28) made of a periodic oscillation circuit (I) stimulating a circuit (II) spontaneously pulsating at a higher frequency. When it is not stimulated, circuit II oscillates spontaneously in an irregular way (Figure

[67] K. Herter, Über das Wesen der Vorzugstemperatur bei Echsen und Nagern, *Zeitschrift für vergleichende Physiologie*, **28** (3), 358–388, 1940.

[68] P. Uhlenbruck, Das Cheyne-Stokessche Atmen, *Zeitschrift für die gesamte experimentelle Medizin*, **59** (1), 656–708, 1928.

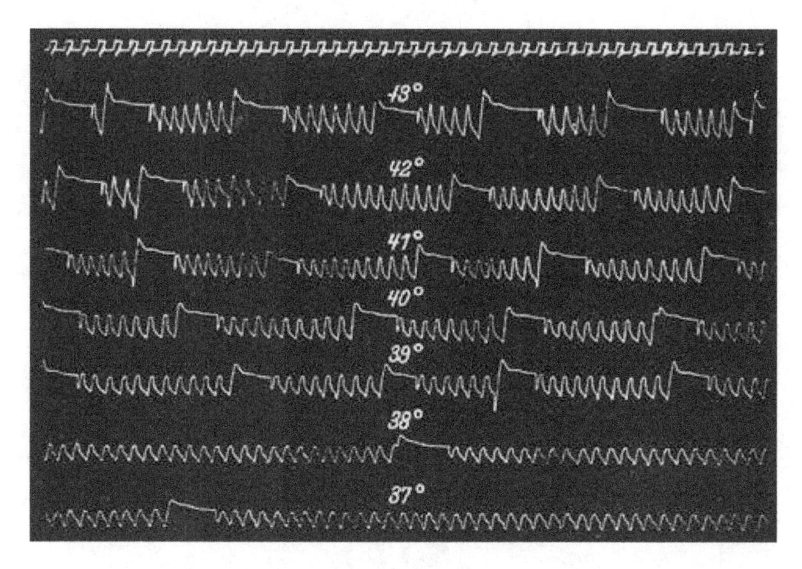

Figure 2.27 Breathing movement with frequent apneas in a *Lacerba vivipera* in anesthesia. This is a kind of Cheyne-Stokes breathing. From Herter, 1940.

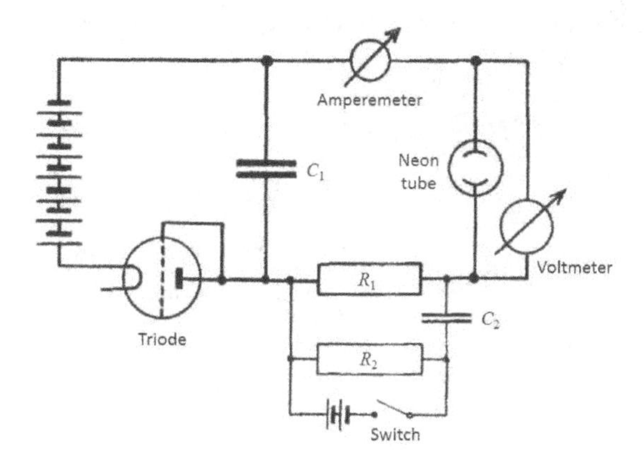

Figure 2.28 Schematic diagram of the switching circuit used by Bethe for reproducing the Cheyne-Stoke breathing patterns. Adapted from Bethe, 1946.

2.29(a)).[69] If this time series could be one of the very first chaotic ones ever published, it is interesting to see that Bethe was able to reproduce various dynamics — not only in shape but also, and more interestingly, in rhythm — by playing with the parameter value of his circuit. He thus used his electronic circuit as a "model" for explaining the rather complex dynamics observed in living systems.

For instance, using the Cheyne-Stokes breathing observed in lizard by Herter as reference (Figure 2.30(a)), Bethe was able to tune the parameter of his circuit to produce a time series (Figure 2.30(b)) which has some properties that the

[69] A. Bethe, Irritabilität, Rhythmik und Periodik, *Naturwissenschaften*, **33** (3), 86–91, 1946.

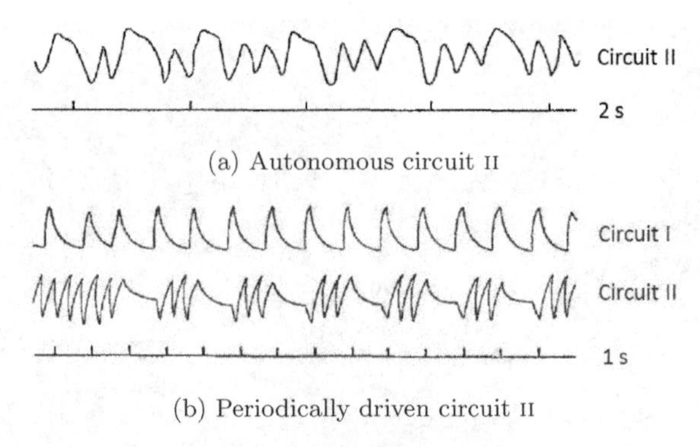

(a) Autonomous circuit II

(b) Periodically driven circuit II

Figure 2.29 Dynamics produced by the electronic circuit (Figure 2.28) used by Bethe in order to reproduce some biological rhythms. (a) Spontaneous aperiodic (?) oscillations when circuit II is autonomous and (b) intermittent oscillations when it is periodically driven. Adapted from Bethe, 1946.

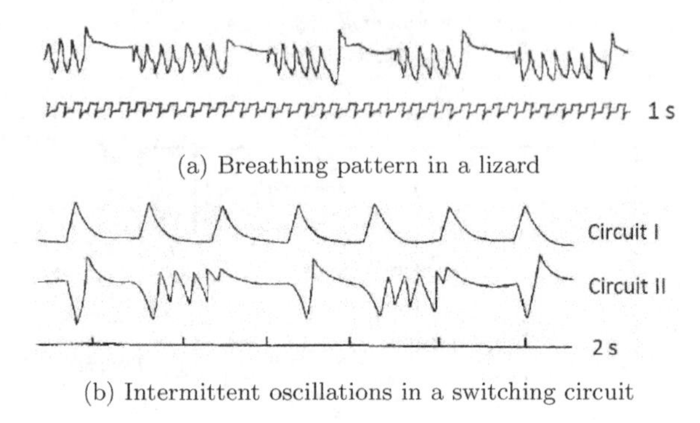

(a) Breathing pattern in a lizard

(b) Intermittent oscillations in a switching circuit

Figure 2.30 Comparison between Cheyne-Stoke breathing patterns in a lizard at 43°C measured by Herter (a) and the dynamics produced by a switching circuit as shown in Figure 2.28. Adapted from Bethe, 1946.

measured signal has. Bethe thus showed that this specific breathing pattern can be well reproduced by the interplay of two oscillators, one driving the other. This type of "*electrical models*" allowed to propose new possible explanation for complex phenomena observed in living systems and which would have been described by too complicated equations for analytical analysis. These electronic circuits were used at these times as we are using today numerical simulations. Nevertheless, when the circuitries become too complicated, as the algebraic structure of their corresponding differential equations, these circuits lose their power for explaining the underlying mechanisms: they are useful for proving that there is an underlying deterministic dynamics but do not offer the possibility to be used for practical applications.

2.3.2 *Simulations with the Simple van der Pol Equation*

Wilhelm Ostwald (1853–1932) stimulated his pupil, Henry Heathcote (some of his experiments are discussed pp. 246–247), for conducting the experiment as follows.[70] When an iron wire in concentrated nitric acid is touched shortly with a zinc rod, the wire becomes active and there is an "*activation*" wave which propagates along the wire from the point of contact: the wire becomes active for a duration which depends on the acid concentration. In that case, there is a wave front of activation followed by a wave front of repassivation; there is thus a moving spot of activity. Ostwald compared this phenomenon to the excitation running along a nerve.

Ralph Lillie (1875–1952), an American physiologist, used that experiment as a model for nervous transmission.[71] He was convinced that this type of model was indeed useful for understanding living systems.

> Biology, because of the complexity of its subject matter and the special need for simplification, has a larger and more diversified assortment of models than other sciences. If we disregard pictures, or other models which aim simply at reproducing the visible aspects of phenomena, we find that in biological models vital processes are usually represented as combinations, more or less complex, of physical or chemical processes. [...] The assumption is that the processes represented in the models are similar in kind to those of the living system. The agreement need not to be complete, but so far as it is real it aids in the understanding of the vital process.

Lillie thus considered that "*the passive iron wire model* [...] *resembles closely the irritable and transmissive protoplasmic systems, especially nerve.*" In the 1940s, Karl Friedrich Bonhöffer (1899–1957) — a German chemist who should not be mistaken with the German neurologist Karl Ludwig Bonhöffer (1868–1948) — further developed this analogy, justifying it by the qualitative properties both systems were sharing.[72]

> It is indeed most astonishing that iron wire and nerve, which from the chemical point of view differ so enormously, function in such a similar way. It does not seem credible that the various functional properties in which the two systems resemble each other could be independent and accidental similarities. There is here a most interesting problem from the point of view of reaction kinetics. The existence of a threshold of activation, of a refractory state, of a transmission of activation, of a

[70] H. L. Heathcote, Vorläufiger Bericht über Passivierung, Passivität und Aktivierung des Eisens, *Zeitschrift für Physikalische Chemie*, **37** (1), 368–373, 1901.
[71] R. S. Lillie, The passive iron wire model of proto-plasmic and nervous transmission and its physiological analogues, *Biological Reviews*, **11** (2), 181–209, 1936.
[72] K. F. Bonhöffer, Activation of passive iron as a model for the excitation of nerve, *Journal of General Physiology*, **32** (1), 69–91, 1948.

> tendency to give rhythmic reactions, and a suggestion that even the so called accommodation effects are not missing in the model, indicated that all these properties, so uncommon in ordinary chemistry, are in some way related to each other.

Thus, after some experimental studies, Bonhöffer showed that these qualitative properties correspond well to undamped electric oscillations. To avoid the natural damping of these oscillations, there must be an influence which compensates it: this is the so-called "*negative resistance*" in the electrical circuit, meaning that an increase in voltage is associated with a decrease in current intensity.

Bonhöffer considered a circuit containing in series a condenser C, a self-inductance L and a resistance R with a voltage $E_R(I)$. He proposed the governing equations

$$\begin{cases} \dot{I} = \frac{E}{L} - \frac{E_R(I)}{L} \\ \dot{E} = -\frac{I}{C} \end{cases} \tag{2.10}$$

where E is the voltage across the condenser. Bonhöffer then explained that the curve $E_R(I)$ must have a S-shape (Figure 2.31), the increasing branch, which is only observed beyond a threshold current I, corresponds to the spontaneous increase of active areas by local currents. Since the refractoriness is produced in a wire becoming active, $\dot{I}$ is positive when E is positive; Bonhöffer then added that "*the rate of increase of activity $\dot{E}$ is produced by the current is diminished by the refractoriness I.*" Since E cannot rise indefinitely, the curve $E_R(I)$ must present a maximum and then decrease again, thus inducing a S-shaped curve (Figure 2.31). Physically, this means that the "*local currents lose their activating power when the whole surface is active.*"

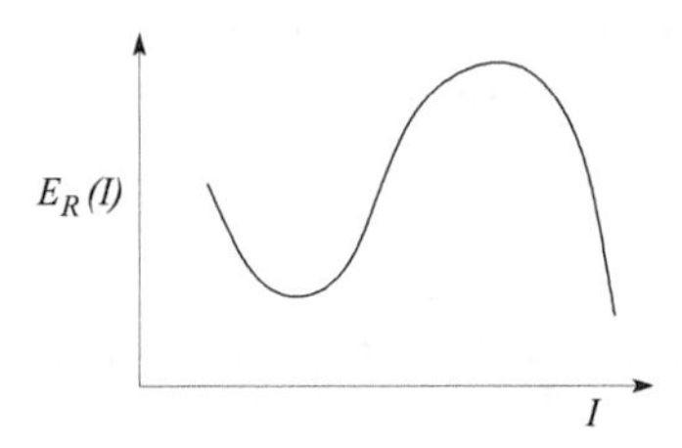

Figure 2.31 S-shaped curve for the activity $E_R(I)$ *versus* the refractoriness I.

Bonhöffer did not propose any algebraic expression for $E_R(I)$. A general form for describing the S-shaped curve can be[73]

$$E_R(I) = -\alpha I + \beta \frac{I^3}{3}\,.$$

[73]This form corresponds to the simple cubic characteristic $i = -\alpha v + \beta v^3$ used by van der Pol in his paper titled "The nonlinear theory of electric oscillations," *Proceedings of the Institute of Radio Engineers*, **22**, 1051–1086, 1934.

The system (2.10) has thus the form

$$\begin{cases} \dot{I} = \dfrac{1}{L}\left(E + \alpha I - \beta \dfrac{I^3}{3}\right) \\ \dot{E} = -\dfrac{I}{C} \,. \end{cases} \tag{2.11}$$

In order to show that this system is equivalent to the van der Pol equation (2.5), let us start from the transformation of coordinates

$$y = \frac{\dot{x}}{\mu} - x + \frac{x^3}{3}$$

introduced by Alfred-Marie Liénard (1869–1953) to prove the existence of a limit cycle in the van der Pol equation (2.5).[74] Differentiating this transformation leads to

$$\dot{y} = \frac{\ddot{x}}{\mu} - (1 - x^2)\dot{x} \,. \tag{2.12}$$

Rewriting the van der Pol equation (2.5) as

$$\frac{\ddot{x}}{\mu} = (1 - x^2)\dot{x} - \frac{x}{\mu} \,,$$

and injecting this expression into equation (2.12), we get $\dot{y} = -\frac{x}{\mu}$. Consequently, the van der Pol equation can be rewritten as

$$\begin{cases} \dot{x} = \mu \left(y + x - \dfrac{x^3}{3}\right) \\ \dot{y} = -\dfrac{x}{\mu} \,. \end{cases} \tag{2.13}$$

This set of two differential equations corresponds to the Bonhöffer system (2.11) where $I = x$, $E = y$, $\alpha = \beta = 1$ and $\frac{1}{L} = C = \mu$. We have thus a direct correspondence between the Bonhöffer model for the activation of passive iron or, by analogy, for the excitation of nerve, and the van der Pol equation (2.5). System (2.13) is often called the Bonhöffer-van der Pol model as suggested by Richard FitzHugh.[75]

Independently, the flow of electric current through the surface membrane of a giant nerve fibre was then described by Alan Hodgkin (1914–1998) and Andrew Huxley (1917–2012) by using an electric circuit as follows.[76] The ionic current carried through a membrane can be divided into a current $I_{\rm Na}$ carried by sodium ions, a current $I_{\rm K}$ carried by potassium ions and a small leakage current $I_{\rm l}$ associated with chloride and other ions. There is also a current charging the membrane capacity. Each of these ionic currents is driven by an electrical potential difference E and a

[74] A.-M. Liénard, Etude des oscillations auto-entretenues, *Revue Générale de l'Electricité*, **23**, 901–912 and 946–946, 1928.

[75] R. FitzHugh, Impulses and physiological states in theoretical models of nerve membrane, *Biophysical Journal*, **1**, 445–466, 1961.

[76] A. L. Hodgkin & A. F. Huxley, A quantitative description of membrane current and its application to conduction and excitation in nerve, *Journal of Physiology*, **117** (4), 500–544, 1952.

permeability coefficient (the inverse of a resistance). The corresponding electrical circuit is shown in Figure 2.32. For describing the dynamics of this system, Hodgkin and Huxley obtained the set of four differential equations

$$\left\{\begin{aligned}
\dot V &= \frac{1}{C_{\rm m}}\left(I - \bar g_{\rm K} n^4 (V - V_{\rm K}) - \bar g_{\rm Na} m^3 h (V - V_{\rm Na}) - \bar g_l (V - V_l)\right)\\
\dot n &= (1-n)\,\frac{0.01(V+10)}{e^{\frac{V+10}{10}} - 1} - 0.125\, n\, e^{\frac{V}{80}}\\
\dot m &= (1-m)\,\frac{0.1(V+25)}{e^{\frac{V+25}{10}} - 1} - 4\, m\, e^{\frac{V}{18}}\\
\dot h &= (1-h)\, 0.07 e^{\frac{V}{20}} - \frac{h}{e^{\frac{V+30}{10}} + 1}
\end{aligned}\right. \tag{2.14}$$

where $\bar g_{\rm K}$, $\bar g_{\rm Na}$ and $\bar g_l$ are the membrane conductances. The total current density through the membrane

$$I = C_{\rm m}\dot V + \bar g_{\rm K} n^4 (V - V_{\rm K}) + \bar g_{\rm Na} m^3 h (V - V_{\rm Na}) + \bar g_l (V - V_l)$$

is obtained from the first equation of system (2.14) and V is the membrane voltage. The dimensionless variables m and n correspond to the proportion of sodium activation and potassium activation in the membrane, respectively. Variable h corresponds to the proportion of sodium inactivation outside of it. This system was quite complicated to investigate. Moreover, its dynamics was rather poor since only corresponding to limit cycles.

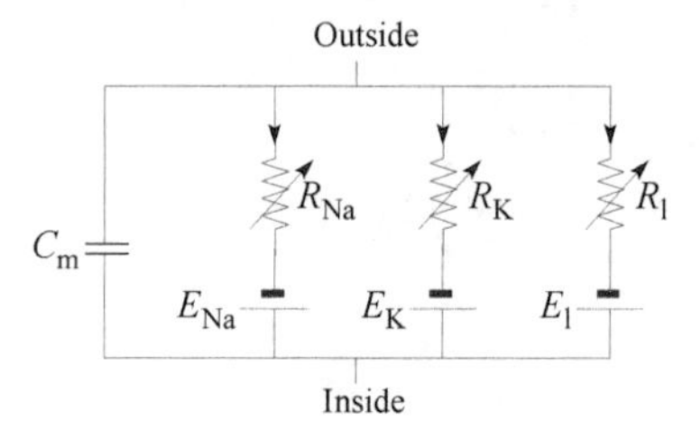

Figure 2.32 Electrical circuit for simulating the membrane current in nerve. Experiments showed that $R_{\rm Na}$ and $R_{\rm K}$ are varying with time. Redrawn from Nagumo *et al.*, 1962.

In order to obtain a lower-dimensional model than the Hodgkin-Huxley one, in the case where the excitation of a nerve is spatially uniform, Richard FitzHugh (1922–2007) restarted from the van der Pol-Bonhöffer system (2.11) but, to improve the fit to time series measured in nerve membrane, he added some terms — apparently in a rather empirical way — to obtain the model[77]

$$\left\{\begin{aligned}
\dot I &= \mu\left(E + I - \frac{I^3}{3} + I_{\rm s}\right)\\
\dot E &= -\frac{1}{\mu}(I - a + bE)
\end{aligned}\right. \tag{2.15}$$

[77] FitzHugh, 1961. *Ibid.*

where I_s is the stimulus intensity corresponding to the membrane current occurring in the Hodgkin-Huxley equation. Roughly, variables of the modified Bonhöffer-van der Pol system corresponds to those of the Hodgkin-Huxley model according to[78]

$$\begin{cases} I = V - 36m \\ E = \dfrac{n-h}{2} . \end{cases}$$

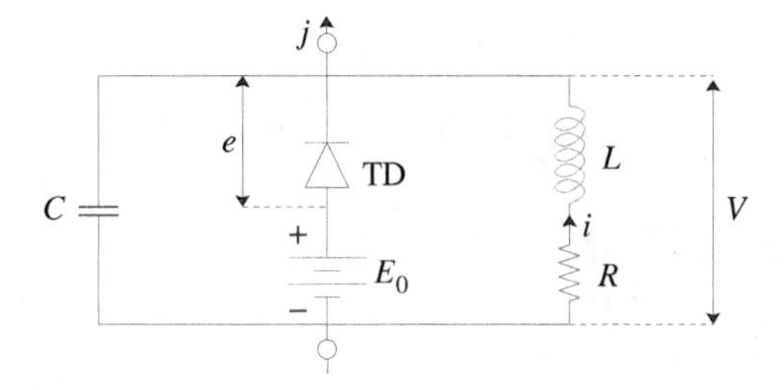

Figure 2.33 Electronic circuit with a tunnel diode (TD) proposed by Nagumo and co-workers for simulating the dynamics of the Bonhöffer-van der Pol system modified by FitzHugh. Redrawn from Nagumo, 1962.

In biology, according to the terminology introduced by FitzHugh, the two-dimensional system (2.15) is in fact a modified Bonhöffer-van der Pol system. Jin-Ichi Nagumo (1926–1999), Suguru Arimoto, and Shuji Yoshizawa (University of Tokyo) proposed an electronic circuit (Figure 2.33) made of a tunnel diode[79] with a cubic current-voltage characteristic and which is described by a system of differential equations equivalent to the system (2.15).[80] This system is now (surprisingly) designated as the FitzHugh-Nagumo system. Parameters of the system (2.15) are thus

$$\begin{cases} \mu = \dfrac{1}{\rho}\sqrt{\dfrac{L}{C}} \\ a = \dfrac{Ri_0 + (e_0 - E_0)}{K} \\ b = \dfrac{R}{\rho} \end{cases}$$

where ρ, K and e_0 are parameters of the cubic current-voltage characteristic of the tunnel diode.

The model (2.15) was the starting point of the studies by FiztHugh on the spike generation in squid giant axons. He was thus able to explain the different phases

[78] J. Nagumo, S. Arimoto & S. Yoshizawa, An active pulse transmission line simulating nerve axon, *Proceedings of the Institute of Radio Engineers*, **50** (10), 2061–2070, 1962.

[79] Tunnel diode was invented in August 1957 by Reona Esaki (also known as Leo Esaki), Yuriko Kurose and Takashi Suzuki while working at Tokyo Tsushin Kogyo (Sony). L. Esaki, New phenomenon in narrow germanium *p-n* junctions, *Physical Review*, **109**, 603–604, 1958. It was patented by Reona Esaki and Yuriko Kurose, Diode type semiconductor device, *US Patent* No 3,033,714, filed on May 8, 1958, granted on May 8, 1962.

[80] Nagumo *et al.*, 1962, *Ibid.*

occurring during an oscillation of the membrane current as shown in Figure 2.34. With his analysis of the modified Bonhöffer-van der Pol system (2.15), FitzHugh also showed that the nonlinear dynamical system theory was able to provide useful insight in applied problems. Note that apparently, FitzHugh is the first to investigate how the nullclines, defined as $\dot{x} = 0$ and $\dot{y} = 0$, structure the state portrait. Other like van der Pol used curves defined as $\dot{x} = k_1$ and $\dot{y} = k_2$ where k_1 and k_2 are two constants which can be nonzero.[81]

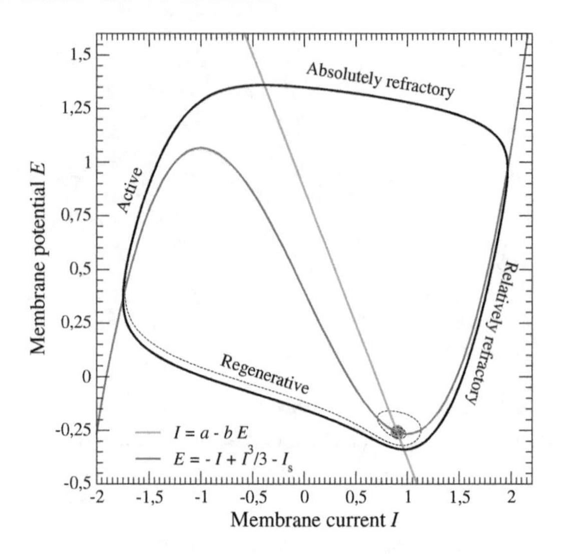

Figure 2.34 Limit cycle produced by the modified Bonhöffer-van der Pol system (2.15). After the active phase, the nerve is refractory. The nerve then progressively recovers its excitability and is again regenerated; it can be stimulated for a new oscillation. Nullclines are defined as $\dot{x} = 0$ (blue) and $\dot{y} = 0$ (green). Parameter values: $\mu = 3$, $a = 0.7$, $b = 0.8$ and $I_s = 0$.

2.4 From Electronics to Dynamical Systems

If the solutions "heard" by van der Pol and van der Mark were quasi-periodic, most likely those investigated by Levinson were chaotic, but they remained rather confidential. Nevertheless, none of these brilliant researchers made an explicit connection with Poincaré's contribution to the nonlinear dynamical systems theory. They only presented their solutions as irregular but not showing appealing pictures stimulating scientists' imaginary world.

2.4.1 *The Hayashi's group*

It seems that one of the very first notable contributions in this direction was that of the group directed by Chihiro Hayashi (1911–1987), professor in the department of electrical engineering at the University of Tokyo. Hayashi published in 1953 a

[81] van der Pol, 1926, *Ibid.*

remarkable book entitled *Nonlinear Oscillations in Physical Systems.*[82] He had studied the works of Lord Rayleigh, Poincaré, Lyapunov, Duffing, and van der Pol. He began experiments in the style of van der Pol on forced oscillators during the period 1942–1948 based on differential equations such as Duffing's equation (1.5). He was particularly drawn to graphical representations of the solutions of these equations. If he used the earliest computers to draw the first state portraits of some solutions to these equations, he only inserted state portrait of limit cycle. When quasi-periodic behaviors were investigated, he provided time series of one variable or a Poincaré section of the state portrait.

When Ueda began his thesis in 1959 under Hayashi's supervision, the use of digital computers was not common, and the calculations that were submitted for his Ph.D. thesis in 1965[83] were all done using analog computers. He studied principally the systems of Duffing and van der Pol. To each of these sets of equations corresponds an electronic circuit, shown in Figure 2.35 and Figure 2.36. The important point is that these circuits are driven by an alternating current, that is, a sinusoidal wave with a certain fixed frequency: this corresponds to the sinusoidal driving term shown, for instance, in equation (2.6).

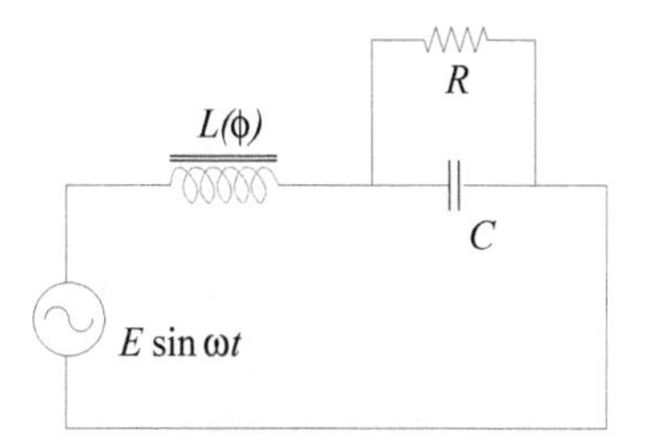

Figure 2.35 Electrical circuit corresponding to the Duffing equation.

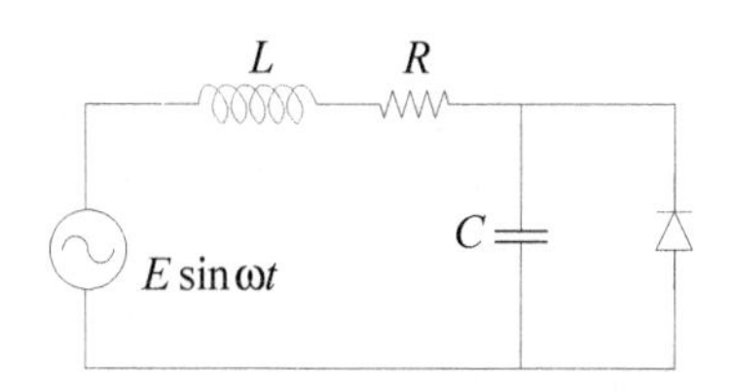

Figure 2.36 Electronic circuit corresponding to the van der Pol equation. The nonlinear element may be a tunnel diode.

Ueda studied the phenomenon of entrainment (another word for synchronization) and the conditions required for its observation.[84]

> When a circuit (oscillator) which would, if left alone, keep on generating an electrical (self-sustained) oscillation with a certain frequency and amplitude, is driven externally with signals whose frequency is different from that of the oscillator, its self-oscillating frequency is drawn to and synchronized with that of the driving frequency. This phenomenon is called frequency entrainment. There are exceptions, of course — depending on the value of the driving frequency and amplitude, entrainment

[82] C. Hayashi, *Nonlinear Oscillations in physical systems*, McGraw-Hill, 1953. .

[83] Y. Ueda, Some problems in the theory of nonlinear oscillations, Ph.D. Thesis, Tokyo University (1965), reproduced in English in *The road to chaos*, Aerial Press, 1992.

[84] Y. Ueda, Strange attractors and the origin of chaos, *International Journal of Nonlinear Science Today*, **2** (2), 1–16, 1992.

> sometimes does not occur. Instead, an aperiodic "*beat oscillation*" with drifting frequencies would appear.

Ueda here described what Appleton introduced in 1921 as the "*synchronization range*" (see p. 101) but without explicit reference to him.[85] In fact, in order to complete his analytic study, Ueda used some approximations (these had the effect of suppressing chaos). He subsequently verified his results by carrying out a numerical integration using an analog computer built by Minoru Abe with vacuum tubes.

On November 27, 1961, while he was finishing a paper on the driven van der Pol equation

$$\ddot{x} - \mu(1 - \gamma x^2)\dot{x} + x^3 = B\cos(\omega t)\,, \tag{2.16}$$

Ueda varied the angular frequency ω and observed a strange trajectory on the screen of his computer:

> It was nothing like the smooth oval closed curves, but was more like a broken egg with jagged edges. My first concern was that my analog computer had gone bad. But I soon realized that that was not the case. It did not take long for me to recognize the mystery of it all — the fact that during the asynchronous phase, the shattered egg appeared more frequently than the smooth closed curves, and that the order of the dots which drew the shattered egg was totally irregular and seemingly inexplicable. As I watched my professor preparing the report without a mention of this shattered egg phenomenon, but rather replacing it with the smooth closed curves of the quasi-periodic oscillation, I was quite impressed by this technique of report writing.[86] But at the same time, I realized that one needs to be very careful in reading reports of this sort.

The "shattered eggs" in fact correspond to a chaotic behavior (Figure 2.37). The attractor's Poincaré section[87] revealed some secrets to Ueda — the points were not distributed at random — but he was not able to investigate this further up until much later. In fact, Hayashi had observed that only periodic or quasi-periodic behavior was discussed in the literature. He thought that the "almost" periodic behavior was simply irregular transients that finally always end up — after a time that could be very long — by converging to a regular behavior. He did not want to hear talking about irregular oscillations:

---

[85] Appleton is quoted a single time in Hayashi's book (for his paper published in 1922 with van der Pol) and none in Ueda's Ph.D. thesis.

[86] C. Hayashi, H. Shibayama & Y. Ueda, Quasi-periodic oscillations in a self-oscillatory system with external force, *Proceedings of the Symposium on Nonlinear Oscillation* (International Union in Theoretical Applied Mechanics Kiev), **1**, 495–509, 1963.

[87] The Poincaré section was constructed following K. W. Blair & W. S. Loud, Periodic Solution of $\ddot{x} + c\dot{x} + g(x) = Ef(t)$ under variation of certain parameters, *Journal of the Society for Industrial and Applied Mathematics*, **8**, 74–101, 1960.

[One day in the fall or winter of 1962], I struggled again for several days in a row, in front of the computer. When the amplitude of the external force increased, the high frequency components in the periodic solution also increased, accelerating the response time, thus making it extremely difficult for the servo multiplier — that represented the nonlinear term — to follow up. Consequently, one had to extend the computer's time scale so as to slow down the response time. I repeated the experiment with one cycle of the external force 2π corresponding to 31.4... seconds. During the process, I encountered enough chaotic oscillations (the source of the Japanese attractor) to make me sick. But Prof. Hayashi told me:

> "*Oh, it's probably taking time to settle down to the subharmonic oscillations. Even in an actual series resonance circuit, such a transient state lingers for a long time.*"

When I look back, though, I seemed to have sensed at that time that chaos was not a phenomenon unique to forced self-oscillatory systems in which quasi-periodic oscillations appeared.

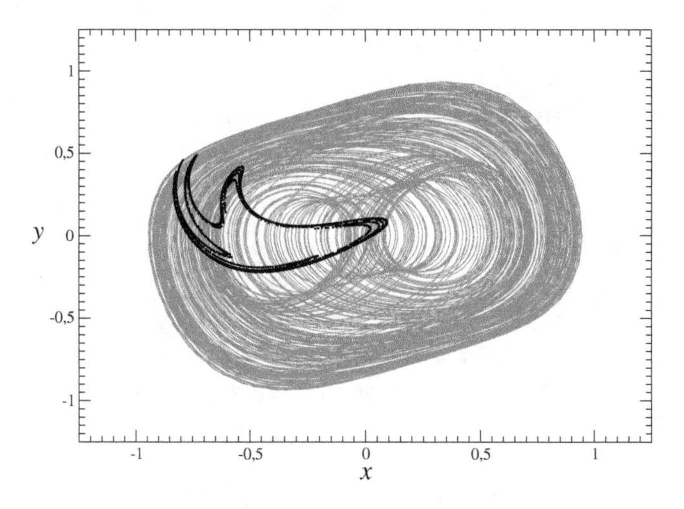

Figure 2.37 Figure similar to those computed by Ueda on November 27, 1961 with an analogic computer. Here the number of points (15,000) plotted in this Poincaré section is larger than the number computed by Ueda, his computations of 50 points required more than hours, while the present computations needed fewer than seconds. Parameter values: $\mu = 0.2$, $\gamma = 8$, $B = 0.35$ and $\omega = 1.02$.

Despite all, Ueda continued to remember this bizarre behavior. In 1963 he read the mathematics course given by Vladimir I. Smirnov (1887–1974), who was familiar with the work of Birkhoff which could have pushed him to be more confident in what he observed in his experiments. Nevertheless, the timidity shown by Hayashi always restrained Ueda. On September 1969, during a student protest movement in his university,[88] that Ueda took the initiative to send, without informing Hayashi who was the first author of the paper, an article describing the beats apart from the synchronization range. The simulations were performed using the system

$$\begin{cases} \dot{x} = y \\ \dot{y} = \mu(1 - \gamma y^2)y - x^3 + B\cos\omega t\,, \end{cases} \tag{2.17}$$

that is, a variant of the driven van der Pol equation (2.16). In the English version originally published,[89] the conclusion was as follows.

> For the external force prescribed outside the regions of entrainment, a beat oscillation results. Two types of beat oscillations were observed. One of them is a quasiperiodic oscillation and the corresponding successive images form a smooth invariant closed curve on the phase plane. Successive images form an extremely complicated figure, and the nature of this point sequance has not been fully investigated.[90]

There Ueda and co-workers pointed out the differences between the Poincaré sections during quasi-periodic motion — simple because they are characterized by a simple closed curve — (Figure 2.38(a)) and during "*irregular and complicated*" motion (Figure 2.38(b)).[91] The second type of beats was found when an infinite number of "*doubly asymptotic points*", that is, an infinite number of intersections between the unstable (α-branch) and stable (ω-branch) manifolds. This description is quite similar to the one which can be found in Poincaré's works, which were quoted.[92] As in Poincaré's work, a clear connection with homoclinic orbit is shown.

Even so, in 1971, Ueda did not yet understand that the origin of the instabilities was intrinsic to the system. Ueda recounted that he was dissuaded from presenting at a seminar the new type of behavior he had observed by Minoru Urabe who was the seminar organizer: "*What you saw was simply the essence of quasi-periodic oscillations. You are too young to make conceptual observations.*" Nevertheless,

[88] Japanese student protests started in the early 1960s. There were stimulated not only by opposition to the Vietnam war but also by a demand for campus reforms. For instance, at Tokyo University, medical students started a long strike against the medical practitioners' lax. They finished by boycotting all classes, forcing the president and the director of the university hospital to resign. In 1969, some reforms were put in practice but this is only in 1971 and 1972 that actually started deeper changes. For more details, see for instance, M. Shimbori, T. Ban, K. Kono, H. Yamazaki, Y. Kano, M. Murakami & T. Murakami, Japanese student activism in the 1970s, *Higher Education*, **9** (2), 139–154, 1980.

[89] There is another English version which was translated in 1992 from the Japanese by Ueda when the book *Road to chaos* was produced.

[90] G. D. Birkhoff, Surface transformations and their dynamical applications, *Acta Mathematica*, **43**, 1–119, 1922.

[91] C. Hayashi, Y. Ueda, N. Akamatsu & H. Itakura, On the behavior of self-oscillatory systems with external force, *Transactions of the Institute of Electronics and Communication Engineers A*, **53** (3), 150–158, 1970.

[92] H. Poincaré, *Les méthodes nouvelles de la mécanique céleste*, Gauthier-Vilars, Tome III, chapter 33, 1899.

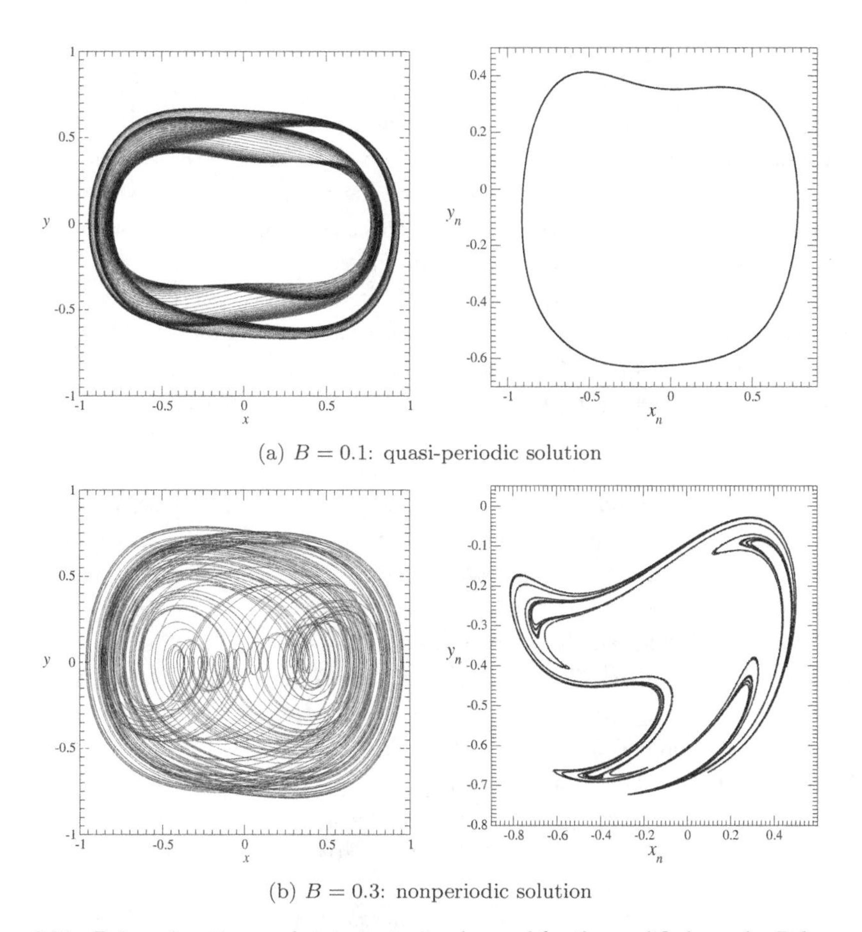

Figure 2.38 Poincaré sections and state portraits observed for the modified van der Pol equation (2.17), as calculated by Ueda in 1969. Several thousands of points are used to construct these sections while Ueda and co-workers had only about fifty due to the limitations of their analog computer. Other parameter values: $\mu = 0.2$, $\gamma = 4$ and $\omega = 1.1$.

if he explained during his presentation that the irregular behavior was organized around the unstable periodic orbits, he concluded:[93]

> However, according to my observation of the phenomenon with the use of a computer, each of the minimal sets which make up the set of central [periodic] points are all unstable, and the steady state seems to move randomly around the vicinity of the minimal sets, influenced by small fluctuations in the oscillatory system or external disturbances.

Here Ueda found himself on the path blazed by Hill and Poincaré: periodic orbits

[93] C. Hayashi, Y. Ueda, N. Akamatsu & H. Itakura, On steady-state solutions of a nonlinear differential equation of the second-order, *Report of the Research Institute for Mathematical Sciences* (Tokyo University), **113**, 1–27, 1971.

organize irregular trajectories. Nevertheless, Ueda continued to speak of random behavior. If that were the case, instead of finding the elegant Poincaré section (Figure 2.38(b)), he would have found a cloud of points without any structure. The presence of a structure is a strong indicator for underlying deterministic processes. However, Ueda had only about fifty points in his Poincaré section, and a structure in his section was not as obvious as the structure in the section shown in Figure 2.38(b) that contains many thousands of points.

These results were then further developed in the Ph.D. thesis defended in 1974 by Norio Akamatsu who was also a co-author of the 1970 paper.[94] This thesis was under the supervision of Hayashi but Akamatsu was "*greatly aided*" by Ueda and Hiroshi Kawakami. Returning to the driven van der Pol equation (2.16), Hayashi's group published in 1973 some of Akamatsu's results.[95] In this work, nonperiodic solutions (Figure 2.39) are presented as made of two components: one set of "*pseudo-recurrent points*" — periodic or almost periodic points — and one set of "*wandering points*". The latter points would correspond in fact to "*computer simulation* [which] *continues to move randomly in the vicinity of the solutions* [of the invariant closed set asymptotically stable] *due to the effect of the minute variation of the system, the error, the disturbance, etc.*" Nonperiodic solutions were thus considered as "*randomly transitional oscillations.*" Clearly chaos was still not understood but interpreted as resulting from some stochastic processes combined with some periodic or quasi-periodic behaviors.

In Akamatsu's Ph.D. thesis, there is no trace of "*noise*" in the description of nonperiodic solutions which were viewed in the neighborhood of "*doubly asymptotic solutions*", exactly as described by Poincaré as already mentioned. When there are nonperiodic solutions, there are also an infinite number of periodic orbits. According to Akamatsu, the set of unstable periodic points corresponds to the "*central points*" introduced by Birkhoff.[96] Central points are points around which the solutions are organized in the state space: they correspond to the skeleton of chaotic attractors. The unstable manifold — the α-branches — were responsible for the wandering of the trajectory around periodic orbits.

Akamatsu observed various nonperiodic behaviors. They were obviously considered as stable since he remarked that, even when he continued the iterations of the mapping, he obtained "*similar points which cover more densely the same domain.*"[97] As a conclusion of his Ph.D. thesis, he asserted that "*the successive images of the mapping continue to move complicatedly without tending to any point, because the α-branches* [(the unstable manifold)] *of* [unstable periodic points] *intersect their ω-branches* [(their stable manifold)] *repeatedly. Therefore we can obtain the*

[94] N. Akamatsu, *On the behavior of self-oscillatory systems with external force*, Tokushima University, 1973.

[95] Y. Ueda, C. Hayashi & N. Akamatsu, Computer simulation of nonlinear ordinary differential equations and nonperiodic oscillations, *Electronics & Communication in Japan*, **56** (4), 27–34, 1973.

[96] G. Birkhoff, 1922, *Ibid.*

[97] Akamatsu, 1973, *Ibid.*

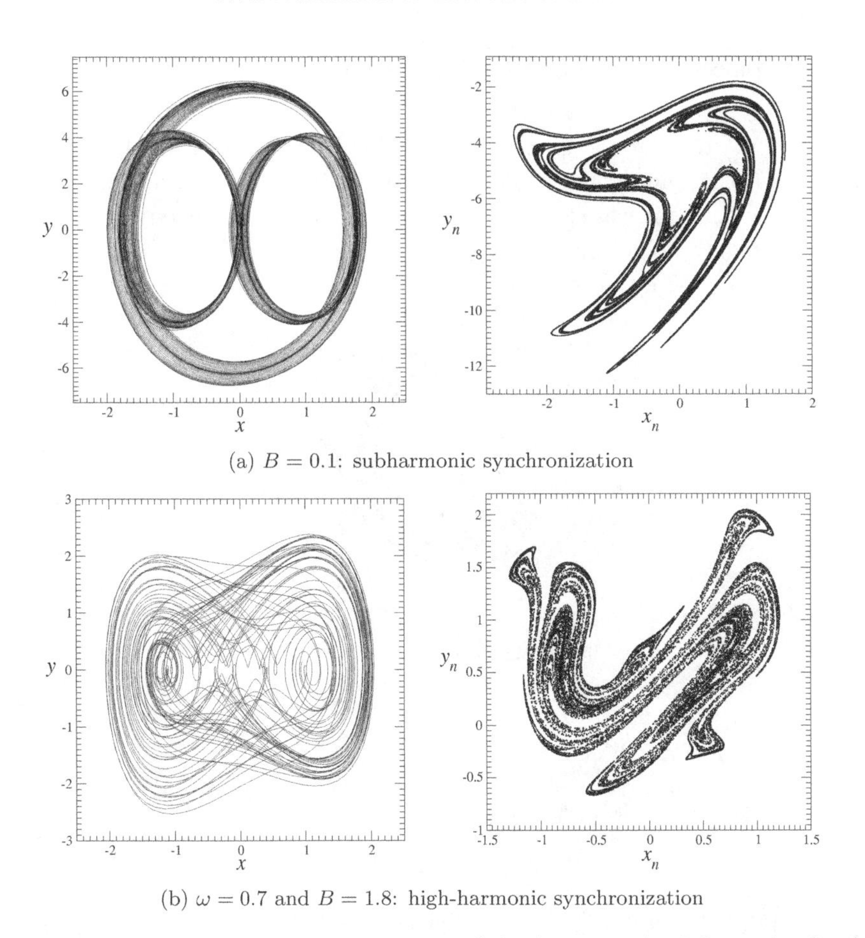

(a) $B = 0.1$: subharmonic synchronization

(b) $\omega = 0.7$ and $B = 1.8$: high-harmonic synchronization

Figure 2.39 State portraits and Poincaré sections of the driven van der Pol equation (2.16), as computed by Akamatsu in his Ph.D. thesis. Several thousands of points are used to construct these sections while Akamatsu had only about one hundred due to the limitations of his computer. Other parameter values: $\mu = 0.2$. $\gamma = 4$ and $\omega = 1.1$. Values of the pulsation ω were slightly modified from the published values in order to recover the beats.

nonperiodic oscillations whose successive images are dispersed in the phase space." Once again this is the argument used by Poincaré for asserting that the restricted three-body problem has inextricable solutions. Nonperiodic solutions were clearly resulting from the intrinsic dynamics of the driven van der Pol system (2.16) and no reference to noise was required.

The contribution of Hayashi's group was finally noticed in the international community when some of its works was recognized in 1978 by David Ruelle.[98] He

[98] D. Ruelle, Strange attractors, *The Mathematical Intelligencer*, **1**, 126–137, 1980.

called one Poincaré section of the Duffing equation[99]

$$\ddot{x} + \mu y + x^3 = B\cos(\omega t)\,, \tag{2.18}$$

the "*Japanese attractor*" (Figure 2.40). At this time, Ueda had sufficiently many points to see the underlying structure but nonetheless he continued to speak of random motion... as it was still too often the case up to the beginning of the 1980s (and unfortunately sometimes today), with the exception of a few of whom we will presently speak.

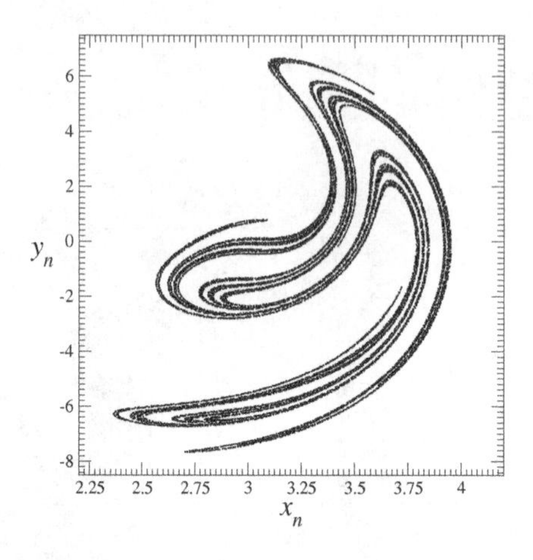

Figure 2.40 "Japanese attractor" as named by Ruelle. Poincaré section of the state portrait of the Duffing oscillator, similar to the one computed by Ueda in 1978. Parameter values: $\omega = 1$, $\mu = 0,1$ and $B = 12$.

For instance in 1981 Ueda and Akamatsu, still using the driven van der Pol equation (2.16), investigated the structure of its chaotic regimes in the Poincaré section (Figure 2.41). The case of Figure 2.41(a) is particularly interesting since it corresponds to a toroidal chaotic attractor, that is, a chaotic trajectory which is developed on a multi-foliated torus. As shown in Figure 2.39, toroidal chaos was in fact already observed in Akamatsu's Ph.D. thesis. The two other cases are more common (at least today). Nevertheless, although there was no longer a mention to random processes, chaos was yet presented as a "*transitional phenomenon.*" The qualification of "*transitional,*" most likely due to Ueda, may leave the impression that chaos only exists as a metastable regime. Note that this is not the case in the review published in 1980 by Hayashi in which he concluded that "*A slight change in the amplitude* [of the driving oscillator] *results in a smaller number of stable periodic points or indefinitely large number of them leading to the chaotic state.*"[100] The use

[99] Y. Ueda, Random Phenomena resulting from nonlinearity: in the system described by Duffing's equation, *Transactions of the Institute of Electronics and Communication Engineers A*, **98**, 167–173, 1978 — Reproduced in English in *International Journal for Nonlinear Mechanics*, **20**, 481–491, 1985.

[100] C. Hayashi, The method of mapping with reference to the doubly asymptotic structure of invariant curves, *International Journal of Non-Linear Mechanics*, **15** (4–5), 341–348, 1980.

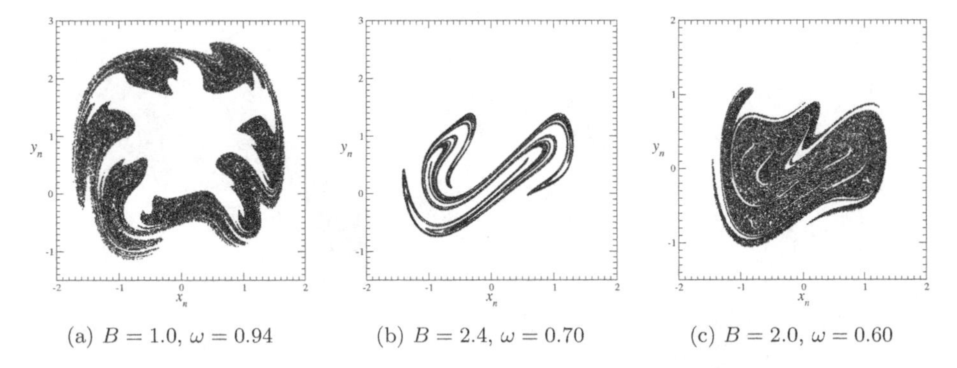

(a) $B = 1.0$, $\omega = 0.94$ (b) $B = 2.4$, $\omega = 0.70$ (c) $B = 2.0$, $\omega = 0.60$

Figure 2.41 Poincaré sections of the chaotic attractors published by Ueda and Akamatsu in 1981. Other parameter values: $\mu = 0.2$ and $\gamma = 1$.

of "*chaotic state*" expresses clearly that Hayashi considered, in 1980, chaotic regimes as a dynamics underlying to the system itself and not from some external noise.

2.4.2 *The Toulouse Group*

Another important contribution was provided in France at the end of the 1960s by Igor Gumowski and Christian Mira (the "Toulouse Research Group").[101] Starting from a paper by C. P. Pulkin[102] who showed that when a one-dimensional noninvertible map has infinitely many unstable periodic orbits it can produce complex solutions, Gumowski and Mira studied the piecewise-linear map[103]

$$\begin{cases} x_{n+1} = (1-\mu)x_n + y_n \\ y_{n+1} = y_n + f(x_n) \end{cases} \tag{2.19}$$

where

$$f(x_n) = \left| \begin{array}{ll} -2\mu x_n - 0.9\mu & x_n < -0.5 \\ -\dfrac{\mu x_n}{5} & \text{if } \; |x_n| < 0.5 \\ -2\mu x_n + 0.9\mu & x_n > -0.5\,. \end{array} \right. \tag{2.20}$$

For appropriate μ-values, they obtained an attractive limit set made of sharply bounded clouds of points as shown in Figure 2.42(a). Since this map is clearly deterministic by construction, there is no doubt that the behavior so produced is chaotic. This could have been the first now called "chaotic" solution produced by a piecewise-linear map reported with an explicit picture. In these late 1960s,

[101] C. Mira, I. Gumowski and a Toulouse Research Group in the "prehistoric times of chaotic dynamics", in *The Chaos avant-garde — Memories of the early days of chaos theory*, World Scientific Series in Nonlinear Science A, **39**, 95–198, 2000.

[102] C. P. Pulkin, Oscillating sequences of iterations (in Russian), *Doklady Akademii nauk SSSR*, **76** (6), 1129–1132, 1950.

[103] I. Gumowski & C. Mira, Sensitivity problems related to certain bifurcations in non-linear recurrence relations, *Automatica*, **5**, 303–317, 1969.

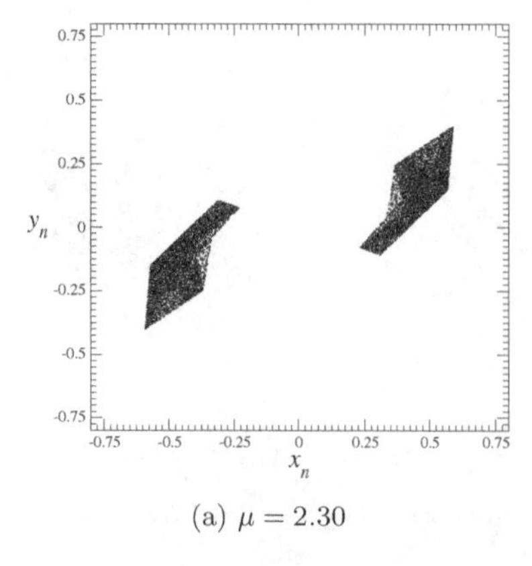

(a) $\mu = 2.30$

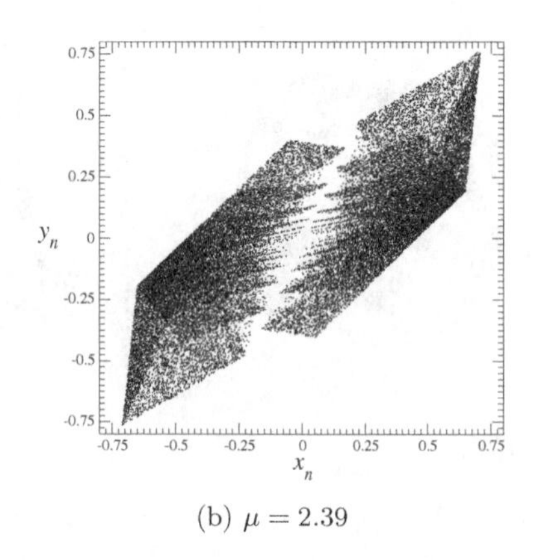

(b) $\mu = 2.39$

Figure 2.42 Chaotic attractor produced by the piecewise-linear map (2.19) as published in 1969 (a). The same map produces a more developed chaos just before a boundary crisis (b).

Gumowski and Mira designated these behaviors as "*Pulkin phenomena*" due to a paper by C. P. Pulkin showing that one-dimensional noninvertible map has many unstable periodic orbits, leading to complex trajectories.

For the two French scientists, the asymptotic nature of this chaotic regime was very clear: it was just another type of dynamics, as were limit cycle or quasi-periodic regimes. The Toulouse group investigated in great details how successive bifurcations were organized, mostly for maps.[104] It should be noted that Gumowski and Mira wrote the first book on chaos, unfortunately for the international community in French.[105] This is only ten years later that first chaotic solutions were widely investigated in electronic circuits.[106]

Since analytical methods very quickly reach their limit when applied to nonlinear differential equations, Gumowski and Mira choose to focus their attention on recurrence maps, taking advantages of contributions by Samuel Lattès (1873–1918) who was a professor at the University of Toulouse from 1911 to 1918, Pierre Fatou (1878–1929) and Gaston Julia (1893–1978). The contributions from these mathematicians were summarized in the book of Paul Montel.[107] A full account of the history of the Toulouse group was written by Mira.[108]

[104] I. Gumowski & C. Mira, Sur les récurrences, ou transformations ponctuelles du premier ordre avec inverse non unique, *Comptes-Rendus de l'Académie des Sciences*, **280**, 905–908, 1975 — Accumulation de bifurcations dans une récurrence, *Comptes-Rendus de l'Académie des Sciences*, **281**, 45–48, 1975 — C. Mira, Accumulation de bifurcations et structures boîtes emboîtées dans les récurrences et transformations ponctuelles, *7th International Conference on Nonlinear Oscillations* (ICNO), Berlin (September 1975), Proceedings, Akademic Verlag, Berlin (1977).

[105] I. Gumowski & C. Mira, *Dynamique chaotique, transformations ponctuelles, transition ordre-désordre*, Cepades édition, 1980.

[106] C. Letellier & J.-M. Ginoux, Development of the nonlinear dynamical systems theory from radio-engineering to electronics, *International Journal of Bifurcation & Chaos*, **19** (7), 2131–2163, 2009.

[107] P. Montel, *Leçons sur les récurrences et leurs applications*, (recueillies et rédigées par Jacques Dufresnoy & Éloi Lefebvre) Gauthier-Villars (Paris), 1957.

[108] C. Mira, I. Gumowski and a Toulouse research group in the "prehistoric" times of chaotic dy-

Among the huge collection of maps which were investigated by this French group, the recurrence map[109]

$$\begin{cases} x_{n+1} = y_n + \mu x_n + \dfrac{2(1-\mu)x_n^2}{1+x_n^2} + \alpha\left(1-\beta y_n^2\right) y_n \\ y_{n+1} = -x_n + \mu x_{n+1} + \dfrac{2(1-\mu)x_{n+1}^2}{1+x_{n+1}^2} \end{cases} \tag{2.21}$$

produced very aesthetic attractors (Figure 2.43) which were presented in 1973 by Mira during the international colloquium *Transformations ponctuelles et leurs applications* in Toulouse.

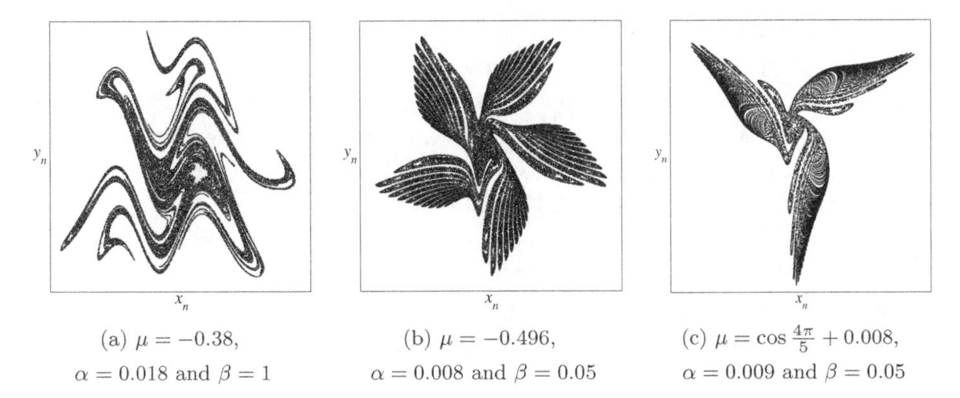

(a) $\mu = -0.38$, $\alpha = 0.018$ and $\beta = 1$

(b) $\mu = -0.496$, $\alpha = 0.008$ and $\beta = 0.05$

(c) $\mu = \cos\frac{4\pi}{5} + 0.008$, $\alpha = 0.009$ and $\beta = 0.05$

Figure 2.43 Three "aesthetic" attractors produced by map (2.21) and presented in 1973 at the colloquium "Point Mapping and Applications" organized in Toulouse.

Mira "*took the liberty of saying that these images had begun to manifest such an emotion in a form opened not only to specialists as Poincaré said, but also to a broad audience, due to the new possibilities offered by numerical simulations.*"[110] Mira also quoted Poincaré to express what he felt while looking at these pictures[111]

> The scientist worthy of such a name, especially the surveyor, experienced in front of his work the same impression as an artist, his enjoyment is as great, and of the same nature. If I was not writing for an audience fond of science, I would not say so, I dread the incredulity of laymen. But here I can express my thoughts. If we work, it is less for these positive

namics, In *The Chaos Avant-Garde. Memories of the early days of the chaos theory*, R. Abraham & Y. Ueda (eds), *World Scientific Series on Nonlinear Science*, Series A, **39**, 95–197, 2000.

[109] C. Mira, Exposé d'Introduction, Colloque International du CNRS **229** *Transformations Ponctuelles et Applications*, (Toulouse September 1973), *Proceedings Editions du CNRS*, Paris, pp. 19–27, 1976.

[110] C. Mira, A Toulouse research group in the "prehistoric" times of chaotic dynamics, in Topology and Dynamics of Chaos, C. Letellier & R. Gilmore (ed), *World Scientific Series on Nonlinear Science Series A*, **84** 39–62, 2013.

[111] H. Poincaré, Note sur Halphen, *Journal de l'Ecole Polytechnique*, **60**, 137–161, 1890.

results which the vulgar believes us only attached, as to feel that aesthetic emotion and communicate it to those who are able to experience it.

Beyond the beauty of these maps, they are not only among the first chaotic maps ever published but also among those whose rich structure is still an open domain of research.

2.5 Chaotic Electronic Circuits

2.5.1 *A Chaotic van der Pol Oscillator*

By the end of the 1970s, other Japanese electronic engineers were investigating the oscillations produced by two coupled nonsynchronized oscillators. For instance, Masanori Shinriki, graduated from Keio University (1965) and working for the Japan Defense Agency at the Technical Research and Development Institute, was developing radar and countermeasures. With Masahiro Yamamoto and Shinsaku Mori, they showed that two coupled oscillation circuits with one positive and one negative nonlinear conductances in series were producing aperiodic oscillations.[112] They used a single oscillation circuit in which a negative conductance and a positive conductance made of two resonators in parallel are connected in series. The two conductances have current-voltage characteristics which can be correctly approximated by the cubic function

$$F(y-z) = a_1(y-z) + a_3(y-z)^3 \tag{2.22}$$

where $y = V_o$ is the voltage applied to the oscillation circuit and $z = V$ is the voltage applied to the nonlinear negative conductance (Figure 2.44). With only the negative conductance, this circuit would have been a van der Pol oscillator; adding a second conductance thus lead to a modified van der Pol oscillator which is three-dimensional and which can produce aperiodic (or "multimode" as used in Shinriki and coworkers' paper) oscillations without being driven by sinusoidal oscillations.

Applying Kirchoff's rules to the Shinriki circuit (Figure 2.44) and after some algebra, Emilio Freire, Leopoldo Franquelo and Javier Aracil (University of Seville, Spain) obtained the system[113]

$$\left\{ \begin{aligned} \dot{x} &= \frac{1}{L} y \\ \dot{y} &= \frac{1}{C} \left[-x - G_2 y - F(y-z) \right] \\ \dot{z} &= \frac{1}{C_0} \left[(a_1 - G_1)x - a_3 z^3 + F(y-z) \right] \end{aligned} \right. \tag{2.23}$$

[112] M. Shinriki, M. Yamamoto & S. Mori, A simultaneous asynchronous oscillator with both nonlinear positive and negative conductances connected in series, *Proceedings of the IEEE*, **67** (2), 322–324, 1979 — Multimode oscillations in a modified van der Pol oscillator containing a positive nonlinear conductance, *Proceedings of the IEEE*, **69** (3), 394–395, 1981.

[113] E. Freire, L. G. Franquelo & J. Aracil, Periodicity and chaos in an autonomous electronic system, *IEEE Transactions on Circuits and Systems*, **31** (3), 237–247, 1984.

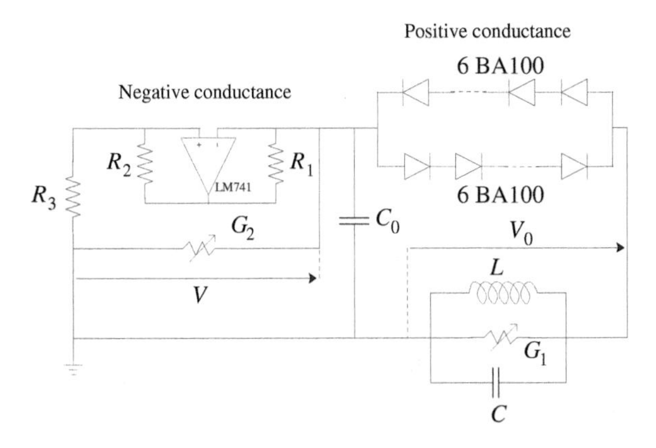

Figure 2.44 Scheme of a Shinriki circuit with two nonlinear conductances slightly modified by Freire and co-workers (1984) for producing a chaotic attractor with parameter values as follows. $R_1 = R_2 = 4.7$ kΩ, $R_3 = 10$ kΩ, $C_0 = 4.7$ nF, $C = 100$ nF, and $L = 110mH$. Parameter G_1 was the bifurcation parameter. Redrawn from Freire *et al.*, 1984.

where $F(y-z)$ is the cubic function (2.22) approximating the current-voltage characteristics. Using numerical simulations of these equations, they obtained an aperiodic behavior which is in fact a chaotic attractor. In 1987, Mori who received in 1965 his Ph.D. in electrical engineering from Keio University, Naohiko Inaba and Toshimichi Saito showed that it was possible to obtained an equivalent dynamics with a simplified system (2.23) by removing the resistor R_3 and the variable resistor G_1 from the circuit: the term a_3 becomes thus equal to zero. With normalized variables and setting $\beta = a_1 - G_1$, they obtained[114]

$$\begin{cases} \dot{x} = y \\ \dot{y} = -x - F(y-z) \\ \dot{z} = \beta x + bF(y-z) \end{cases} \tag{2.24}$$

where the cubic function (2.22) was replaced with the piecewise linear function

$$F(y-z) = \left| \begin{array}{lll} \alpha\left[(y-z)-\delta\right]+\epsilon & & y-z \geq \delta \\ \epsilon(y-z) & \text{if} & |y-z| < \delta \\ \alpha\left[(y-z)+\delta\right]-\epsilon & & y-z \leq \delta\,. \end{array} \right.$$

The current-voltage characteristic is plotted in Figure 2.45(a). The chaotic attractor produced by this system is a so-called "double-scroll" attractor (Figure 2.45(b)). As we will see, this type of attractor was in fact not new (see p. 231). Moreover, we will see in the next section that a simpler circuit and, consequently, a simpler set of equations can produce an equivalent chaotic attractor.

[114]N. Inaba, T. Saito & S. Mori, Chaotic phenomena in a circuit with a negative resistance and an ideal switch of diodes, *Institute of Electronics, Information and Communication Engineers Transactions*, **70** (8), 744–754, 1987.

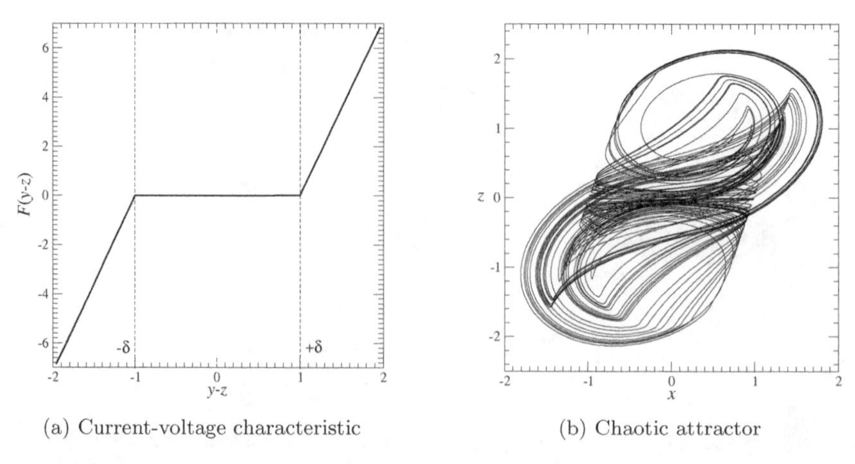

(a) Current-voltage characteristic

(b) Chaotic attractor

Figure 2.45 Chaotic attractor (b) produced by the simplified system (2.24) with a piecewise-linear current-voltage characteristic. Parameter values: $\alpha = 7.14$, $\beta = 0.79$, $b = 2.605$, $\epsilon = 0.00437$ and $\delta = 1$.

2.5.2 *Chua's Zoo of Chaotic Circuits*

Among various contributions to chaotic regimes observed in electronic circuits, Leon Chua's contribution is relevant qualitatively as well as quantitatively.[115] Some of his contributions are here selected for explaining how progressively scientists switch from purely mathematical analyses to investigations mostly driven by numerical simulations.

Born June 28, 1936, Leon Chua was a pupil of Levinson. He thus received a deep background in nonlinear electronic circuits as well as in the nonlinear dynamical systems theory. He is well reputed for his suggestion for new elements in electronic circuits and contributed to design nonlinear or piecewise-linear resistors[116] as already used by Andronov's school. Strongly motivated by the mathematical beauty of symmetry, he thus suggested the memristor in 1971,[117] an electronic element which was only recently designed by Hewlett Packard Laboratories.[118] While he was a student at Massachusetts Institute of Technology (1962), Chua was studying the qualitative approach of the nonlinear dynamical systems from books by Viktor Nemytsky (1900–1967) and Vyacheslav Stepanov (1889–1950)[119] as well as by

[115]Most of this section was originally published as C. Letellier, Chaos in electronic circuits: Chua's contribution (1980–2000), in *Chaos, CNN, Memristors and Beyond*, A. Adamatzky & G. Chen (Ed.), World Scientific Publishing, pp. 211–236, 2013.

[116]L. O. Chua, Synthesis of new nonlinear network elements, *Proceedings of the IEEE*, **56** (8), 1325–1243, 1968.

[117]L. O. Chua, Memristor — the missing circuit element, *IEEE Transaction on Circuit Theory*, **18**, 507–519, 1971.

[118]D. B. Strukov, G. S. Snider, D. R. Stewart & R. S. Williams, The missing memristor found, *Nature*, **453**, 80–83, 2008.

[119]V. V. Nemytsky & V. V. Stepanov, *Qualitative Theory of Differential Equations*, Princeton University Press, 1960.

Solomon Lefschetz (1884–1972).[120] He also read the three-volume Poincaré's book on celestial mechanics.[121] While contributing to the general theory for nonlinear electronic circuits, Chua was always motivated by making a connection between the architecture of the circuit and its resulting dynamics. This is a major problem which is directly related to the still open question of the relationships between the algebraic structure of differential equations and the topology of the dynamics they produce.

Commonly, as inherited from Poincaré's works, one investigates a given dynamical system by studying the stability of its singular points, the qualitative nature of its asymptotic behaviors, etc. This is the *direct problem*. But sometimes, it is desirable to write down some governing equations producing some predetermined features like the number and the nature of the singular points, some given time series, etc. This is what is called the *inverse problem*. One of the first problems related to the nonlinear dynamical system theory attacked by Leon Chua was the inverse problem. In 1971, he proposed a way to write some governing equations which possess a finite number of prescribed singular points, as well as a prescribed set of eigenvalues associated with each singular points.[122]

Two years later, Chua provided a second contribution on this inverse problem with Douglas Green.[123] Their aim was to find a class of differential equations producing a limit cycle with a prescribed pulsation ω and a prescribed waveform. One of their conclusions was that such a problem can be positively addressed but there is, in fact, an infinite number of different types of possible systems, all producing the same limit cycle. This problem was addressed for chaotic solutions much later by James Crutchfield and Bruce McNamara,[124] once Floris Takens (1949–2010) had proposed his theorem for reconstructing the state portrait from a single scalar time series.[125] This became what is called today *global modeling* whose objective is to obtain a set of equations whose numerical integration produces a time series with the same underlying dynamics as for the experimental data.[126]

In his early dynamical analyses, Chua and his colleagues worked in a direct continuation of what was performed in the 1960s, that is, using techniques mostly based on frequency domain analysis.[127] Then they started to investigate the

[120] S. Lefschetz, *Differential Equations: geometric theory* (1957), Reprinted by Dover, 1977.

[121] H. Poincaré, *Les Méthodes Nouvelles de la Mécanique Céleste*, Gauthier-Vilars (1892–1899).

[122] L. O. Chua, Synthesis of nonlinear systems with prescribed singularities, *IEEE Transactions on Circuit Theory*, **18** (3), 375–382, 1971.

[123] L. O. Chua & D. Green, Synthesis of nonlinear periodic systems, *IEEE Transactions on Circuit and Systems*, **21** (2), 286–294, 1973.

[124] J. P. Crutchfield & B. S. McNamara, Equations of motion from a data series, *Complex Systems*, **1**, 417–452, 1987.

[125] F. Takens, Detecting strange attractors in turbulence, *Lecture Notes in Mathematics*, **898**, 366–381, 1981.

[126] L. A. Aguirre & C. Letellier, Modeling nonlinear dynamics and chaos: A review, *Mathematical Problems in Engineering*, **2009**, 238960, 2009.

[127] L. O. Chua & C.-Y. Ng, Frequency domain analysis of nonlinear systems: general theory, *Electronic Circuits and Systems*, **3** (4), 165–185, 1979.

property of singular points, using for instance the Hopf theorem[128] for studying almost sinusoidal oscillations.[129] Chua considered electronic circuits as dynamical systems in the continuation of his early contributions. In 1990, Chua published a survey describing the qualitative behaviors produced by nonlinear *RLC* electronic circuits made of a resistance, an inductor and a capacitor.[130] His motivation was to better understand the sometimes "bizarre" solutions observed for particular initial conditions. If classical textbooks devoted to the nonlinear dynamical systems theory applied to electronic circuits as Nikolai Minorski's[131] and Hayashi's one[132] were quoted, Chua's approach was still quite mathematical and in the spirit of Levinson. Note that a paper by Gollub and co-workers about chaos in a system of two coupled relaxation oscillators made of a tunnel diodes[133] was quoted. In this work, it was observed that "*the existence of chaotic* [regimes] *is more dependent on the nature of the coupling than on the number of degrees of freedom.*" Such a remark motivated Chua and co-workers to remain more focused on the conditions required for producing aperiodic oscillations than on characterizing their nature.

Two papers from Hayashi's group dealing with chaos in the Duffing[134] and van der Pol[135] equations were also mentioned. These references are quite important in the sense that they are probably the first explicit references to a chaotic attractor in an electronic circuit in Chua's published papers. As in many books related to electronics like those by Minorsky and Hayashi, the Duffing and van der Pol equations were treated as typical examples for producing nonlinear oscillations. As others,[136] Chua wanted to have a proof of the chaotic nature of these solutions. Chua questioned himself whether Lorenz's results[137] were actually asymptotic behaviors and not artefact. With co-workers, he was therefore pushed to develop some algorithms to get reliable numerical solutions.

---

[128] E. Hopf, Abzweigung einer periodischen Lösung von einer stationären Lösung eines Differentialsystems, *Berichten der Mathematisch-Physischen Klasse der Sächsischen Akademie der Wissenschaften zu Leipzig*, **94**, 1–22, 1942.

[129] A. I. Mees & L. O. Chua, The Hopf bifurcation theorem and its applications to nonlinear oscillations in circuits and systems, *IEEE Transactions on Circuit and Systems*, **26** (4), 235–254, 1979.

[130] L. O. Chua, Dynamic nonlinear networks: state-of-the-art, *IEEE Transactions on Circuit and Systems*, **27** (11), 1059–1087, 1980.

[131] N. Minorsky, *Nonlinear Oscillations*, Princeton, 1962.

[132] C. Hayashi, *Nonlinear oscillations in physical systems*, McGraw-Hill, 1964.

[133] J. P. Gollub, T. O. Brunner & B. G. Danly, Periodicity and chaos in coupled nonlinear oscillators, *Science*, **200**, 48–50, 1978.

[134] Ueda, 1980, *Ibid.*

[135] Ueda & Akamatsu, 1981, *Ibid.*

[136] C. T. Sparrow, Chaos in a three-dimensional single loop feedback system with a piecewise linear feedback function, *Journal of Mathematical Analysis and Applications*, **83**, 275–291, 1981 — A. Arnéodo, P. Coullet & C. Tresser, Possible new strange attractors with spiral structure, *Communications in Mathematical Physics*, **79**, 573–579, 1981 — R. F. Brockett, On conditions leading to chaos in feedback systems, *Proceedings of the 21st IEEE Conference on Decision and Control*, **2**, 932–936, 1982.

[137] E. N. Lorenz, Deterministic nonperiodic flow, *Journal of the Atmospheric Sciences*, **20**, 130–141, 1963.

Chua and Akio Ushida therefore started by checking that the asymptotic behavior was actually reached in the case where the solution has a very long period.[138] The choice of such solutions was motivated by their relative simplicity and by the possibility to easily characterize them using a Fourier analysis. To fulfill these criteria, Chua and Ushida investigated the driven Duffing equation

$$\begin{cases} \dot{x} = y \\ \dot{y} = -0.1y - 2x - x^3 + A\left(\cos\omega_1 t + \cos\omega_2 t + \cos\omega_3 t\right) \end{cases} \tag{2.25}$$

The motivation was that, although describing a symmetrical mechanical pendulum (see p. 84), the Duffing equation was nonlinear, often studied by Hayashi's group, and often quoted in books dealing with electronic circuits. The Duffing oscillator was therefore forced with multiple input frequencies. Only an excerpt of a time series was proposed by Chua and his co-workers. With all the conditions specified in the paper, a period-211 limit cycle is obtained as exhibited by computing 50,000 points in the Poincaré section after the transient regime (Figure 2.46(b)). Thus, in spite of a an apparently aperiodic state portrait (Figure 2.46(a)) which could lead to conclude to a chaotic solution, the asymptotic behavior is periodic as correctly stated by Chua and Ushida. This is also a good example for showing why a simple state portrait is not sufficient for "proving" the existence of chaos.

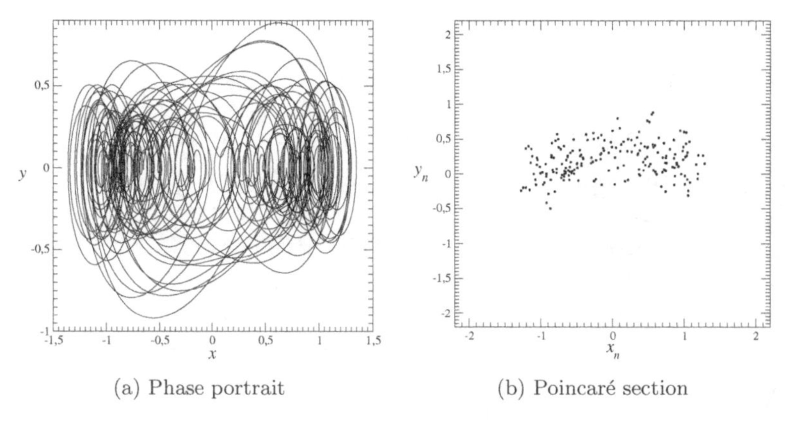

(a) Phase portrait (b) Poincaré section

Figure 2.46 Solution produced by the Duffing equation (2.25) forced with multiple sinusoidal terms as investigated by Chua and Ushida. Initial conditions: $x_0 = 0.69667$ and $y_0 = -0.18304$. Only 211 different intersections with the Poincaré section (based on the frequency ω_1) were distinguished among the 50,000 intersections computed. Parameter values: $A = 0.4$, $\omega_1 = 1$, $\omega_2 = 0.35$ and $\omega_3 = 0.155$.

The first chaotic attractor displayed in Chua's works was obtained with the help of two scientists involved in numerical studies, namely Jacques Neirynck who spent few years in the Philips Laboratories and was in charge of Computer-Aided Design,

[138] L. O. Chua & A. Ushida, Algorithms for computing almost periodic steady-state response of nonlinear systems to multiple input frequencies, *IEEE Transactions on Circuit and Systems*, **28** (10), 953–971, 1981.

and Philippe Verburgh who was in the Circuit Theory Group of the Swiss Federal Institute of Technology (Lausanne). One of their motivations was to demonstrate that all properties for a chaotic motion were indeed observed, that is, sensitivity to initial conditions, hyperbolicity, existence of a chaotic attractor and a broadband frequency spectrum. This study was performed "*through a long series of mathematical analyses of a piecewise linear system.*"[139]

The electronic circuit designed for this study was made of a single nonlinear element, an inductor (Figure 2.47(c)) with a piecewise-linear characteristic reading as

$$I(\phi) = \left| \begin{array}{ll} \dfrac{(\phi - \phi_1)}{L_1} & \phi > \phi_0 \\ \dfrac{\phi}{L_0} & \text{for } |\phi| < \phi_0 \\ \dfrac{(\phi + \phi_1)}{L_1} & \phi < -\phi_0 \end{array} \right. \tag{2.26}$$

where $\phi_1 = \phi_0 \left(1 - \dfrac{L_1}{L_0}\right)$. The two differential equations governing the dynamics underlying the circuit are

$$\left\{ \begin{array}{l} \dot{\phi} = -\dfrac{R_1 R_2}{R_1 + R_2} I(\phi) - \dfrac{R_2}{R_1 + R_2}(V - E\cos\omega t) \\ \dot{V} = \dfrac{R_2}{c(R_1 + R_2)} I(\phi) - \dfrac{1}{c(R_1 + R_2)}(V - E\cos\omega t) \,. \end{array} \right. \tag{2.27}$$

This circuit mainly differs from the circuit (Figure 2.47(a)) investigated by Ueda and Akamatsu by its nonlinearity: in particular, the central branch of the piecewise-linear function (Figure 2.47(d)) has a positive slope, contrary to the cubic nonlinearity commonly observed in a van der Pol circuit (Figure 2.47(b)).

Chua and co-workers investigated the stability of periodic solutions and, finally, some chaotic behaviors as shown in Figure 2.48. They noted the sensitivity to initial conditions and checked that the chaotic regime was a "*real phenomenon*" not caused by numerical instability. As they claimed, "*these results represent the most reliable numerical confirmation to date of chaotic motion in a real physical circuit*", that is, realistically modeled by ordinary differential equations.

They presented some periodic solutions whose projections in the Φ-$\frac{V}{\omega}$ plane provide a rough idea of the shape of the chaotic attractor shown in Figure 2.48(a). They also constructed a Poincaré section providing the signature of an attractive set. They were thus able to conclude that "*these points seem to be all* attracted *toward certain well-defined curves in the state space.*" Although the sensitivity to initial conditions was often associated with a lack of reliability in numerical simulations, Chua and co-workers were sufficiently confident in their own results to conclude that

[139] L. O. Chua, M. Hasler, J. Neirynck & Ph. Verburgh, Dynamics of a piecewise-linear resonant circuit, *IEEE Transactions on Circuit and Systems*, **29** (8), 535–547, 1982.

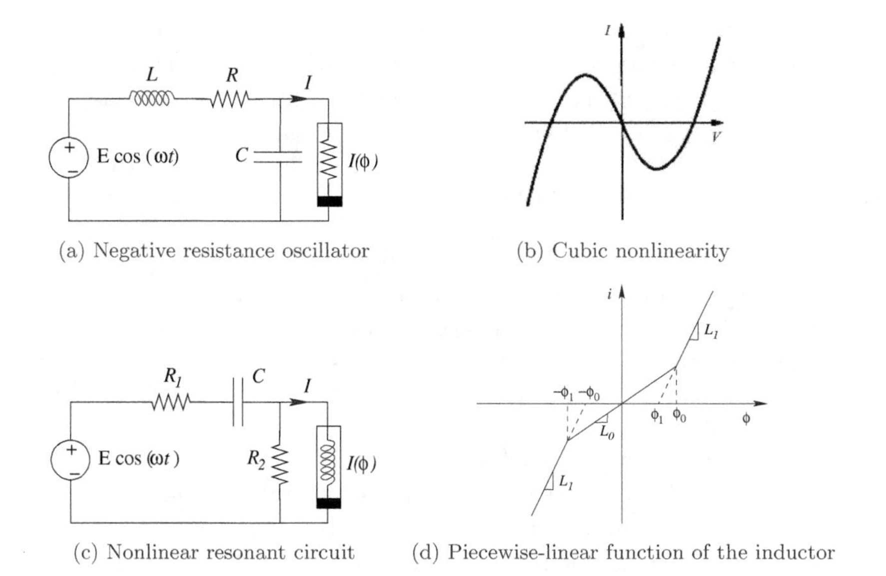

(a) Negative resistance oscillator (b) Cubic nonlinearity

(c) Nonlinear resonant circuit (d) Piecewise-linear function of the inductor

Figure 2.47 The negative resistance oscillator as investigated by Ueda and Akamatsu in 1981 (a) and the piecewise-linear resonant circuit (b) investigated by Chua and co-workers in 1982.

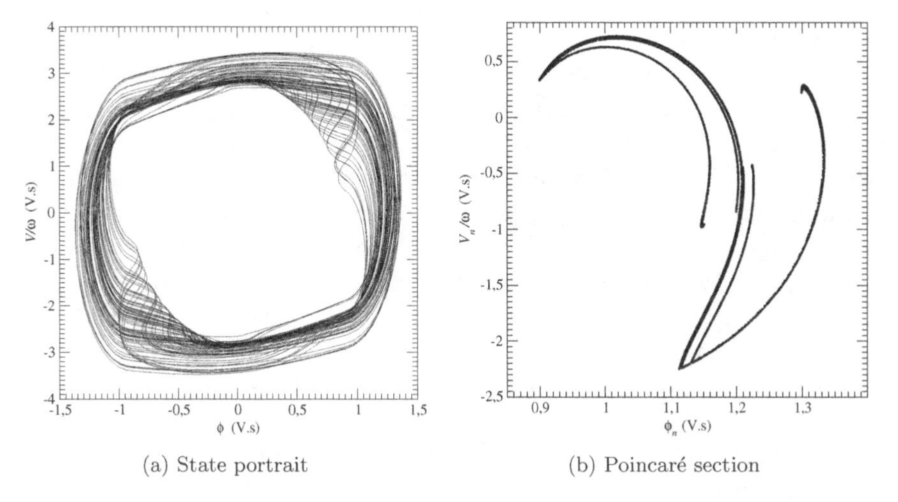

(a) State portrait (b) Poincaré section

Figure 2.48 Aperiodic solution to the driven piecewise-linear resonant circuit (2.27) for $E =$ 800 V, $R_1 = 50\ \Omega$, $R_2 = 50\ \mathrm{k}\Omega$, $C = 250$ nF, $L_0 = 33.33$ H, $L_1 = 1.28$ H, $\phi_0 = 0.92$ V.s, and $\frac{\omega}{2\pi} = 50$ Hz.

"One may suspect this apparent instability to be caused by accumulating numerical errors at the boundaries rather than an intrinsic property of the true solution. To overcome such an objective we have checked the accuracy of the computed solutions [...]. It turns out that

> for this circuit (with $E = 800$ V) the errors at boundaries do accumulate and thus *the solutions can be calculated with sufficient precision only for a certain length of time.* [...] Hence, the drifting apart of neighboring solutions [...] is a *real phenomenon not caused by numerical instability.*"

This conclusion was made possible because their

> "roundoff errors at different time steps within each *linear region* are independent of each other and do not get amplified over long time intervals. Hence, [their] piecewise-linear solutions are much more accurate and reliable compared to traditional numerical or analog (i.e. hardware) simulations."

The correctness of numerical simulations is one of the main advantages of piecewise-linear circuits that allow to overcome the serious flaw that "*long-term chaotic motions obtained by numerical integration diverge rapidly from the actual waveforms.*" In fact, there is a theorem, due to Rufus Bowen (1947–1978) — the so-called *shadowing lemma*[140] — which overcomes this lack of accuracy, it can be interpreted as follows. A numerically computed trajectory remains always in the neighborhood of a true trajectory: one could say that a numerical trajectory is shadowed by a true one. For electrical engineers, the fact that chaotic behaviors were actual phenomena and not artefacts started to be clarified.

The Poincaré section shown in Figure 2.48(b) is an example of the "*well-defined curve*" Chua and co-worker observed and which can be considered today as a numerical proof for the existence of a chaotic attractor. At this point, it is possible to draw the path followed by Chua and co-workers before investigating chaotic behaviors. First, Chua introduced some nonlinear elements for producing new nonlinear electronic circuits. Then, he investigated the stability of the periodic solutions produced by these new nonlinear dynamical systems. The evolution of the asymptotic behaviors — when some parameter values of the circuits were varied — was investigated (for instance) in terms of Hopf bifurcation. Then with his coworkers he developed new algorithms to numerically integrate the equations (to be ensured that numerical instabilities were avoided) and, finally, they investigated the dynamics produced by their nonlinear circuits which were not satisfying any known stability theorem. This whole path was traced within the field of electronics with his original background provided by Levinson.

In 1983 with Thomas S. Parker, Chua investigated relaxation oscillations using a piecewise-linear version of the van der Pol equation.[141] The electronic circuit (Figure 2.49) was simplified compared to the one used by Ueda and Akamatsu

[140] R. Bowen, ω-limit sets for Axiom A diffeomorphisms, *Journal of Differential Equations*, **18**, 333–339, 1975 — S. Hammel, J. A. Yorke & C. Grebogi, Do numerical orbits of chaotic dynamical processes represent true orbit?, *Journal of Complexity*, **3**, 136–145, 1987.

[141] T. S. Parker & L. O. Chua, A computer-assisted study of forced relaxation oscillations, *IEEE Transactions on Circuit and Systems*, **30** (8), 518–533, 1983.

(Figure 2.47(a)). The governing equations are

$$\begin{cases} \dot{x} = y \\ \dot{y} = \dfrac{1}{\mu}\left[-f(x)y - x + B\cos\omega t\right] \end{cases} \tag{2.28}$$

where the piecewise-linear function corresponding to a cubic nonlinearity was

$$f(x) = \left| \begin{array}{lll} Rx + 2Rx_0 & & x < -x_0 \\ -Rx & \text{for} & |x| < x_0 \\ Rx - 2Rx_0 & & x > +x_0 \,. \end{array} \right. \tag{2.29}$$

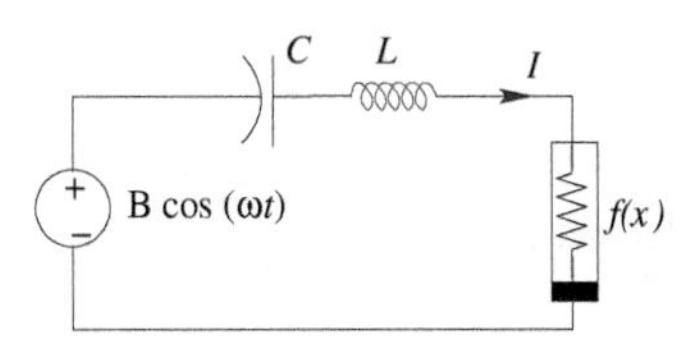

Figure 2.49 Block diagram of the electronic circuit corresponding to a driven van der Pol equation and producing relaxation oscillations investigated by Parker and Chua.

Mostly, periodic solutions were investigated for providing an "*intuitive understanding*" of relaxation oscillations in connection with the mathematical papers by Levinson[142] and Mark Levi.[143] In particular, Levi "*proved what types of behavior are possible and how this behavior is structured as B is varied.*" In order to do that, Levi used rotation numbers as introduced by Levinson. Using numerical simulations, Parker and Chua showed "*how the different subharmonic solutions to the piecewise-linear relaxation oscillation equation are intimately related.*" It should be clear that B actually plays the role of an initial condition for system (2.28) since this system can be rewritten in the autonomous form

$$\begin{cases} \dot{x} = y \\ \dot{y} = -x + \dfrac{-f(x)y + u}{\mu} \\ \dot{u} = v \\ \dot{v} = -\omega^2 u \,. \end{cases} \tag{2.30}$$

Parameter B is thus "hidden" in the autonomous form as an initial condition $u_0 = B$. This is therefore the state space which is investigated and not the parameter space.[144] Parker and Chua thus provided tables of rotation numbers in agreement with Levi's results.

[142] Levinson, 1949, *Ibid.*

[143] M. Levi, Qualitative analysis of the periodically forced relaxation oscillations, *Memoirs of the American Mathematical Society*, **32**, 244, 1981.

[144] O. Ménard, C. Letellier, J. Maquet, L. Le Sceller & G. Gouesbet, Analysis of a non synchronized sinusoidally driven dynamical system, *International Journal of Bifurcation & Chaos*, **10** (7), 1759–1772, 2000.

In the other hand, Levinson found that "*most of the solutions* [...] *are certainly not periodic.* [...] *Of the continuum of sequences there is a countable infinity of periodic sequences.*" This led Parker and Chua to remark that for some μ and B values, Levinson showed that "*given any (perhaps nonperiodic) sequence of component subharmonics, there exists a trajectory which follows that sequence.*" The existence of "*essentially random behavior*" was mentioned in the conclusion. When numerical simulations are performed, it can be observed that most of parameter values lead to a limit cycle but we identified a quasi-periodic regime (Figure 2.50(a)) and a metastable toroidal chaos (Figure 2.50(b)) which ends with a period-2 limit cycle. Although chaotic attractors were not yet clearly investigated, plane projections of state portraits were already widely used.

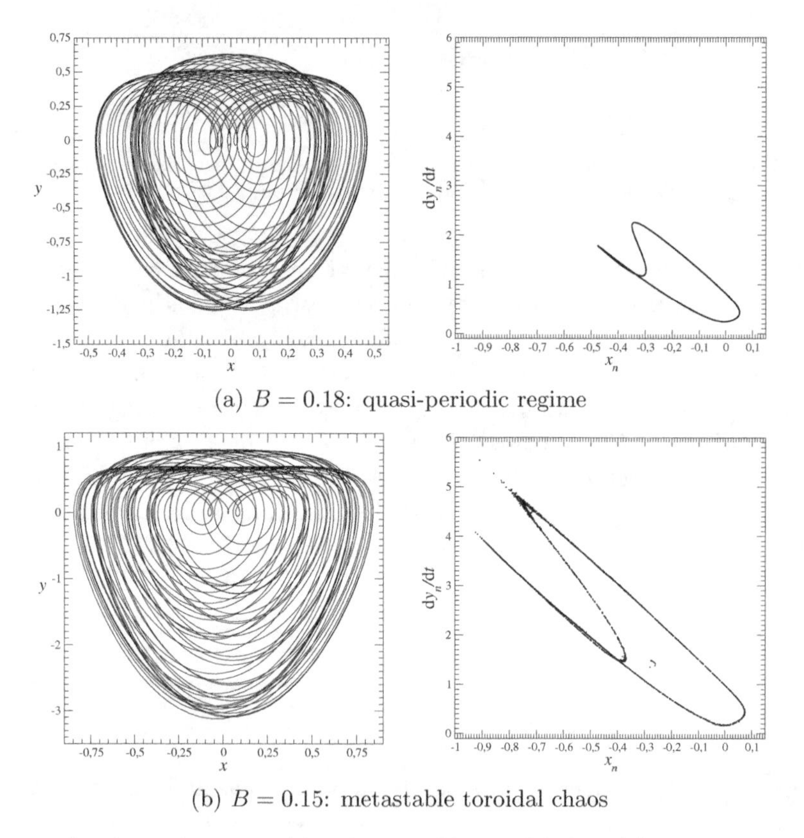

Figure 2.50 Quasi-periodic regime (a) and metastable toroidal chaos (b) solution to the driven piecewise-linear van der Pol equation (2.28). Parameter values: $\mu = 0.1825$, $\omega = 1$ rad.s^{-1}, $R = 1\ \Omega$, and $x_0 = 1$ A.

With Alistair Mees, Chua investigated in an extended way the Hopf bifurcation and chaos as a lack of synchronization between the oscillation circuit and the driving term in the case of a driven van der Pol equation.[145] If most of the papers were devoted to the occurrence of limit cycles, chaos was defined by its properties: i) sensitivity to initial conditions, ii) non periodicity, iii) broad band Fourier spectrum, and iv) complicated recurrences. They investigated chaotic motion using a kind of symbolic dynamics (again, Levinson's heritage) validated by numerical simulations. Again, the analytical approach was preferred for providing a proof for chaotic motion. Note that two papers which became key papers in chaos theory were quoted. One, by Tien-Yien Li and James Yorke, provides a criterion for "proving" the existence of chaos in quadratic recurrence map using the presence of a period-3 orbit.[146] The second paper was published by David Ruelle and Floris Takens: it is devoted to the fact that a dynamics characterized by a broad band Fourier spectrum is not necessarily produced by a system associated with a very large dimensional state space.[147] Another one by John Guckenheimer is less known but is more directly related to the type of work developed by Chua and his coworker since it is devoted to the driven van der Pol equation investigated in terms of symbolic dynamics in the spirit of Levinson and Levi.[148] These quotations reveal the growing interest of Chua for chaos theory.

Once the problem for proving the reality of chaos more or less addressed, Chua and co-workers started to look for finding the simplest electronic circuit that would produce chaotic regimes. In 1984, Takashi Matsumoto, Leon Chua and Satoshi Tanaka found a rather simple electronic circuit made of a series connection of a linear resistor, a linear inductor, and a two-segment, piecewise-linear capacitor driven by a sinusoidal voltage source (Figure 2.51).[149] A detailed study of the bifurcation diagram was then completed in a slightly different R-L-diode circuit (Figure 2.51(b)).[150] The two-dimensional map

$$\left\{ \begin{array}{l} x_{n+1} = y_n - 1 + \left| \begin{array}{ll} +\alpha_1 \, x_n & \text{if } \; x_n \geq 0 \\ -\alpha_2 \, x_n & \text{if } \; x_n < 0 \end{array} \right. \\ y_{n+1} = b \, x_n \, , \end{array} \right. \tag{2.31}$$

was proposed to reproduce "*all essential features of the experimentally observed bifurcation phenomena:*" the resulting bifurcation diagram is shown in Figure. 2.51(b). They observed that the ultimate scenario consists in three kinds of bifurcation: i) saddle-node bifurcations, ii) period-doubling cascades, and iii) crisis. They were thus able to show that chaotic regimes can be produced by very simple systems.

[145] A. Mees & L. O. Chua, Synchronization and chaos, *IEEE Transactions on Circuits & Systems*, **30** (9), 620–626, 1983.

[146] T. Li & J. A. Yorke, A period-three implies chaos, *American Mathematics Monthly*, **82**, 985–992, 1975.

[147] D. Ruelle & F. Takens, On the nature of turbulence, *Communications in Mathematical Physics*, **20**, 167–192, 1971.

[148] J. Guckenheimer, Symbolic dynamics and relaxation oscillations, *Physica D*, **1**, 227–235, 1980.

[149] T. Matsumoto, L. O. Chua & S. Tanaka, Simplest chaotic non autonomous circuit, *Physical Review A*, **30** (2), 1155–1157, 1984.

[150] S. Tanaka, T. Matsumoto & L. O. Chua, Bifurcation scenario in a driven R-L-diode circuit, *Physica D*, **28**, 317–344, 1987.

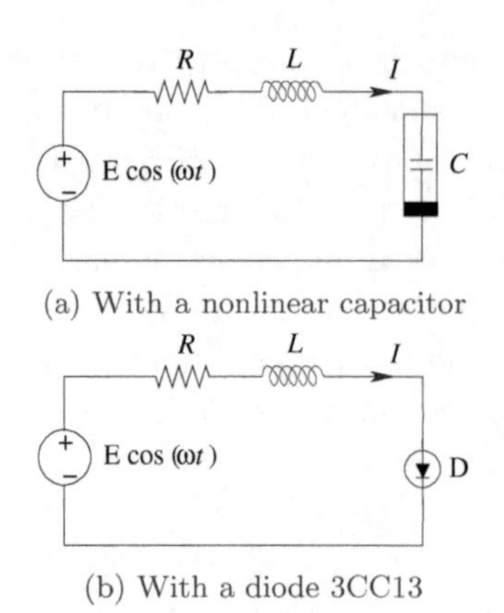

Figure 2.51 Two simple non-autonomous circuits producing chaotic regimes, one with a nonlinear capacitor (a), and one with a diode 3CC13 (b).

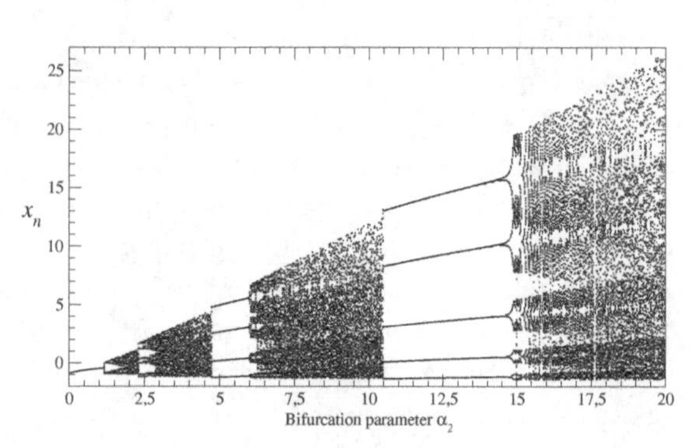

Figure 2.52 Bifurcation diagram of the two-dimensional map (2.31) for reproducing the essential feature of the simplest nonautonomous chaotic electronic circuit. Parameter values: $b = -0.13$ and $\alpha_1 = 0.7$.

With Michael Kennedy, Chua examined a simple experimental circuit with a negative resistance which was quite similar to the circuit used by van der Pol and van der Mark in 1927 (see Figure 2.20(a), p. 107) for investigating frequency demultiplication. The aim of Kennedy and Chua was clearly to reproduce the results obtained by the two Dutch scientists. They therefore considered a sinusoidally-driven neon bulb relaxation oscillator (Figure 2.53). A high-voltage dc supply $E \approx 100$ V with a large source resistance $R \approx 1$ MΩ was attached to a shunt connection of neon bulb and capacitor C, forming the relaxation oscillator. In series with the neon bulb was inserted a sinusoidal voltage source $E_0 \sin \omega t$ (a small current sense resistor R_s was inserted in series with the neon bulb to detect the current flowing in it).[151]

The natural frequency of the undriven oscillation circuit was set to 1 kHz by tuning the capacitance C to C_0. Then a sinusoidal signal $E_0 \sin \omega t$ was applied with a frequency $\frac{\omega}{2\pi} = 1$ kHz (Figure 2.53). The resulting frequency of the voltage pulses measured across the resistance R_s was then recorded as the value of the bifurcation parameter C which was gradually increased from C_0 to larger values. As the capacitance was progressively increased, the system started to oscillate at 1 kHz up to a C-value at which the frequency "suddenly" drops to 1000/2 Hz. Still increasing the value of the capacitance C, the frequency dropped to 1000/3 Hz, then 1000/4 Hz, 1000/5 Hz, and so on up to 1000/20 Hz, exactly as reported by van der Pol and van der Mark in 1927.

From October 1983 to January 1984, Chua visited Matsumoto with whom he already published few papers. As reported by Chua,[152] Matsumoto was not

[151]M. P. Kennedy & L. O. Chua, The devil's staircase: The electrical engineer's fractal, *IEEE Transactions on Circuit and Systems*, **36** (8), 1133–1139, 1989.

[152]L. O. Chua, A zoo of strange attractors from the canonical Chua's circuits, *Proceedings of the 35th Midwest Symposium on Circuit and Systems*, **2**, 916–926, 1992.

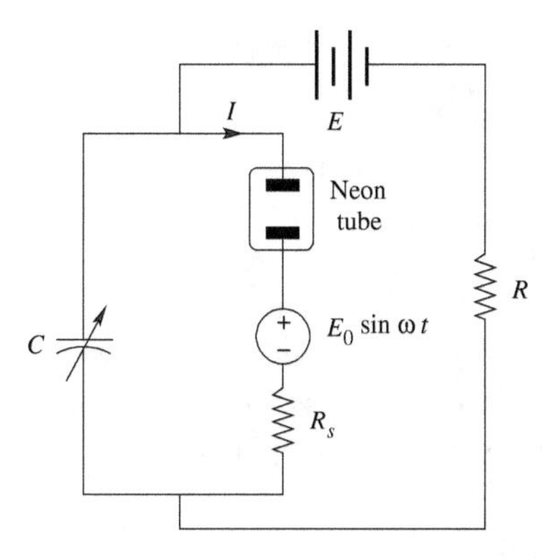

Figure 2.53 Sinusoidally-driven by a relaxation oscillator made of a neon tube as investigated by Kennedy and Chua.

successful in his attempt to design an electronic circuit for reproducing the dynamics underlying the Lorenz system (see Chapter 3, p. 161). In fact, the Lorenz system was only introduced in the Journal of the Institute of Electrical and Electronic Engineers (IEEE) in August 1983 by Colin Sparrow.[153] Matsumoto was most likely motivated by this paper. An electronic circuit producing the Lorenz attractor was later proposed by Frank Neville Robinson (1925–1996) in 1990.[154] In order to replace such a difficult task, Chua rather suggested a new autonomous circuit with a piecewise-linear resistor (Figure 2.54), that is, a circuit without a periodic driving term.

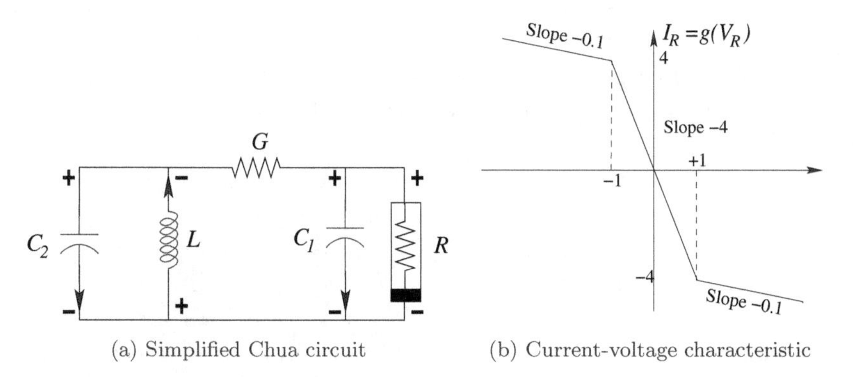

Figure 2.54 Electronic circuit designed by Chua and used by Matsumoto for producing a double-scroll attractor. Redrawn from Matsumoto, 1984.

[153] C. Sparrow, An introduction to the Lorenz equations, *IEEE Transactions on Circuit and Systems*, **30** (8), 533–542, 1981.

[154] F. N. H. Robinson, Analogue electronic model of the Lorenz equations, *International Journal of Electronics*, **68** (5), 803–819, 1990.

Matsumoto quickly produced a double-scroll attractor by using numerical integrations of the set of equations

$$\begin{cases} C_1 \dot{V}_{C_1} = G\left(V_{C_2} - V_{C_1}\right) - f\left(V_{C_1}\right) \\ C_2 \dot{V}_{C_2} = G\left(V_{C_1} - V_{C_2}\right) + I_L \\ \dot{I}_L = -V_{C_2} \end{cases} \tag{2.32}$$

proposed by Chua and where V_{C_1}, V_{C_2} and I_L are the voltage across C_1, the voltage across C_2, and the current through L, respectively. According to the notations later used, the piecewise-linear characteristics (Figure 2.54(b)) reads as

$$f\left(V_{C_1}\right) = m_0 V_{C_1} + \frac{1}{2}\left(m_1 - m_0\right)\left|V_{C_1} + B_p\right| + \frac{1}{2}\left(m_0 - m_1\right)\left|V_{C_1} - B_p\right| . \tag{2.33}$$

The "*double-scroll attractor*" was therefore numerically produced by using these equations on October 1983, that is, at the beginning of Chua's stay at Waseda University.

A few weeks later, while Chua was back to the University of California at Berkeley, Matsumoto sent him a draft of a paper by fax (dated on April 17, 1984). With Chua's green light, Matsumoto submitted his paper on April 20, 1984. Matsumoto introduced himself the circuit (designed by Chua) made of "*only one nonlinear element; a 3-segment R piecewise-linear resistor. It* [was] *a simplified version of a circuit suggested by Leon Chua.*"[155] Only the modified circuit is described, without reference to the original circuit. Matsumoto himself named that circuit by Chua's name as seen from the title of his paper.

Providing a state portrait of the attractor he obtained (Figure 2.55(a)), Matsumoto showed that the structure of the attractor was not equivalent to the structure of the already well-known Lorenz attractor (see Figure 3.7, p. 174) or of the Rössler attractor (Figure 4.12, p. 206). Nevertheless, he correctly remarked that his system possesses an inversion symmetry while the Lorenz system has a rotation with respect to the z-axis.

Today, the Chua circuit is one of the three most often quoted systems (1420 quotations[156]) producing chaos, after the Lorenz system (19524 quotations) and the Rössler system (3554 quotations). These three systems have the advantage compared to the driven Duffing and driven van der Pol systems, that they produce chaotic behaviors without a driving term. In other words, they are autonomous, a property which simplifies a lot the dynamical analysis. As its two companions, the Chua circuit emerged within a series of contributions, providing a bridge between one classical field of science, here electronics, and a new approach which is now known as "chaos theory." The Lorenz system is a hydrodynamical system (Rayleigh-Bénard convection) and the Rössler system is an abstract chemical system.

[155] T. Matsumoto, A chaotic attractor from Chua's circuit, *IEEE Transactions on Circuits and Systems*, **31** (12), 1055–1058, 1984.

[156] According to Google on August 30, 2018 and using the paper published by Matsumoto in 1984 and by Matsumoto, Chua and Komuro in 1985.

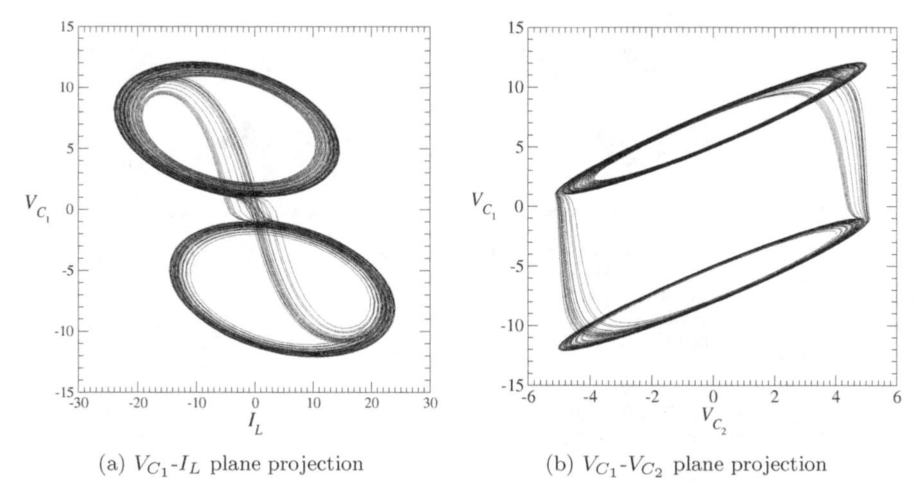

(a) V_{C_1}-I_L plane projection

(b) V_{C_1}-V_{C_2} plane projection

Figure 2.55 Two plane projections of the two-scroll chaotic attractor produced by the system (2.32) as used by Matsumoto for describing the Chua circuit. Parameter values: $G = 0.7$, $C_1 = 1/10$, $C_2 = 1/0.5$, $m_0 = -0.1$, $m_1 = -4$, $B_p = 1$ and $L = 1/7$.

2.6 A van der Pol Oscillator for Describing Plasma Experiments

2.6.1 *Periodic Pulling in Q Machine*

When a voltage is applied to a discharge tube, the electrons emitted by the cathode ionize the gas filling the tube before reaching the anode. The main problem encountered with this type of experimental devices is that the resulting plasma presents many instabilities which are difficult to constrain. In order to simplify the underlying dynamics, Nathan Rynn (University of California at Irvine) and Nicola d'Angelo proposed to create the plasma by using two hot plates of tungstene ($T_{\rm plate} \approx 2000$ K) located at the ends of a cylindrical vacuum chamber:[157] electrons are thus emitted through thermionic emission. Ions are then created by contact with cesium atoms — that have a low ionization potential — produced by two ovens close to the two elliptical plates (≈ 3 cm) as shown in Figure 2.56. The vacuum chamber is placed inside a solenoid which produces a uniform magnetic field ($B \approx 2000$ Gauss). The vapor pressure of cesium is controlled by the temperature of the walls. The chamber walls are cooled ($T_{\rm wall} \approx 15^o$C) in such a way that cesium atoms condense on them and are thus rapidly pumped out of the plasma: it is therefore possible to reach a large fractional ionization (99%). Another advantage of such a device is that the ions and electrons are at a temperature close to the one of the hot plates and, consequently, at a lower temperature than encountered in common plasma. All these properties help to reduce the instabilities in the resulting plasma.

[157] N. Rynn & N. d'Angelo, Device for generating a low temperature, highly ionized cesium plasma, *The Review of Scientific Instruments*, **31** (2), 1326–1333, 1960.

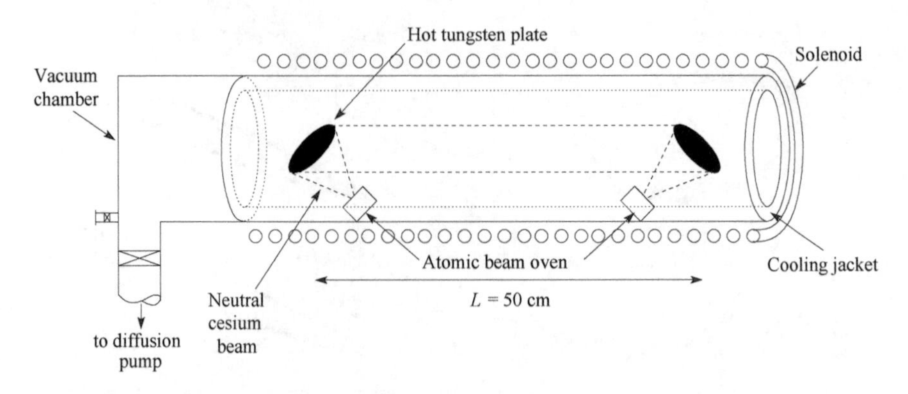

Figure 2.56 Scheme of the Q machine conducted by Rynn and d'Angelo. The vacuum chamber walls are cooled by means of a water jacket. (Redrawn from Ryn and d'Angelo, 1960.)

This type of device allows to produce plasma with reduced fluctuations in its properties. It was used by the group led by Herbert Lashinsky[158] (1921–1980) (Maryland Science Institute) for investigating the transition to turbulence in plasma. In particular, Lashinsky showed that the introduction of new frequencies in the Fourier spectrum measured in one of the first two variables of the driven van der Pol system

$$\begin{cases} \dot{x} = y \\ \dot{y} = \mu(1 - x^2)y - x + u \\ \dot{u} = v \\ \dot{v} = -\omega^2 u \end{cases} \tag{2.34}$$

can be associated with a phenomenon he designated as "*periodic pulling.*"[159] Periodic pulling was defined as the incomplete entrainment of an oscillator by a perturbation whose frequency and amplitude are close to the *synchronization range*[160] evidenced by Appleton (see p. 101). Periodic pulling is a special case of the beats investigated by Hayashi's group. Under these conditions, the oscillations are modulated in frequency and amplitude, inducing multiple frequencies in the Fourier spectrum. According to Lashinsky and co-workers, periodic pulling is characteristic of van der Pol-like systems.

[158] I am too fond of Jazz for avoiding to note that Lashinsky was a friend of the great bassist and composer Charles Mingus (1922–1979) that he met when he served the US army and played piano in a dance band. From L. C. Krisher & T. J. Rosenberg, Herbert L. Lashinsky, *Physics Today*, **33** (9), 84–85, 1980.

[159] H. Lashinsky, Periodic pulling and the transition to turbulence in a system with discrete modes, *in Turbulence of Fluids and Plasmas*, (J. Fox, ed.), Wiley (New York), pp. 29–46, 1969.

[160] R. H. Abrams, Jr., E. J. Yadlowsky & H. Lashinsky, Periodic pulling and turbulence in a bounded plasma, *Physical Review Letters*, **22** (7), 275–278, 1969.

They also showed that a driven van der Pol equation can correctly describe some dynamics observed in plasma as produced by a Q machine.[161] Such results were obtained for an argon plasma. The growth rate of instabilities in a positive column of a neon arc discharge was well predicted from a driven van der Pol equation.[162] It was shown that the density perturbations of the ion-sound instability plasma can be described by a driven van der Pol equation.[163] Thomas Klinger (University of Kiel, Germany) and co-workers investigated periodic pulling in the driven van der Pol system and observed this phenomenon in a weakly magnetized discharge column.[164] Periodic pulling was also observed in a nonlinear electronic oscillation with a reinjection transistor as the nonlinear element in the electrical circuit.[165]

Periodic pulling is here exemplified in the driven van der Pol equation (2.16) by using parameter values close to those reported by Tomaz Gyergyek and co-workers.[166] The pulsation $\omega_{\rm d}$ of the driven is used as the bifurcation parameter. First, in the synchronization range, the dynamics produced by the driven van der Pol equation is a period-1 limit cycle (Figure 2.57(a)). Beyond each ends of this range, there is a small interval in which periodic pulling is observed (Figure 2.57(b)–(c) and 2.57(e)–(f)). The duration of the phase associated with nearly periodic oscillations progressively increases when the frequency approaches the synchronization range. Sufficiently far from the synchronization range, the dynamics is quasi-periodic (Figure 2.57(d) and 2.57(g)).

As shown by Lashinsky and co-workers, periodic pulling is associated with the emergence of new frequencies in the Fourier spectrum (Figure 2.58), a feature they associated with a transition to (weak) turbulence.

Nevertheless, contrary to what they claimed, the dynamics far from the synchronization range is not periodic but quasi-periodic, that is, already characterized by at least two incommensurate frequencies ($\frac{f_{\rm o}}{f_{\rm d}} \neq \frac{p}{q}$ where p and q are two integers). If this is always difficult to accurately check the commensurability between frequencies in a Fourier spectrum, it is quite easy to check the quasi-periodic nature of the behavior by computing a Poincaré section or a first-return map to a Poincaré section of the state portrait. This is performed for the quasi-periodic regime observed beyond the synchronization range (Figure 2.59(a)): the first-return map clearly shows the annular structure, that is, typical of a torus (the trajectory associated with a quasi-periodic regime is located in the surface of a torus).

---

[161] Abraham *et al.*, 1969, *Ibid.*

[162] B. E. Keen & W. H. W. Fletcher, Suppression of a plasma instability by the method of "asynchronous quenching", *Physical Review Letters*, **24**, 130–134, 1970.

[163] B. E. Keen & W. H. W. Fletcher, Suppression and enhancement of an ion-sound instability by nonlinear resonance effects in a plasma, *Physical Review Letters*, **23** (14), 760–763, 1969.

[164] T. Klinger, A. Piel, I. Axnäs & S. Torvén, The bifurcation structure of periodically forced current disruptions, *Physica Scripta*, **56**, 70–85, 1997.

[165] M. E. Koepke & D. M. Hartley, Experimental verification of periodic pulling in a nonlinear electronic oscillator, *Physical Review A*, **44**, 6877–6887, 1991.

[166] T. Gyergyek, M. Čerček & M. Stanojević, Experimental evidence of periodic pulling in a weakly magnetized discharge plasma column, *Contributions to Plasma Physics*, **37** (5), 399–416, 1997.

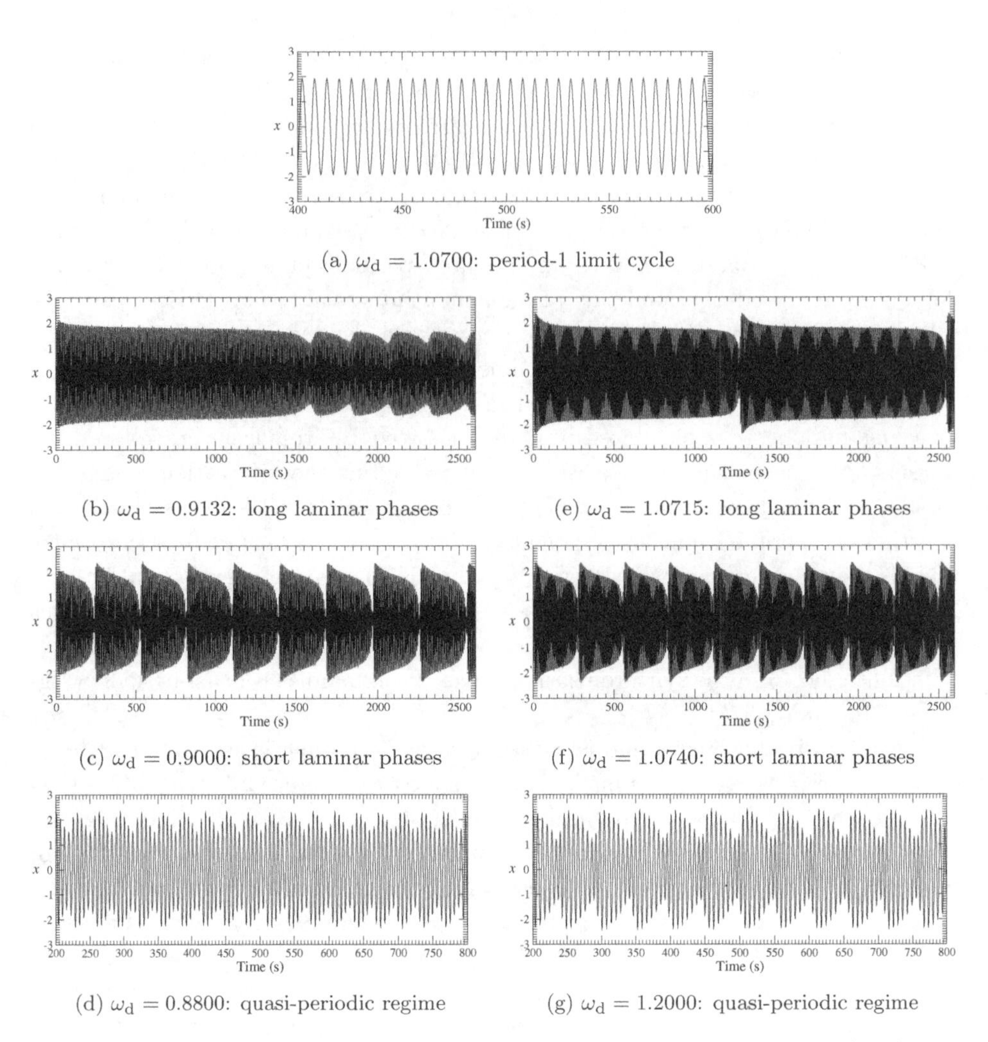

(a) $\omega_d = 1.0700$: period-1 limit cycle

(b) $\omega_d = 0.9132$: long laminar phases

(e) $\omega_d = 1.0715$: long laminar phases

(c) $\omega_d = 0.9000$: short laminar phases

(f) $\omega_d = 1.0740$: short laminar phases

(d) $\omega_d = 0.8800$: quasi-periodic regime

(g) $\omega_d = 1.2000$: quasi-periodic regime

Figure 2.57 Evolution of the dynamics produced by the driven van der Pol equation (2.34) when the pulsation ω_d of the driving term is varied around the period-1 synchronization range. Periodic pulling is observed before and after the synchronization range. Other parameter value: $\mu = 0.3$. Initial conditions: $x_0 = 1$, $y_0 = 0.1$, $u_0 = 0.3$, and $v_0 = 0$.

The mechanism responsible for periodic pulling is as follows. The torus associated with the quasi-periodic regime is progressively deformed when the driving pulsation ω_d is varied up to a value at which the first-return map touches the first bisecting line (Figure 2.59(b)): just before, the trajectory is trapped into a small channel (see the insert Figure 2.59(b)). In this example, the trajectory is trapped in the neighborhood of a period-1 limit cycle; it is almost periodic. When it goes out of this channel, the trajectory describes a quasi-periodic burst before returning to a new almost periodic phase. Periodic pulling is therefore associated with a tangent bifurcation as the three types of intermittencies described by Yves Pomeau and

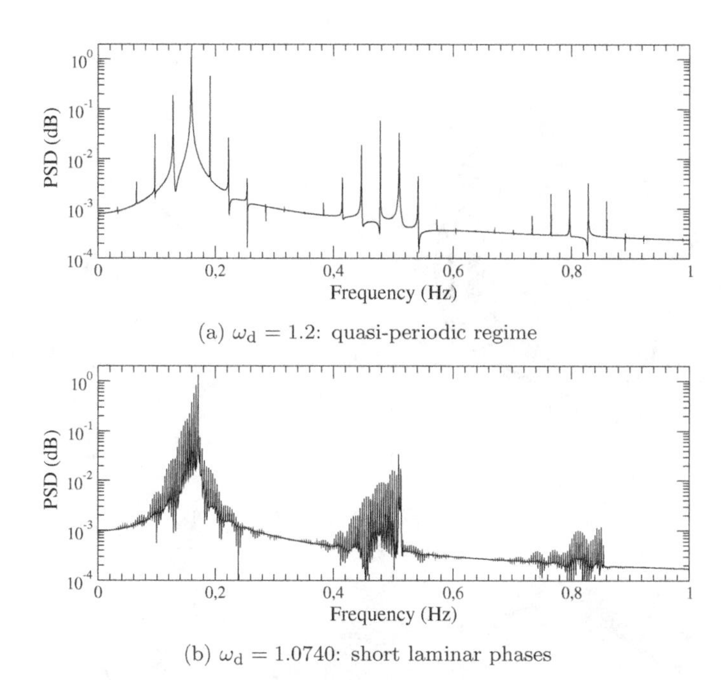

(a) $\omega_{\mathrm{d}} = 1.2$: quasi-periodic regime

(b) $\omega_{\mathrm{d}} = 1.0740$: short laminar phases

Figure 2.58 Emergence of frequencies through periodic pulling produced by the driven van der Pol system (2.34). Other parameter values: $\mu = 0.3$, and $A = 0.3$.

Paul Manneville.[167] Periodic pulling is therefore a particular type of intermittency. Since associated with a quasi-periodic regime, it could be more accurate to speak about quasi-periodic pulling rather than periodic pulling.

The pulling phenomenon corresponds to the fact that, close to the synchronization range, the driving oscillator changes the response pulsation ω of the driven oscillator: when this perturbed pulsation becomes equal to the natural pulsation ω_{o} of the driven oscillator, a full synchronization between the two oscillators occurs. The pulsation ω_{o} of the driven oscillator then evolves linearly with the pulsation ω_{d} of the driving oscillator (Figure 2.60(b)). When ω becomes again too different from the natural pulsation ω_{o}, the synchronization is broken *via* intermittency. This is in a full agreement with the bifurcation diagram showing the synchronization range (Figure 2.60(b)).

2.6.2 *A Chaotic Thermionic Diode*

As we developed in this chapter, many electronic circuits are made of thermionic diode and are well described by a driven van der Pol equation. Let us close this chapter with a circuit made of a thermionic diode which was carried out by Klinger

[167] Y. Pomeau & P. Manneville, Intermittent transition to turbulence in dissipative dynamical systems, *Communications in Mathematical Physics*, **74**, 189–197, 1980. See p. 178 of Chapter 3.

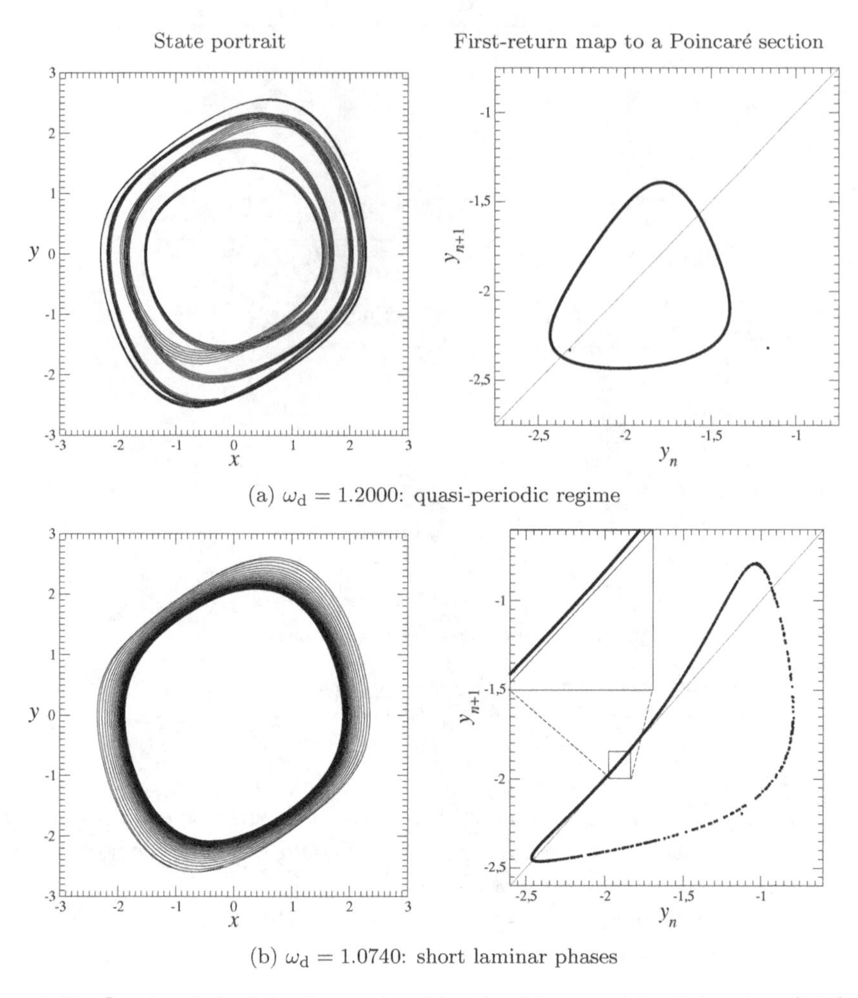

(a) $\omega_\mathrm{d} = 1.2000$: quasi-periodic regime

(b) $\omega_\mathrm{d} = 1.0740$: short laminar phases

Figure 2.59 Quasi-periodic behavior produced by the driven van der Pol system (2.34) at a tangent bifurcation. Other parameter values: $\mu = 0.3$ and $A = 0.3$.

and his colleagues,[168] and for which a strong dynamical relationship with the dynamics produced by a diven van der Pol equation will be shown. The experiments was constructed with a tungsten filament (cathode) placed in a 15 cm diameter cylinder. A plate of stainless steel (anode) was inserted at a distance of 10 cm from the cathode (Figure 2.61). In principle, this is nothing but a Fleming diode. The diode is driven by a static potential on the top of which is superposed a sinusoidal component.

The discharge current I_d was measured. The state portrait produced by this circuit is shown in Figure 2.62 with a first-return map to a Poincaré section. The

[168]T. Mausbach, T. Klinger & A. Piel, Chaos and chaos control in a strongly driven thermionic plasma diode, *Physics of Plasmas*, **6** (10), 3817–3823, 1999.

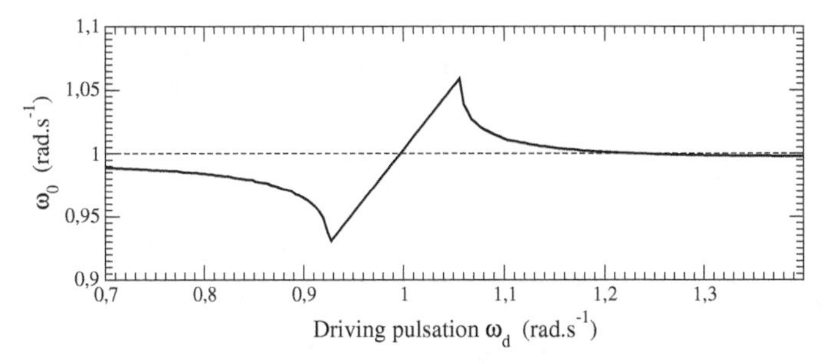

(a) Pulsation of the driven van der Pol system

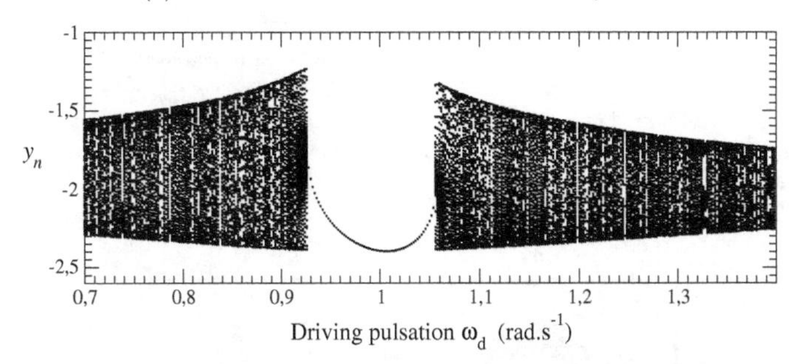

(b) Bifurcation diagram of the driven van der Pol system

Figure 2.60 Evolution of the pulsation ω_0 of the driven system when the driving pulsation $\omega_{\rm d}$ is increased. Bifurcation diagram of the van der Pol system (2.34) around the synchronization window $0.928 < \omega_{\rm d} < 1.056$ rad.s^{-1}. Other parameter values: $A = 0.3$ and $\mu = 0.3$. Initial conditions: $x_0 = 1$, $y_0 = 0.1$, $u_0 = A$ and $v_0 = 0$.

latter is a plot of x_{n+1} against x_n, where x_n is the nth intersection of the state space trajectory with a Poincaré section of the state portrait. These figures permit us to conclude that the dynamics responsible for the state portrait is not random but has a clear underlying structure: the dynamics is therefore deterministic. A more thorough study of this structure shows that the behavior is chaotic.[169]

Since the van der Pol equation was shown to reliably reproduce the dynamics of electronic circuit as the one shown in Figure 2.61, it must be possible to reproduce the experimental dynamics (Figure 2.62) by numerically integrating the driven van der Pol equation (2.16) with appropriate parameter values. Even though the driven van der Pol equation does not take into account of all the experimental details, it contains the essential ingredients for qualitatively reproducing the experimental dynamics. After many trials and errors, an attractor and its first-return map to a Poincaré section (Figure 2.63(b)) were found with the main features evidenced by the experimental dynamics (Figure 2.62(b)). The dynamical characteristics these two systems share include the general smooth unimodal first-return map, with an atypical decreasing branch — on the right — which is doubled (see the insert in

[169]C. Letellier, O. Ménard, Th. Klinger, A. Piel & G. Bonhomme, Dynamical analysis and map modelling of a thermionic diode plasma experiment, *Physica D*, **156**, 169–178, 2001.

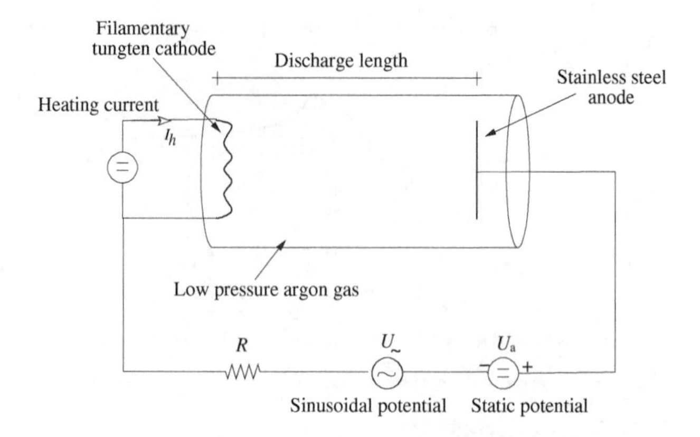

Figure 2.61 Layout of the thermionic diode experiment. The external resistance R was chosen equal to 100 Ω and the heating current $I_h = 4.2$ A. The cylinder was filled with argon to a pressure of $P_0 = 0.4$ Pa.

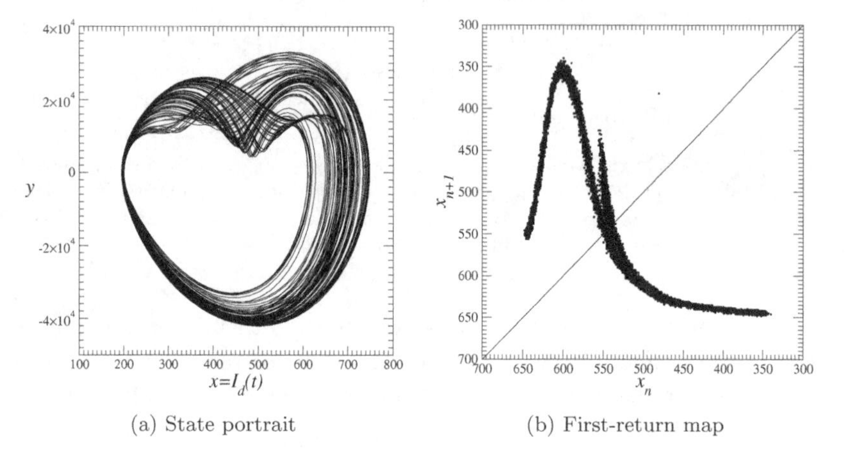

(a) State portrait (b) First-return map

Figure 2.62 Chaotic behavior of the thermionic diode. (a) Projection of the state portrait reconstructed with the derivative coordinates and (b) the corresponding first-return map to the Poincaré section.

Figure 2.63(b)): the foliated decreasing branch is the key property difficult to reproduce. The two first-return maps (Figure 2.62(b) and 2.63(b)) are quantitatively similar, a feature which can be considered as another proof of the natural relationship between a thermionic diode and the driven van der Pol equation. Since the experimental state portrait has no symmetry, the inversion symmetry in the driven van der Pol equation is modded out by applying the coordinate transformation[170]

$$\Phi = \left| \begin{array}{l} X = 2xy \\ Y = x^2 - y^2 \, . \end{array} \right. \tag{2.35}$$

[170] C. Letellier & R. Gilmore, Covering dynamical systems: Two-fold covers, *Physical Review E*, **63**, 016206, 2001. See more details p. 301.

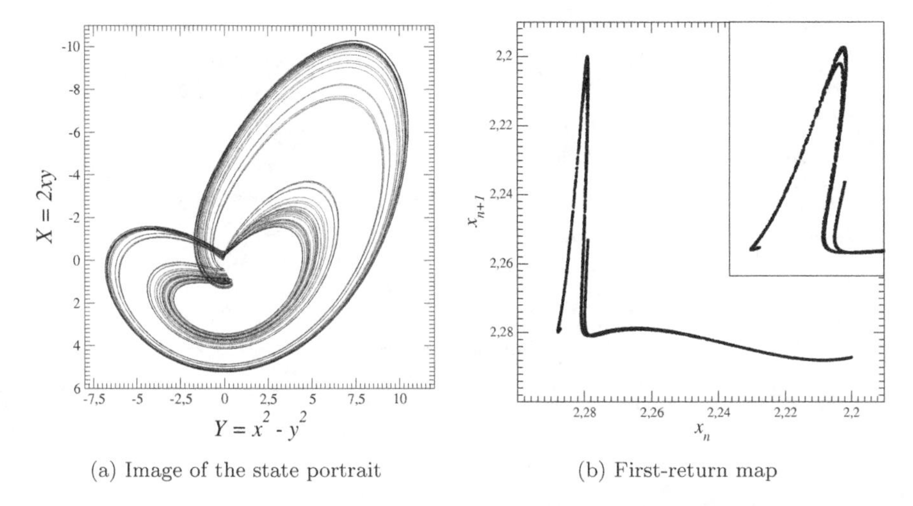

(a) Image of the state portrait

(b) First-return map

Figure 2.63 Chaotic behavior solution to a driven van der Pol equation (2.16) with a first-return map to a Poincaré section with the same structure than the structure observed in the thermionic diode experiments. Parameter values: $\mu = 0.48$, and $\omega = 0.7722$. Initial conditions: $x_0 = 1$, $y_0 = 0$, $u_0 = 3$ and $v_0 = 0$.

The state portrait thus obtained (Figure 2.63(a)) has no residual symmetry and presents some coarse similarities with the experimental one (Figure 2.62(a)).

The important qualitative properties of these two curves are: a maximum where the derivative can be calculated, and the foliated structure of the decreasing branch. The slight differences in form result from the simplifications made in passing from the electronic circuit (Figure 2.61), to the driven van der Pol equation (2.16). Qualitatively — or, in an equivalent manner, dynamically — the behaviors are equivalent. A more faithful, but more complicated, model than the driven van der Pol equation would permit a better quantitative agreement. Certain properties specific to the thermionic diode, imply a slightly different organization of the dynamics which can be obtained by a continuous deformation (without cutting) of the state portrait and of the first return map.

The route to chaos for this chaotic attractor is a period-doubling cascade (Figure 2.64) as observed when the heating current is varied in the experimental device. For weak currents a period-one oscillation is observed (Figure 2.65(a)), as shown by a main peak at the frequency f_0 in the Fourier spectrum (the small peak at the very left in the spectrum is related to the secondary oscillation that occurs at 400 mA). When the heating current is slightly increased the periodicity of the oscillation changes and becomes twice as large (Figure 2.65(b)): a second peak at $\frac{f_0}{2}$ can be seen.[171] A further small increase in the heating current triggers another period-doubling (or frequency halving) (Figure 2.65(c)) and a frequency $\frac{f_0}{4}$ also appears.

[171] As in the spectrum corresponding to the period-2 oscillations, linear combinations between frequencies of the form $pf_0 + q\,\frac{f_0}{2}$ appear.

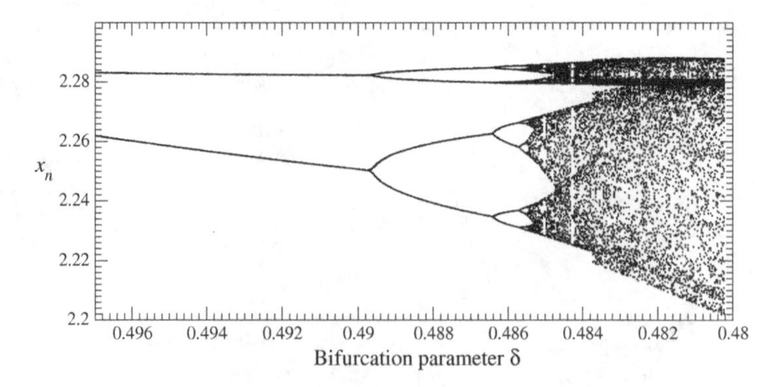

Figure 2.64 Bifurcation diagram of the driven van der Pol equation used as a simple model for the thermionic diode experiments.

Finally, above a threshold heating current, chaotic behavior is seen (Figure 2.65(d)): the spectrum contains an infinite number of frequencies. One should notice the series of frequencies f_0, $\frac{f_0}{2}$, $\frac{f_0}{4}$,...: this is characteristic of a type of chaotic behavior resulting from a period-doubling cascade as a route to chaos.

A period-doubling cascade can thus be found in the driven van der Pol equation by varying one of its parameters. To our knowledge, there is a single period-doubling cascade reported in the driven van der Pol equation[172] as well as in the thermionic experiments.[173] This recent thermionic diode producing chaotic behavior was just a return to the origins, that is, to Fleming's thermionic diode.

2.7 Conclusion

The early developments of electronic circuits provided a stimulating field for introducing new techniques for characterizing non-trivial dynamics (more complex than periodic oscillations). Up to the late 1940s, electronic circuits were mostly investigated by mathematical analysis. Some important phenomena as synchronization between nearly identical systems were already discussed. Then, biologists and physiologists used electronic circuits — more or less complicated — to reproduce some dynamics that were observed in living systems. There are at least three important contributors for having initially popularized the van der Pol equation in this domain, namely Karl F. Bonhöffer and Albrecht Bethe. Then, neuronal dynamics was investigated with the major contributions by Alan Hodgkin, Andrew Huxley, and Richard FitzHugh.

The next period (1960–1980) corresponds to the emergence of the analog computers whose results were initially checked by investigating the electronic circuits corresponding to the equations which were numerically integrated. In this approach,

[172] U. Parlitz & W. Lauterborn, Period-doubling cascades and devil's staircases of the driven van der Pol oscillator, *Physical Review A*, **36** (3), 1428–1433, 1987.
[173] Mausbach *et al.*, 1999. *Ibid.*

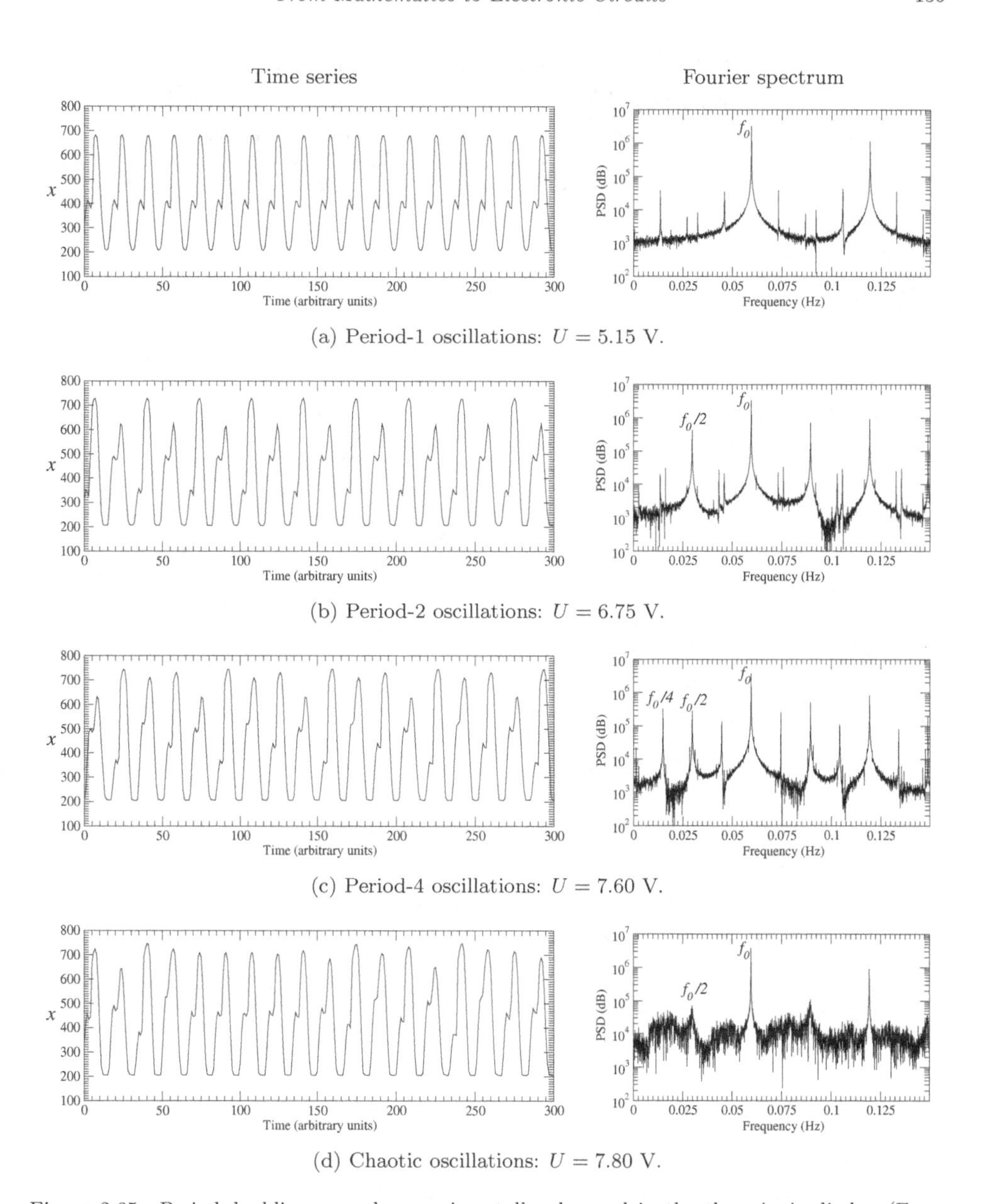

(a) Period-1 oscillations: $U = 5.15$ V.

(b) Period-2 oscillations: $U = 6.75$ V.

(c) Period-4 oscillations: $U = 7.60$ V.

(d) Chaotic oscillations: $U = 7.80$ V.

Figure 2.65 Period-doubling cascade experimentally observed in the thermionic diode. (From data provided by Thomas Klinger.)

the Japanese school led by Chihiro Hayashi had a very important contribution although it did not fully realize the relevance of "chaotic behaviors", being trapped in the classical stream according which only periodic or quasi-periodic solutions were investigated. From this aspect, Leon Chua and co-workers developed a relevant bridge with Poincaré's heritage *via* Norman Levinson, combining an advanced mathematical approach with solid numerical simulations — as well as a solid knowledge of the "*historical*" contributions. As we will see in the next chapter, there is yet another way electronics contributed to the emergence of "chaos theory."

Chapter 3

From Meteorology to Chaos: The Second Wave

3.1 Prediction in Meteorology

Historically, the first noteworthy example of chaotic behavior in a dissipative system came to us from the field of meteorology and was made by Edward Lorenz in 1963. Already in 1876, James Clerk Maxwell pointed out that "*like causes produce like effects*" only "*when small variations in the initial circumstances produce only small variations in the final state of the system.*"[1] He already understood that there are some "*unstable*" system which could provide a "*limitation on any postulate of universal physical determinacy such as Laplace was credited with.*"[2] Indeed, Maxwell mentioned systems "*in which a small initial variation may produce a very great change in the final state of the system, as when the displacement of the "points" causes a railway train to run into another instead of keeping its proper course.*" He thus added that "*the weather may be due to an unlimited assemblage of local instabilities, it may not be amenable to a finite scheme of law at all.*" In 1908, in the same vein, Poincaré understood that atmospheric motions were a natural site of dynamics that were complicated and difficult to predict:[3]

> Why have meteorologists such difficulty in predicting the weather with any certainty? Why is it that showers and even storms seem to come by chance, so that many people find it quite natural to pray for rain or fine weather, when they would consider it ridiculous to ask for an eclipse by prayer? We see that great disturbances are generally produced in regions where the atmosphere is in unstable equilibrium. The meteorologists see very well that the equilibrium is unstable, that a cyclone will be formed somewhere, but exactly where they are not in a position to say; a tenth of a degree more or less at any given point, and the cyclone will burst here and not there, and extend its ravages over districts it would otherwise have spared. If they had been aware

[1] J. C. Maxwell, *Matter and motion* (1876), Reprinted by the Society for Promoting Christian Knowledge (London), 1920.

[2] See p. 35.

[3] H. Poincaré, *Science et Méthode*, Flammarion, p. 69, 1908.

> of this tenth of a degree, they could have known it beforehand, but the observations were neither sufficiently comprehensive nor sufficiently precise, and that is the reason why it all seems due to the intervention of chance. Here, again, we find the same contrast between a very triffling cause that is inappreciable to the observer, and considerable effects, that are sometimes terrible disasters.

Most likely, Lewis Fry Richardson (1881–1953) published in 1922 one of the first books about weather forecasting. He addressed the problem for getting a model correctly describing the underlying processes as well as obtaining initial observations with an accuracy sufficient for reliable computations.[4] He evaluated that he needed six weeks "*to draw up the computing forms and to work out the new distribution in two vertical columns for the first time.*" Consequently,

> if the time-step were 3 hours, then 32 individuals could just compute two points so as to keep pace with the weather, if we allow nothing for the very great gain in speed which is invariably noticed when a complicated operation is divided up into simpler parts, upon which individuals specialize. If the co-ordinate chequer were 200 km square in plan, there would be 3200 columns on the complete map of the globe. In the tropics the weather is often foreknown, so that we may say 2000 active columns. So that $32 \times 2000 = 64,000$ computers would be needed to race the weather for the whole globe.

In fact, the growth of meteorology was stimulated by the arrival of computers. During the Second World War, weather predictions were vital in planning military operations as for the D-day. Further, in 1946, John von Neumann (1903–1957) who was involved in the Manhattan project that developed the first atomic bombs, realized that the speed of numerical calculations provided by these new devices could lead to solution of numerous scientific problems and launched a project at Princeton University aimed at using computers to address meteorological problems. The objective was to collect data and to make numerical calculations with sufficient speed as to allow weather predictions 24 hours in advance over the entire American country. In 1950, with Jule Charney and Agnar Fjörtoff, von Neumann were able to compute a twenty-hour of weather forecast in... twenty-four hours.[5] They performed this with an Electronic Numerical Integrator and Computer (ENIAC), a computer made of 17,468 vacuum tubes, 7200 crystal diodes, 1500 relays, 70,000 resistors, 10,000 capacitors and approximately 5,000,000 hand-soldered joints. Beyond the technological issue, the difficulties were enormous because it was necessary to make reasonable simplifying approximations to allow numerical integration of the equations describing atmospheric dynamics; it was also necessary to make precise

[4] L. F. Richardson, *Weather forecasting by numerical process*, Cambridge University Press, 1922.
[5] J. Charney, A. Fjörtoff and J. von Neumann, Numerical integration of the barotropic vorticity equation, *Tellus*, **2**, 237–254, 1950.

measurements over the entire country to initialize these calculations. The strategy adopted was to begin with a simple model, to add terms later that were initially neglected, and finally to reproduce the best observations. Von Neumann and co-workers estimated that the causes of forecast errors were due to the space resolution and from the misalignment between the gradient of pressure and the gradient of density in the stratified fluid (the so-called baroclinicity) that is the atmosphere. They were particularly concerned about numerical instabilities and were aware that "*the small-scale motions for which there is inevitably a large distortion may possibly be amplified in the course of computation to such an extent that they will totally obscure the significant large-scale motions.*" They were also working with a strongly approximated model. The number of grid points — each made of 15×18 space intervals equal to $\delta x = 736$ km — was adjusted to match the limited internal memory capacity of the ENIAC. They were thus able to provide forecasts for January 5, 1949. They choose a situation such that forecasting was not possible to made by a simple extrapolation. Their results are shown in Figure 3.1. As they concluded themselves, the forecast was rather poor because a too small displacement of the cyclone was predicted and its shape was distorted. Reasons for such features were due to the replacement of the differential equation by a discretized equation (unavoidable in numerical simulations), approximation in the wind variation, the baroclinicity, and the simplified model. One may say that real-time operational numerical weather prediction was operative on July 1, 1954, when the Joint Numerical Weather Prediction Unit (JNWPU) was created by the U.S. Weather Bureau, the U.S. Air Force, and the U.S. Navy.[6]

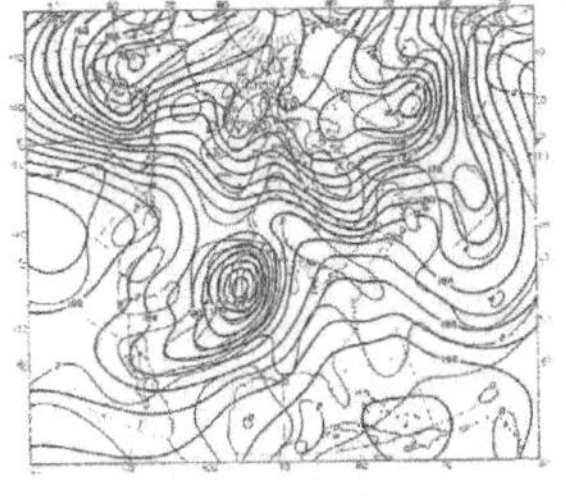

(a) Initial observations

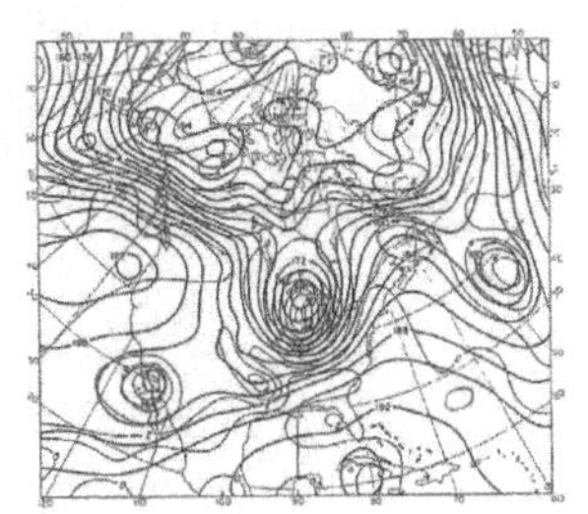

(b) Observations 24 hours later

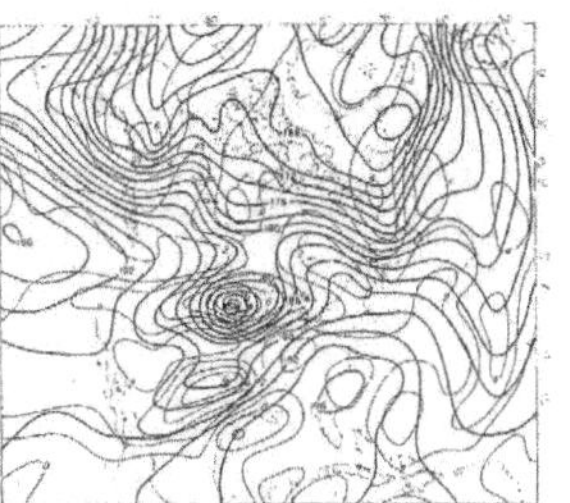

(c) Predicted observations

Figure 3.1 Height contours (in units of 100 ft) and the isolines of absolute vorticity (in units of $\frac{1}{3} \cdot 10^{-4}$ s^{-1}). Initial observations (a), 24 hours later (b), and predicted conditions by von Neumann and co-workers (c).

Nevertheless, problems persisted because it did not seem possible to make longer term predictions and it was difficult to determine if this was because of the simplifying approximations or due to the accumulation of errors during the numerical integrations. As we have already seen in celestial mechanics, there are two possible

[6] K. Harper, L. W. Uccellini, E. Kalnay, K. Carey and L. Morone, 50th anniversary of operational numerical weather prediction, *Bulletin of the American Meteorological Society*, **88** (5), 639–650, 2007.

approaches to this problem. One can gradually make more complex models to describe atmospheric dynamics in order to make better predictions (this perturbation theory approach was adopted in celestial mechanics). Or one could analyze the global dynamics of the system, determining its major properties before attempting to determine the source of the difficulties (this is the global analysis begun by Hill and Poincaré for the restricted three-body problem). As in the case of celestial mechanics, the two approaches are complementary. Once the source of difficulties was understood, meteorologists could return to their models and, by judicious addition of appropriate terms, make predictions with improved accuracy.

Following Poincaré's example, in 1957 Philipp Duncan Thompson considered the effect of the uncertainties in the initial conditions (the observations) and their growth in time, on the accuracy of predictions.[7] The principle difficulty was that the growth of errors over the course of time lead to predictions that were not much better than those based on random guesses: meteorologists were confronted with the problem of the rapid growth of small uncertainties.

In 1960, Edward Norton Lorenz, of the Department of Meteorology at the Massachusetts Institute of Technology (MIT) hoped to understand the origin of, and limits to, long term prediction. His impact in meteorology is similar to Hill's role in celestial mechanics. The description of weather variations demands knowledge of an enormous number of variables such as temperature and water vapor pressure as a function of height from the earth's surface, solar radiation and the influence of cloud cover and the ozone layer on it, surface height profiles, ocean currents and temperatures... These quantities are related by hundreds of differential equations. The solution of these differential equations was a very difficult problem and Lorenz realized that to make any headway he had to content himself with studies of enormously simplified systems. He summarized the problem between the two possible approaches:[8]

> The various phenomena which are observed in our atmosphere, and the changes in the state of the atmosphere from one time to another, are supposedly governed by a set of physical laws. The dynamic meteorologist does not usually regard the discovery of these laws as one of his tasks, being willing to concede that the laws have already been established, at least in approximate form, by workers in other fields. Instead, he includes among his problems the prediction of future states of the atmosphere by means of these laws, and the explanation of typical observable phenomena in terms of these laws. He ordinarily finds it convenient to express the laws as a set of mathematical equations.
>
> In order to make the best attainable forecast of the future weather, it would be desirable to express the physical laws as exactly as possible, and determine the initial conditions as precisely as possible. Yet the ultimate achievement of producing perfect forecasts, by applying

[7]Ph. D. Thomson, Uncertainty of initial states as a factor in the predictability of large scale atmospheric flow patterns, *Tellus*, **9**, 275–295, 1957.

[8]E. Lorenz, Maximun simplification of the dynamics equations, *Tellus,* **13** (3), 243–254, 1960.

> equations already known to be exact to initial conditions already known to be precise, if such a feat were possible, would not by itself increase our understanding of the atmosphere [...].
>
> Our present methods of weather observations, and also any foreseeable future methods, yield systematically incomplete initial conditions, and our present mathematical techniques do not allow as to solve the dynamics equations without previous systematic simplification, whether or not the equations may originally be expressed in exact form. Beyond these unavoidable inaccuracies, further simplifications have so far been necessary for the sake of economy. Thus it is that the recent studies in numerical weather prediction, besides yielding creditable although not optimum forecasts, have made vast contributions to our understanding of common weather phenomena.

In fact, following Hill's approach in celestial mechanics, Lorenz approached the problem of understanding the origins of these limitations as would a mathematician. He searched for the simplest possible model that would lead to long term prediction errors of the type encountered in meteorology. Lorenz's objective was to find a mathematical model as simple as possible that was able to produce an aperiodic solution ("infinite" period) because he knew that atmospheric motion never repeats itself exactly. In 1961 Lorenz visited his former student Barry Salzman, of the Traveler Weather Center, who had also chosen to understand the origins of prediction limitations and who, as a result, was searching for very simple models. Saltzman was working on a simplified model of convection that contained the essential ingredients describing atmospheric motions:[9]

> With but little exception, the motions of the atmosphere, on all scales, are of convective origin. This is to say that the primary causes for air motions are the thermal inequalities which are constantly being imposed upon the atmosphere, mainly by solar heating. The particular forms which these motions take vary greatly in scale and character, ranging from chaotic thermal "turbulence" to highly organized systems such as hurricanes. For all cases, however, there is, among others, the common property that the motions which develop will transport heat and vorticity (momentum) and it is these processes which introduce a basic non-linear content to atmospheric behavior.
>
> As a first step towards understanding the complicated forms of this non-linearity it seems necessary to study model systems of much greater simplicity than are actually encountered. One class of such simple systems, capable of elucidating the non-linear properties of the convective process, is that formed by representing the spatial variations of the motion and temperature which evolve in Bénard-type experiments by a fixed and limited number of Fourier components.

[9]B. Saltzman, Finite amplitude free convection as an initial value problem-I, *Journal of the Atmospheric Sciences,* **19**, 329–341, 1962.

Lorenz adopted Saltzman's model of the convection experiments carried out by Henri Bénard in 1900[10] that showed the existence of convective turbulence in a container of fluid heated from below.[11]

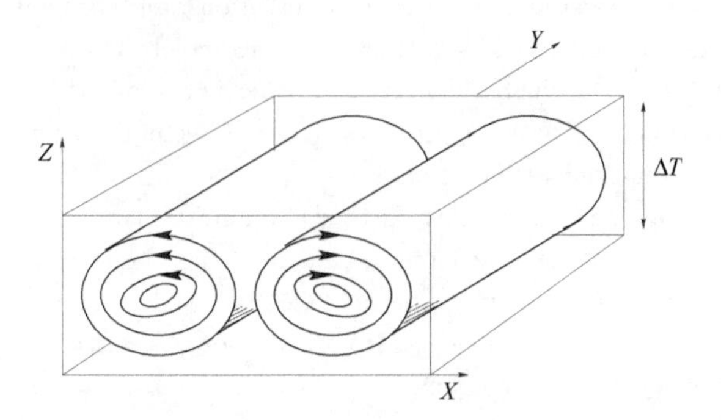

Figure 3.2 Rayleigh-Bénard convection rolls in a rectangular cell. ΔT is the temperature difference between the lower face of the cell and the free surface of the fluid, and the rectangular cell is longer in the Y direction than the X direction.

Convection transports heat due to fluid motion that is caused by temperature and density gradients. Rayleigh-Bénard convection develops when a fluid is placed in a small cell of height H when the temperature difference ΔT between the bottom and top of the cell (Figure 3.2) is held constant using an external heat source. To simplify the problem, the geometry of the small rectangular cell can be fixed so that only two or three rolls develop. This artifice allows to truncate the degrees of freedom of the system and, as a result, to reduce the complexity of the model.[12] The rectangular geometry used imposes an unambiguous constraint on the rolls that develop: the rotation axes are parallel to the longest side of the cell (Figure 3.2).

3.2 The Lorenz System

By simplifying Saltzman's equations Lorenz was able to obtain a set of three differential equations that could not be integrated (exactly) since there was no constant of motion. By contrast, they could easily be integrated numerically (by computer) from any initial condition. Since Lorenz was a student of George Birkhoff (1884–1944), one of the few who adopted Poincaré's methods, he used a number of concepts introduced by Poincaré.

[10]H. Bénard, Etude expérimentale des courants de convection dans une nappe liquide — Régime permanent; tourbillons cellulaires, *Journal de Physique*, **9**, 513–525, 1900.
[11]This experiment is theoretically described since works by Lord Rayleigh (1842–1919) published in 1916: On Convection Currents in a horizontal layer of fluid when the higher temperature is on the under side, *Philosophical Magazine*, **32**, 529–546, 1916. This is now called the *Rayleigh-Bénard convection*.
[12]A. Libchaber & J. Maurer, A Rayleigh-Bénard Experiment: helium in a small box, in *Nonlinear Phenomena at Phases Transitions*, Ed. T. Riste, 1982, pp. 259–286.

3.2.1 *State Space*

Lorenz started his paper[13] by an introduction on turbulent flows and weather forecasting. Focusing on "*deterministic equations which are idealizations of hydrodynamical systems*", Lorenz concentrated on "*solutions which never repeat their past history exactly.*" The second section was devoted to general definitions about trajectories in state space.[14] One clear breakthrough in the study of dynamical systems re-introduced by Lorenz was the use of projection of state space. He did not that in an empirical way, but stated rather clearly that a system governed by the set of equations

$$\dot{X}_i = F_i(X_1, X_2, ..., X_M)\,, (i = 1, ..., M) \tag{3.1}$$

"*may be studied by means of phase space — an M-dimensional Euklidean space* Γ *whose coordinates are* $X_1, ..., X_M$." Lorenz then was very clear about what was represented here and who introduced the concept:

> Each *point* in phase space represents a possible instantaneous state of the system. A state which is varying in accordance with (3.1) is represented by a moving *particle* in phase space, traveling along a *trajectory* in phase space. For completeness, the position of a stationary particle, representing a steady state, is included as a trajectory.
>
> Phase space has been a useful concept in treating finite systems, and has been used by such mathematicians as Gibbs[15] in his development of statistical mechanics, Poincaré[16] in his treatment of the solutions of differential equations, and Birkhoff[17] in his treatise on dynamical systems.

No doubt that Lorenz was acquainted to such background through Birkhoff's work. Birkhoff was Dean of the Faculty of Arts and Science at Harvard University where he taught since 1912. Lorenz got his AM in mathematics from Harvard University in 1940 and, he attended to Birkhoff's lectures (in 1938). Birkhoff is well known to be one of the continuators of Poincaré's work as told by Oswald Veblen:[18]

> as remarked by Marston Morse "Poincaré was Birkhoff's true teacher." I remember well how frequently, in the walks we used to take together during his sojourn in Princeton, Birkhoff used to refer to his reading in Poincaré's *Les Méthodes Nouvelles de la Mécanique Céleste*, and I know that he was intensively studying all of Poincaré's work on dynamics. In a very literal sense Birkhoff took up the leadership in this field at the point where Poincaré laid it down.

---

[13]E. N. Lorenz, Deterministic nonperiodic flow, *Journal of the Atmospheric Sciences,* **20**, 130–141, 1963.

[14]Depending on the field, state space or phase space is used. I choose "state space". Nevertheless, in the quotations, I left the original terminology used by the author.

[15]J. W. Gibbs, *Elementary principles in statistical mechanics*, Scribner (New York), 1902.

[16]H. Poincaré, Mémoire sur les courbes définies par une équation différentielle, *Journal de Mathématiques*, III, **7**, 375–422, 1881.

[17]G. D. Birkhoff, *Dynamical Systems*, American Mathematical Society, New York, 1927.

[18]O. Veblen, George David Birkhoff: a biographical memoir, *Biograhical Memoirs* **80**, 45–58, 2001.

There is therefore a clear bridge between Poincaré and Lorenz.

The use of state space was one of the very key points in Lorenz's paper. In contrast to this, many other contributions using electronic or analog computers published around the 60's did not use that concept. Those we identified were as follows.

(1) The model

$$\begin{cases} \dot{x} = -\mu x + yz \\ \dot{y} = -\mu y + (z - \alpha)x \\ \dot{z} = 1 - xy \end{cases} \tag{3.2}$$

where $\alpha = \mu \left(K^2 - \frac{1}{K^2} \right)$, x and y are the electric currents in each disk and z is the angular velocity. It described a two disk dynamo model that Tsuneji Rikitake (1921–2004) proposed in 1958 for investigating earth magnetic field reversals;[19]

(2) Arkadii Grasiuk and Anatoly Oraevsky who investigated in 1964 dynamics of a laser system (see p. 182);[20]

(3) Derek Moore and Edward Spiegel who studied in 1966 a simple model for pulsating stars (see p. 323).[21]

But these three other contributions only showed excerpts from time series as reported in Figure 3.3. Note that all these systems are quadratic — including linear and nonlinear terms up to the second degree — with a symmetry property. Rikitake's model is a set of three ordinary differential equations with a rotation symmetry — as also the Lorenz system has — and the Moore and Spiegel system is a set of three differential equations with an inversion symmetry. The Grasiuk and Oraevsky's model is four dimensional with a rotation symmetry. All of them produce very similar time series. At first sight, one could conclude that the underlying dynamics are equivalent but a topological analysis — in state space — reveals that only the attractor solution to the Rikitake model is topologically equivalent to that of the Lorenz system. The Moore and Spiegel attractor has a much more complex topology,[22] and the attractor produced by the Grasiuk and Oraevsky model looks like a Lorenz attractor rotating around its rotation axis.

[19]T. Rikitake, Oscillations of a system of discs dynamos, *Proceedings of the Cambridge Philosophical Society* **54** 89–105, 1958.

[20]A. Z. Grasiuk & A. N. Oraevsky, The dynamics of quantum oscillators, in *Quantum Electronics and Coherent Light* (Academic Press New York), pp. 192–197, 1964.

[21]D. W. Moore & E. A. Spiegel, A thermally excited nonlinear oscillator, *Astrophysical Journal*, **143**, 871–887, 1966.

[22]C. Letellier and J.-M. Malasoma, Universalities in the chaotic generalized Moore & Spiegel equations, *Chaos, Solitons & Fractals*, **69**, 40–49, 2014.

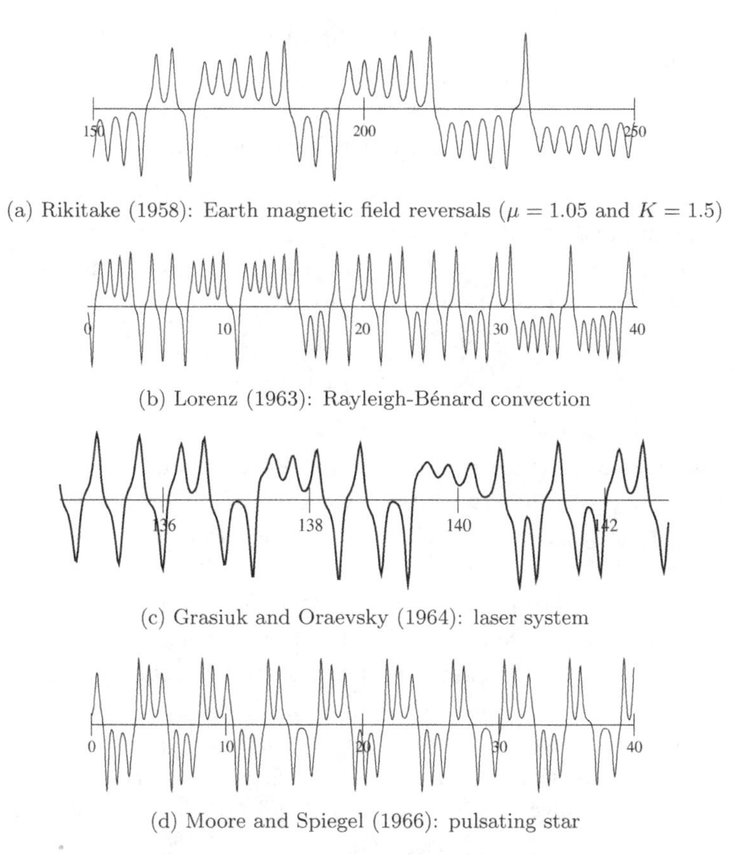

(a) Rikitake (1958): Earth magnetic field reversals ($\mu = 1.05$ and $K = 1.5$)

(b) Lorenz (1963): Rayleigh-Bénard convection

(c) Grasiuk and Oraevsky (1964): laser system

(d) Moore and Spiegel (1966): pulsating star

Figure 3.3 Time series similar to those observed around the 1960s by numerical integration of the ordinary differential equations modelling the respective systems investigated.

3.2.2 *The Stability of Periodic Solutions*

The third section of Lorenz's paper introduced some definitions about the stability of "*nonperiodic flow.*" This was performed with the mathematical background inherited from Birkhoff since Lorenz admitted that his paper was prepared "*guided by Birkhoff's treatment of dynamical systems.*" Viktor Nemytsky and Vyacheslav Stepanov's book[23] was also quoted but Lorenz himself wrote that this quotation was added because it was required by one of the referees of his paper.[24] Some definitions about stable and unstable points, periodic, quasi-periodic and nonperiodic solutions were provided. He also stated that "*two states differing by imperceptible amounts may eventually evolve into two considerably different states*". As a consequence, "*an acceptable prediction of an instantaneous state in the distant future may well be impossible.*" Such sensitivity to initial conditions was one of the relevant points

[23]V. V. Nemytsky & V. V. Stepanov, *Qualitative theory of differential equations*, Princeton University Press, 1960.

[24]E. Lorenz, *The essence of chaos*, p. 142, University College London, 1993.

highlighted by David Ruelle by the mid of the 1970s to distinguish chaos from other qualitative types of dynamical behavior.[25]

3.2.3 *Numerical Integration and Application of Linear Theory*

The procedure for integrating numerically nonconservative systems was then discussed by Lorenz and, he described the convection equations for the Rayleigh-Bénard convection introduced by Saltzman. Lorenz reduced them to the set of three ordinary differential equations

$$\begin{cases} \dot{x} = \sigma(y - x) \\ \dot{y} = Rx - y - xz \\ \dot{z} = -bz + xy \end{cases} \tag{3.3}$$

This system depends on three *parameters*: the Prandtl number σ — adimensional number defined as the ratio between the heat transport by conduction and viscosity effects —, and the Rayleigh number, R — another adimensional number characterizing the degree of instabilities in the experiments. Convection phenomena arise when the Rayleigh number is greater than a threshold value R_c. Below this value, fluid is at rest. The last parameter, b, is a function of the aspect ratio (length over width) of the rectangular cell containing the rolls. Lorenz then applied linear theory to these equations to investigate their properties. He showed that the trajectory was always bounded,[26] and that "*each small volume shrinks to zero*" as the time goes to infinity, that is, that the system was dissipative (nonconservative). Lorenz also showed that the solution oscillates around the two singular points defined by

$$S_\pm = \left| \begin{array}{l} x_\pm = \pm\sqrt{b(R-1)} \\ y_\pm = \pm\sqrt{b(R-1)} \\ z_\pm = R - 1\,. \end{array} \right.$$

Numerical computations were performed on a Royal McBee LGP-30 electronic computer. Lorenz provided 6,000 iterations. Since one second was required per iteration, each run took roughly one hour and forty minutes. Lorenz showed short portion of the trajectory, typically 500 iterations, chosen after the first 1400 iterations from the initial conditions $x_0 = 0$, $y_0 = 0.1$ and $z_0 = 0$. A recomputed trajectory with a modern computer and the same parameters leads to the trajectory shown in Figure 3.4.

3.2.4 *Topological Analysis*

To provide an idea of how the trajectory was organized in three-dimensional state space, Lorenz introduced "*isopleths*"[27] that return the value of x as a smooth single-

[25] D. Ruelle, The Lorenz attractor and the problem of turbulence, *Lecture Notes in Mathematics*, **565**, 146–158, 1976.

[26] Once the trajectory entries in a given volume of the state space $\mathbb{R}^3(x, y, z)$, it never goes out.

[27] A line drawn on a map through all points having the same value of some measurable quantity. Isopleths are commonly used in meteorology.

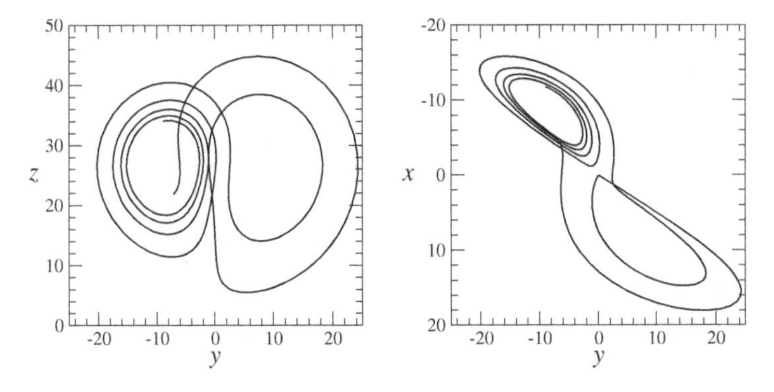

Figure 3.4 Numerical solution to the Lorenz equations. Projections on the x-y and the y-z planes in state space of the segment of the trajectory extending from iteration 1400 to 1900. These segments slightly differ from those obtained by Lorenz in 1963. Parameter values: $R = 28$, $\sigma = 10$ and $b = 8/3$.

valued function of y and z. Isopleths allow to represent the "surface" on which the trajectory evolves (Figure 3.5(a)). Lorenz was thus able to show that the trajectory "*passes back and forth from one spiral to the other without intersecting itself.*" This surface was topologically equivalent to what is now called a branched manifold — or a template — on which all trajectories can be drawn (Figure 3.5(b)). Such a manifold was used since the middle of 1970s by Franck Williams for describing the Lorenz attractor[28] as "*a picture already present in Lorenz's paper*" (compare Figure 3.5(a) and 3.5(b)). As Williams wrote, "*a computer gives the same picture up to a smooth deformation when programmed to find the attractor of the system.*" The branched manifold was important as a knot holder, that is, to synthesize the relative organization of unstable periodic orbits embedded within the attractor, as later shown by Joan Birman and Williams.[29]

3.2.5 *First-return Map to Maxima*

Lorenz also proposed a first-return map to maxima of variable z in order to identify the possible periodic sequences that can be produced. It helped him to conclude that

> the periodic trajectories, whose sequences of maxima form a denumerable set, are unstable, and only exceptional trajectories, having the same sequences of maxima, can approach them asymptotically. The remaining trajectories, whose sequences of maxima form a nondenumerable set, therefore represent deterministic nonperiodic flow.

[28] R. F. Williams, The structure of Lorenz attractors, *Lecture Notes in Mathematics*, **615**, 94–112, 1977 — R. F. Williams, The structure of Lorenz attractors, *Publications Mathématiques de l'IHES*, **50**, 73–99, 1979.
[29] J. S. Birman & R. F. Williams, Knotted periodic orbits in dynamical systems I: Lorenz's equations, *Topology* **22**, 47–82, 1983.

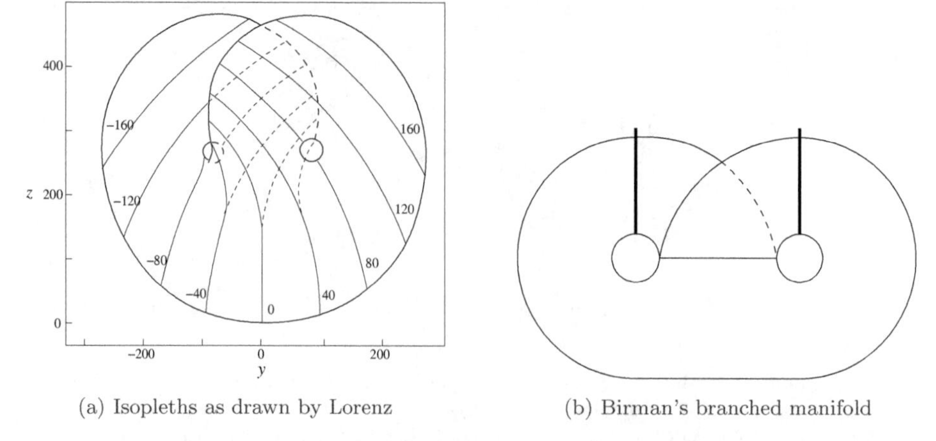

(a) Isopleths as drawn by Lorenz

(b) Birman's branched manifold

Figure 3.5 (a) Isopleths of x as a function of y and z (thin solid curves). Where two values of x exist, the dashed lines are isopleths of the lower value. Heavy solid curve, and extensions as dotted curves, indicate natural boundaries of surfaces. (b) Representation of the associated branched manifold drawn by Williams. The two-component Poincaré section associated with the maxima of variable z is also drawn.

This argument was used to show that trajectories were actually nonperiodic since unstable periodic orbits were "*exceptional*" since the probability to have a trajectory remaining in the neighborhood of a periodic orbit is nearly zero.

Lorenz then used a first-return map to describe the dynamics governing the transitions from one spiral to the other:

> ... the trajectory apparently leaves one spiral only after exceeding some critical distance from the center. Moreover, the extent to which this distance is exceeded appears to determine the point at which the next spiral is entered; this is in turn seems to determine the number of circuits to be executed before changing spirals again.

In order to investigate that feature carefully, Lorenz used the successive maximum values of z. He thus plotted the value of the $(n+1)$th maximum value of z versus the nth maximum (Figure 3.6). This is what is now called a *first-return map* to a Poincaré section. Lorenz introduced that tool for having "*an empirical prediction scheme*" allowing to predict the number of "*circuits*" (oscillations around one of the focus singular point) described by the trajectory between two successive transitions from one spiral to the other. With such a map, it is possible to follow through how the trajectory visits the attractor using a simple geometric construction (Figure 3.6). The increasing branch (left part of the map) corresponds to the successive oscillations around the same focus and the decreasing branch (right part) is associated with transition from one spiral to the other. For instance, as shown in Figure 3.6, starting from point 1, there are thus two oscillations in the initial spiral (points 2 and 3), then one transition in the other spiral (point 4) and, finally, a return to the initial spiral (point 5) before new oscillations in the initial spiral, and so on.

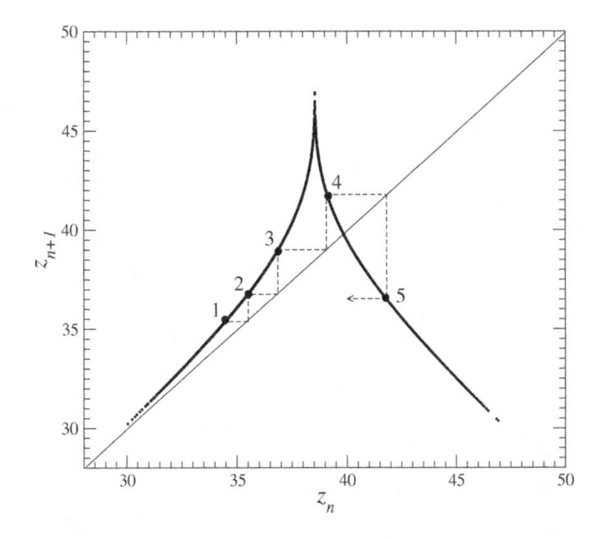

Figure 3.6 Successive values of relative maximum plotted as z_{n+1} versus z_n as shown in Lorenz's original paper. The bisecting line has been added to make explicit the geometric construction (dashed line) that allows to track the evolution of the trajectory within the attractor.

To conclude, the most important concepts used by Lorenz were i) plotting the trajectory in plane projections of the state portrait, ii) showing that the trajectory can be described as evolving on a surface (a template) and iii) using a first-return map (or a Poincaré map) to show that the trajectory is nonperiodic with the help of periodic sequences.

3.3 Sensitivity to Initial Conditions

Lorenz thus found an aperiodic attractor (Figure 3.7) which, because of its peculiar properties, was called "*strange*" by David Ruelle and Floris Takens in 1971.[30] This term "strange" summarized the perplexity of scientists who encountered this object for the first time.

Lorenz succeeded in finding a rapid growth of small perturbations. Here are some of his recollections describing this discovery:[31]

> At one point I decided to repeat some of the computations in order to examine what was happening in greater detail. I stopped the computer, typed in a line of numbers that it had printed out a while earlier, and set it running again. I went down the hall for a cup of coffee and returned after about an hour, during which time the computer had simulated about two months of weather. The numbers being printed were nothing like the old ones. I immediately suspected a weak

[30] D. Ruelle & F. Takens, On the nature of turbulence, *Communications in Mathematical Physics*, **20**, 167–192, 1971.

[31] E. Lorenz, *The Essence of chaos*, UCL Press, London, pp. 134–136, 1993.

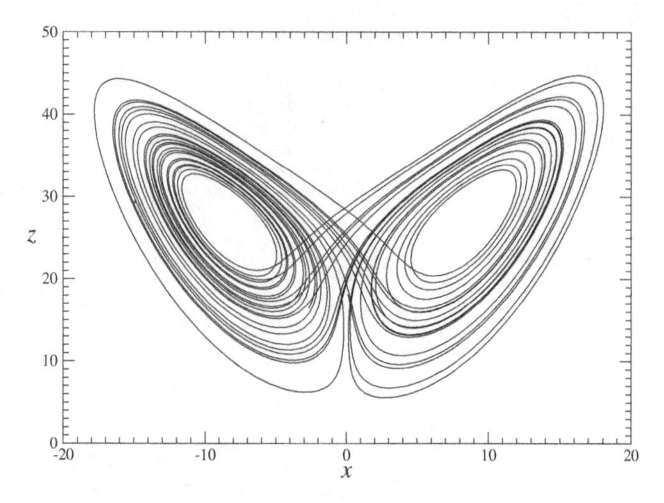

Figure 3.7 Aperiodic attractor, numerical solution of the Lorenz equations (3.3). Only the asymptotic behavior is shown. The transient regime between the initial conditions and the attractor is not shown here. Almost all initial conditions are responsible for trajectories that relax to the object shown here. Parameter values: $R = 28$, $b = 8/3$ and $\sigma = 10$.

> vacuum tube or some other computer trouble, which was not uncommon, but before calling for service I decided to see just where the mistake had occurred, knowing that this could speed up the servicing process. Instead of a sudden break, I found that the new values at first repeated the old ones, but soon afterward differed by one and then several units in the last decimal place, and then began to differ in the next to the last place and then in the place before that. In fact, the differences more or less steadily doubled in size every four days or so, until all resemblance with the original output disappeared somewhere in the second month. This was enough to tell me what had happened: the numbers that I had typed in were not the exact original numbers, but were the rounded-off values that had appeared in the original printout. The initial round-off errors were the culprits; they were steadily amplifying until they dominated the solution. In today's terminology, there was chaos.

Lorenz's magnificent contribution was to recognize this behavior as typical of nonlinear systems. Small errors in initial conditions guarantee that computers cannot preserve all the decimals in the numbers used to initiate the computations. Because of memory storage capabilities, numerical input is always rounded off and only a certain number, fixed *a priori* by storage capabilities, of significant figures (without counting the zeroes) are used. The computer that Lorenz used kept six figures and printed three. Lorenz used the numbers that he had copied down, to initiate a second calculation. These were not exactly the numbers in the computer's memory. The difference between these numbers was small, but large enough so that the error amplification mechanism soon lead to large deviations. This rapid growth of small errors is shown for two solutions of the Lorenz equations initiated from very nearby initial conditions (Figure 3.8). For these two solutions the evolution is very similar for the short term ($t < 10$ s, Figure 3.8), but later they become very different and, as a result, it is not possible to make good long term predictions for this system. Even a system as simple as the one studied by Lorenz does not allow for long term predictions. With this model Lorenz understood that the source of the difficulties was not the simplifications made in the equations that describe atmospheric dynamics. Rather, they are inherent in the nature of the processes responsible for those dynamics.

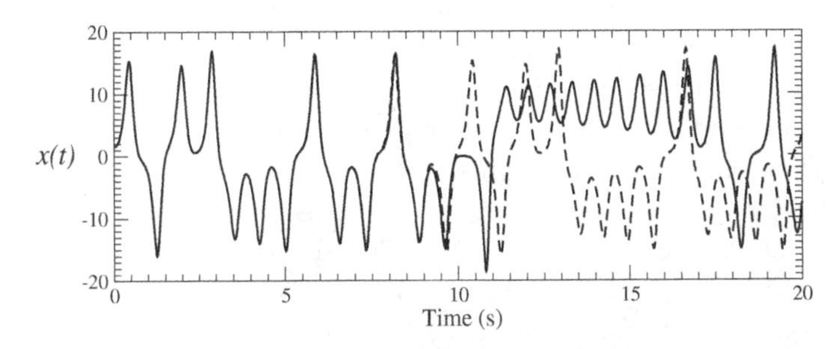

Figure 3.8 Time evolution of the variable x of the Lorenz system for two initial conditions separated by $\epsilon = 0.001$. After describing similar evolution for some time, the trajectories go their separate ways. This is the phenomenon of sensitivity to initial conditions that prohibits long term predictions in meteorology.

From this type of simulations, Lorenz understood that "*the mathematically predicted weather diverges farther and farther from the real weather, as the cumulative effect of the approximations becomes more and more dominant.*"[32] There is therefore no possibility for the meteorologists to obtain the accuracy of predictions of solar eclipses. This failure does not result from the fact that "*meteorologists are not in a class with astronomers*" but, as Lorenz concluded, from the fact that "*no method of predicting the weather can ever compare in accuracy to the prediction of eclipses.*" The motion of a fluid and the motion of discrete heavenly bodies are simply not governed by the same type of laws. Lorenz well understood that the sensitivity to initial conditions responsible for this lack of accurate predictions was inherent to aperiodic (nonperiodic) solutions whose characteristics are very different from those observed in periodic or quasi-periodic behaviors. As already noted by Poincaré, aperiodic solutions "*may come close to repeating a previous state, but the histories following the two occurrences do not remain close, except temporarily.*"[33]

This led Lorenz to distinguish three kinds of predictability: i) the *intrinsic predictability* which depends only upon the underlying dynamics as for the chaotic systems, ii) the *attainable predictability* which is also limited by the unavoidable

[32] E. Lorenz, The predictability of hydrodynamic flow, *Transactions of the New York Academy of Sciences*, **25** (4), 409–432, 1963.
[33] Lorenz, 1963, *Ibid.*

inaccuracies in measurement and, iii) the *practical predictability* which is further limited by our present inability to identify the most suitable formulas. In the present meteorology, most likely, better predictions can be achieved by improving the accuracy (in space as well as in time) of measurements. Perhaps, the governing equations could incorporate processes, today neglected, but for sure, the horizon of prediction will remain quite limited because there is an intrinsic sensitivity to initial conditions: this last aspect is the main discovery by Lorenz.

As a consequence of the rapid growth of small errors, the correct trajectory, which corresponds exactly to the initial conditions specified, cannot be calculated. Depending on the numerical precision retained for the calculations, the trajectory computed follows the exact trajectory for longer or shorter times. Under these conditions, it is not possible to calculate the trajectory really observed because the initial conditions are known with a finite precision and the numerical calculations are made using small approximations. It was Rufus Bowen (1947–1978)[34] who offered a solution to this problem by a very surprising mathematical result, known by the name of the "*shadowing lemma*". The shadowing lemma guarantees that the uncertainty in the initial conditions and the round off errors wash out: there is a trajectory, a rigorous solution of the system of equations, that coincides with the numerically computed trajectory to the precision retained in the computation. The two trajectories coincide even for a computer that retains only a few significant figures. We point out that only the rigorous trajectory, guaranteed by the shadowing lemma, is a real solution of the dynamical system (in the mathematical sense of the term): each point in the trajectory is determined from the previous point in the trajectory, without error, by a rigorous mapping determined from the equations that define the system. The important point is that, globally, the numerical trajectory describes an object, the attractor, that is identical to that described by the exact trajectory. From this point of view, the principle benefit of the global analysis is not related at all to better prediction (the core of the scientific problem), but rather to the identification of some invariant structure as the attractor.

Even so, do not forget that in the real world (as opposed to the world of mathematics) every physical system always evolves in the presence of "external gremlins", more or less important, who influence the evolution of the system: physicists call this "noise". This term hides everything that physicists either do not understand or cannot control in their experiments. Due to this, the numerical trajectory retains its importance because it is, in a certain sense, noisy and it describes the evolution of an experimental system that is also noisy. The shadowing lemma assures us that the noisy trajectory is always close to the exact trajectory, so that it is not possible to distinguish the one from the other. This is very close to Poincaré's viewpoint that it is always possible to find a periodic orbit in the neighborhood of an arbitrary

[34] R. Bowen, ω-Limit sets for axiom A diffeomorphisms, *Journal of Differential Equations*, **18**, 333–339, 1975. The shadowing lemma was proposed for discrete maps. Its version for the set of ordinary differential equations was proposed two years later: J. E. Franke & J. F. Selgrade, Hyperbolicity and chain recurrence, *Journal of Differential Equations*, **26**, 27–36, 1977.

trajectory:[35]

> ... we can always find a periodic solution (whose period, it is true, could be very long), such that the difference between the two solutions is as small as you wish, during as long a time as we wish.

3.4 Turbulence, Aperiodic Solutions, and Chaos

Lorenz's results had little impact on the scientific community at the time they were published. At that time *turbulence*, which is a complicated movement of fluids that was observed in a large number of situations (for example, boiling water undergoes turbulent motion) was poorly understood as a phenomenon in fluid motion. The theory that seemed most plausible was due to the independent work of Lev Landau[36] (1908–1968) and Eberhard Hopf[37] (1902–1983). According to this theory, a fluid makes a transition from regular motion, in hydrodynamics this is called "*laminar*", to irregular motion, turbulent, by the appearance of successive degrees of freedom. Recall that each degree of freedom of an integrable system is associated with an oscillator, and corresponds to a sharp characteristic frequency. This theory of turbulence is based on the assumption that a hydrodynamic system could be considered as a set of weakly coupled oscillators (almost integrable system) where each oscillator is associated with a degree of freedom and, as a result, has a characteristic frequency. In this framework, turbulence, the apparently disordered motion of a fluid, results from interactions among a large number of oscillators, which become increasingly strong as the energy in the system increases. For example, if one begins heating a pot of water at a low temperature, then gradually turns up the heat, the energy progressively increases, increasing numbers of oscillators interact with those already interacting, new frequencies appear and the movement becomes progressively more complicated.

Nevertheless, Hopf already knew that such a model did not actually corresponds to the reality, in particular, due to not only Kolmogorov's theory of turbulence,[38] but also the theories due to Carl von Weizsäcker[39] and Werner Heisenberg[40] that already took into account interactions between the different "oscillators" as induced by the viscosity. In the latter theories, there is indeed interactions between the

[35]H. Poincaré, *Méthodes Nouvelles de la mécanique céleste*, Tome I, p. 782, 1892.
[36]L. D. Landau, Sur le problème de la turbulence (in russian), *Doklady Akademii Nauk SSSR*, **44**, 8, 339–342, 1944. See also L. Landau & E. Lifchitz, Fluid Mechanics, *Theoretical Physics*, **6**, MIR Editions, 2nd edition, 1989. Note that these authors used the term turbulence to designate what is now called *chaos*.
[37]E. Hopf, A mathematical example displaying the features of turbulence, *Communications in Pure and Applied Mathematics*, **1**, 303–322, 1948.
[38]A. N. Kolmogorov, The local structure of turbulence in incompressible viscous fluid for very large Reynolds numbers, *Dokladi Akademii Nauk SSSR*, **30** (4), 299–303, 1941. Translated by V. Levin, *Proceedings of the Royal Society of London A*, **493**, 9–13, 1991.
[39]C. von Weizsäcker, Das Spektrum der Turbulenz bei groβen Reynoldsschen Zahlen, *Zeitschrift für Physik*, **124**, 614–627, 1948.
[40]W. Heisenberg, Zur Statischen Theorie der Turbulenz, *Zeitchrift für Physik*, **124**, 628–657, 1948.

different oscillators required for describing the spatial pattern, which are entirely absent in Hopf's theory. Hopf tried a rational theory of statistical hydrodynamics and not a theory based on a "*semi-empirical picture of turbulent fluid motion*" as he presented these other theories. But in order to do this, he had to neglect the interactions due to viscosity.

At the close of the 1960s David Ruelle, of the Institut des Hautes-Études Scientifiques in Bures-sur-Yvette, had many discussions with his mathematical colleague René Thom (1923–2002), creator of the theory of catastrophes, and with Stephen Smale, to whom we owe a fundamental model of chaotic systems, as we shall see in a few pages. As a result of these interactions we find the ideas of Poincaré at the heart of modern developments in the theory of dynamical systems. In this context, it seemed unlikely to Ruelle that a weakly coupled set of "oscillators" could account for the behavior of turbulent fluids. More specifically, it seemed that for viscous fluids different oscillators would have to interact strongly, viscosity (frictional losses) being responsible for this coupling. He therefore tried to take into account, in a rational theory, the interactions neglected by Hopf. Further, he knew that simple equations with few degrees of freedom could produce complicated behavior, as Smale had already shown this. As a result, David Ruelle and Floris Takens, a Dutch mathematician, proposed a new theory for the development of turbulence in 1971.[41]

The essential idea is that because of the nonlinear coupling between oscillators, there is no need for an infinite number of degrees of freedom to obtain complicated behavior (the Lorenz system is a good example). A small number of degrees of freedom is sufficient to produce aperiodic behavior. Ruelle and Takens proposed a scenario according to which four strongly coupled oscillators were sufficient to obtain turbulent behavior. They found attractors whose characteristics were similar to those obtained by Lorenz almost ten years earlier. For the first time the adjective "*chaotic*" was used in a mathematical context to identify motion that was at the same time complicated and deterministic. In 1963 Lorenz entitled his paper "*Deterministic turbulence*", but the editor, Norman Philipps, remarked that his model did not conform to the accepted idea of turbulence at all and the title was replaced by the less explicit title "*Deterministic nonperiodic flows.*" In 1971 Ruelle and Takens identified turbulence with the surprising figures that they found with their mathematical models, and which they called "*strange attractors.*"

3.5 Hydrodynamics and the Lorenz Attractor

In fact, when the Rayleigh-Bénard experiments were carried out, the behaviors observed as the temperature difference ΔT is increased did not correspond at all to those computed with the model — too simplified — of Lorenz. The basic reason is that the approximations made to obtain the Lorenz system are not applicable unless the fluid is at rest (there is no convection in the fluid). In the midst of the

[41]D. Ruelle & F. Takens, On the Nature of turbulence, *Communications in Mathematical Physics*, **20**, 167–192, 1971.

1970s, as the Lorenz system began to be adopted as a description for some types of irregular behavior, an experiment was conceived to correspond to the dynamics described by the Lorenz equations:[42] it was the inverse of the usual procedure. Usually the model is modified to describe the experiment; this time the experiment was designed to suit the model.

The experiment consisted of an annular ring, with internal diameter d, in a vertical orientation (Figure 3.9). The ring has diameter D. A fluid is allowed to circulate within the tube. The liquid is heated by a heating ribbon in the lower half of the tube and cooled by a water cooling jacket in the upper half of the tube. The fluid temperature is measured at two diametrically opposite points in the ring, in the cooled part of the ring (Figure 3.9).

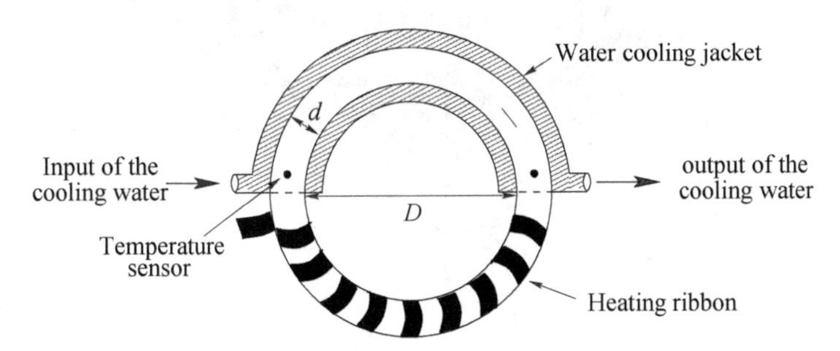

Figure 3.9 Schematic description of the convection experiment in an annular tube. The bottom half is heated with a heating ribbon and the top half is cooled with a water jacket.

Following the procedure used by Lorenz the equations of fluid mechanics (called the Navier-Stokes equations) were reduced to the three ordinary differential equations

$$\begin{cases} \dot{x} = \sigma(y - x) \\ \dot{y} = -y - xz \\ \dot{z} = -z + xy - R \end{cases}$$

where R is the Rayleigh number and σ the Prandtl number.[43] These equations are not exactly similar to those obtained by Lorenz, but the departure does not imply notable changes in the nature of its solution.[44] All the types of behavior observed in the Lorenz system were also found in this model. Further, when these equations are numerically integrated, this system produce trajectories that describe oscillations typical of those of the Lorenz system, that is, they were embedded in an attractor (Figure 3.10) — topologically — equivalent to the attractor produced by the

[42]H. F. Creveling, J. F. de Paz, J. Y. Baladi & R. H. Schoenhals, Stability characteristics of a single thermal convection loop, *Journal of Fluid Mechanics*, **67**, 65–84, 1975.

[43]Y. Wang, J. Singer and H. H. Bau, Controlling chaos in a thermal convection loop, *Journal of Fluid Mechanics*, **237**, 479–498, 1992.

[44]See for instance, C. Letellier, T. Tsankov, G. Byrne & R. Gilmore, Large-scale structural reorganization of strange attractors, *Physical Review E*, **72**, 026212, 2005.

Lorenz system (Figure 3.7). When the temperature difference between the upper and lower part of the annulus (characterized by the Rayleigh number) is varied, the observed dynamics of the fluid corresponds to that predicted by the model. In this context, the dynamics of the Lorenz system corresponds to an experimentally observed dynamics. This result gave his work credibility and provided the widespread recognition that he enjoys today.

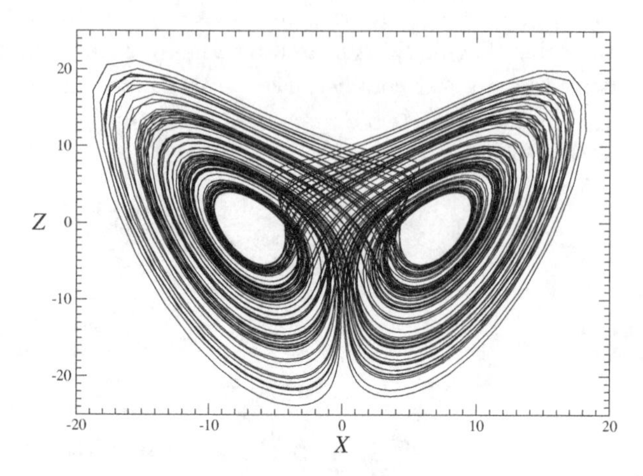

Figure 3.10 Chaotic attractor for the model of convection in the annular ring. This attractor has the same structure as the Lorenz attractor (Figure 3.7). Parameter values: $R = 48$ and $\sigma = 10$.

3.6 Laser Dynamics and the Lorenz System

Laser systems (*Light Amplification by Stimulated Emission of Radiation*) are sources of light that is stimulated, or induced, as opposed to the more usual sources of light — bulbs with incandescent filaments — where the light emission is spontaneous. Lasers are of great interest because they can transmit relatively large energy densities in the form of light.

Every since Niels Bohr (1885–1962) proposed the spectral model in 1913[45] it has been known that electrons surround the nucleus with different energy levels, and one could jump from a level with energy E_2 to a level with energy $E_1 < E_2$ by emitting a photon of energy $h\nu = E_2 - E_1$, where h is Planck's constant and ν the frequency of the emitted photon. As Albert Einstein (1879–1955) showed in 1917,[46] the emission could be either spontaneous or induced (stimulated). In the first case the photon is emitted in an arbitrary direction at any time. *Induced* emission occurs when an atom is subjected to an electromagnetic field — a light wave — with a frequency ν corresponding to the transition $E_2 \to E_1$: the electromagnetic field

[45] N. Bohr, On the Theory of the decreases of velocity of moving electrified particles on passing through matter, *Philosophical Magazine*, **25**, 10–31, 1913.

[46] A. Einstein, Quantentheorie der Strahlung, *Physikalische Zeitschrift*, **38**, 121–128, 1917.

induces a de-excitation of the electron. The photon is emitted with a frequency that is exactly the same as that of the inducing electromagnetic field, with the same phase, and in the same direction. Induced emission therefore corresponds to an amplification of the inducing radiation.

Unfortunately, under the usual temperature conditions, the number N_2 of electrons — in fact, this is the number of excited atoms or ions — in the excited state with energy E_2 is very much smaller than the number N_1 of the nonexcited state with energy E_1. In order for the laser to operate, it is not only necessary that $N_2 > N_1$, but also that the probability of induced emission is greater than the probability of spontaneous emission. The first difficulty to resolve is obtaining a population inversion so that $N_2 > N_1$: it was Alfred Kastler (1902–1984) who first realized this goal by *optical pumping.*[47] This principle is now explained for the case of the red ruby crystal, which we will encounter again below. Ruby is a crystal of alumina (Al_2O_3) in which a small fraction of Al^{3+} ions have been replaced by chromium Cr^{3+} ions, which give it a red hue. It is the Cr^{3+} that allows a population inversion. Green and blue radiation lift the Cr^{3+} ions from the state with energy E_1 to the states with energies E_2 and E_2', which are very close to each other (Figure 3.11). The excited chromium ions very rapidly lose some of their energy through nonradiative transitions — no light is emitted — to fall into a metastable state with energy E_3: the spontaneous emission probability $E_3 \to E_1$ is very small compared to the induced emission probability. In this way energy is lifted by optical pumping, stored in a metastable state, and then transferred to the emitted beam.

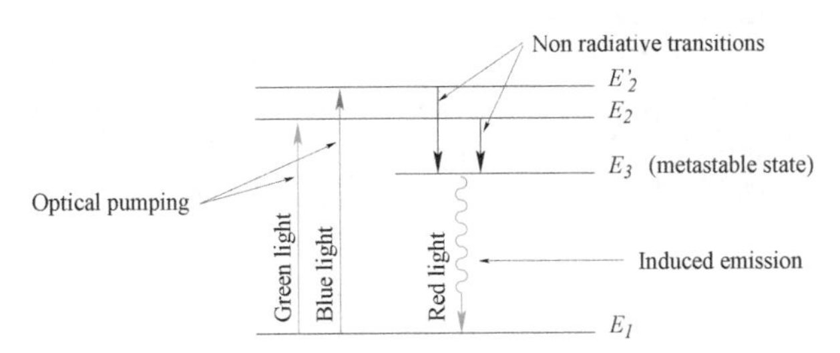

Figure 3.11 Energy level diagram for Cr^{3+} ions. The transition $E_3 \to E_1$ occurs primarily through induced emission because of the long lifetime (order of 10^{-3} s) of the energy level E_3.

Using optical pumping, microwave radiation amplifiers (Maser, with M for microwave) were built. Difficulties remained for building amplifiers in the visible. Two problems needed to be resolved: determining the right operating conditions and finding the right materials to use. The first problem was solved in 1958 by Charles Townes (1915–2015) and Arthur Schawlow (1921–1999) of Columbia

[47]A. Kastler, Quelques suggestions concernant la production optique et la détection optique d'une inégalité de population des niveaux de quantifigation spatiale des atomes. Application à l'expérience de Stern et Gerlach et à la résonance magnétique, *Journal de Physique et du Radium*, **11**, 255–265, 1950 — A. Kastler, Optical methods of atomic orientation and of magnetic resonance, *Journal of the Optical Society of America*, **47** (6), 460–465, 1957.

University: they proposed to place the amplifying material between two highly reflecting mirrors that created a resonant cavity.[48] This made it possible to obtain a beam for which the frequency dispersion has been reduced.[49] Townes and Schawlow suggested that a crystal could be used — specifically a sapphire crystal — to obtain a maser emitting in the visible. Somewhat skeptically, they wrote:

> In a solid there may also be rapid decay by nonradiative processes. If the storage time is long, [...] there is more time for competing processes to occur. Even lines which are sharp for solids are likely to be broader than those obtainable in gases. This larger width makes the attainment of maser oscillation more difficult, and it adds greatly to the difficulty of selecting a single mode [of emission].

On top of this we add the problem of optical pumping. Two years later, in 1960, Theordore Maiman (1927–2007) published a description of a laser working with a ruby crystal.[50] Optical pumping was carried out using lightflashes from a vacuum tube containing a low pressure Xenon, which emits in the green and the blue (Figure 3.12). Weak spontaneous emission served to initiate stimulated emission. The resonant cavity served as a positive feedback loop. Very quickly a pulse of red light was emitted through the weakly transmitting mirror (only a few percent of the reflected light) at one of the ends of the cavity. Since the optical pumping was carried out with a flashlamp the laser did not emit continuously. A continuously operating laser was finally obtained in 1962 by Donald F. Nelson and William S. Boyle who replaced the tube by an arc lamp.[51]

In 1964, we saw that Grasiuk and Oraevsky published a time series quite similar to the evolution of variable x or y of the Lorenz system. They thus showed that instabilities could appear in laser systems. To do this they used the equations

$$\left\{\begin{aligned} \dot{x} &= y \\ \dot{y} &= -y - 2\epsilon(\delta x + h_0 y + 2ku) - 2k\epsilon^2(-2h_2 v - 2h_2(1+w)x) \\ \dot{u} &= v \\ \dot{v} &= -u - 2h_2\epsilon[v + (1+w)x] \\ \dot{w} &= \epsilon[-h_1 w + 2h_2 x(v + h_2\epsilon u)] \end{aligned}\right. \tag{3.4}$$

[48]A. L. Schawlow and C. H. Townes, Infrared and optical masers, *Physical Review*, **112**, 1940–1949, 1958.

[49]The suggestion concerning the two mirrors was also proposed by Aleksandr M. Prokhorov, (1916–2002), Molecular amplifier and generator for submillimeter waves, *Journal of Experimental and Theoretical Physics*, **34**, 1658–1659, 1958 and by Robert H. Dicke (1916–1997), Molecular amplification and generation systems and methods, U.S. Patent 2,851,652 on September 9, 1958. Prokhorov shared the Nobel prize with Townes and Schawlow in 1964.

[50]T. H. Maiman, Stimulated Optical Radiation in ruby, *Nature*, **187** (4736), 493–494, 1960, and Optical and microwave-optical experiments in ruby, *Physical Review Letters*, **4**, 564–566, 1960.

[51]D. F. Nelson and W. S. Boyle, A continuously operating ruby optical maser, *Journal of Applied Optics*, **1** (2), 181–183, 1962.

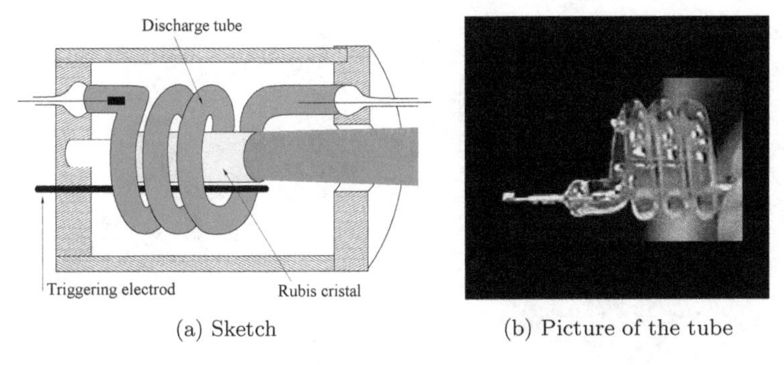

(a) Sketch (b) Picture of the tube

Figure 3.12 Laser cavity with ruby crystal and Xenon flash tube.

where x is the electric field, u the polarization and w the population inversion due to the pump process. These equations correspond to a model for dipole-dipole interaction between the quantum oscillators in an active material and an electromagnetic field. They numerically integrated the differential equations that they found: the evolution of the electric field (Figure 3.3(c)) that they obtained revealed an astonishing similarity with the evolution of the x variable of the Lorenz system (Figure 3.3(b)).

Grasiuk and Oraevsky designated evolution as a "periodic modulation of the amplitude which can be named *automodulation*". But their objective was to explain the pulsing mode of the ruby laser. Too focused on their objective — to explain the pulses observed in these lasers — they did not realize the importance of the aperiodic behavior of their solution. If they had plotted the time evolution of their lasers in state space, as had Lorenz, they would have obtained a figure (Figure 3.13) resembling that previously obtained by him.

The analogy between the Lorenz system and the laser system was not established until 1975 when the Lorenz system became better known: we owe this to Hermann Haken who attended the congress where the work of Grasiuk and Oraevsky was presented.[52] Beginning with the Maxwell-Bloch equations, and under certain conditions, Haken was able to exactly derive some equations producing a Lorenz attractor. In order to do this, he started from the equations governing the laser field propagating in x direction which read[53]

$$\left\{ \begin{array}{l} \dot{E} = \kappa P - \kappa E - c\dfrac{\partial E}{\partial x} \\ \dot{D} = \gamma_{\|}(\lambda + 1) - \gamma_{\|} D - \gamma_{\|}\lambda E P \\ \dot{P} = -\gamma P + \gamma E D \end{array} \right. \tag{3.5}$$

[52]Haken presented a contribution entitled *Theory of laser action in solid-state, gaseous and semiconductor systems*, with H. Sauermann, in *Quantum Electronics and Coherent Light*, Ed. P. A. Miles, Academic Press, New York, 1964, p. 111.

[53]H. Haken, Analogy between higher instabilities in fluids and laser, *Physics Letters A*, **53**, 77–78, 1975.

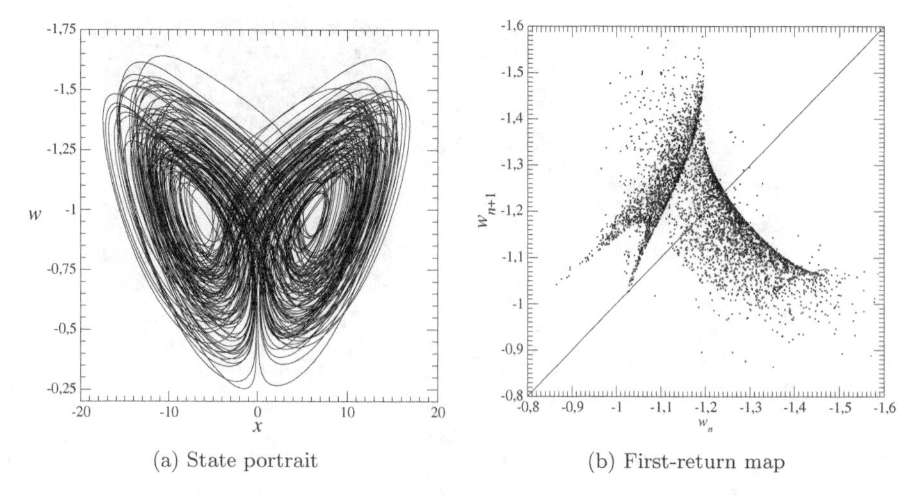

(a) State portrait (b) First-return map

Figure 3.13 Chaotic behavior produced by the system (3.4) proposed by Grasiuk and Oraevsky. The general resemblance to that of the Lorenz system is clear. Parameter values: $h_0 = 5$, $h_1 = 2$, $h_2 = 0.595$, $k = 155$, $\epsilon = 2.5$ and $\delta = 0,192$. The parameter values used by Grasiuk and Oraevskij were not those given in their paper. A random search for the values providing a Lorenz-like attractor is quite difficult because there are six parameters to find.

where E is the electromagnetic field, P the polarisation and D the inversion. Parameter κ is the cavity loss, γ the linedwidth, $\gamma_{||}$ the inverse longitudinal relaxation time, and $\lambda = \frac{D_0 - D_c}{D_c}$ where D_0 is the unsaturated inversion. D_c is the critical inversion for getting the laser phenomenon. If the partial derivative $\frac{\partial E}{\partial x}$ is vanished, the system is reduced to a single mode laser. Using the coordinate transformation

$$\begin{cases} E \mapsto \alpha x \\ P \mapsto \alpha y \\ D \mapsto z \\ t \mapsto \frac{\sigma}{\kappa} t' \end{cases}$$

where $\alpha = \frac{1}{\sqrt{b(R-1)}}$ and the parameter transformation

$$\begin{cases} \gamma_{||} \mapsto \dfrac{\kappa b}{\sigma} \\ \gamma \mapsto \dfrac{\kappa}{\sigma} \\ \lambda \mapsto R - 1\,, \end{cases}$$

the set of three equations

$$\begin{cases} \dot{x} = \sigma(y - x) \\ \dot{y} = -y + xz \\ \dot{z} = bR - bz - xy \end{cases} \tag{3.6}$$

is obtained. This is not exactly the same system as the Lorenz system (3.3). This is in fact, another set of equations which belongs to the class of Lorenz-like systems. Using the same parameter values as for the Lorenz system (3.3), an attractor, topologically equivalent to the Lorenz attractor, is obtained (Figure 3.14).

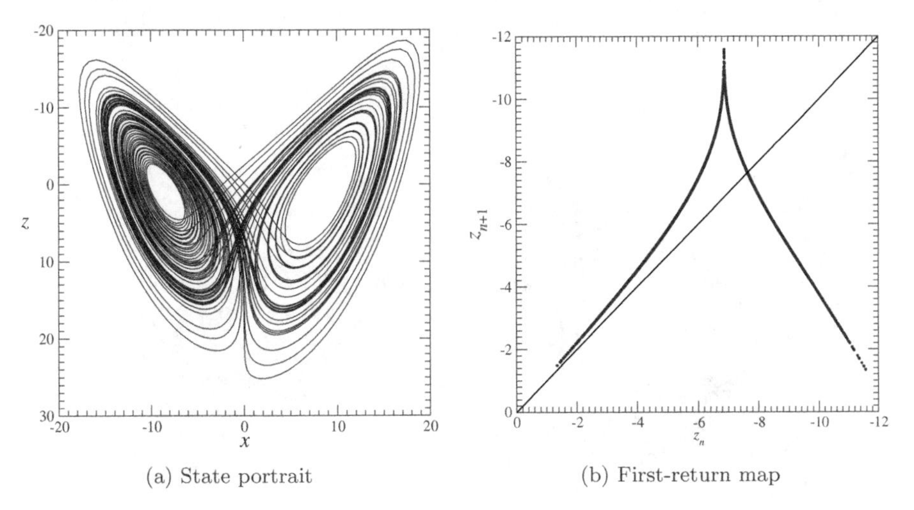

(a) State portrait (b) First-return map

Figure 3.14 Chaotic attractor produced by the Haken system (3.6). Parameter values: $R = 28$, $\sigma = 10$ and $b = 8/3$.

The experimental development of a laser with Lorenz dynamics was finally realized 1986 by Carl O. Weiss and J. Brock.[54] Their laser used a gas, ammonia (NH_3). The variable measured was the light intensity, which is related to the electric field strength. It is possible to compare the experimental data[55] with the model (Figure 3.15). The most striking feature is the first return map which presents the maximum as a cusp, very characteristic of the Lorenz system. The foliated structure of this map results from a slight symmetry breaking in the experimental system. With all of these experimental confirmations, the Lorenz system became a reference model for demonstrating the possibility of chaotic behavior in real physical systems.

3.7 Conclusion

The Lorenz system with its very suggestive attractor became the most quoted ones from chaos theory. The fact that it was used by Ruelle as providing a good example of his own "*strange attractor*" contributed to that popularity. Lorenz was a meteorologist and, too often, it is believed that the Lorenz system is a model for

[54] C. O. Weiss & J. Brock, Evidence for Lorenz-type chaos in a laser, *Physical Review Letters*, **57**, 2804–2806, 1984.

[55] The data are issued from Dingyuan Tang's Ph.D. thesis — *Chaotische Amplituden- und Phasendynamik des optisch angeregten NH_3 Einmodenringlasers und Vergleich mit den reellen und komplexen Lorenz-Gleichangen*, Hannover University, 1993 — and were kindly provided by C. Weiss.

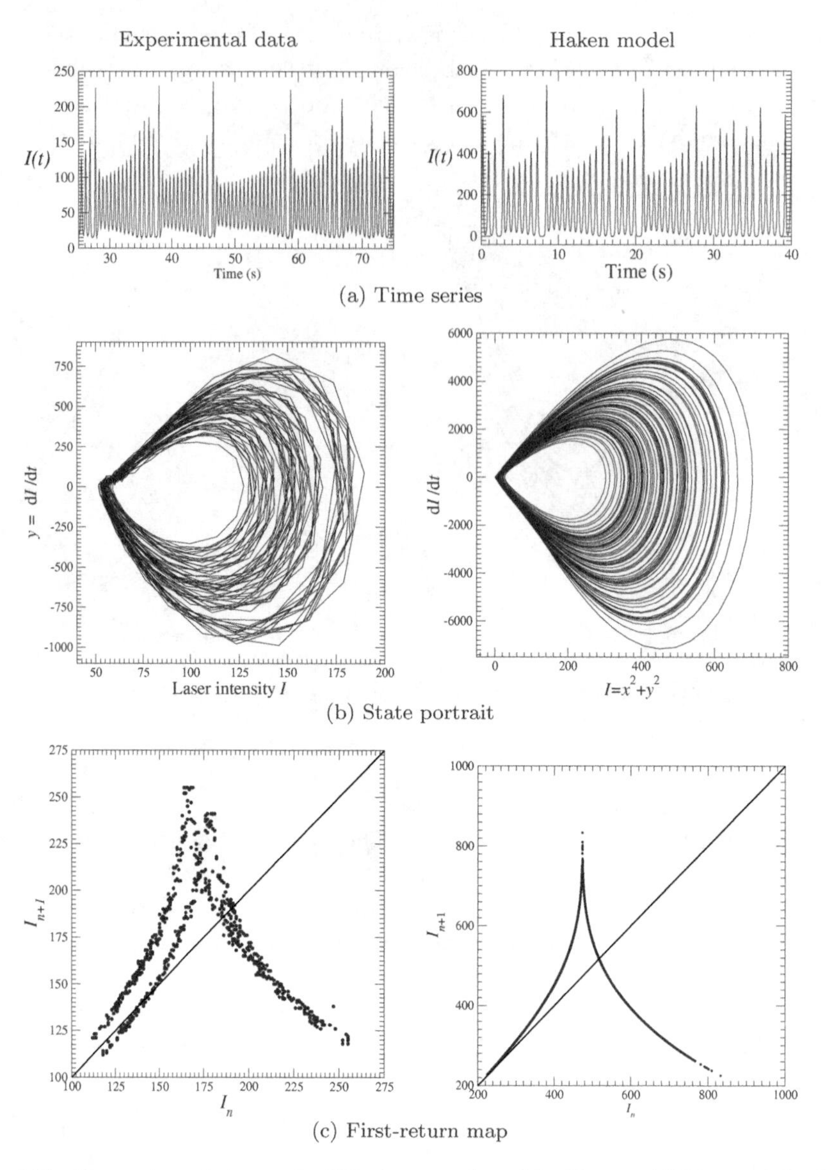

Figure 3.15 Comparisons between the NH_3 laser conducted by Tang and Weiss, and the Haken model (3.6). The laser has a pump intensity of 6 W/cm^2, a gas pressure of 10 Pa and a pump frequency of 20 MHz. Parameter values used for integrating the Haken model: $R = 25$, $\sigma = 10$ and $b = 8/3$.

weather prediction: it is not! This is a very simplified model for the Rayleigh-Bénard convection. Lorenz knew that the problem of weather forecasting can be identified with the problem of solving the governing dynamical equations: this was already the approach considered in 1904 by Vilhelm Bjerknes (1862–1951).[56] Thus Lorenz used the great sensitivity to initial conditions observed in his model for supporting the short-term predictability of weather conditions. He used this understanding to extrapolate that it would not be possible to predict "*with any confidence what the phase of the sunspot cycle will be 100 years from now*", because "*the cumulative effect of the approximations becomes more and more dominant.*"[57]

Moreover, Lorenz insisted on the fact that there is no tendency to recurrences of certain typical features in the variables of a twelve-dimensional meteorological model. He investigated how he was able to forecast the evolution of the system depending on the errors in initial conditions: he observed that, when the behavior is non-periodic, small errors were growing rapidly. These small errors were sufficient to prevent any reliable forecasting for more than two or three days. He thus concluded that "*if the theory were correct, one flap of a sea gull's wings would be enough to alter the cause of the weather forever.*"[58]

Among the possible sources of failure in providing "perfect" weather forecasts, Lorenz thought that the human activity was affecting the atmosphere and, assuming that human behavior is not deterministic, at some point, the atmospheric behavior is not deterministic too. Nevertheless, "*such a lack of determinism is not a significant contributing cause to our present failures in forecasting.*"[59] This lack of observations about the present (and past) state of the atmosphere combined with a nonperiodic component (chaos) necessarily leads to "*poorer and poorer forecasts as the range of prediction increases.*"

The evolution of small uncertainties was one of the key features investigated in Lorenz's works. At the 139th meeting of the American Association for the Advancement of Science (December 29, 1972), Lorenz gave a talk entitled "*Predictability: does the flap of a butterfly's wings in Brazil set off a tornado in Texas?*" This title focussed the attention on this very suggestive picture that a small butterfly could provoke a tornado: arbitrarily small causes could induce large scale and powerful events! This is not true, of course, and this was clarified in Lorenz's talk since he explained that "*over the years minuscule disturbances neither increase nor decrease the frequency of occurrence of various weather events such as tornados; the most that they may do is to modify the sequence in which these events occur.*"[60] Moreover

[56] V. Bjerknes, Das Problem der Wettervorhersage, betrachtet vom Standpunkte der Mechanik und der Physik, *Meteorologische Zeitschrift*, **21**, 1–7, 1904 — English translation by Esther Volken and Stefan Brönnimann, The problem of weather prediction, considered from the viewpoints of mechanics and physics, *Meteorologische Zeitschrift*, **18**, 663–667, 2009.

[57] E. N. Lorenz, The predictability of hydrodynamic flow, *Transactions of the New York Academy of Sciences*, **25**, 409–432, 1963.

[58] E. N. Lorenz, 1963, (*Ibid.*)

[59] E. N. Lorenz, A study of the predictability of a 28-variable atmospheric model, *Tellus*, **17**, 321–333, 1965.

[60] E. N. Lorenz, Predictability: Does the flap of a butterfly's wings in Brazil set off a tornado in Texas?, Talk presented on December 29, 1972, for the American Association for the Advancement of Science Section on Environmental Sciences, New Approaches to Global Weather, Sheraton Park Plaza Hotel (Boston, Massachusetts), 1972.

this would not be the result of the single flap of butterfly's wings but rather the flaps of millions of butterflies, "*not to mention the activities of innumerable more powerful creatures, including our own species.*" He also added that "*the influence of a single butterfly is not only a fine detail, it is confined to a small volume.*" Moreover, and this is in agreement with all his theoretical studies, "*the influence of butterfly's wings will spread in turbulent air, but not in calm air.*" In other words, behaviors are sensitive to initial conditions only when there are nonperiodic: chaos or turbulence is required for such a dependency to small causes. The "butterfly effect" is therefore a powerful picture to stimulate imagination but has some strong limitations.

Lorenz ended his talk with the still valid advise as follows.

> *Today's errors in weather forecasting cannot be blamed entirely nor even primarily upon the finer structure of weather patterns. They arise mainly from our failure to observe even the coarser structure with near completeness, our somewhat incomplete knowledge of the governing physical principles, and the inevitable approximations which must be introduced in formulating these principles as procedures which the human brain or the computer can carry out.*

Today, global warming becomes a major concern. For sure, I would not argue against the fact that humans are polluting the Earth at a level for which its equilibrium is strongly in danger, if we did not already pass the point of no return.[61] Concerning the climate, Lorenz claimed that "*climate is not universally identified with averages over infinite time intervals.*"[62] If we use the expression "*change of climate*", this is due to our use of "*averages over long but finite time intervals.*" Lorenz even asserted that "*there is no* a priori *reason why a climate need exist*, then explaining how the weather changed over the milleniums.

[61]See for instance the 1992 *World Scientists' Warning to Humanity.*

[62]E. N. Lorenz, The problem of deducing the climate from the governing equations, *Tellus*, **16**, 1–11, 1964.

Chapter 4

The Architecture of Chaotic Attractors

With the studies of Lorenz, Ruelle and Ueda it began to be appreciated that a set of simple differential equations could produce chaotic behavior: at the same time this type of behavior began to be discovered in several very simple systems starting to the late 1970s. However, in order to become a real scientific discipline, it was necessary to identify the invariant structures underlying chaotic attractors. For dissipative systems there were several ideas that allowed a discussion of the architecture of chaotic behavior. To identify them, it was useful to study a system as simple as possible in order to identify in detail the ingredients that were necessary to produce chaotic behavior. This chapter is somewhat more technical than the previous chapters. Even read rapidly, it will give an idea of the concepts that are used to characterize chaos. The reader will note, however, that (s)he can read most of this book without mastering the contents of this chapter.[1]

4.1 The Rössler System

4.1.1 *A Brief Biography*

Otto E. Rössler was born in 1940. His father, Otto Rössler (1907–1991), was a linguist recognized for having introduced a new system of Egypto-Semitic consonant correspondences and the term "Afro-semitic" languages. Strongly impressed by the "open mind" of his father and his religious mother, Otto E. tried to find his own way. As an adolescent, he built his own radio-transmitter and thus got acquainted with electronics while still in highschool at Tübingen. In 1957, he got an individual licence (DL9 KF) from the Deutscher Amateur Radio Club. He then studied medicine up to 1966 at the University of Tübingen. In 1966, he defended his inaugural dissertation — supervised by Erich Letterer (1895–1982) — for getting his grade of doctor in medicine.[2] Deeply interested how the Life could come from

[1]The first part of this chapter was initially published as C. Letellier & V. Messager, Influences on Otto E. Rössler's earliest paper on chaos, *International Journal of Bifurcation & Chaos*, **20** (11), 3585–3616, 2010.

[2]O. E. Rössler, *Dauerimmunisierung von Albinomäusen mit Rinder-γ-Globulin* [Long-term Immunization of Albino Mice with Bovine-γ-Globulin], University of Tübingen, 1966.

a "*chemical soup*", he exchanged letters with Carl-Friedrich von Weizsäcker (1912–2007) and met him. Under his recommendation, he spent one year (1966–1967) at the Max-Planck Institute for the Physiology of Behavior (SeeWiesen) supervised by Konrad Lorenz (1903–1989) and Erich von Holst (1908–1962). Otto then spent two years at the University of Marburg where he was a medical assistant under the supervision of Reimara Waible who became his wife, one year later. During that period, Otto wrote — in German — a first paper entitled "Contributions to the theory of spontaneously evolving systems I: a simple model class" to the *Journal of Theoretical Biology.* The editor, Robert Rosen (1934–1998), who was reading German, accepted the paper for publication but required a translation in English. Not yet fluent in English, Otto never made it and the paper remained unpublished. Interested enough by this first paper, Rosen retained Otto's application for a one-year position at the Center of Theoretical Biology (State University of New York at Buffalo). At this center, a very stimulating atmosphere was present, as Vahe Bedian reported from one of his stays (slightly after Rössler visited):[3]

> In the early 1970s, the temporary Ridge Lea campus of SUNY/Buffalo was home to the Center for Theoretical Biology and the Department of Biophysical Sciences, where I was a graduate student. It was a stimulating and supportive place to think and learn from some of the best in the field: Robert Rosen, Fred Snell, Robert Spangler, Robert Rein and Howard Pattee. In front of chalkboards and in the hallways, we discussed everything from the uncertainty principle, to von Neumann's automata, to neural networks, to Stuart Kauffman's binary switch networks, to the complexity of quantum mechanical computations.

Bedian also mentioned that Spangler was the one to go "*beyond iterative simulations* [to] *formalize the model as a non-linear dynamical system.*" This is exactly what Spangler and Snell did with the oscillating chemical reaction they simulated in 1961 with a digital computer[4] and in 1967 with an analog computer.[5] In the latter, they showed few periodic oscillations and a state portrait of a limit cycle, which they identified with the synonymous concept in the textbook *Nonlinear Oscillations* published in 1962 by Minorsky. Although Rössler did not meet Spangler and Snell during his stay, he later quoted their 1967 paper in 1975. Rössler started to investigate some differential equations during his stay at Buffalo.

Friedrich-Franz Seelig who had a chair ("Lehrstuhl") for Theoretical Chemistry at the University of Tübingen offered Otto to join his new group with a stipend from the Deutsche Forschungsgemeinschaft (DFG). In the early 60s, Seelig had done his diploma work with Hans Kuhn and Fritz-Peter Schäfer to build an analog computer consisting of a network of electrical oscillators, connected to capacitors to solve the

[3]V. Bedian, Self-description and the origin of the genetic code, *Biosystems* **60**, 39–47, 2001.

[4]R. A. Spangler & F. M. Snell, Sustained oscillations in a catalytic chemical system, *Nature*, **191**, 457–458, 1961.

[5]R. A. Spangler & F. M. Snell, Transfer function analysis of an oscillatory model chemical system, *Journal of Theoretical Biology*, **16**, 381–405, 1967.

two-dimensional Schrödinger equation.[6] This system was excited by means of a radio frequency generator. In 1965, Seelig solved a two-dimensional Schrödinger equation with a digital computer (IBM 7090).[7] Rössler had met Seelig via Hans Kuhn who was working on the origin of Life, Otto's first research topic. Kuhn handed down Rössler to Seelig as it were. Sharing an interest for the origin of Life, in differential equations and electronics (computers), they agreed that nonlinear systems like Otto's evolutionary soup and electronic systems (without self-induction and without coupling condensers) were virtually isomorphic. This triggered a cooperation project between Seelig — a quantum chemist — and Rössler — a medical physiologist — to look for reaction-kinetic analogs to electronic circuits.

Rössler joined Seelig at Tübingen returning from Buffalo in 1970. After having been sent by the Division of Theoretical Chemistry to attend an Enterprise Application Integration course on analog computing, he had to teach that topic, for which his radio-amateur past was useful. With the founding money obtained with his new position at Tübingen, Seelig bought (with 80 000 DM) an analog computer — a Dornier DO 240 (Figure 4.1) — equipped with digital potentiometers, a digital clock and two function generators... With this computer, Seelig obtained limit cycles — plotted in state space — with computer simulation of a linear chemical model[8] and of a model for a spike oscillator.[9] As a Stipend-holder" of the DFG Rössler was free in his research and started to study few-variable systems with Seelig. He started by investigating a chemical multivibrator,[10] that is, a chemical equivalent to the electronic circuit developed by Henri Abraham (1868–1943) and Eugène Bloch (1878–1944).[11] To learn about the dynamics of such an electronic circuit, he read the textbook by Andronov, Khaikin and Witt in its 1966 English edition.

Inspired by a little book entitled " *Measuring-signal generators, Frequency Measuring Devices and Multivibrators* from the Radio-Amateur Library,[12] Rössler and Seelig began to "translate" electronic systems into nonlinear chemical reaction systems (among them the RC-oscillator shown in Figure 44 of that book as shown in Figure 4.2). Morphogenetic reaction systems, devised by Nicolas Rashevsky

[6]F. F. Seelig, W. Huber & H. Kuhn, Analogiebetrachtungen und Analogrechner zur Behandlung der Korrelation von Elektronen, *Zeitschrift für Naturforschung A*, **17**, 114–121, 1962.

[7]F. F. Seelig, Numerical solution of 2- and 3-dimensional Schrödinger equations for any molecular potential by iterative variation of numerical test functions with a digital computer — I. Theoretical principles: description of a computer program for solution of 2-dimensional Schrödinger equation, *Zeitschrift für Naturforschung A*, **20**, 416–427, 1965.

[8]F. F. Seelig, Activated enzyme catalysis as a possible realization of the stable linear chemical oscillator model, *Journal of Theoretical Biology*, **30**, 497–514, 1971.

[9]H. R. Karfunkel & F. F. Seelig, Reversal of inhibition of enzymes and the model of a spike oscillator, *Journal of Theoretical Biology*, **36** pp. 237–253, 1972.

[10]O. E. Rössler, Basic circuits of fluid automata and relaxation systems, *Zeitschrift für Naturfoschung B*, **27**, 333–343, 1972.

[11]H. Abraham and E. Bloch, Mesure en valeur absolue des périodes des oscillations électriques de haute fréquence, *Annales de Physique*, **9** (1), 237–302, 1919.

[12]H. Sutaner, *Meßender Frequenzmesser und Multivibratoren*, Radio-Praktiker Bucherei **128/130** (Franzis Verlag, Munich), 1966.

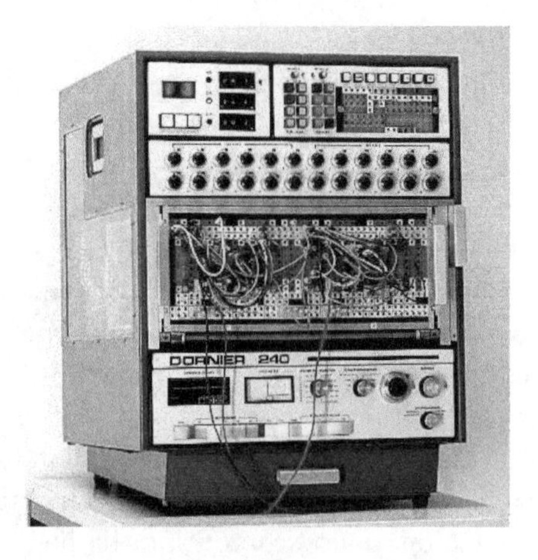

Figure 4.1 Analog computer Dornier DO 240 as bought by Seelig in 1970.

(1899–1972)[13] and Alan Turing (1912–1954),[14] fitted in, enabling the design of a chemical oscillator based on a chemical flip-flop, that is, a bistable multivibrator that has two stable states in a subsystem and hence can be used as one bit of memory. The latter had been invented by William Eccles (1875–1966) and Franck Jordan.[15] Rössler remained fascinated by the multivibrator[16] and the electronic Eccles-Jordan trigger as he called it in.[17] This had led to the "flip-flop" studied with Seelig. Rössler necessarily associated the multivibrator with the universal circuit introduced by Khaikin[18] and its description in state space as in Andronov and coworkers' book. Most of Rössler's early papers — say between 1972 and 1975 — were devoted to chemical reactions that reproduce the dynamics underlying some electronic circuits, and many of them explicitly discussed the multivibrator. In 1972, with Dietrich Hoffmann, Rössler provided "*a first evidence that the Belousov-Zhabotinsky reaction is a Bonhoeffer oscillator, that is, a special type of chemical hysteresis oscillators.*"[19] A link was explicitly made with relaxation oscillations as done by Bonhoeffer in 1948 when he investigated a model for the excitation of

[13] N. Rashevsky, An approach to the mathematical biophysics of biological self-organization and a cell polarity, *Bulletin in Mathematical Biophysics*, **2**, 65–67, 1940.
[14] A. M. Turing, The chemical basis of morphogenesis, *Philosophical Transactions of the Royal Society B*, **237**, 37–72, 1952.
[15] W. H. Eccles & F. W. Jordan, *Improvements in ionic relays*, British patent number: GB 148582, (filed June 21, 1918 and published August 5, 1920) — W. H. Eccles & F. W. Jordan? Sustaining the vibration of a tuning fork by a triode valve, *The Electrician* **82** p. 704, 1919.
[16] O. E. Rössler, A multivibrating switching network in homogeneous kinetics, *Bulletin of Mathematical Biology*, **37**, 181–192, 1975.
[17] O. E. Rössler, Chemical automata in homogeneous and reaction-diffusion kinetics, *Lecture Notes in Biomathematics*, **4**, 399–418, 1974.
[18] S. E. Khaikin, Continuous and discontinuous oscillations, *Zhurnal Prikladnoi Fiziki*, **7**, 21, 1930.
[19] O. E. Rössler & D. Hoffmann, Repetitive hard bifurcation in a homogeneous reaction system, in *Analysis and Simulations of Biochemical Systems*, H. C. Hemkers & B. Hess (Ed.), Proceedings of the 8th FEBS-Meeting (Amsterdam, North-Holland), pp. 91–102, 1972.

nerves.[20] Rössler was exactly in the spirit of Bonhöffer's works, trying analogies between physiological or chemical problems and electronic circuits.

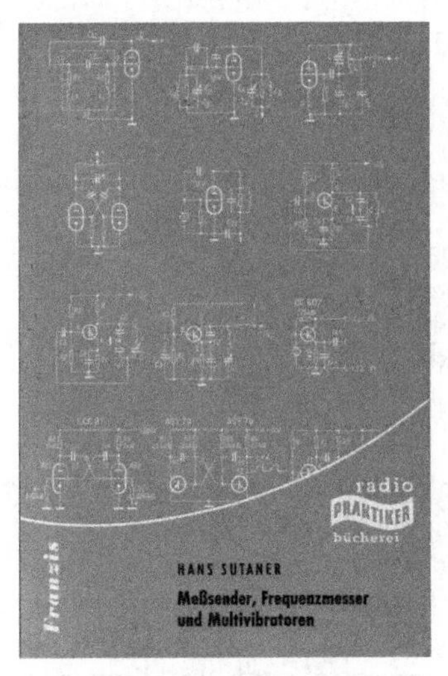

(a) Cover of Hans Sutaner's book published in 1966

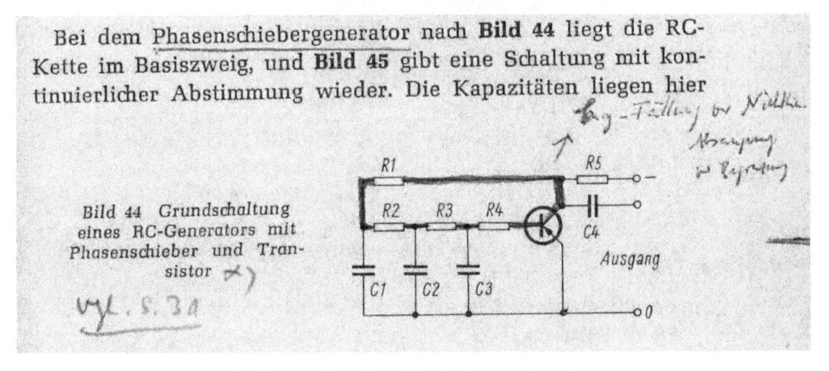

Bei dem Phasenschiebergenerator nach **Bild 44** liegt die RC-Kette im Basiszweig, und **Bild 45** gibt eine Schaltung mit kontinuierlicher Abstimmung wieder. Die Kapazitäten liegen hier

Bild 44 Grundschaltung eines RC-Generators mit Phasenschieber und Transistor

(b) Figure 44 with Rössler's hand writings

Figure 4.2 Scheme of the basic circuit of an RC-oscillator with phase shifter as investigated by Rössler and Seelig.

In this vein, Rössler and Seelig proposed in 1972 a two-cellular homogeneous chemical multivibrator described by the set of three ordinary differential equations

$$\left\{ \begin{aligned} \dot{A} &= -k_2 A - k_3 B \frac{A}{K+A} + k_1 + k_6 C \\ \dot{B} &= -k_2 B - k_3 A \frac{B}{K+B} + k_1 + \beta_B \\ \dot{C} &= k_4 B - k_5 C \end{aligned} \right. \tag{4.1}$$

[20] See p. 117.

which was found on the analog computer by Otto: it is an homogeneous system involving a two-variable bistable system (switch). This system is still quoted as one of the very first chemical reaction system designed to implement logic circuits.[21] Computer output of this abstract chemical reaction was compared to an electronic multivibrating device discussed by Chrilian.[22] Then starting to investigate the subsystem A-B by replacing term k_6C in the first equation with a constant term β_A, Rössler commented in the paper submitted in 1971 (but only published in 1975):

> The equations of this partial system are well-known in electronics where they apply to the usual symmetrical RS flip-flop: the so-called Eccles-Jordan trigger; only the nonlinear terms [...] are normally replaced by a more generally formulated class of functions (see Andronov *et al.*, p. 309, Eq. (5.61)). However, the very system [A-B] is obtained, even in the electronic case, if n-channel field-effect transistors are employed as the active elements.
>
> If the standard analytical techniques used in electronics (Andronov *et al.*, p. 310) are applied to the present special case, it is again found (a) that either equation, when set equal to zero, yields a curved nullcline; (b) that both nullclines intersect each other in either 1 or 3 steady states; (c) that the intermediate steady state is a saddle-point and the other ones (or the remaining one, respectively) are stable nodes; and (d) that the presence of additional limit sets (limit cycles) is excluded.

It is thus clear that Rössler was deeply influenced by the contribution of Andronov's group. This not only framed his early studies on chemical reactions but also his first studies on chaos as we will show in this paper.

4.1.2 *Rössler's Main Influences*

According to an abstract submitted on December 1st, 1975 for the 1976 *Biological Society Meeting* (Figure 4.3), inspiring influences for Rössler were i) Lorenz's 1963 paper, ii) Li-Yorke theorem and iii) a paper by Khaikin about the universal circuit. But let us follow the chronology.

As mentioned in the short biography, Rössler was consequently quite acquainted with electronics. Since he was also attracted by dynamical systems (to which he was acquainted during his stay at Buffalo), the textbook by Andronov, Khaikin and Witt became one of his favorite books in the early 1970s. Indeed as soon as he realized that equations for describing life would be too complicated as an exclusive object of research, he concentrated his interest on the basic chemical elements that could be used to build complex chemical reactions. The very first elementary circuit he investigated was a two-variable multivibrator as investigated by Abraham and Bloch. In fact, according to Andronov himself,[23] the Russian scientist and his

[21] K.-P. Zauner, Molecular information technology, *Critical Reviews in Solid State and Material Sciences*, **30**, 33–69, 2005.

[22] P. M. Chrilian, *Electronic Circuits: Physical Principles, Analysis and Design*, McGraw-Hill (New York), 1971.

[23] A. Pechenkin, The concept of self-oscillations and the rise of synergetics ideas in the theory of nonlinear oscillations, *Studies in History and Philosophy of Modern Physics*, **33** 269–295, 2002.

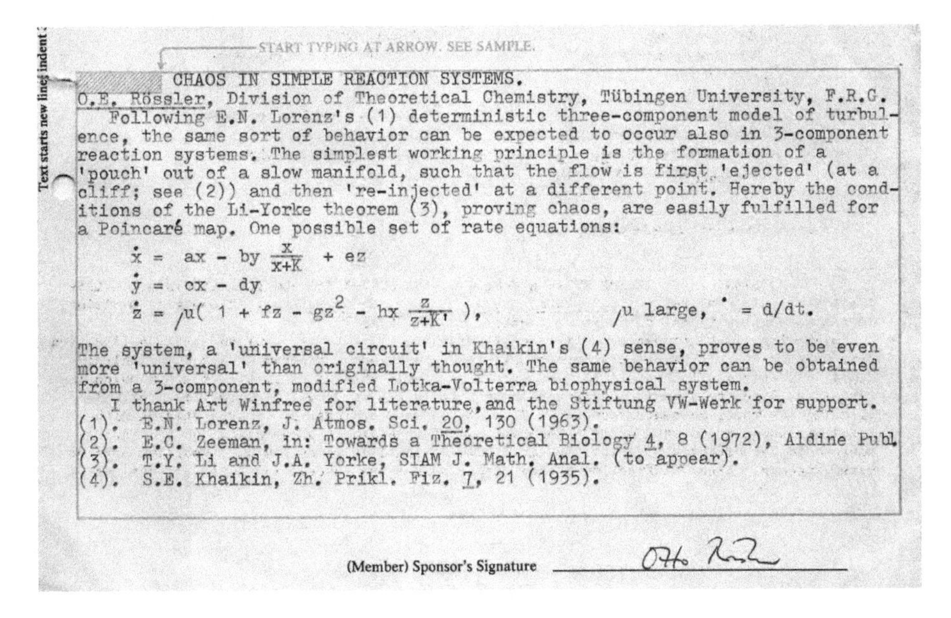

START TYPING AT ARROW. SEE SAMPLE.

Text starts new line; indent

CHAOS IN SIMPLE REACTION SYSTEMS.
O.E. Rössler, Division of Theoretical Chemistry, Tübingen University, F.R.G.
Following E.N. Lorenz's (1) deterministic three-component model of turbulence, the same sort of behavior can be expected to occur also in 3-component reaction systems. The simplest working principle is the formation of a 'pouch' out of a slow manifold, such that the flow is first 'ejected' (at a cliff; see (2)) and then 're-injected' at a different point. Hereby the conditions of the Li-Yorke theorem (3), proving chaos, are easily fulfilled for a Poincaré map. One possible set of rate equations:

$$\dot{x} = ax - by \frac{x}{x+K} + ez$$
$$\dot{y} = cx - dy$$
$$\dot{z} = \mu\left(1 + fz - gz^2 - hx \frac{z}{z+K'}\right), \qquad \mu \text{ large}, \quad \dot{} = d/dt.$$

The system, a 'universal circuit' in Khaikin's (4) sense, proves to be even more 'universal' than originally thought. The same behavior can be obtained from a 3-component, modified Lotka-Volterra biophysical system.
I thank Art Winfree for literature, and the Stiftung VW-Werk for support.
(1). E.N. Lorenz, J. Atmos. Sci. 20, 130 (1963).
(2). E.C. Zeeman, in: Towards a Theoretical Biology 4, 8 (1972), Aldine Publ.
(3). T.Y. Li and J.A. Yorke, SIAM J. Math. Anal. (to appear).
(4). S.E. Khaikin, Zh. Prikl. Fiz. 7, 21 (1935).

(Member) Sponsor's Signature

Figure 4.3 Abstract submitted by Otto E. Rössler on December 1st, 1975 for the Biological Society Meeting planned for 1976.

co-workers started to investigate the multivibrator in 1929. They quickly focussed their interest on an intermediary circuit between a double RC circuit and a multivibrator. This so-called *universal circuit* — a circuit as simple as possible with a wide variety of behaviors — was described in Andronov's book by the three differential equations

$$\left\{\begin{array}{l} \mu\dot{u} = E_a - Ri_a(u) - \left(1 + \dfrac{R}{R_1}\right)u + (1-\beta)\dfrac{R}{R_1}z - v_1 \\ \dot{v}_1 = z \\ \dot{z} = \dfrac{C_1}{\beta(1-\beta)C_2}u - \left(1 + \dfrac{C_1}{\beta C_2}\right)\dfrac{z}{1-\beta} \end{array}\right. \tag{4.2}$$

where $\mu = \frac{RC_{\rm a}}{R_2C}$ and $i_a(u)$ corresponds to the current-voltage characteristic of the pair of Audions, u being the potential measured at one of these two triodes (Figure 4.4). Potential v_1 is measured at condenser C_1 located between the two Audions. Condenser $C_{\rm a}$ is a small capacitance such as $C_{\rm a} \ll C_1, C_2$. When this condition holds, $z = R_2i_1$ and is equal to the derivative $\dot{v}_1$ of the potential v_1. This universal circuit is an intermediate between a two-mesh RC circuit ($\beta = \frac{R_1}{R_2} = 0$) and a multivibrator with one RC circuit ($\beta = 1$). Varying β via the potentiometer allows to change from continuous to discontinuous oscillations.

The universal circuit thus requires three variables to describe its motion in a state space (Figure 4.5). This is one of the most important methodological breakthroughs introduced by Andronov and co-workers. They described the trajectory drawn in the three-dimensional space spanned by the three variables u, z and v_1 as follows.

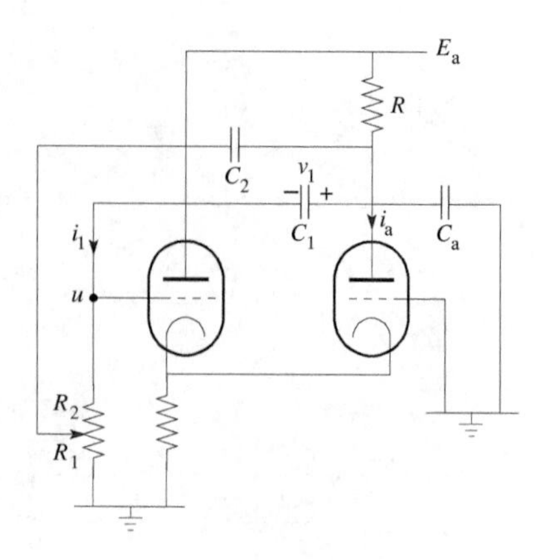

Figure 4.4 The universal circuit as investigated by Andronov's school. It is an intermediate circuit between a generator with two RC-oscillators ($\beta = \frac{R_1}{R_2} = 0$) and a multivibrator with one RC-oscillator ($\beta = \frac{R_1}{R_2} = 1$). Adapted from Andronov *et al.*, 1966.

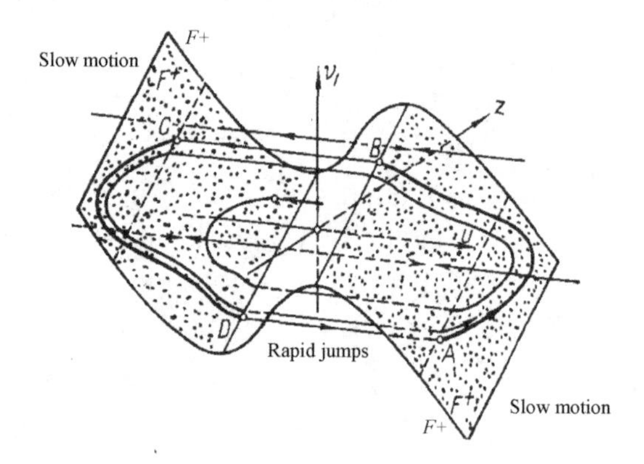

Figure 4.5 Sketch used by Andronov and his co-workers to describe the trajectory produced by the universal circuit. What is noticeable is that they used a qualitative description in a three-dimensional state space. The trajectory is organized around the "S"-shaped surface F where slow and fast motions are distinguished, the slow motion occurring in the F^+ surface.

> [...] the phase paths of "rapid" motion (jump) in the u, z, v_1 phase space recede away from the region $|u| \leq u_*$ of the surface F [...]. For $|u| \leq u_*$ only jumps of the voltage u are possible [...]. On the remaining part of the surface F (for $|u| > u_*$) [...] the paths of "rapid" motion approach the surface F [...] On the portion F^+ of F where $|u| \leq u_*$ there are "slow" motions along paths [...]. Outside F^+ $u \to \infty$, for $\mu \to +0$ but $\dot{z}$ and $\dot{v}_1$ remain finite, therefore there are "rapid" motions along the paths z =const, v_1 =const which lead to the surface F^+ where they pass into paths of "slow" motions. In due course all paths of "slow" motion pass into discontinuous jumps at $u = +u^*$ or at $u = -u^*$. It can easily be shown that all phase paths tend to a unique and stable limit cycle for $t \to +\infty$. Thus [...], whatever the initial conditions, discontinuous oscillations build up in the system.

In this description, Andronov and co-workers used a three-dimensional space to clearly distinguish "slow" and "fast" motions. They also explained why "jumps of the voltage" cannot be avoided. This therefore represents a dynamical analysis of the universal circuit.

This contribution was impressive enough to frame Rössler's mind in two ways: i) it kept his attention focused on the multivibrator and ii) it introduced an S-shaped two-dimensional surface to explain how to produce non trivial oscillating solutions. By "trivial" it is here meant a limit cycle with a nearly constant speed. From a dynamical point of view, the background provided by Andronov and his co-workers was the most important influence on Rössler's mind before 1975.

Lorenz's paper also strongly influenced the way in which Rössler's first paper on a chaotic system was written. The best testimony to this influence is provided by the structure of the Lorenz's paper which was detailed in the previous chapter and which is roughly the structure Rössler retained for writing his first paper.

The third important influence on Rössler was the paper published in 1975 by Tien-Yien Li and James Yorke[24] remains highly reputed for i) having introduced the term chaos and ii) providing a theorem that can be understood as follows: as soon as a system has a period-3 orbit for solution, then there is chaos. The term chaos was introduced for designating "*complicated phenomena* [that] *may sometimes be understood in terms of simple model*." Chaos was here used in a quite adequate way and not as in the traditional one which designates the "*indescribable* state of Earth before creation." A simple difference equation (a second-order polynomial) may have surprisingly complicated dynamic behavior, complicated meaning here "not actually understood." Similar conclusions could be obtained from the adverb "*chaotically*" used once in Ruelle and Takens' paper published in 1971.[25] James Yorke himself recently conceded that defining clearly what chaos is remains an open problem, particularly because it depends on the context in which it is used.[26] It has to be noted that the word "chaos" also appeared in the title of a paper published by May in 1974 in which he quotes Li and Yorke's preprint, and in the subsequent preprint by John Guckenheimer, George Oster and Ipaktchi. We will see that all of these works were sent by Art Winfree (1942–2002) to Rössler, just before he wrote his first paper on a chaotic system.

[24]T.-Y. Li & J. Yorke, Period-three implies chaos, *American Mathematics Monthly*, **82**, 985–992, 1975.
[25]D. Ruelle & F. Takens, On the nature of turbulence, *Communications in Mathematical Physics*, **20**, 167–192, 1971.
[26]J. Yorke, Response to David Ruelle, Letter to the editor, *Notices of the American Mathematical Society*, **56**, 1232, 2009.

Second, the most important theorem proved by Li and Yorke[27] roughly states that when the system has a period-3 orbit for solution, then it has at least one orbit of each period for solution too. Furthermore, there is an uncountable subset of points x in the visited interval J which are not even asymptotically periodic. This means that there is an uncountable subset of unstable periodic orbits. This is a proof of the argument previously used by Lorenz in his 1963 paper as the letter by Winfree to Rössler dated on September 17, 1975 seems to confirm. In the other hand, it has to be noted that the Li-Yorke theorem is in fact included in the Sharkovsky's theorem.[28]

Chaotic behaviors will only be encountered when there is no stable periodic point. This last property is quite hard to prove and, for instance, a computer assisted proof for the chaoticity of the Lorenz attractor was only obtained in 1999.[29] In the other hand, the Lozi map[30]

$$\begin{cases} x_{n+1} = y_n + 1 - a|x_n| \\ y_{n+1} = bx_n \end{cases} \tag{4.3}$$

widely known for providing a two-dimensional chaotic attractor was recently proved as only having "*giga-periodic orbits*" when iterated with finite precision.[31] For

[27]The theorem was provided in the form as follows.

> Let J be an interval and let $F : J \mapsto J$ be continuous. Assume there is a point $a \in J$ for which the points $b = F(a)$, $c = F^2(a)$ and $d = F^3(a)$, satisfy
>
> $$d \leq a < b < c \quad (\text{or } d \geq a > b > c)\,.$$
>
> Then
>
> (1) for every $k = 1, 2, \ldots$ there is a periodic point in J having period k.
> (2) Furthermore, there is an uncountable set $S \subset J$ (containing no periodic points), which satisfies the following conditions:
>
> (a) for every $p, q \in S$, with $p \neq q$,
>
> $$\lim_{n \mapsto \infty} \sup |F^n(p) - F^n(q)| > 0$$
>
> and
>
> $$\lim_{n \mapsto \infty} \inf |F^n(p) - F^n(q)| = 0\,.$$
>
> (b) for every $p \in S$ and periodic point $q \in J$,
>
> $$\lim_{n \mapsto \infty} \sup |F^n(p) - F^n(q)| > 0\,.$$

[28]A. N. Sharkovsky, Co-existence of cycles of a continuous mapping of the line into itself, *Ukrainian Mathematical Journal*, **16**, 61–71, 1964. In Russian.

[29]W. Tucker, The Lorenz attractor exists, *Comptes-Rendus de l'Académie des Sciences* (Paris), **328**, 1917–1202, 1999.

[30]R. Lozi, Un attracteur étrange du type attracteur de Hénon, *Journal de Physique* (France), **39**, C5-9–C5-10, 1978.

[31]R. Lozi, Giga-periodic orbits for weakly coupled tent and logistic discretized maps, In: *Modern*

instance, for parameter values for which the obtained behavior was proved as corresponding to a chaotic solution (Figure 4.6(a)),[32] a giga-periodic limit cycle of period 436,170,188,959 was obtained after 19 hours of computation. Two different limit cycles were obtained for the Hénon map[33]

$$\begin{cases} x_{n+1} = y_n + 1 - a x_n^2 \\ y_{n+1} = b x_n \end{cases} \tag{4.4}$$

with period equal to 3,800,716,788 and 310,946,608, respectively. These two limit cycles were obtained from different initial conditions. It therefore seems impossible to actually obtain an aperiodic orbit using numerical simulation. Consequently, when a map of the interval has a period-3 orbit, one can conclude that there is at least one orbit of each period and these orbits are nondenumerable. But it remains to prove that there is no stable periodic point embedded, something that remains non trivial to be shown in most cases.

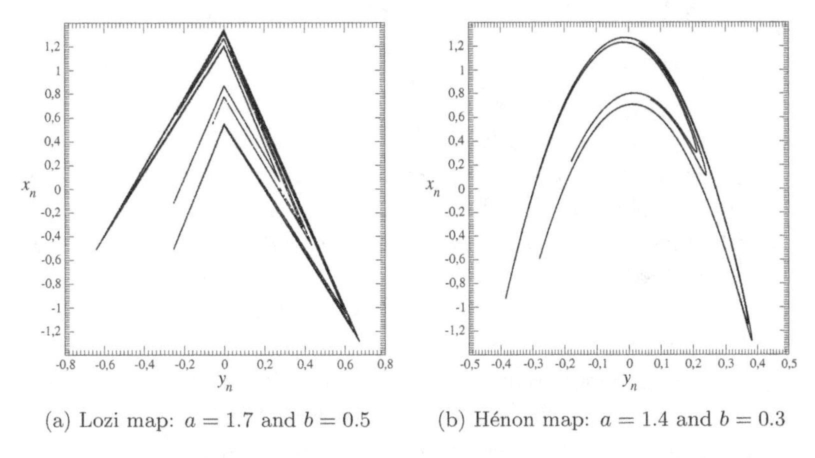

(a) Lozi map: $a = 1.7$ and $b = 0.5$ (b) Hénon map: $a = 1.4$ and $b = 0.3$

Figure 4.6 Chaotic attractors produced by the Lozi and the Hénon maps.

Strictly speaking, showing that there is a period-3 orbit in a uni-dimensional map is not enough to prove that the behavior is chaotic. But it is sufficient to show that you have an infinite number of periodic orbits and that any periodicity is realized as a periodic orbit. In addition to that, if a proof for the underlying determinism is obtained (trivial when the trajectory results from iterations of a set of deterministic equations) as well as a proof of the boundedness of the behavior (numerically, it is a rather good approximation to wait for a long time and to check whether there is a bounded surface that is never crossed again once the trajectory is inside) and a proof for the sensitivity to initial conditions, it may quite confidently be concluded

Mathematical Models, Methods and Algorithms for Real World Systems, A. H. Siddiqi, I. S. Duff & O. Christensen (Eds), Anamaya Publishers, (New Delhi), 80-14, 2006.

[32]M. Misiurewicz, Strange attractors for the Lozi mappings, *Annals of the New York Academy of Science*, **375**, 348–358, 1980.

[33]M. Hénon, A two-dimensional mapping with a strange attractor, *Communications in Mathematical Physics*, **50** (1), 69–77, 1976.

that the behavior under investigation is chaotic. (But remember that the Lozi map is a good counter-example.) For scientists working with an experimental data set or with "computer experiments", there is no rigorous way to distinguish an arbitrarily long periodic orbit from a chaotic solution. Thus, numerical experimentalists often used the existence of a period-3 orbit as a proof for an uncountable subset of non periodic points and implicitly assumed that the studied solution was chaotic.

4.1.3 *A Chaotic Chemical Reaction*

Rössler started to design some three-variable oscillator by coupling a two-variable bistable system to a slowly moving third-variable. The resulting three-dimensional system was only producing limit cycles at the time. In this period, Rössler also introduced *dynamical automata* as components for the building up of complex chemical reaction systems: in other words, he had in mind to build chemical reaction systems as complex as electronic circuits are. At an international congress on *Rhythmic functions in biological systems* held on September 8–12, 1975 in Vienna, he met Arthur Winfree again — a theoretical biologist who started his career as an engineering physicist and studied chemical waves,[34] circadian rhythm,[35] and cardiac arrhythmia.[36] Winfree — also an expert in computers — was regularly exchanging letters with Rössler about oscillating chemical reactions or dynamical systems. Winfree was looking for a "*kinetics with a source and no limit cycle.*"[37] The concepts invoked in these letters were nullclines and bistability,[38] Lorenz equations[39] with Art's comment "*Guckenheimer, Li and Yorke are doing a long job on this Equ. now; not yet ready for press,*" differential systems, saddle and stable foci, damped oscillations, chemical monoflop, limit cycles, self-oscillations that Otto "*had already seen* [as] *behavior of monoflops on the analog computer: when a chemical monoflop was just above the threshold of being self-oscillating, irregular spikes of differing amplitudes occurred.*"[40]

At this conference in Vienna, Winfree challenged Rössler to find a biochemical reaction reproducing the Lorenz attractor. To stimulate Otto, Art sent a collection of reprints and preprints with a letter dated on October 7, 1975. The paper sent were:

(1) E. N. Lorenz, Deterministic Nonperiodic Flow, *Journal of the Atmospheric Sciences,* **20** (1963) 130–141;

[34] A. T. Winfree, Spiral waves of chemical activity, *Science*, **175**, 624–636, 1972.
[35] A. T. Winfree, *The geometry of biological time*, Springer (Berlin), 1980.
[36] A. T. Winfree, Electrical instability in cardiac muscle: phase singularities and rotors, *Journal of Theoretical Biology*, **138**, 353–405, 1989.
[37] Letter from Art to Otto, May 25, 1975.
[38] Letter from Otto to Art, June 23, 1975.
[39] Letter from Art to Otto, September 17, 1975.
[40] Letter from Otto to Art, September 30, 1975.

(2) R. May & G. F. Oster. Bifurcations and dynamic complexity in simple ecological models, (preprint later published[41]);
(3) F. C. Hoppensteadt & J. M. Hyman. Periodic solutions of a logistic difference equation, (preprint later published[42]);
(4) T. Y. Li & J. A. Yorke. Period-three implies chaos, (preprint later published[43]);
(5) J. Guckenheimer, G. F. Oster & A. Ipaktchi. Dynamics of density-dependent population models, (preprint later published[44]).

Otto was strongly impressed by Lorenz's paper: he thus proposed Winfree to write a "*joint paper, entitled* Chemical Nonperiodic Flow, 3 examples"[45] but Winfree declined this offer.[46] Lorenz's paper's influence on Rössler is confirmed by the explicit quotation to it found in the abstract of Rössler's first paper about chaos.[47] As it will be shown, Li and Yorke's paper also had a strong influence on Rössler's mind and was crucial for providing a numerical proof of chaos. By these times, Rössler failed to find a chemical or biochemical reaction producing the Lorenz attractor[48] but he instead found a simpler type of chaos in a paper he wrote during the 1975 Christmas holidays. This paper will be detailed below as well as the style in which it was written. It is only much later that Otto discovered jointly with Peter Ortoleva a biochemical reaction scheme producing a Lorenz-like dynamics.[49] The obtained attractor does not have the rotation symmetry the Lorenz attractor has but it is characterized by a map equivalent to the one published by Lorenz in 1963.

In the collection of papers and reprint sent by Winfree, Rössler had references to all the essential works available in this field: references to the global analysis with the articles of Stephen Smale and Edward Lorenz, access to the earliest articles on chaotic dynamics in simple systems through the other articles. Rössler refined his objective to obtain a chaotic chemical reaction with a system of three variables. It was not until December 15, 1975 that he found his first model with three variables that produced chaotic oscillations. Rössler explained the way by which he came to his first set of equations. He revealed how he was influenced by Andronov and co-workers' book. He started out with the Khaikin's universal circuit and the latter's S-shaped surface (Figure 4.5) which he then modified (Figure 4.7(d)) to get a dynamics different from the one investigated by Andronov's school. The key was to modify

[41] R. May & G. F. Oster, Bifurcations and dynamic complexity in simple ecological models, *The American Naturalist*, **110**, 573–599, 1976.
[42] F. C. Hoppensteadt & J. M. Hyman, Periodic solutions of a logistic difference equation, *SIAM Journal of Applied Mathematics*, **32**, 73–81, 1977.
[43] Ibid. Li, 1975
[44] J. Guckenheimer, G. F. Oster & A. Ipaktchi, Periodic solutions of a logistic difference equation, *Journal of Mathematical Biology*, **4**, 101–147, 1976.
[45] Letter from Otto to Art, October 15, 1975.
[46] Letter from Art to Otto, October 22, 1975.
[47] O. E. Rössler, Chaotic behavior in simple reaction system, *Zeitschrift für Naturforschung A*, **31**, 259–264, 1976.
[48] As Mastumoto tried few years later, see p. 146.
[49] O. E. Rössler & P. J. Ortoleva, Strange attractors in 3-variable reaction systems, *Lecture Notes in Biomathematics*, **21**, 67–73, 1978.

(bend-over more and more) the S-shaped surface in order to have an additional "*orientation of flowing*" on the other half, that is, eventually a motion with a "*twist*" would form. Again, the way in which this was expressed in Rössler's first paper on chaos was not so clear:

> ...a slight modification is sufficient to turn the device into chaos generating machine: by simply introducing a different orientation of flowing on the other [lower] stable branch of the slow manifold (with the consequence of a "reinjection" of part of the flow after its having past through twisted roundabout loop).

The original picture he added (Figure 4.7(d)) shows a "*reversed direction of flow*" reinjecting the trajectory (upstair) in a nonlinear way, thereby allowing for an aperiodic trajectory (see Figure 4.7(d) with its original caption). When the surface is nearly flat (Figure 4.7(a)), only limit cycle can be produced, according to the Poincaré-Bendixson theorem. When the S-shape is more evident, relaxation oscillations can be produced but there are still periodic cycles (Figure 4.7(b)). It is necessary to introduce a "*reverse direction*" in the lower branch to introduce a "*variable*" reinjection of the trajectory in the neighborhood of the unstable focus point (Figure 4.7(d)).

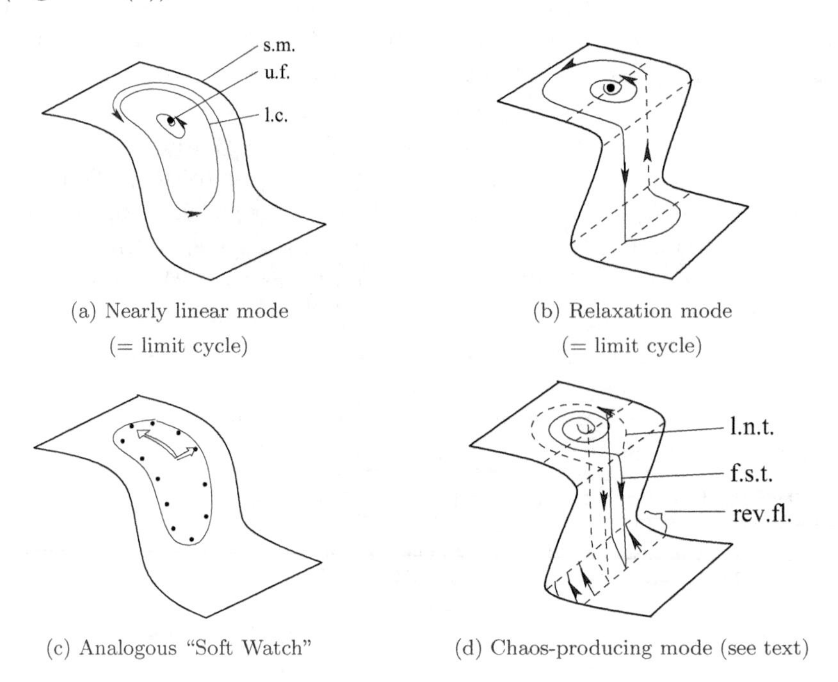

(a) Nearly linear mode (= limit cycle)

(b) Relaxation mode (= limit cycle)

(c) Analogous "Soft Watch"

(d) Chaos-producing mode (see text)

Figure 4.7 Main trajectorial flow of a universal circuit. s.m.= slow manifold, u.f.= unstable focus, l.c.= limit cycle, the intermediate part of slow manifold in (b) and (d) is unstable, f.s.t. "first switched trajectory", l.n.t.= "last non switched trajectory", rev.fl.= reversed direction of flow "downstairs".

With this collection of figures, Rössler's way of presenting things certainly reached its height since he introduced in one of the panels the "*soft watch*" painted by Salvador Dali. The single objectively existing connection is the analogy with the S-shaped surface. We asked Otto many times for a justification of this including this soft watch in the original paper. Among the answers we got, the one which convinced us the most was:

> I had a knack for watches ever since I dismantled my grandmother's big table watch, with its S-shaped curves to the left and right on the top, at age three. And never being punished for not having been able to reassemble it from the little cogwheels and springs that I had retrieved from it.[50]

This type of clock present actually a S-shape (Figure 4.8). Nevertheless, the presence of Dali's soft watch questioned the reader, destabilizing him from the main purpose of the sequence of figures.

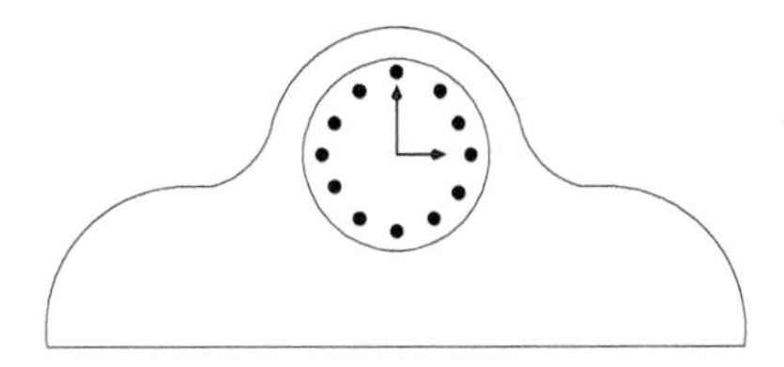

Figure 4.8 Sketch of the clock that Otto dismantled.

For Dali, the "soft watch" is a representation of the perception of time and space, and of the behavior of the memory, acquiring soft forms that adjust themselves to the circumstances,[51] but Otto said "*the distortion of memory did not come to my mind.*" Dali's soft watch could serve to speak to a broad audience, to stimulate the reader. But if Dali's soft watch can provoke smiles during a talk for a broad audience, it would surely leave strict scientists perplexed.

Returning to the way in which equations were obtained, Rössler combined an oscillator described by Turing — a chemical oscillator with two variables — with an on-off switch devised by Barry Edelstein[52] — a chemical system with a single variable that exhibited hysteresis. The combination of the oscillator with the hysteresis loop was treated schematically by Rössler as shown in Figure 4.9. This combination of oscillator and switch produced a chemical oscillator that is but a single example in a large selection of possible oscillating models.

Now there is a gap between the S-shaped surface proposed in Figure 4.7(d) and the obtained equations. The intermediary step consists in a reaction scheme (Figure 4.10) where each arrow stands for a source or sink of the concentration of the substances A, B or C. Arrows directed toward other arrows indicate catalytic

[50] Otto E. Rössler, personal communication, 2010.

[51] S. Dali, *The disintegration of the persistence of memory*, 1952.

[52] B. B. Edelstein, A Biomedical Model with multiple steady states, *Journal of Theoretical Biology*, **29**, 57–62, 1970.

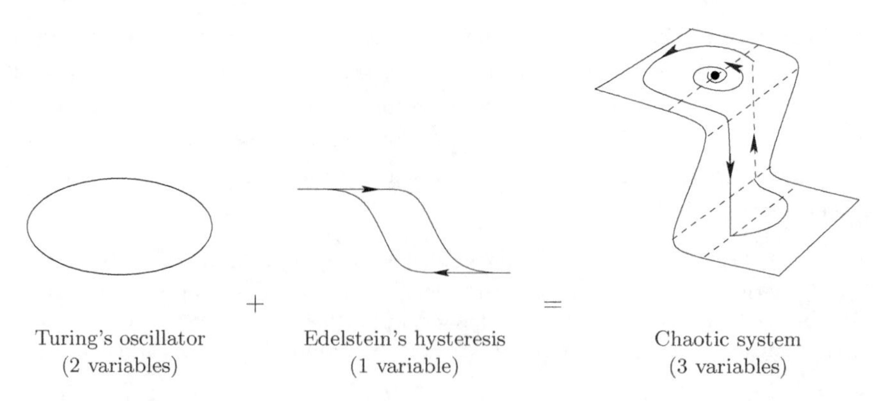

Figure 4.9 Combination of a Turing oscillator and an Edelstein switch to obtain a three-variable system exhibiting chaotic behavior.

rate control. This scheme results from a two-dimensional chemical multivibrator published in 1972 and a third variable, the so-called Edelstein switch. Rössler described it as follows:

> The following reaction scheme (Figure 4.10) constitutes **one possible way** to realize the principle by chemical means. It combines a 2-variable chemical oscillator (variable a, b) with a single-variable chemical hysteresis system (c), as prescribed by the recipe. The system obeys, under the usual assumptions of wellstirredness and isothermy as well as an appropriate concentration range, [to the set of three differential equations]
>
> $$\left\{\begin{aligned} \dot{a} &= k_1 + k_2 a - \frac{(k_3 b + k_4 c)a}{a+K} \\ \dot{b} &= k_5 a - k_6 b \\ \mu\dot{c} &= k_7 a + k_8 c - k_9 c^2 - \frac{k_{10} c}{c+K'} \end{aligned}\right. \tag{4.5}$$
>
> where a denotes the concentration of substance A, etc., $k_{10} = k'_{10} e_0$, e_0 =constant, and K, K' are Michaelis constants.[53]

[53] As René Lozi remarked (personal communication, 2010), this set of rate equations is not "exact" in the sense that it does not correspond exactly to the scheme shown in Figure 4.10. It rather should be:

$$\left\{\begin{aligned} \dot{a} &= k_1 + k_2\, a - \frac{(k_3\, b + k_4\, c)\, a}{a+K} \\ \dot{b} &= k_5\, a - k_6\, b - \frac{k_3\, ab}{a+K} \\ \mu\dot{c} &= k_7\, a + k_8\, c - k_9 c^2 - \frac{k_{10}\, c}{c+K'} - \mu\frac{k_4\, ac}{a+K}\,. \end{aligned}\right. \tag{4.6}$$

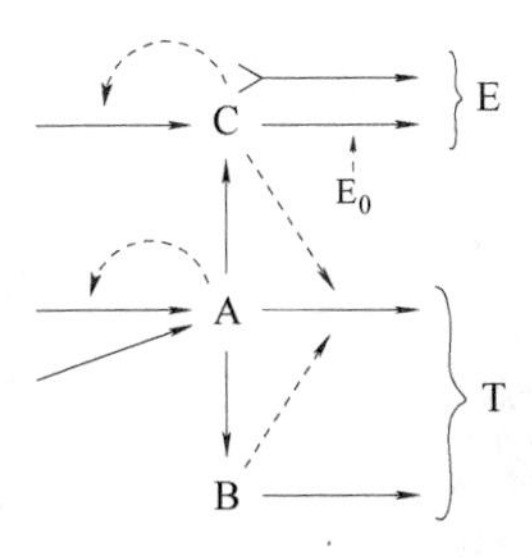

Figure 4.10 Combination of an Edelstein switch with a Turing oscillator in a reaction system producing chaos. E = switching subsystem, T = oscillating subsystem ; constant pools (sources and sinks) have been omitted from the scheme as usual. (Adapted from Rössler, 1976.)

In fact, once the "*ideal*" reaction scheme — which only represents "*a possible way*" — is drawn, there is a lot of intuition and time was spent on the analog and/or digital computer varying the coefficients to get the result. This is confirmed by the system

$$\begin{cases} \dot{a} = k_2\, a - \dfrac{k_3\, ab}{a+K} + c \\ \dot{b} = k_5\, a - k_6\, b \\ \dot{c} = \mu \left(1 - k_8\, c - k_9 c^2 - \dfrac{k_4'\, ac}{c+K} \right) \end{cases} \tag{4.7}$$

that was proposed in the abstract Otto sent by December 1st, 1975 (Figure 4.3).[54]

The S-shaped surface therefore served to design the general structure of the equations and then the parameters were determined by a manual "maieutic" technique. In other words, the "*principle for generating chaos*" can be summed up into a procedure to pre-define some qualitative properties of the expected behavior and to then use different components introduced as chemical automata in 1972 to design roughly the structure of the equations (or exactly in a limit). The final part of the work is just... time and patience in front of a computer (Figure 4.11).[55]

This means that many parameters were tried and only those leading to the expected dynamical behavior were retained. In other words, during his search for appropriate parameter values, a few terms were set to zero. In the present case, the two rational terms recovered by René Lozi were in fact removed. Such empirical steps were not described in the original paper.

[54]The system was thus, term $\frac{k_4 ac}{a+K}$ in the first equation of (4.5) was reduced to a linear term c, the term $\frac{k_3 ab}{a+K}$ was removed from the second equation, and the linear term $k_7 a$ was removed from the third equation where the two nonlinear terms were mixed together. This system is a variant of the exact form (4.6) proposed by Lozi and of the system actually published in Rössler's first paper on chaos.

[55]The value of parameter μ was changed here compared to the one published (1/25) to recover the picture published. Such misprint is quite rare in Rössler's papers.

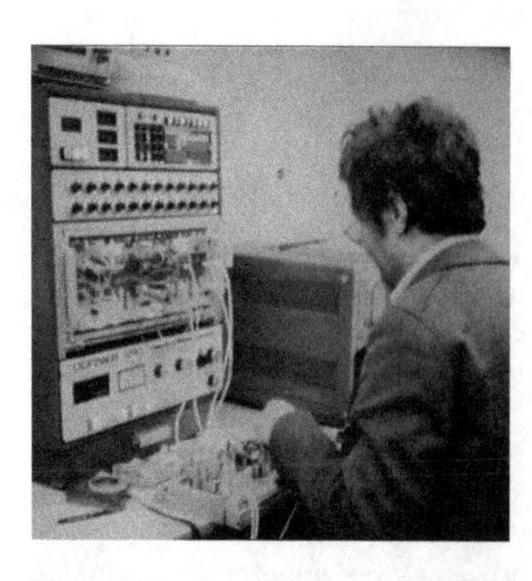

Figure 4.11 Otto E. Rössler in front of his computer in 1979.

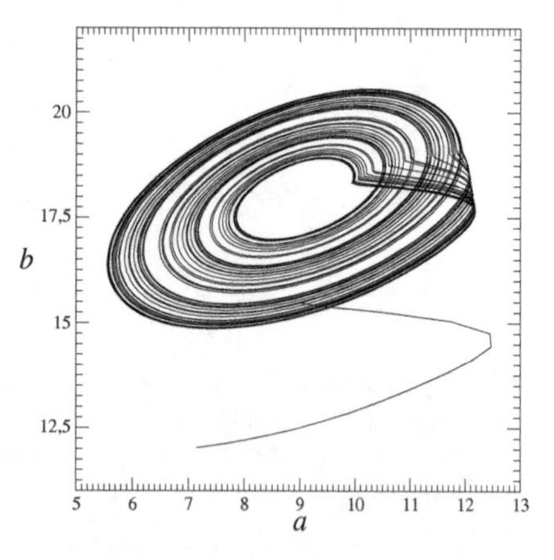

Figure 4.12 Chaotic attractor produced by the first chaotic system Rössler published in 1976. Parameter values: $k_1 = 37.8$, $k_2 = 1.4$, $k_3 = 2.8$, $k_4 = 2.8$, $k_5 = 2$, $k_6 = 1$, $k_7 = 8$, $k_8 = 1.84$, $k_9 = 0.0616$, $k_{10} = 100$, $K = 0.05$, $K' = 0.02$, $\mu = 1/500$; $a_0 = 7$, $b_0 = 12$, $c_0 = 0.2$, $t_0 = 0$ and $t_{\text{end}} = 43.51$.

4.1.4 *The Rössler System*

Otto Rössler claimed that his simple set of equations for continuous chaos — known as the so-called Rössler system —

$$\begin{cases} \dot{x} = -y - z \\ \dot{y} = x + a\,y \\ \dot{z} = b + z\,(x - c) \end{cases} \tag{4.8}$$

was derived from the first chemical reaction scheme (Figure 4.10). This was implicitly expressed as:[56]

> Therefore, a simpler equation which directly produces a similar flow and forms only a single spiral (a term may be of interest, even if this equation has, as a "model of a model", no longer an immediate physical interpretation).
>
> Eq. (4.7) incidentally illustrates a more general principle for the generation of "spiral type" chaos:[57] combining a two-variable oscillator (in this case x and y) with a switching-type subsystem (z) in such a way that the latter is being switched by the first while the flow of the first is dependent on the switching state of the latter. Eq. (4.7) has in fact been derived from the more complicated equation for which this "*building-block principle*" has been shown to apply strictly.

The simpler system was obtained after nights and days spent in front of his computer. His objective was actually to simplify the set of original equations (4.7) to obtain a simpler one that "*contains just one (second-order) nonlinearity in one*

[56] O. E. Rössler, An equation for continuous chaos, *Physics Letters A*, **57**, 397–398, 1976.

[57] O. E. Rössler, Chaos in abstract kinetics: two prototypes, *Bulletin of Mathematical Biology*, **39**, 275–289, 1977.

variable" as mentioned in the abstract of Rössler's most quoted paper. The reaction scheme (Figure 4.10) was thus used by Rössler as a starting point to predefine the algebraic structure of the set of differential equations he tried to simulate on his computer. Switching from the general model (4.6) to the reduced one (4.8) was actually performed according to an empirical way.

Once he got a chaotic solution to his equation (Figure 4.12), Rössler came to the conclusion that "*qualitative properties cannot be deduced from simulation alone*" and, as Lorenz had done, the dynamics would be better understood by using a first-return map. In contrast to what Lorenz had done, Rössler did not compute the first-return maps he had provided. He rather drew them after many visual inspections of the dynamics using stereoscopic projections as used in many of his papers (to verify the analytical limiting result he had obtained first). Thus, and in agreement with his combining an oscillating circuit with a switch, the map is made up from two branches. One branch is associated with the relaxation process induced by the switching nonlinear mechanism. At a certain threshold value, the linear process is interrupted by the switch, thereby limiting the diverging spiral. The crucial point in this part of the paper is that Rössler drew the map with a qualitatively correct curvature (Figure 4.13). For instance, he could have idealized his map by a tent map as Lorenz did at the end of his paper. The general shape of the map was checked by computing a first-return map to a Poincaré section (Figure 4.14). It reveals that Otto's ability to read state space was quite accurate.

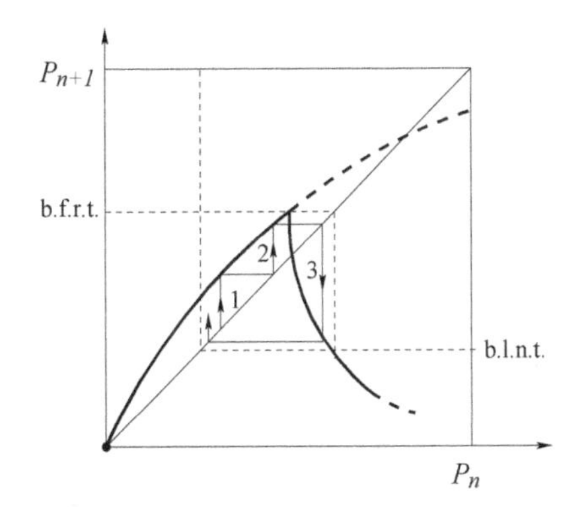

Figure 4.13 First-return map to a Poincaré section of the simple chemical reaction (4.7) in the chaotic mode (see Figure 4.7(d)). b.f.r.t. = border-line determined by first reinjected trajectory; b.l.n.t. = borderline determined by last non-reinjected trajectory; 1, 2, 3 = steps proving chaos.

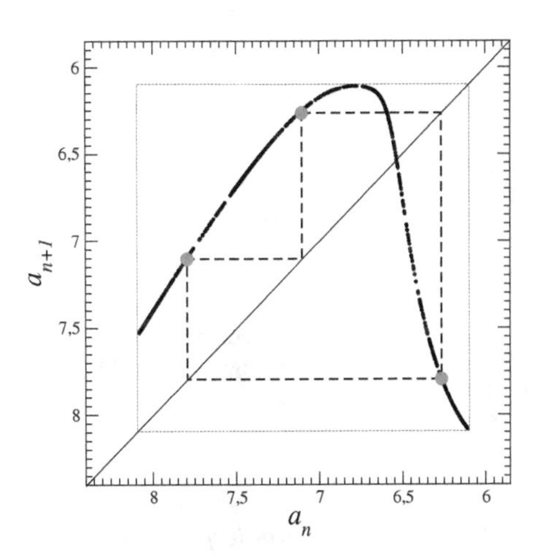

Figure 4.14 First-return map to a Poincaré section for the chaotic chemical reaction (4.7). The box within which the period-3 orbit is observed is drawn with a thin dashed line. The three periodic points are linked by thick dashed lines.

He thus used the opportunity to show that the trajectory was bounded in state space by showing that the "*cut*", that is, the threshold at which the relaxation mechanism cuts the linear expansion, induces a "*quadratic box*" — the term "*quadratic box*" has no clear meaning and was later replaced with "*Li-Yorke box*" — whose edges are bounding the behavior. This results from a common geometric construction for the first-return map. Such proof can be considered as a numerical proof for a bounded trajectory although drawn by hand. Slightly later, Rössler clarified his interpretation of the Li-Yorke theorem by stating: this "*path* [is] *proving that period-3, and hence chaos, is possible within the box.*" Rössler then showed that there is a period-3 orbit within his map (Figure 4.13). Using the Li and Yorke theorem, he was thus able to deduce the "*existence of an uncountable set of repelling periodic attractors of measure zero.*" The conclusion was nearly the same as Li and Yorke's one.

As a result, Rössler was able to show that the behavior exhibited by his system was chaotic. We point out that the use of the first return map to characterize an attractor remains, even today, the best tool. The period-three orbit extracted from the attractor is shown in Figure 4.15.

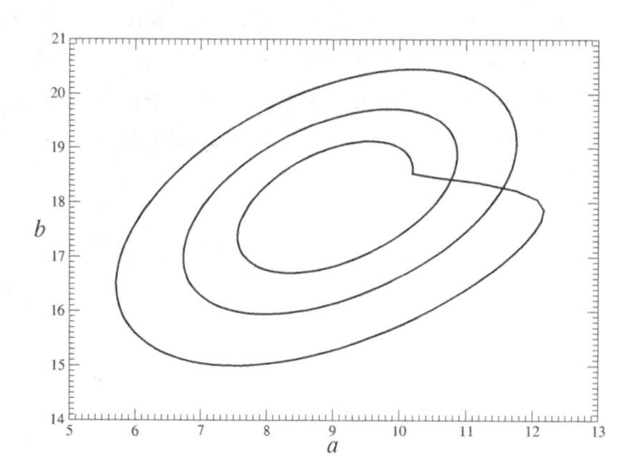

Figure 4.15 Period-three orbit coded by the sequence (100) — cf. Section 4.3 — extracted from the attractor produced by the first Rössler system integrated using the same parameter values as those used for producing Figure 4.12. This can be used as a "proof" that the attractor shown in this figure is actually chaotic.

4.1.5 *A First Topological Analysis*

Following this, Rössler made a connection with the work of Stephen Smale (who we will run across again in Section 4.3) by proposing a schematic representation — based on Figure 4.12 and 4.13 — that summarizes the major properties of the system. With this description (Figure 4.16(a)) Rössler developed a global analysis: he identified two strips, labelled respectively 0 and 1 (Figure 4.16(a)). Strip 0 is only *stretched* while strip 1 is both *stretched* and *folded* onto strip 2. Stretching and folding are the two ingredients needed to obtain chaotic behavior: stretching guarantees sensitivity to initial conditions while folding ensures the recurrence properties of trajectories. Both conjugated induce the mixing of trajectories that guarantees the long term unpredictability of the system. Starting from this schematic representation, Rössler introduced an "*allowed cut*" — at the boundary between strips 0 and 1 — and deformed this blender as if it were made of rubber, without cutting it. By doing this he obtained a normal strip that corresponds to a section of a cylinder, and a Möbius strip[58] that undergoes a half-turn (Figure 4.16(b)). The two strips have different topological properties. Rössler simplified this description and reduced it to a paper model (Figure 4.17), which he called "*origami*" after the Japanese art of paper folding.[59] This is an outstanding example of global analysis that produced the first template for a chaotic attractor.

The Rössler attractor (Figure 4.18) can be explained as follows.[60] As we learned from Poincaré, the analysis of such a system begins with a search for the singular points around which the typical state space trajectories move. Two singular points

$$S_\pm = \left| \begin{array}{l} x_\pm = \eta_\pm = \dfrac{c \pm \sqrt{c^2 - 4ab}}{2} \\ y_\pm = -\dfrac{\eta_\pm}{a} \\ z_\pm = \dfrac{\eta_\pm}{a}. \end{array} \right.$$

These singular points $S_\pm$ are obtained by setting $\dot{x} = 0$, $\dot{y} = 0$, and $\dot{z} = 0$. The system is at rest at these points; as a result, these are also called *fixed points* or *equilibrium points*. One can show that these singular points are of saddle-node type (Figure 4.18(a)), that is, associated with a two-dimensional plane in which there is a divergent (convergent) spiral and an axis, transverse to that plane, driving the trajectory toward (outward of) the spiral. Numerical integration shows that this Rössler system produces an attractor which is structured around these singular points (Figure 4.18(a)).

A trajectory begins by spiraling away from the singular point S_- in a plane parallel to the x-y plane (divergent spiral). When the amplitude of the oscillation is large enough, the non-linearity — the hysteresis — becomes active and ejects the trajectory upward from that plane towards larger values of z; it is then reinjected downwards along the Oz axis towards the singular point S_-, in preparation for another cycle. This singular point is therefore a combination between an unstable focus point and a stable direction driving the trajectory towards the midst of the

[58]A Möbius strip has a single face, due to its single half-turn. It was introduced by August Ferdinand Möbius (1790–1868), Über die Bestimmung des Inhaltes eines Polyeders, *Berichte über die Verhandlungen der Sächsischen Akademie der Wissenschaften zu Leipzig*, **17**, 31–68, 1865.

[59]O. E. Rössler, Chaos in abstract kinetics: two prototypes, *Bulletin of Mathematical Biology*, **39** (2), 275–289, 1977.

[60]The Rössler system (4.8) can be decomposed into to sub-systems. The sub-system x-y produces a diverging spiral — this is a bidimensional Turing oscillator — while the third equation in z ensures the nonlinear reinjection in the midst of the diverging spiral — this is a hysteresis.

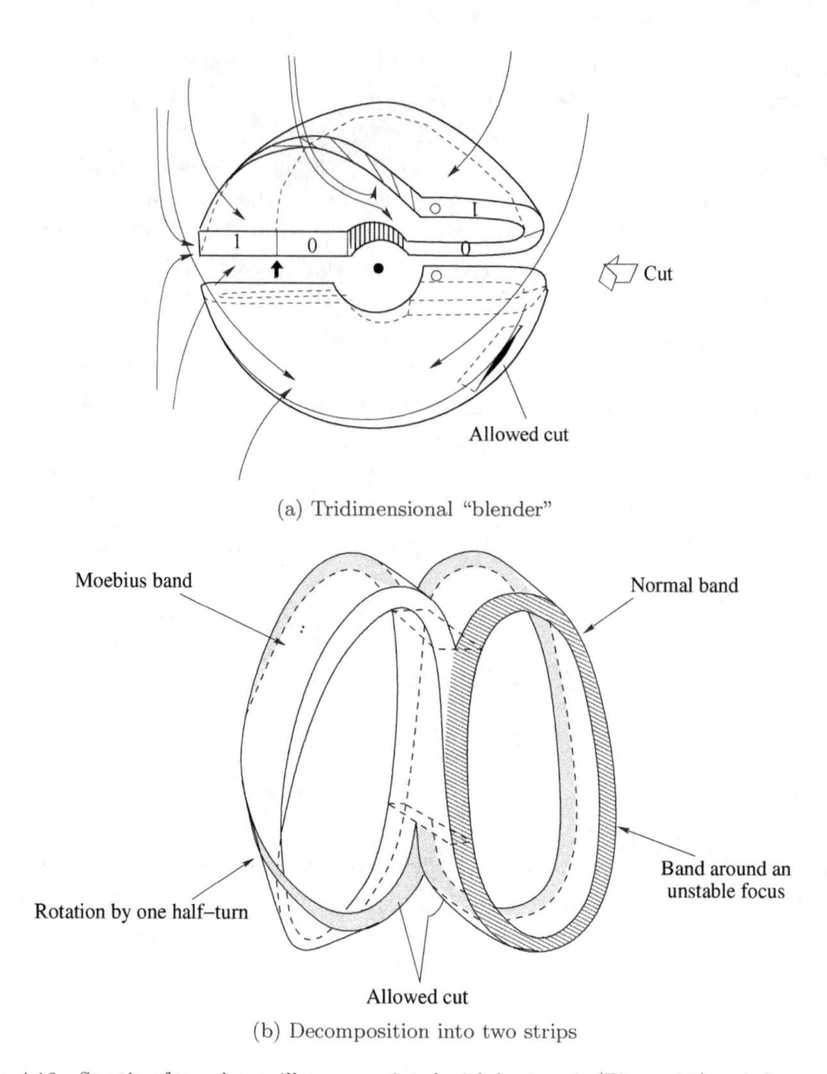

(a) Tridimensional "blender"

(b) Decomposition into two strips

Figure 4.16 Starting from the oscillator associated with hysteresis (Figure 4.9) and the representation of the chaotic attractor (Figure 4.12(a)), Rössler found a schematic representation which he called a "three-dimensional blender" (a). With the help of an "allowed cut" he separated his "blender" into two strips with different properties (b). These two representations are topologically equivalent.

spiral. Since it has stable and unstable directions, this point is also a node point; it is therefore a saddle-node point. We point out that the nonlinear return action acts as a folding mechanism and occurs after the stretching caused by the spiral motion away from the singular point. Stretching guarantees rapid growth of small differences in initial conditions and folding guarantees that the trajectory is both bounded and recurrent. This alternation and repetition of stretching and folding is characteristic of chaotic behavior. At each point on the trajectory there is always a

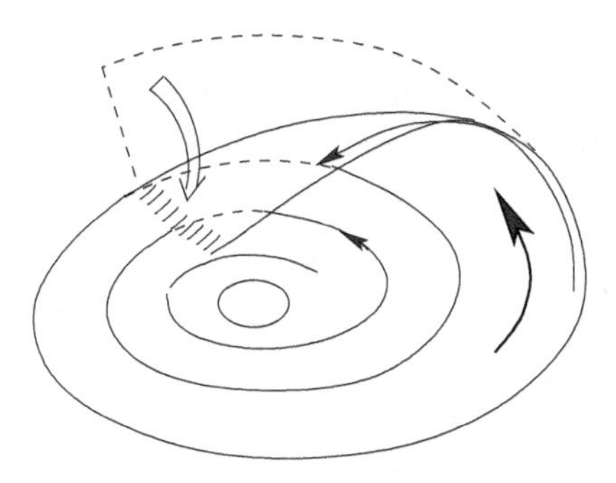

Figure 4.17 Paper model topologically equivalent to a blender.

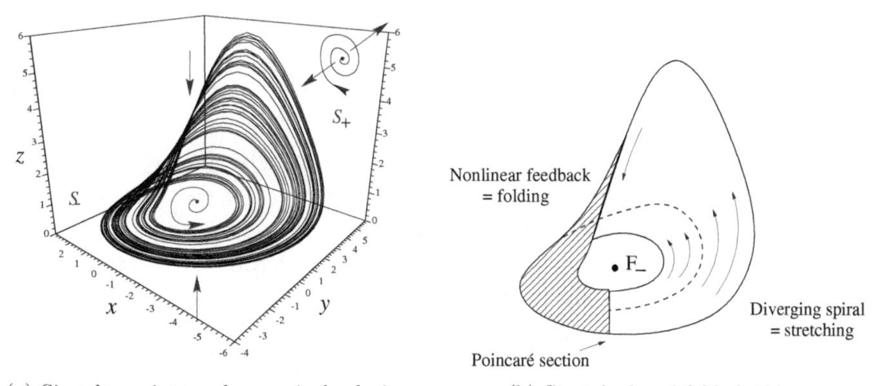

(a) Singular points and numerical solution (b) Stretched and folded ribbon

Figure 4.18 Chaotic attractor organized around the singular points of the Rössler system. The singular point S_- is associated with a diverging spiral motion and a converging direction while the singular point S_+ is associated with converging spiral motion and a diverging direction. Because of energy dissipation, folding assures that trajectories are reinjected on the very weak stretching band in a way that ensures a zero volume: the repetition of stretching and folding guarantees the chaotic nature of the motion. The dashed line corresponds to the "allowed cut" between the two domains of the attractor (see next Section). Parameter values: $a = 0.398$, $b = 2$ and $c = 4$.

diverging direction and a converging direction, as we saw for homoclinic trajectories (Figure 5.10(c), p. 59). When the system is conservative, on average the divergence rigorously balances the contraction while for dissipative systems the contraction is always larger. This allows a simplification in the structure of the attractor.

To end with Rössler's contribution, it is quite clear that, with his first paper on chaos, Otto E. Rössler continued the "*tour de force*" — already achieved by Lorenz in uncompleted form — to provide a rather extended analysis of his system. The main results got by Rössler were a second dissipative continuous systems investigated in the state space for which the underlying structure was interpreted using a topological analysis. By distinguishing two topologically inequivalent domains, no doubt that Rössler provided a more advanced understanding of his chaotic attractor.

But the reason why Rössler's paper does not always leave the reader with a positive feeling is for sure the writing style. With his mathematical presentation, Lorenz left the reader with the impression that most of the concepts he introduced — inherited from Birkhoff — to investigate his chaotic system were well under control. Rössler, with his use of a flowery style, seemingly left the impression that he was not too conversant with the concepts. We believe that the detailed analysis here provided shows that the concepts were rather deeply understood and that he touched on the remaining key points some of which he later completed himself: like distinguishing between different types of chaos from the topological point of view by the use of paper models, providing suspension of different Poincaré maps, laying the ground for hyperchaos... But his fascination for mathematics and his displayed lack of self-confidence while writing mathematics pushed him toward a writing style quite rarely found — not to say unusual — in mathematical papers. It should be mentioned that such a way of writing was not so pregnant in his earlier papers where he combined chemical reactions and electronic circuits, two fields where he had a strong background.

The inclusion of Dali's soft watch strikes us as an advertisement to say "*dear reader I am not comfortable with writing mathematics, consequently, please, forgive me if I am not rigorous.*" As a consequence, Rössler was successful according to one of his aims: not to be too seriously considered by less pictorially oriented colleagues but, at the same time he also was thereby not able to attract enough scientists to stimulate deep investigation into his own contributions so far. This was already pointed out in a letter from Winfree to Rössler[61] (Figure 4.19):

> Many thanks for your marvelous preprint on chaos which is too compact; you need to expand, spell out more explicitly. Diagrams especially are a wonder of richness, but fear will take time to study with the needed care. [...] I love the sense of humor latent in your writing. But wish you would write more explicitly, more detail so I can fully understand.

Rössler wanted to be reachable, so as to speak to everybody. As a side effect always encountered in popularization, many points had to remain implicit including key details. Another problem is that he often jumps too quickly from one idea to the next, which renders the actual content of his papers very dense. His writings are therefore sometimes quite difficult to read and a "decoder" is required — as we did in this chapter regarding his first contribution to chaos theory.

Rössler did not provide enough detail to be fully understood by non specialist readers and perhaps by numerous specialists not yet focusing on his type of questions. Most likely, his pictorial writing style comes from his unsystematic mathematical background — remember that his education was in medicine and his Ph.D. thesis in physiology. He had the advantage of not being intimidated by mathematical difficulties but, unfortunately, Rössler was not rigorous enough in introducing a new terminology: Rather than using Greek or Latin roots for his new notions as

[61] Letter from Art to Otto, April 1976.

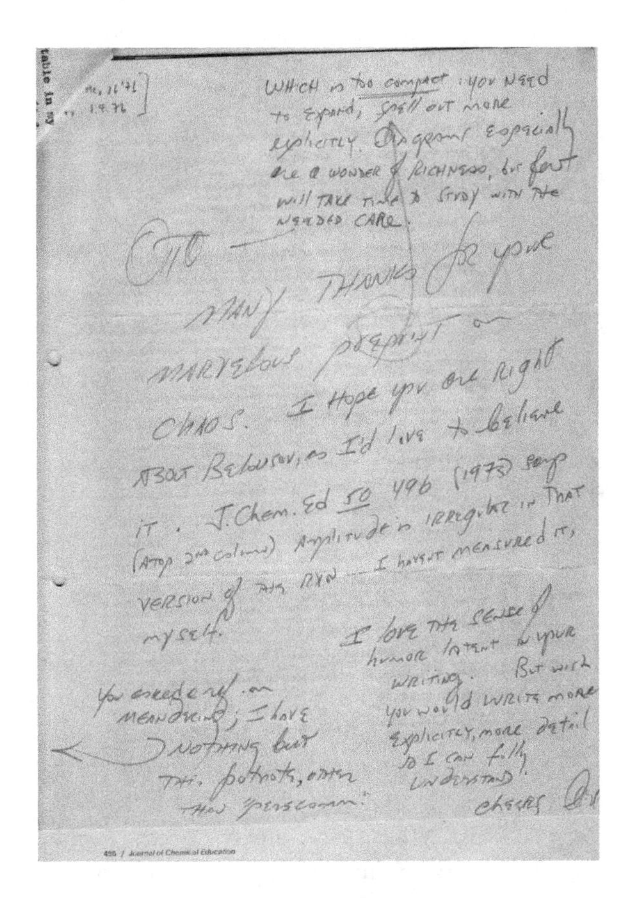

Which is too compact: you need to expand, spell out more explicitly. Diagrams especially are a wonder of richness, but few will take time to study with the needed care.

Otto — many thanks for your marvelous preprint on chaos. I hope you are right about Belousov, as I'd love to believe it. J. Chem. Ed 50 496 (1973) says (atop 2nd column) amplitude is irregular in that version of the rxn — I haven't measured it myself.

I love the sense of humor latent in your writing. But wish you would write more explicitly, more detail so I can fully understand!

Cheers Art

You succeeded in meandering; I have nothing but the footnotes, other than "pers comm"!

496 / Journal of Chemical Education

Figure 4.19 Scan of the letter sent by Art Winfree to Otto Rössler on April 1976.

recommended by Louis Guyton de Morveau (1737–1816) for neologisms.[62] Rössler used informal terms from daily life — like "*pancake*", "*cap-shaped*", "*veined pattern*", "*blender*", "*walking stick*", "*folded towel*"... The same ideas dressed with a more mathematical clothing and with clear statements of the concepts used would have led to a reference paper for many years already.

4.2 Poincaré Section

In order to characterize a chaotic attractor, as Rössler did, we should use a Poincaré section. It is convenient to place a plane in the part of the attractor where no folding takes place. In the case of the Rössler system, a Poincaré section can be defined as the set of intersections of a typical trajectory with a half-plane: all intersections with this half plane are from the same side. The Poincaré section that is obtained is

[62] L. Guyton de Morveau, Mémoire sur les dénominations chimiques, la nécessité d'en perfectionner le système, et les règles pour y parvenir, *Observations sur la physique, sur l'histoire naturelle et sur les arts* **19**, p. 370, 1782.

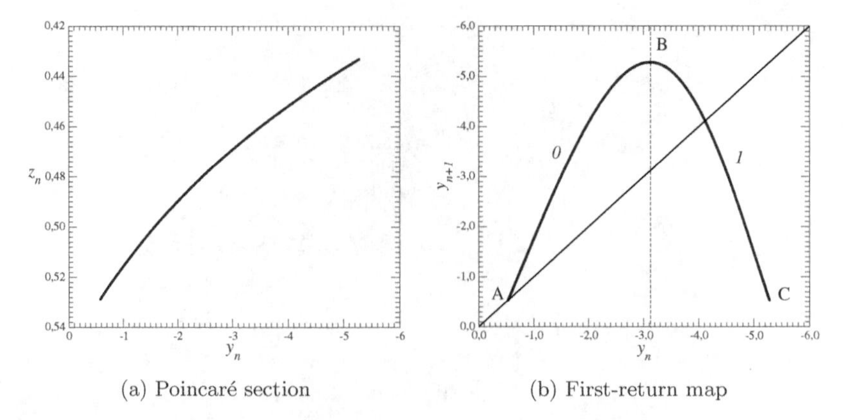

(a) Poincaré section (b) First-return map

Figure 4.20 Poincaré section and first-return map associated with the Rössler attractor. Parameter values: $a = 0.432$, $b = 2$, and $c = 4$.

a simple curve, evidencing the strong dissipation of the underlying dynamics (Figure 4.20(a))

The Poincaré section teaches us little about the chaotic behavior. To learn about this behavior we must use the first-return map, which tells us how the $n+1$st intersection with the Poincaré section depends on the nth intersection. To do this we plot $y_{n+1} = g(y_n)$. Iterating the map g corresponds to making a revolution in the attractor (around the singular point S_-). The figure obtained is a smooth curve with one maximum (Figure 4.20(b)). In this map we see two monotonic branches separated by a critical point B: an increasing branch AB and a decreasing branch BC. Now look at the general behavior of each of these two monotonic branches under iteration. The increasing segment AB is only stretched under iteration while the decreasing segment BC is both stretched and inverted (Figure 4.21), forcing this branch to make a half-twist. Because of this, there are two different regions, called strips, in the attractor. One is associated with the increasing branch, which undergoes only stretching while the other, associated with the decreasing branch, is both stretched and twisted. The critical point B partitions the attractor into two zones in which these two different processes take place. This justifies the "allowed cut" made by Rössler to decompose his "blender" into two strips.

4.3 Symbolic Dynamics

These two strips exhibit different topological properties. One, associated with the increasing branch, can be viewed as contained in a plane while the other, associated with the decreasing branch, shows a rotation through half of a full turn, the standard fingerprint of folding. These topological differences, characteristic of different types of time evolution, allow us to encode chaotic trajectories. Designate by "0" the strip without rotation and by "1" the strip with a half-twist. Each time the trajectory

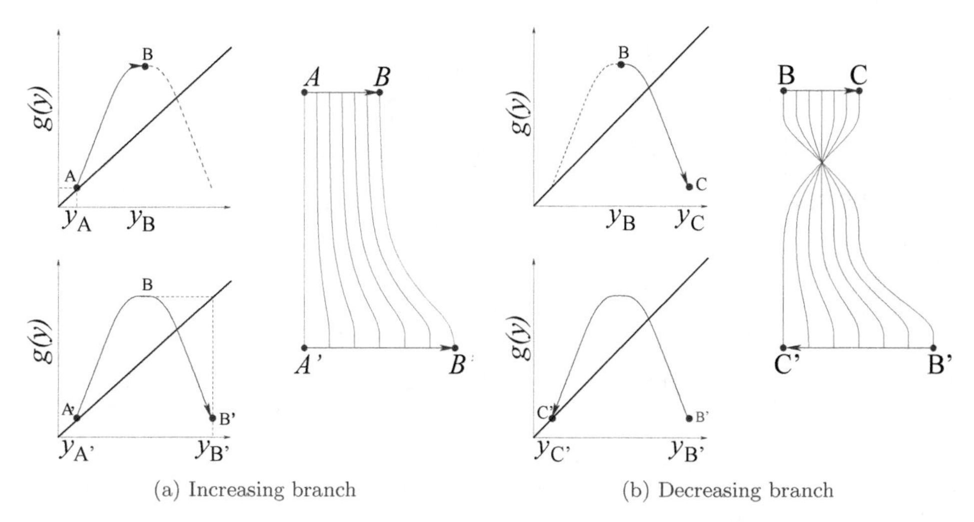

Figure 4.21 Dynamical behavior associated with each of the two monotonic branches of the first return map. The iterate of the point A is the point A', the iterate of B is B' and similarly for C and C'. We find A'=A, B'=C and C'=A. In fact, if y_A is the y coordinate of point A, we have $y_{A'} = g(y_A)$, where g is the Poincaré return map giving the $(n+1)$st intersection as a function of the nth.

passes through the strip 0 the revolution around the singular point S_- is coded by 0 and each time the trajectory passes through the strip 1, the revolution is coded by 1. A chaotic trajectory is thus encoded by a series of symbols 0 and 1 which never repeats since the trajectory is not periodic. This encoding of a trajectory by a series of symbols is called *symbolic dynamics*.

In fact, this concept dates to the works of Jacob Bernoulli (1667–1748) dealing with combinatorial and probabilistic problems.[63] Jacques Hadamard (1865–1963) revived these ideas in the context of surfaces of negative curvature in 1897.[64] These studies were taken up again by Marston Morse (1892–1977),[65] George Birkhoff,[66] and Norman Levinson. With this background Stephen Smale developed an idealization of the Poincaré map (first-return map to the Poincaré section) for chaotic systems.[67] For that, he used the fact that the two ingredients for obtaining chaotic behavior are stretching and folding (Figure 4.22).

[63] J. Bernoulli, *Ars conjectandi, opus posthumum. Accedit Tractatus de seriebus infinitis, et epistola gallicé scripta de ludo pilae reticularis*, Thurneysen Brothers (Basel), 1713.
[64] J. Hadamard, Les Surfaces à courbures opposées et leurs lignes géodésiques, *Journal de Mathématiques Pures et Appliquées*, **4**, 27–73, 1898.
[65] M. Morse, Recurrent Geodesis on a surface of negative curvature, *Transactions of the American Mathematical Society*, **22**, 84–100, 1921.
[66] G. D. Birkhoff, *Dynamical Systems*, American Mathematical Society, 1927.
[67] S. Smale, Differentiable dynamical systems, *Bulletin of American Mathematical Society*, **23**, 747–817, 1967.

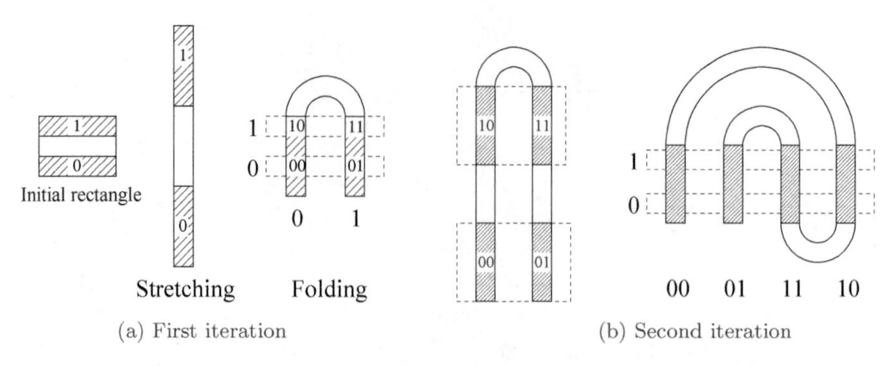

(a) First iteration (b) Second iteration

Figure 4.22 Idealization of the stretching and folding process. The first rectangle is stretched vertically, then folded. If one recalls the convention adopted for the first-return map of the Rössler system, the strip 0 is only stretched and the strip 1 undergoes, in addition, a half-turn. The grey zones represent the part of the rectangle that remains inside the rectangle after the first iteration of the map. Only this part of the rectangle is treated to avoid difficulties associated with the curved parts.

Because of its shape, this map is now called the *horseshoe map* or the *Smale horseshoe*. Smale considered only the points that remain within the original rectangle under this map. This allows us to avoid the difficulties associated with the curved regions and to concentrate on the properties that come out of the marriage of the stretching and folding processes. After n iterations a large number of symbolic sequences are allowed. For example, after three iterations (Figure 4.23) we find eight symbolic sequences ordered as follows

$$000 \prec_I 001 \prec_I 011 \prec_I 010 \prec_I 110 \prec_I 111 \prec_I 101 \prec_I 100\,,$$

where $\prec_I$ is the implication order.[68]

For instance, the sequence '001' means that this panel is only stretched during the first two iterates, and then stretched and folded in the third iterate. With the relative location of each panel and the associated symbolic sequence, a "*natural order*" appears in the symbolic sequences. We designate it using the mathematical symbol $\prec_{\mathrm{I}}$. Order $\prec_{\mathrm{I}}$ should be read as follows: $000 \prec_{\mathrm{I}} 001$ means that *the sequence 001 implies the sequence 000.* This is very useful to determine how the periodic orbits are organized with respect to each other in the Poincaré section. A periodic orbit is clearly represented by a symbolic sequence that is repeated infinitely. For example, the sequence 100 100 100 ... describes a period three orbit that goes through strip 1 once, followed by two revolutions through band 0 before repeating itself. We simplify this by representing the orbit by (100), the parentheses indicating that the sequence repeats infinitely often. The horseshoe map allows us to conclude that there is exactly one orbit for any given symbolic sequence. An orbit of period

[68]Hao Bai-Lin, *Elementary Symbolic Dynamics and Chaos in Dissipative Systems*, World Scientific Publishing, 1989 — C. Letellier, P. Dutertre & B. Maheu, Unstable periodic orbits and templates of the Rössler system: toward a systematic topological characterization, *Chaos*, **5**(1), 272–281, 1995.

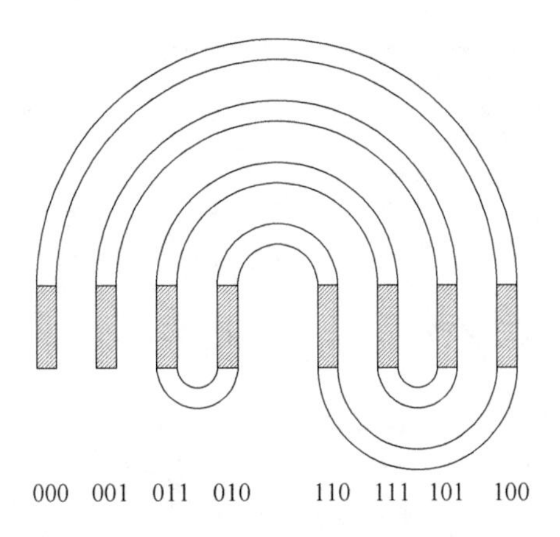

Figure 4.23 Third iteration of the horseshoe map.

three intersects the Poincaré section at three distinct points before repeating. These three points are labeled by the cyclic permutations of (100): specifically 100, 001, and 010. We switch from one cyclic permutation to the other according to the *Bernoulli shift* σ which maps the sequence of symbols

$$s_1, s_2, s_3, ..., s_n, ...$$

into

$$s_2, s_3, s_4, ..., s_{n+1}, ...$$

The three cyclic permutations of the symbolic sequences are thus

$$... \xrightarrow{\sigma} 100 \xrightarrow{\sigma} 001 \xrightarrow{\sigma} 010 \xrightarrow{\sigma} 100 \xrightarrow{\sigma} ...$$

Applying the Bernoulli shift is therefore equivalent to perform one revolution in the attractor, that is, to switch from one intersection with the Poincaré section to the next one.

The period-3 orbit visits successively the points 100, 001, and 010 then returns to 100, and so forth. The *third* iteration of the horseshoe map teaches us that the periodic points of the periodic orbits (0), (1), (100) and (101), respectively labeled $1_a, 1_b, 3_a$, and 3_b, are ordered in the Poincaré section as follows:

$$\begin{array}{cccccccc} 0 & 001 & 011 & 010 & 110 & 1 & 101 & 100 \\ \bullet & \bullet & \bullet & \bullet & \bullet & \bullet & \bullet & \bullet \\ 1_a & 3_a & 3_b & 3_a & 3_b & 1_b & 3_b & 3_a \end{array}$$

This can be checked for the Rössler system (Figure 4.24).

An arbitrary chaotic trajectory is organized by the skeleton of periodic orbits (all unstable) and visits the neighborhoods of these orbits in turn. As a result, to know the relative organization of the periodic orbits is to know the architecture of the chaotic orbit. The skeleton of periodic orbits constitutes, to use a phrase of Poincaré's, "*the sole breach to reach this unaffordable place*". The skeleton of

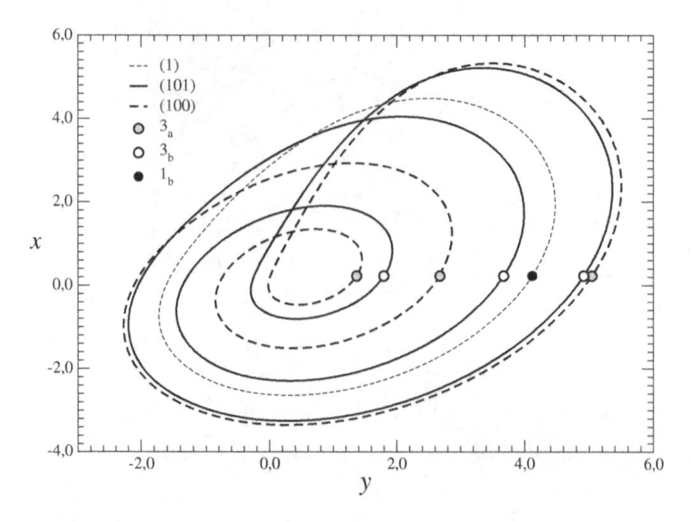

Figure 4.24 Relative organization of several periodic orbits from the Rössler attractor. The order produced by the horseshoe map idealization corresponds exactly to the order observed in the Poincaré section. In the Rössler system, the periodic point 1_a is in fact identified with the singular point S_-.

periodic orbits satisfies an order produced by a mapping as simple as the horseshoe map. Chaotic behavior is therefore governed by an underlying order arising from simple laws. This is the first demonstration that order underlies chaos. Somewhat in the manner of the KAM theory, it is possible to show that chaotic trajectories occur in the presence of periodic orbits. In a similar manner, each point in a Poincaré section of a chaotic trajectory is between two periodic points.

4.4 Characterization by Template as Periodic Orbits Holder

We have seen that every chaotic trajectory evolves around periodic orbits, so that these periodic orbits are the *skeleton* of the attractor. It now remains to synthesize all this into some kind of object. For that, we imagine the stretching and folding strip in the same way as we did for the solution of the Rössler equations (Figure 4.18(b)): a template is obtained (Figure 4.25(c)). This final object, the *template*, is a consequence of concept introduced in 1983 by Joan Birman and Robert Williams.[69]

This describes the essentials of the structure of the attractor in the same sense as the idealized horseshoe map: to find the template of the attractor is equivalent to characterizing its topology. Starting from the template it is possible to determine the relative organization of all the periodic orbits that can be found, thanks to symbolic dynamics. For example, the orbits (1), (100) and (101) are shown on the template (Figure 4.26). Once the template is known the entire topological structure

[69] J. S. Birman & R. F. Williams, Knotted periodic orbits in dynamical systems — I. Lorenz's equations, *Topology*, **22** (1), 47–82, 1983. Works by Birman and Williams were developed independently from Rössler's works.

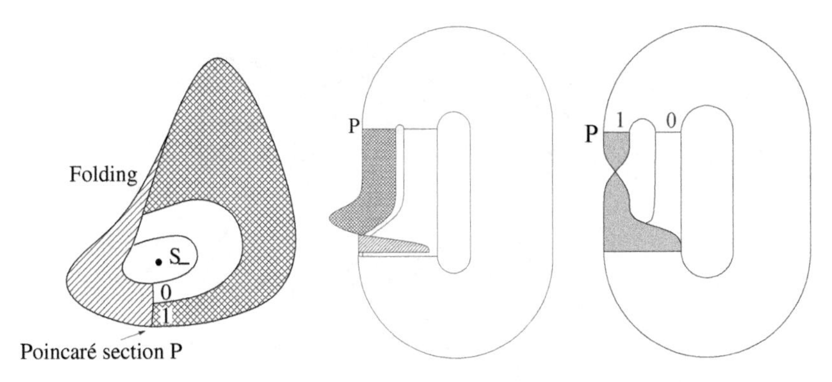

Figure 4.25 Idealization of structure of the stretching and folding strips representing the chaotic attractor produced by the Rössler equations. P designates a Poincaré section on which the periodic orbits can be ordered.

of the attractor is known: the chaotic attractor is an organized structure, invariant and describable, provided with somewhat surprising properties if one recalls the original meaning of the word *chaos*.

4.5 A Simple Model for the Poincaré Map

Consider the very simple recurrence map

$$x_{n+1} = \mu x_n \tag{4.9}$$

where x_n could represent, for example, the value of a population of individuals on January 1 in the nth year and x_{n+1} represents the population on January 1 of the following year. The value during the $(n+1)$st year depends on the value during the nth year according to equation (4.9). Thus, starting from the year 0, the evolution of the population is completely determined by the knowledge of this map, which defines a dynamical system. In this form, the parameter μ in the recurrence map (4.9) roughly represents the rate of growth of the population from one year to the next. This map is a linear system (the map defines a straight line). Only three types of evolution are possible (Figure 4.27):

(1) the rate of reproduction μ is too small and the population disappears;
(2) the reproduction rate μ is sufficient to maintain the population at a constant value;
(3) the rate μ is too large and the population grows indefinitely.

The previous map does not correspond to what is experimentally observed, in particular, that there is a simple value of the rate of growth for which the population remains nearly constant. A second observational fact which is not reproduced by the recurrence map (4.9) is that the growth of a population is in general limited to

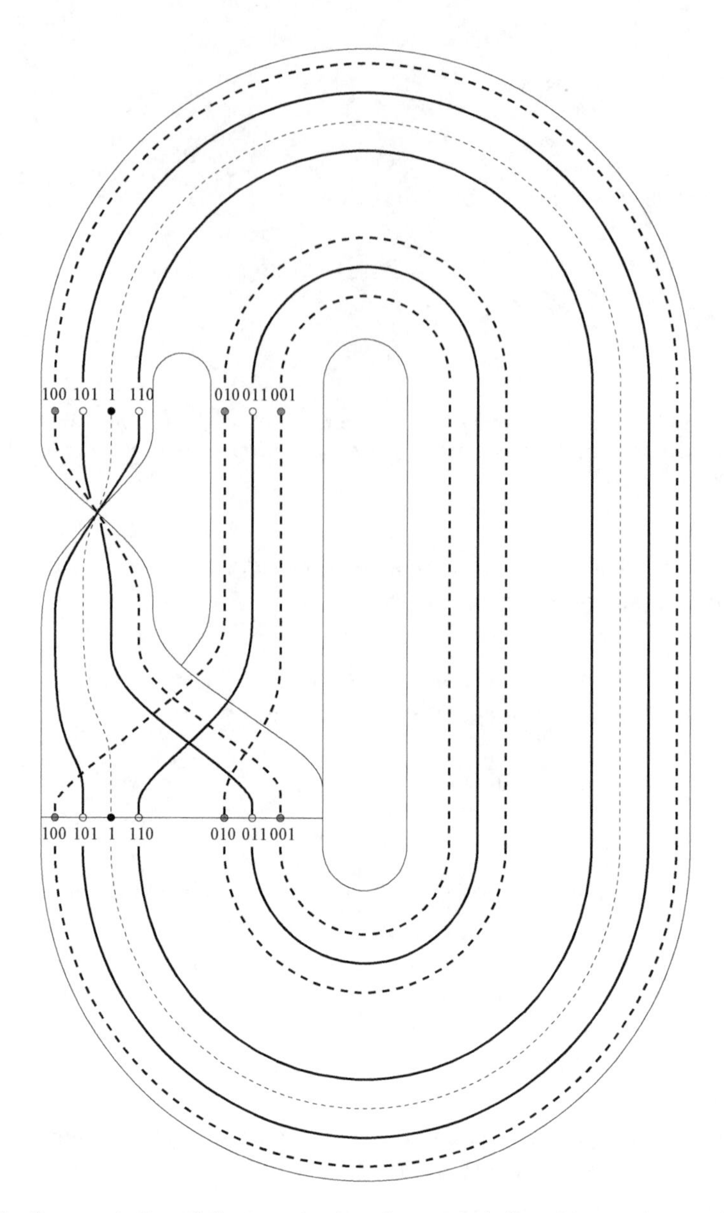

Figure 4.26 Representation of the organization of some periodic orbits on the template for the Rössler attractor. This organization should be compared with the structure observed by extracting these periodic orbits directly from this attractor (Figure 4.24).

the amount of food available. Pierre-François de Verhulst (1804–1849) introduced a second term in the equation (4.9) to take into account this feature. The so-called

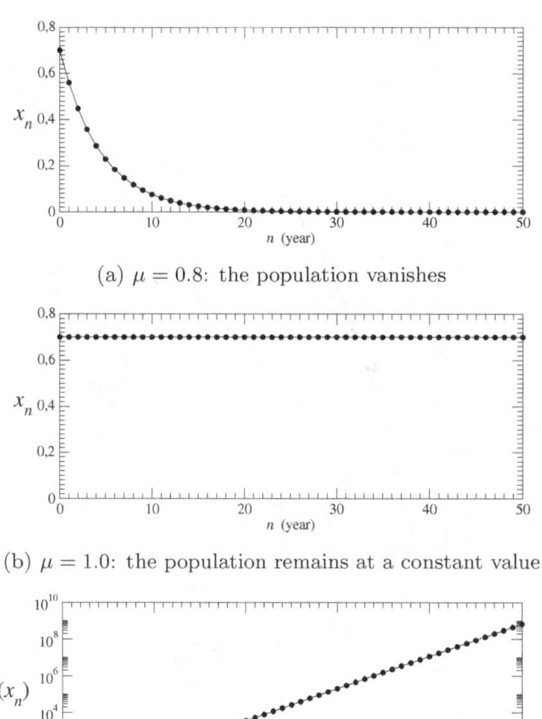

(a) $\mu = 0.8$: the population vanishes

(b) $\mu = 1.0$: the population remains at a constant value

(c) $\mu = 1.5$: the population increases

Figure 4.27 Evolution of the population described by the linear function $x_{n+1} = \mu x_n$. For each value of μ the initial population is equal to 0.7. When the reproduction rate is above 1 the growth is exponential, as shown by the semi-logarithmic representation in (c).

logistic map[70]

$$\begin{aligned} x_{n+1} &= \mu x_n - \mu x_n^2 \\ &= g(x_n)\,, \end{aligned} \tag{4.10}$$

is thus obtained. It is a simple but nontrivial discrete dynamical system. The term μx_n still represents the rate of reproduction of the members of the population while the term $-\mu x_n^2$ is a damping factor representing excess mortality due to overpopulation (the available food is no longer sufficient). This quadratic equation defines a smooth curve with a unique maximum — a bell shaped curve — in the

[70]P.-F. Verhulst, Recherches mathématiques sur la loi d'accroissement de la population, *Nouveaux Mémoires de l'Académie Royale des Sciences et Belles-Lettres de Bruxelles*, **18**, 1–42, 1845. In his paper, Verhulst investigated in fact the differential equation $\dot{x} = \mu x - \mu x^2$. From a relatively small value for the population, an exponential growth is first observed, followed by a saturation of the population at $x = 1$, the inhibiting term $-\mu x^2$ becoming preponderant. He designated the curve produced by this equation the "logistic".

interval $x_n \in [0,1]$. The maximum is at $x_n = \frac{1}{2}$ (Figure 4.28). The dynamics underlying this map is very frequently encountered, as we will have occasion to see below.

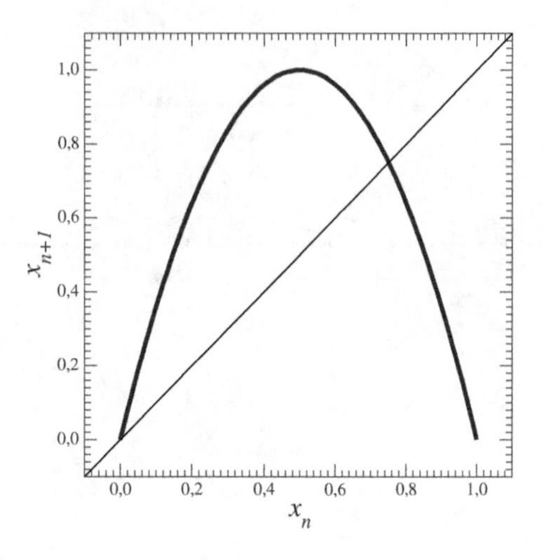

Figure 4.28 The logistic map (4.10) defines a smooth curve with a single maximum. This has an increasing branch and a decreasing branch separated by a maximum where the curve is differentiable ($\mu = 4$).

When we consider the behavior produced by the logistic map (4.10) it is not so simple. There are many different types of behavior depending on the value of the growth rate. If μ remains less than 1 the term μx_n^2 does not play an important role and the population disappears (Figure 4.29(a)). For all values of μ between 1 and 3 it is possible to show that the population stabilizes and then remains constant at $x_c = \frac{\mu-1}{\mu}$, independent of the initial conditions (provided that $x_c \in [0;1]$). The solution x_c defines the attractor which is very simple since it is a single point towards which the value of the population converges; there is a *transient regime* during which population is not "stable" (Figure 4.29(b)).

Truly surprising behavior occurs when the reproduction rate exceeds 3. When $\mu \in]\mu_1 = 3; \mu_2 = 3.449\,489...[$, the value of the population converges to a regime of period two, that is, the population assumes the same value every other year (Figure 4.29(c)). The attractor consists of two periodic points. Once the transients die out, the population oscillates between these two values. When the reproduction rate is further increased, $\mu \in]\mu_2; \mu_3 = 3.544\,090..[$, the population oscillates periodically between four values, and so it continues. *Bifurcations* occur at the values $\mu_1, \mu_2, \mu_3...$. This means that the behavior changes drastically at these values. In the present case a solution of period p becomes a solution of period $2p$: there is a *period-doubling* bifurcation. When the parameter μ is increased, we observe successively a trajectory of period 2, period 4, period 8... There is in fact a cascade of period-doubling bifurcations, leading successively to stable orbits of period 2^n.

Table 4.1 Number N of period-p orbits that a quadratic map may have.

p	1	2	3	4	5	6	7	8	9
N	2	1	2	3	6	9	18	30	56

Pekka Juhana Myrberg (1892–1976) showed that the cascade ends at $\mu_\infty = 3.56995$ with a period-2^∞ orbit: this point is the accumulation point.[71] He also showed that a quadratic map has N period-p orbits as reported in Table 4.1.[72]

There is also a beautiful analysis of the logistic map provided by Lorenz in 1967.[73] In particular, he remarked that for $\mu = 4$, it was possible to show that the value of x_n were determined by the residual of a real number θ modulo 1.[74] In particular, when θ is rational, x_n necessarily belongs to a periodic orbit while the solution is not periodic for irrational θ. Aperiodic solutions are therefore related to periodic solutions as irrational and rational number are. Lorenz thus understood that any stable solution of period-p is in fact stable for some range of μ-values, today called *periodic window*. He intuited that between two different values μ' and μ'' for which the solution is non-periodic, there is always a range of μ values such as $\mu' < \mu < \mu''$ and corresponding to a periodic window. The μ-values for which the solution are periodic form an everywhere dense set, while those for which the solutions are non periodic form a nowhere dense set. Consequently, arbitrarily close to any value of μ, it is possible to find another value of μ for which the solution is periodic. This μ-value lies within a periodic window. There are no aperiodic windows. To end with this contribution, Lorenz also understood that the width of the period-p window "*decreases rapidly as p increases.*" He numerically evidenced these results by computing the average value $\overline{x}$ *versus* the value of parameter μ (Figure 4.30). Some of these results were popularized by Robert May in the mid 1970s.[75]

In fact an infinite number of successive period-doubling bifurcations occur at values μ_i that get closer and closer together. In 1978 Mitchell Feigenbaum[76] and,

---

[71] P. J. Myrberg, Sur l'Itération des polynomes réels quadratiques, *Journal de Mathématiques Pures et Appliquées*, **41** (9), 339–351, 1962 — P. J. Myrberg, Iteration der reellen Polynome zweiten Grades III, *Annales Academiae Scientiarum Fennicae*, **336**, 3–16, 1963. In fact, Myrberg investigated the quadratic recurrence map $x_{n+1} = x_n^2 - \mu$, but it may be shown that any quadratic map has the same qualitative behavior as the logistic map.

[72] P. J. Myrberg, Iteration von Quadratwurzelnoperationen, *Annales Academiae Scientiarum Fennicae*, **259**, 3–16, 1958.

[73] E. N. Lorenz, The problem of deducing the climate from the governing equations, *Tellus*, **16**, 1–11, 1967.

[74] This results from the fact that for $\mu = 4$, the logistic map has $x_n = 4\sin^4(2^n \pi\theta)$ for solution. This solution was first found by Ernst Schröder (1841–1902): E. Schröder, Über iterirte Functionen, *Mathematische Annalen*, **3** (2), 296–322, 1871.

[75] R. May, Simple mathematical models with very complicated dynamics, *Nature*, **261**, 459–657, 1976.

[76] M. J. Feigenbaum, Quantitative Universality for a class of nonlinear transformation, *Journal of Statistical Physics*, **19** (1), 25–52, 1978.

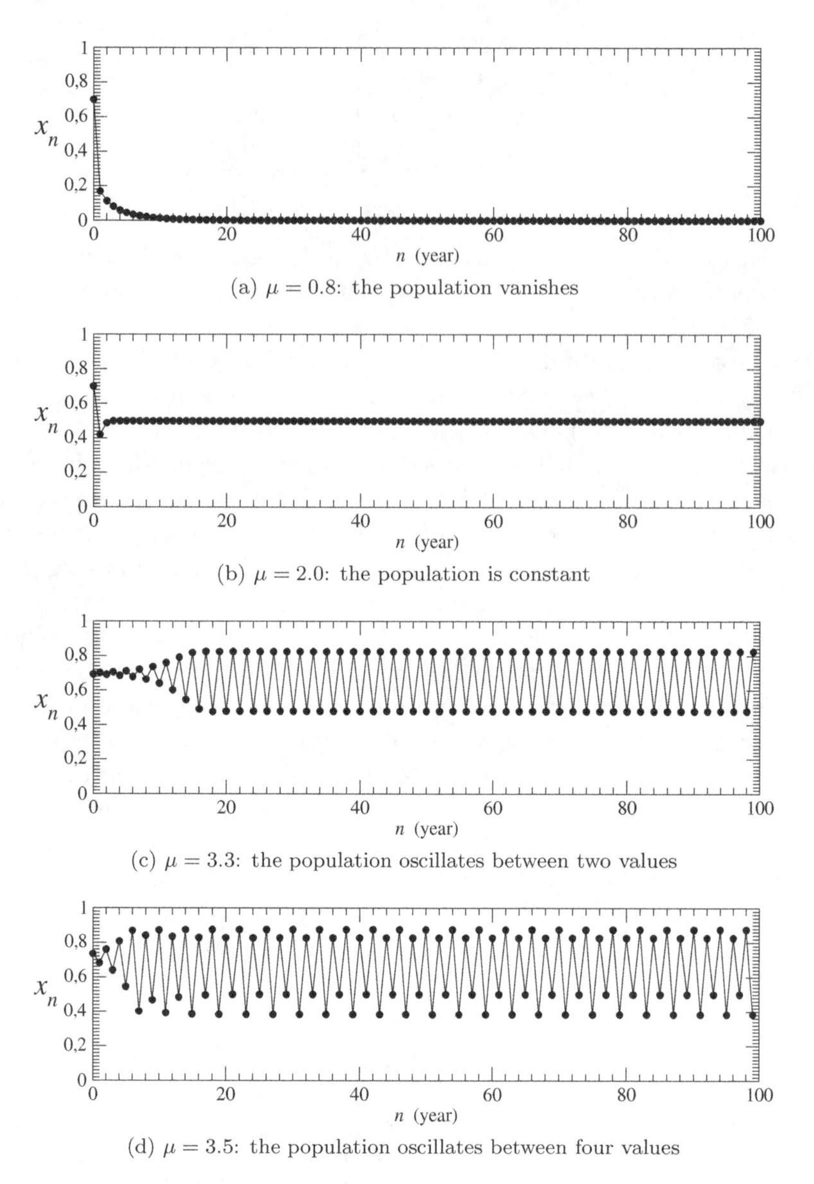

(a) $\mu = 0.8$: the population vanishes

(b) $\mu = 2.0$: the population is constant

(c) $\mu = 3.3$: the population oscillates between two values

(d) $\mu = 3.5$: the population oscillates between four values

Figure 4.29 Evolution of the population described by the logistic function (4.10) for different values of the reproduction rate. The initial condition for each is 0.7.

independently Pierre Coullet and Charles Tresser[77] showed that these values are not arbitrary but that they are related to each other by something called a *scaling*

[77]P. Coullet & C. Tresser, Itérations d'endomorphismes et groupe de renormalisation, *Journal de Physique*, **8** (39), C5-25, 1978.

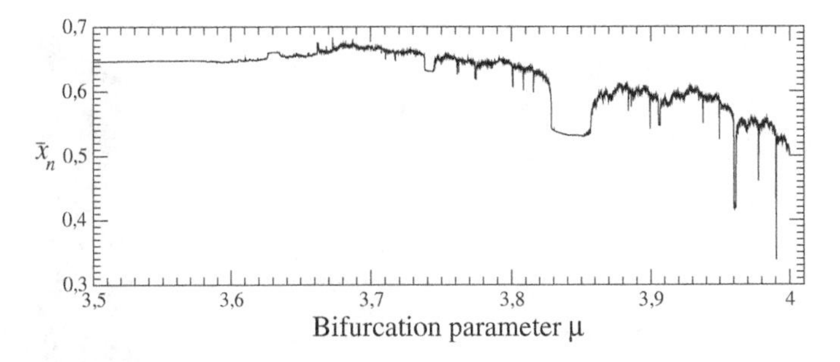

Figure 4.30 Mean value of x_n *versus* the bifurcation parameter μ. When the solution is periodic, the mean value may significantly differ from the one computed for chaotic solution. Thus, the period-3 window is clearly seen for $\mu \in [3.83; 3.85]$ and the period-5 window for $\mu \in [0.3738; 0.3744]$.

law expressed as

$$\delta = \lim_{i \to \infty} \frac{\mu_{i+1} - \mu_i}{\mu_i - \mu_{i-1}} = 4,669\ 201\ 609\ 102\ 9... \tag{4.11}$$

One of the surprising things is that the number δ is the same independent of the mapping function provided it has one increasing branch, a decreasing branch and the two branches are separated by a quadratic maximum where the derivative exists, that is to say, that the function is a smooth unimodal curve. One of the first experimental measurements of this universal number δ was carried out on a small Rayleigh-Bénard convection cell containing mercury.[78] Every recurrence map associated with a smooth unimodal curve produces a period-doubling cascade when a parameter such as μ is varied and the values μ_i at which period-doubling bifurcation occur satisfy the scaling law (4.11), with exactly the same constant δ.

A useful way to show how the population varies as a function of the parameter μ is to show all values that the population can assume over the years as a function of the parameter μ (Figure 4.31). This is called a *bifurcation diagram.*[79] For example, for $\mu = 3.5$ four values are visited (after transients die out): the population "stabilizes itself" and oscillates through four different values. In this diagram one can see that the successive period-doubling bifurcations occur more and more quickly when μ is increased. Very quickly the value of μ is such that the behavior has infinite period: the behavior is aperiodic and there is chaos! In fact, following the end of the cascade the population assumes various values on the interval — depending on the value of μ — without ever repeating (Figure 4.32).

A particular property is seen when the behavior is chaotic: *sensitivity to initial conditions.* Starting at two nearby initial conditions the trajectories begin by evolving in a very similar way, but, after some appropriate time (18 years in our figure) their evolutions become completely different (Figure 4.33).

[78]A. Libchaber, C. Laroche & S. Fauve, Period-doubling cascade in mercury, a quantitative measurement, *Journal de Physique* (Lettres), **43**, L-211–L-216, 1982.

[79]The first bifurcation diagram was possibly published by Robert May and George Oster, Bifurcations and dynamics complexity in simple ecological models, *The American Naturalist*, **110** (974), 573–599, 1976 — but only the beginning of the cascade was shown.

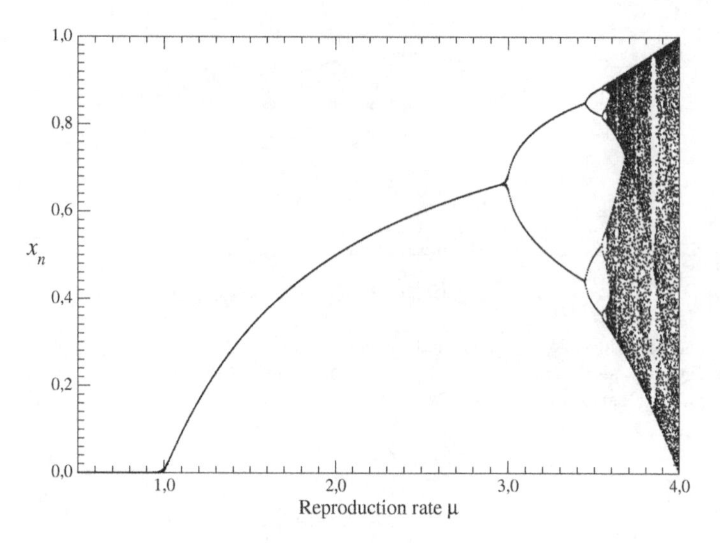

Figure 4.31 Bifurcation diagram for the logistic map. Depending on the reproduction rate, the evolution of the population x_n can assume different values. Beyond the period-doubling cascade the behavior is chaotic. The cascade ends ($p = 2^{\infty}$) at $\mu = 3.56995....$

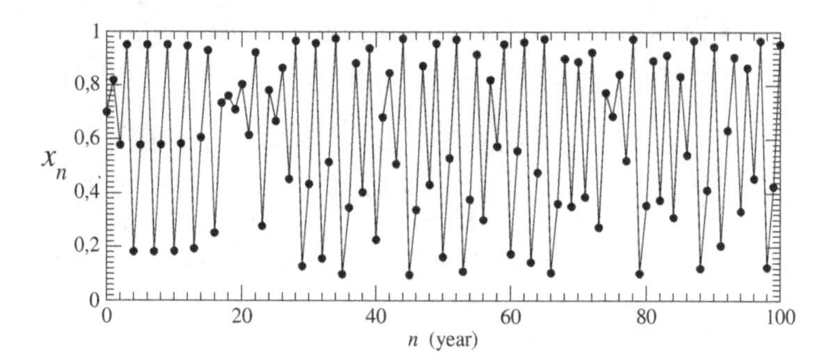

Figure 4.32 Chaotic evolution of the population x_n produced by the logistic map ($\mu = 3.9$).

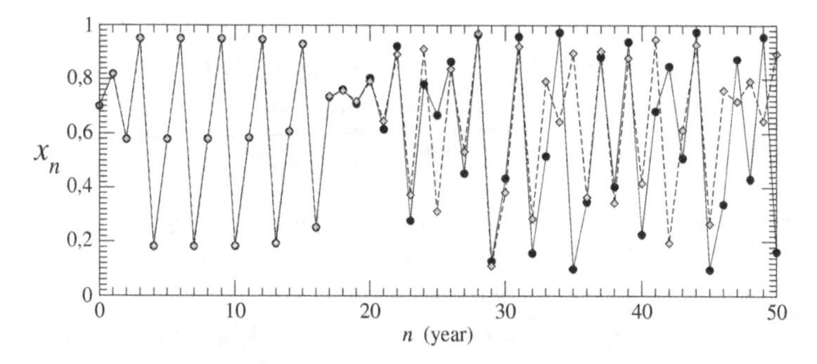

Figure 4.33 Sensitivity to initial conditions in the evolution of a population produced by the logistic map. The two trajectories have neighboring initial conditions with $x_0 = 0.7$ and $x_0 = 0.7 + 0.0000001$.

There are two important features in chaotic behavior that prevent long term predictions: sensitivity to initial conditions which we have just seen, and hopeless expectation to be able to predict the long term future. We demonstrate the second feature as follows. Begin from the initial condition $x_0 = 0.6$ and compute with a pocket computer the next few values of the population using the logistic map (4.10) with the value $\mu = 4$: you should obtain

$$\begin{aligned} x_0 &= 0.6 \\ x_1 &= 0.96 \\ x_2 &= 0.1536 \\ x_3 &= 0.5200281 \\ x_4 &= 0.9983954 \end{aligned}$$

Notice that the number of significant figures after the decimal doubles with each iteration. As a result, because of the limited precision of our calculator (here limited to 7 digits), the value of the population x_3 at the end of three years is approximate because the calculator can provide only seven figures after the decimal: all values following the first seven figures are lost as errors that then grow very quickly. Thus, when numerical calculations are made, one can never exactly know the trajectory because the calculator or computer uses only a finite number of decimal places for these calculations. Even so, round off errors are always done in the same way, so that a computer calculation reproduces the same trajectory time after time, despite the round-off errors. Contrary to this, any small perturbation becomes significant as the number of figures increases in the previous example. The shadowing lemma guarantees that the numerically computed trajectory is near an exact solution.

Observe that long term prediction is impossible. What is true of numerical calculations is even more so for experimental systems because they are inevitably contaminated by environmental noise or measurement imprecisions which make long term predictions impossible. To illustrate, we iterate a population starting from the same initial condition x_0 twice; once using the logistic map (4.10) directly, the second time adding a random variable (with amplitude less than 0.01) at each iterate. This represents external perturbations of the system (measurement noise does not affect the long term evolution of the system because it is added on top of the value x_i in the trajectory). The two trajectories diverge (Figure 4.34) even more quickly than when a small error is added to the initial conditions and the evolution occurs without noise (Figure 4.33). These results show clearly that long term prediction for chaotic systems is not possible, even though they are deterministic.

4.6 Different Topologies for Chaos

Rössler found a relatively simple model of chaotic systems. He continued his work and developed a variety of different types of attractors. For instance, he proposed

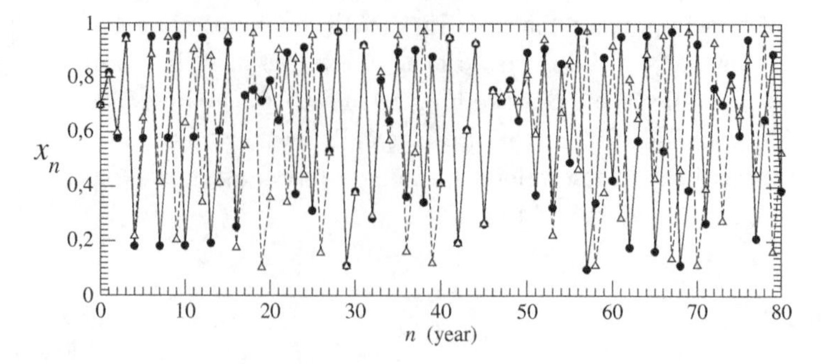

Figure 4.34 Evolution of a population produced by the logistic map, with (solid line) and without noise (dashed line), starting from the same initial condition ($x_0 = 0.7$) for $\mu = 3.9$. A very rapid divergence of the two trajectories occurs. The random perturbations that were added to simulate experimental noise were drawn at random from numbers uniformly distributed between ± 0.01.

the system

$$\begin{cases} \dot{x}_1 = k_1 + k_2' x_1 - \dfrac{k_3 x_2 x_1}{x_1 + K} \\ \dot{x}_2 = k_4 x_1 - k_5 x_2 + k_6 x_3 x_2^2 \\ \dot{x}_3 = k_7 - k_6 x_3 x_2^2 \end{cases} \tag{4.12}$$

that produces an attractor which differs from the Rössler attractor (Figure 4.18(a)) by a global torsion (Figure 4.35(a)):[80] it is thus described by a template with an additional global torsion (compare Figure 4.35(b) to Figure 4.25).

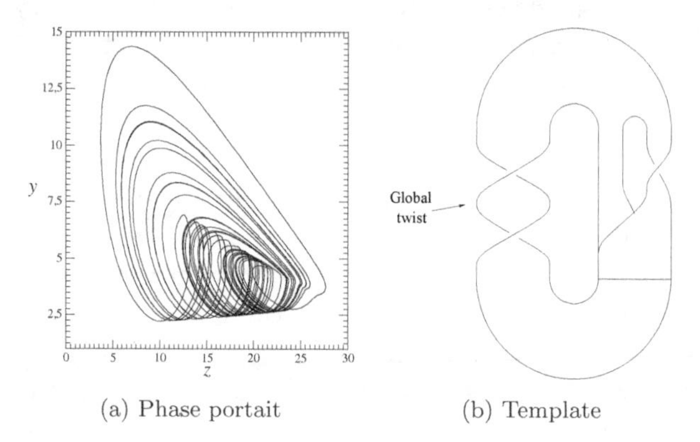

(a) Phase portait (b) Template

Figure 4.35 Another of Rössler's chaotic attractors. The attractor is produced by the system (4.12) and is described by a template with a global torsion of one — the return flow has a full twist. Parameter values: $k_1 = 2$; $k_2' = 0,9$; $k_3 = k_4 = 1$; $k_5 = 0,5$; $k_6 = 0,005$; $k_7 = 1,95$ and $K = 0,1$.

[80] O. E. Rössler, Chaos in abstract kinetics: two prototypes, *Bulletin of Mathematical Biology*, **39** (2), 275–289, 1977.

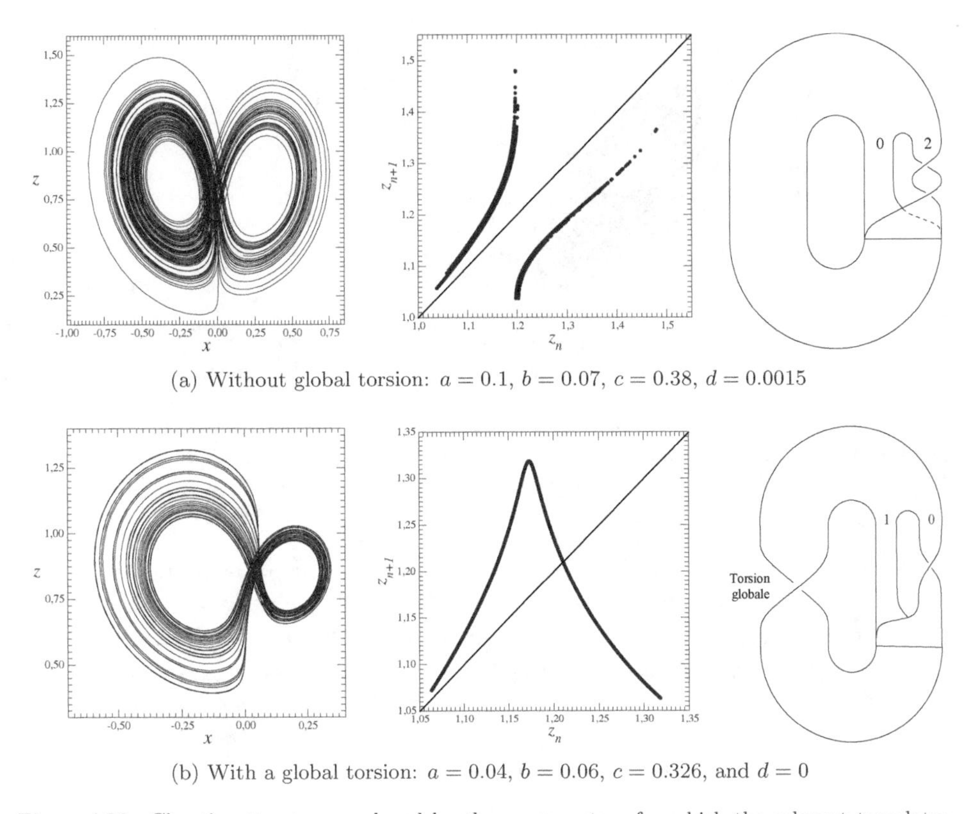

(a) Without global torsion: $a = 0.1$, $b = 0.07$, $c = 0.38$, $d = 0.0015$

(b) With a global torsion: $a = 0.04$, $b = 0.06$, $c = 0.326$, and $d = 0$

Figure 4.36 Chaotic attractors produced by the same system for which the relevant templates and first-return maps clearly show that they are not topologically equivalent.

Otto Rössler was indeed concerned by finding various types of chaotic attractors, that is, which were not topologically equivalent. He thus proposed the system

$$\begin{cases} \dot{x} = x - xy - z \\ \dot{y} = x^2 - ay \\ \dot{z} = bx - cz + d \end{cases} \tag{4.13}$$

which describes a theoretical chemical reaction.[81] Depending on parameter values, this system produces different attractors which are not topologically equivalent. For instance, the chaotic attractor shown in Figure 4.36(a), is particularly interesting because it presents a unimodal first-return map (Figure 4.36(b)) but, contrary to what is observed in almost chaotic attractors characterized by a smooth unimodal first-return map, the two monotonic branches are both increasing, that is, both associated with a strip with an even number of half-turns (preserving order branches). This is only possible when there is a large gap between the two branches at the critical point. Choosing different parameter values led to another attractor

[81] O. Rössler, Different types of chaos in two simple differential equations, *Zeitschrift für Naturforschung A*, **31**, 1664–1670, 1976.

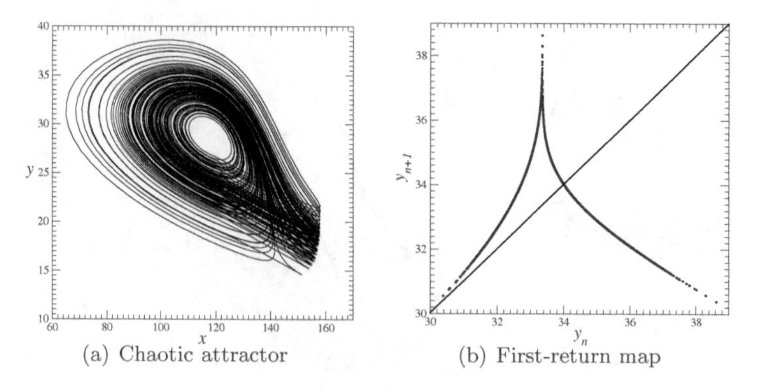

(a) Chaotic attractor (b) First-return map

Figure 4.37 A chaotic attractor solution to the system (4.13) with a "Lorenz map" but without any symmetry. Parameter values: $a = 33$, $b = 150$, $c = 1$, $d = 3.5$, $e = 4815$, $f = 410$, $g = 0.59$, $h = 4$, $j = 2.5$, $k = 2.5$, $l = 5.29$, $m = 750$, $K_1 = 0.01$ and $K_2 = 0.01$.

which, although presenting roughly similar aspects (compare the attractors shown in Figure 4.36(a) and 4.36(b)), is not topologically equivalent to the previous one, a feature evidenced by the first-return map as well as by the templates.

Pursuing his researches for various types of chaos, Rössler also identified the system[82]

$$\begin{cases} \dot{x} = ax + by - cxy - \dfrac{(dz + e)x}{x + K_1} \\ \dot{y} = f + gz - hy - \dfrac{jxy}{y + K_2} \\ \dot{z} = k + lxz - mz \end{cases} \tag{4.14}$$

which produces an attractor which has a first-return map with a look similar to the Lorenz map (compare Figure 4.37 with Figure 3.6) but without the rotation symmetry the Lorenz system has. The chaotic attractor presents a tearing in the neighborhood of the singular point (see Figure 4.37). The template characterizing this attractor does not differ from those associated with the simply stretched and folded ribbon (Figure 4.22). But these two attractors differ by the mechanism responsible for the sensitivity to initial conditions: the model (4.8) published in 1976 involves a folding whereas the chemical system (4.14) proposed with Ortoleva uses a tearing. Both have similar effects on the trajectories but lead to different types of first-return map to a Poincaré section. Folding is characterized by a map with a "continuous" maximum and tearing is associated with a map presenting a cusp located at its extremum.[83] A last system chosen in the large collection of Rössler systems will be now presented because it will be recovered in a famous electronic

[82] O. E. Rössler and P. J. Ortoleva, Strange attractors in 3-variable reaction systems, *Lecture Notes in Biomathematics*, **21**, 67–73, 1978.

[83] G. Byrne, R. Gilmore and C. Letellier, Distinguishing between folding and tearing mechanisms in strange attractors, *Physical Review E*, **70**, 056214, 2004.

circuit. In his attempt to list the different types of chaos, Rössler proposed the system

$$\begin{cases} \dot{x} = -ax - y(1 - x^2) \\ \dot{y} = \mu(y + 0.3x - 2z) \\ \dot{z} = \mu(x + 2y - 0.5z) \end{cases} \tag{4.15}$$

which has the symmetry of Khaikin's universal circuit, that is, there are two symmetric foci around which slow motions occur related by fast jumps.[84] Two plane projections of the chaotic attractor are shown in Figure 4.38(a) and 4.38(b). The structure of the attractor is quite complex. A first-return map is computed using two components for the Poincaré section as required for such a chaotic attractor with symmetry properties.[85] The first-return map is made up of 16 branches (Figure 4.38(c)). The corresponding template therefore has 16 branches (not shown!).

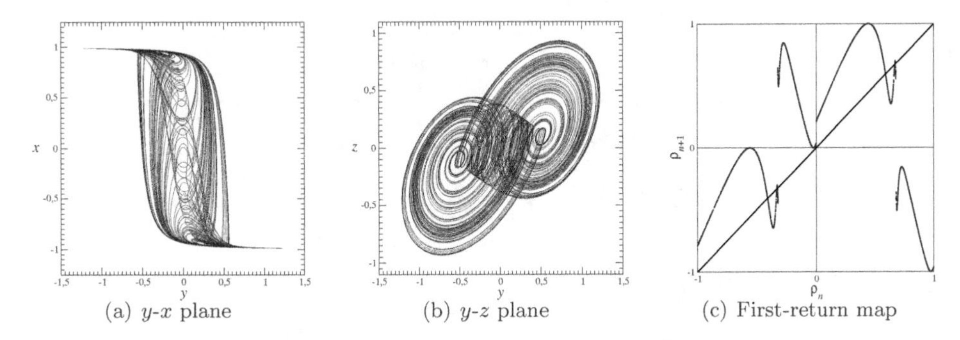

(a) y-x plane (b) y-z plane (c) First-return map

Figure 4.38 The attractor and first-return map associated with a chaotic solution to the system (4.15) with a symmetry. Parameter values: $a = 0.03$ and $\mu = 0.1$ (and not 10 as reported in the Rössler's paper). Initial conditions are chosen such as $x_0 = -1$, $y_0 = 0.55$ and $z_0 = 0.12$.

This two-scroll attractor is topologically equivalent to the attractor produced by the simpler system[86]

$$\begin{cases} \dot{x} = y - \delta z \\ \dot{y} = -x + 2\gamma y + \alpha z \\ \mu\dot{z} = x + z - z^3 \end{cases} \tag{4.16}$$

governing the dynamics of the electronic circuit (Figure 4.39(a)) proposed in 1978 by Arkady Pikovsky and Mikhail Rabinovich. Parameters of this system are related

[84] O. E. Rössler, Continuous chaos, In *Synergetics* (H. Haken, ed.), Proceedings of the International Workshop on Synergetics at Schloss Elmau (Bavaria, May 2–7, 1977), Springer-Verlag, pp. 184–197, 1977.

[85] C. Letellier, E. Roulin and O. E. Rössler, Inequivalent topologies of chaos in simple equations, *Chaos, Solitons & Fractals*, **28**, 337–360, 2006.

[86] A. S. Pikovski & M. I. Rabinovich, A simple autogenerator with stochastic behavior, *Soviet Physics Doklady*, **23** (3), 183–185, 1978.

to the element of this circuit according to

$$\begin{cases} \alpha = 1 + \beta - 2\gamma\delta \\ \gamma = \dfrac{gL - CR}{2\sqrt{LC}} \\ \delta = \sqrt{\dfrac{C}{L}} \dfrac{U_0}{I_0} \\ \mu = \dfrac{\delta C_1}{C} \,. \end{cases}$$

This circuit produces a double-scroll attractor shown in Figure 4.39(b).

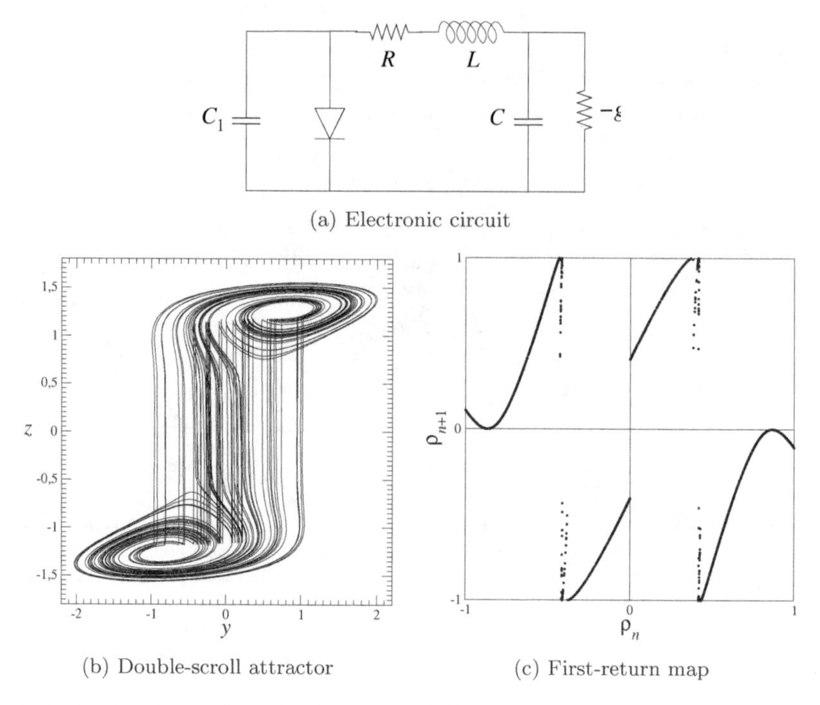

Figure 4.39 Electronic circuit made of a tunnel diode and a negative conductance $-g$ proposed by Pikovsky and Rabinovich for producing a double-scroll attractor. Parameter values: $\alpha = 0.33$, $\gamma = 0.4$, and $\delta = 0.66$.

The best known double-scroll attractor — equivalent to the two previous ones — is produced by the Chua circuit.[87] Chua, always motivated by elegant solutions, that is, the simplest ones, simplified the original set of equations used by Matsumoto (see p. 148) and got the dimensionless equations

$$\begin{cases} \dot{x} = \alpha \left[y - x - f(x) \right] \\ \dot{y} = x - y + z \\ \dot{z} = -\beta y \end{cases} \tag{4.17}$$

[87] T. Matsumoto, L. O. Chua and M. Komuro, The double scroll, *IEEE Transactions on Circuits and Systems*, **CS-33**, 797–818, 1985.

where the characteristic is the piecewise-linear function

$$f(x) = \begin{vmatrix} bx + a - b & & x \geq 1 \\ ax & \text{for} & |x| \leq 1 \\ bx - a + b & & x \leq -1 \end{vmatrix} \tag{4.18}$$

The double-scroll attractor (Figure 4.40(a)) produced by this circuit was topologically characterized under the impulsion of Motomasa Komuro (Department of Mathematics, Tokyo University, Tokyo). This mathematician was highly involved in nonlinear dynamics[88] and was aware about Williams' works on branched manifolds. It was therefore natural for him to describe the structure of the attractor in the state space with great details and in terms of a branched manifold (Figure 4.40(b)).

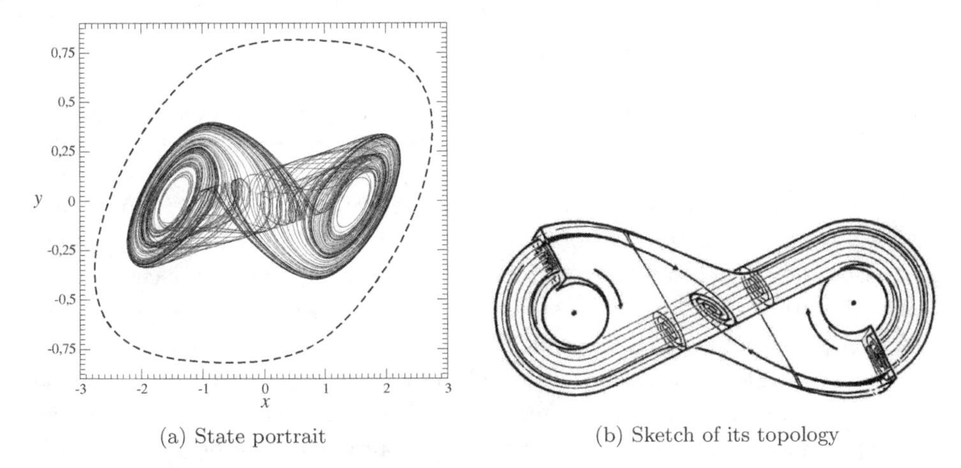

(a) State portrait (b) Sketch of its topology

Figure 4.40 Two-scroll chaotic attractor and its surrounding unstable limit cycle produced by the Chua system (4.17). Parameter values: $\alpha = 9$, $\beta = 10/0.7$, $a = -\frac{8}{7}$ and $b = -\frac{5}{7}$. Initial conditions for the unstable periodic orbit: $x = 2.532735$, $y = 1.285458 \cdot 10^{-3}$ and $z = -4.810689$. A sketch of the topology of the two-scroll attractor, as investigated by Matsumoto, Chua and Komuro in 1985, is also shown.

For slightly different parameter values ($\alpha = 7$ and $6.5 \leq \beta \leq 10.5$), Robert Ghrist and Philip Holmes showed that the Chua system (4.17) satisfies the four properties as follows.[89]

(1) The equations are equivariant under inversion symmetry;
(2) The singular point at the origin is a focus point with eigenvalues $\{\lambda_{\rm s} \pm i\omega, \lambda_{\rm u}\}$ such as $0 < -\lambda_{\rm s} < \lambda_{\rm u}$;

[88] M. Komuro, On embeddings of subshifts of finite type, *Lecture Notes in Mathematics*, **1021**, 299–301, 1983 — M. Komuro, Lorenz attractors do not have the pseudo-orbit tracing property, *Journal of the Mathematical Society of Japan*, **37** (3), 489–514, 1985.
[89] R. Ghrist & P. Holmes, An ODE whose solutions contain all knots and links, *International Journal of Bifurcation & Chaos*, **6** (5), 779–800, 1996.

(3) There is a homoclinic connection at the origin (Figure 4.41);[90]
(4) The homoclinic orbit is unknotted.

In that case, the template describing the topology of the two-scroll attractor contains all possible knots.

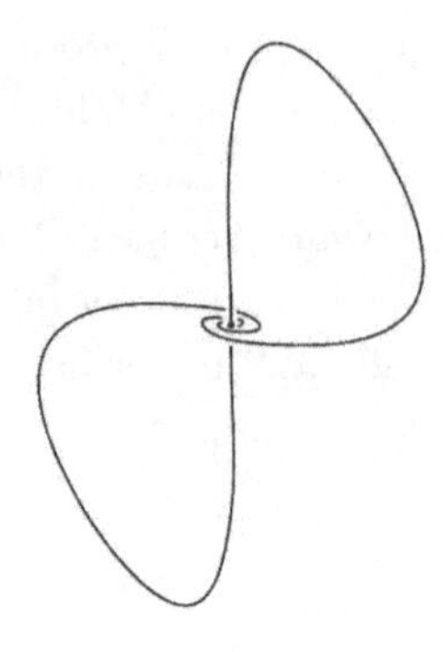

Figure 4.41 Homoclinic connection as proposed by Ghrist and Holmes for the Chua system (4.17). Chua and co-workers proved that the homoclinic connection was realized in the Chua circuit (1986).

The template for the two-scroll chaotic attractor (Figure 4.42(a)) produced by the Chua circuit (4.17) with parameter values as used by Ghrist must be made of eight branches as evidenced in the first-return map to a two-component Poincaré section (Figure 4.42(b)). Note that due to the inversion symmetry — an order-2 symmetry — that the Chua circuit has, a convenient Poincaré section must be made of two components, one in each scroll as shown in Figure 4.42(a).[91] There are indeed four different monotonic branches in each scroll, labelled "0", "1", "3", and "4", respectively. Since each branch of the first-return map must be associated with one branch of the template, a template (Figure 4.42(c)) made of eight branches was proposed for this double-scroll attractor.[92]

The template proposed by Ghrist (Figure 4.43(c)) has obviously only four branches and not eight. The "universal" template, containing all type of knots, must therefore be the subtemplate of the eight-branch shown in Figure 4.42(c). Since only branches "0" and "4" do not present local torsion (writhe), it is possible to start from the subtemplate made of these four branches (Figure 4.43(a)) and to transform it in the universal template under an isotopy (a continuous deformation without using cisors). This is schemed by two moves whose results are shown in Figure 4.43(b) and 4.43(c), thus proving that the double-scroll contains all knots.

[90]This was proved by L. O. Chua, M. Komuro and T. Matsumoto, The Double Scroll Family, *IEEE Transactions on Circuit and Systems*, **33** (11), 1073–1118, 1986.

[91]C. Letellier Modding out a continuous rotation symmetry for disentangling a laser dynamics, International Journal of Bifurcation and Chaos, 13 (6), 1573–1577, 2003 — C. Letellier & R. Gilmore, Poincaré sections for a new three-dimensional toroidal attractor, *Journal of Physics A*, **42**, 015101, 2009.

[92]C. Letellier and R. Gilmore, The universal template is a subtemplate of the double-scroll template, *Journal of Physics A*, **46**, 065102, 2013.

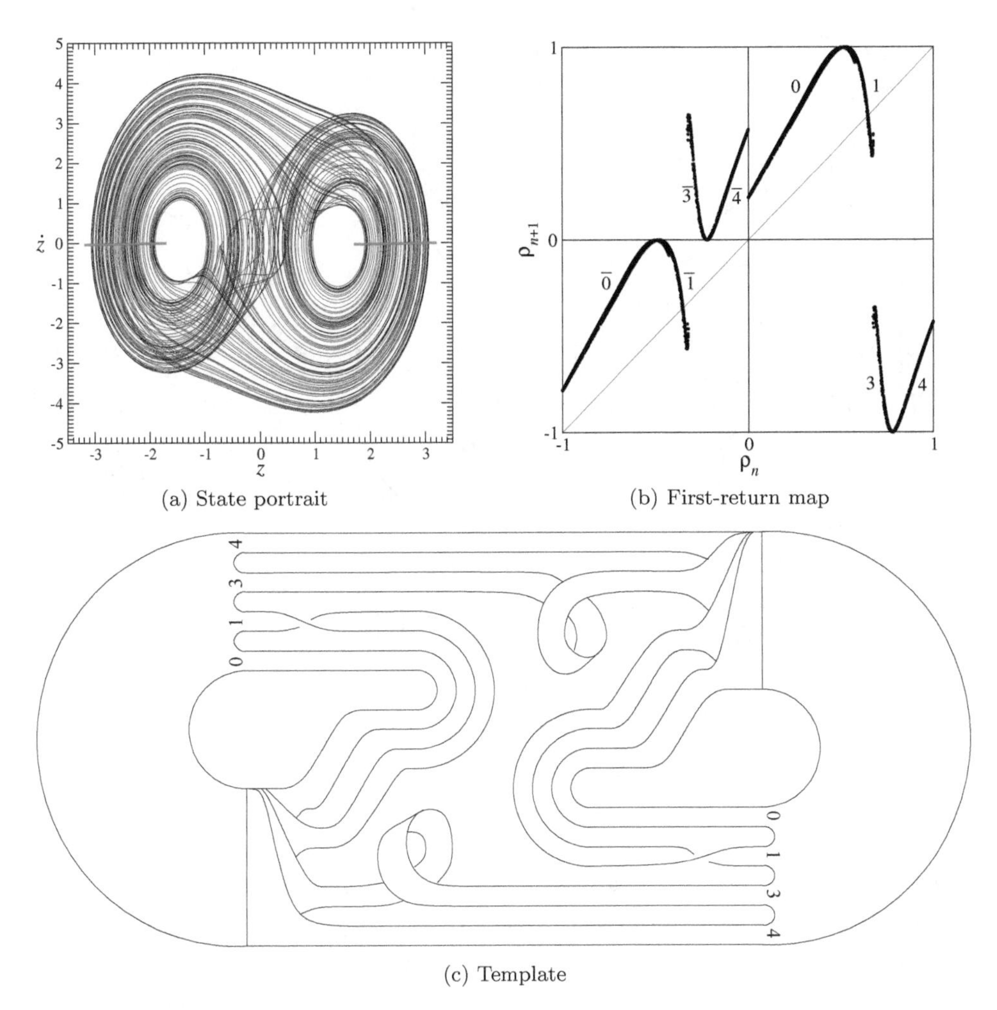

(a) State portrait (b) First-return map

(c) Template

Figure 4.42 Chaotic attractor produced by the Chua system (4.17). Parameter values: $\alpha = 7$ and $\beta = 9$. Adapted from Letellier and Gilmore, 2013.

As a result, double-scroll attractors are rather complex attractor not very easy to characterize and, from that point of view, be considered with precautions when used for testing a new method for analyzing chaotic dynamics.

4.6.1 *A Zoo of Chaotic Attractors*

Using the slightly modified Chua equations

$$\begin{cases} \dot{x} = \kappa\alpha\,(y - x - \phi) \\ \dot{y} = \kappa\,(x - y + z) \\ \dot{z} = -\kappa\,(\beta y + \gamma z) \end{cases} \tag{4.19}$$

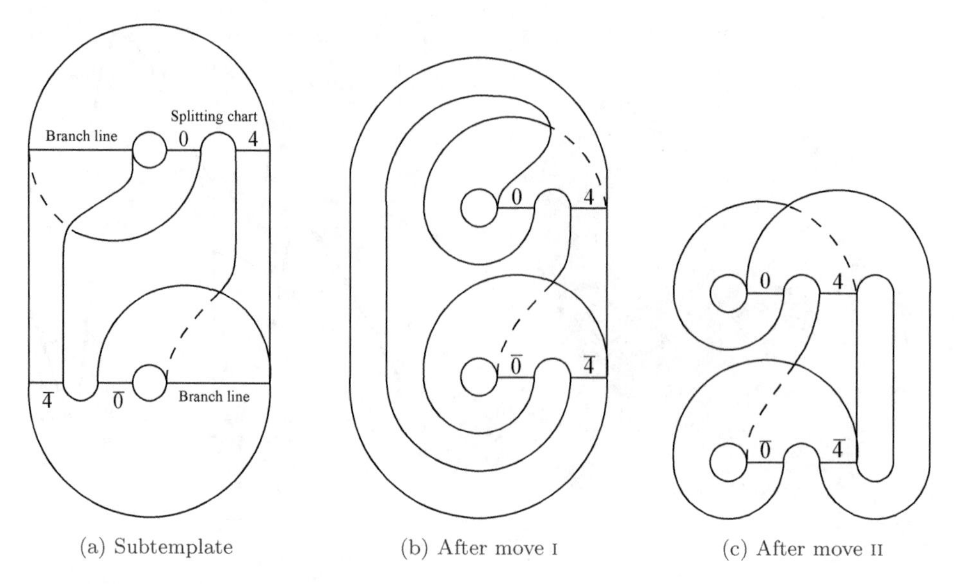

(a) Subtemplate (b) After move I (c) After move II

Figure 4.43 A subtemplate is obtained by removing branches 2 and 3 from the double-scroll template shown in Figure 4.42(c) by removing the four branches labelled "1" and "3". Move I: the upper branch line is identified with the upper splitting chart and the bottom splitting chart is identified with the bottom branch line (b). Move II: branch 4 is moved from the left to the right, leading to the universal template (c).

where the piecewise-linear function is

$$\phi = bx + \frac{(a-b)\left(|x+1| - |x-1|\right)}{2}, \tag{4.20}$$

Chua and co-workers obtained various chaotic attractors with different topologies (Figure 4.44).[93] For each different topology, the most suggestive plane projection is shown. Let us start with two asymmetric funnel attractors (Figure 4.44(a)) which can fuse into a single symmetric attractor through a merging attractor crisis when one of the parameters is varied: the resulting symmetric attractor is shown in Figure 4.44(b). This is not exactly a common double-scroll attractor in the sense that there are foldings in each scroll in the latter but not in the former. Depending on parameter values, the winding number in the funnel may vary but there is no crucial departure in the resulting topology.

A very special attractor, here named the "cord" attractor according to the "cords" linking the two scrolls, is shown in Figure 4.44(c). To our knowledge, this attractor was never reported elsewhere. Another cord attractor was found by Luis A. Aguirre.[94]

[93]L. O. Chua, M. Komuro & T. Matsumoto, A universal circuit for studying and generating chaos — Part II: Strange attractors, *IEEE Transactions on Circuit and Systems*, **40** (10), 745–761 (1993).

[94]C. Letellier & L. A. Aguirre, Required criteria for recognizing new types of chaos: Application to the "cord" attractor, *Physical Review E*, **85**, 036204, 2012.

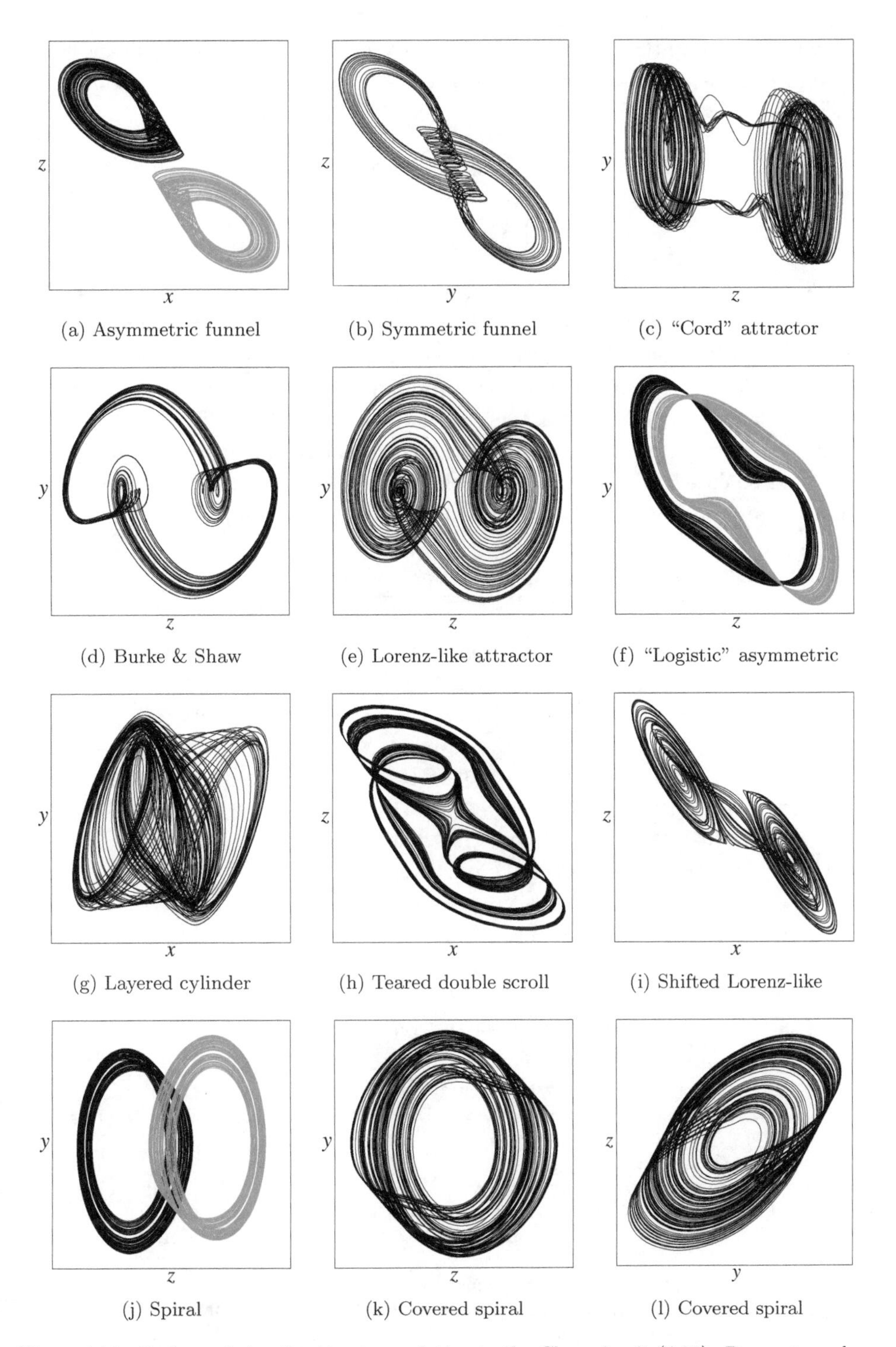

(a) Asymmetric funnel
(b) Symmetric funnel
(c) "Cord" attractor
(d) Burke & Shaw
(e) Lorenz-like attractor
(f) "Logistic" asymmetric
(g) Layered cylinder
(h) Teared double scroll
(i) Shifted Lorenz-like
(j) Spiral
(k) Covered spiral
(l) Covered spiral

Figure 4.44 Zoology of chaotic attractors solution to the Chua circuit (4.19). Parameter values are reported in Table 4.2.

The symmetric attractor shown in Figure 4.44(d) looks like a Burke and Shaw attractor, that is, an attractor which can be observed in the Burke and Shaw system[95]

$$\begin{cases} \dot{x} = -S(x+y) \\ \dot{y} = -y - Sxz \\ \dot{z} = Sxy + V \end{cases} \tag{4.21}$$

with $S = 10$, and $V = 4.272$. Such an attractor is rather common in Lorenz-like systems.[96] In fact, there is also a Lorenz attractor (Figure 4.44(e)) produced by the system (4.19) but it has an inversion symmetry and not a rotation symmetry like the original Lorenz attractor. It is also possible to observe in the Chua circuit (4.19) two attractors obtained after a period-doubling cascade as observed in the Lorenz system for large R values.[97] These attractors have a Logistic-like first-return map to a Poincaré section. Once again, these attractors are related by an inversion symmetry and not by a rotation symmetry as observed in the Lorenz system.

Table 4.2 Parameter values used to produce the attractors with system (4.19).

Fig.	α	β	γ	a	b	κ
4.44a	-1.5590535	0.0156453	0.1374556	-0.24385532	-0.0425189	-1
4.44b	-1.5590535	0.0156453	0.1574556	-0.2438532	-0.0425189	-1
4.44c	-1.3184010	0.0125741	0.1328593	-0.2241328	-0.0281101	-1
4.44d	-4.08685	-2.0	0	-1.142837	-0.7142858	+1
4.44e	-4.898979	-3.624135	-0.00118088	-2.501256	-0.9297201	+1
4.44f	-1.3635256	-0.0874054	-0.3114345	1.292150	-0.49717	-1
4.44g	3.7091002	24.0799705	-0.8592556	-2.7647222	0.1805569	+1
4.44h	-1.458906	-0.0930819	-0.3214346	1.218416	-0.5128436	-1
4.44i	143.1037	207.34198	-3.8767721	-0.855372	-1.09956	-1
4.44j	6.5792294	10.8976626	-0.0447440	-1.1819730	-0.6523354	+1
4.44k	8.4562218	12.0732335	0.0051631	-0.7056296	-1.1467573	-1
4.44l	-75.6	31.25	-3.125	-2.4	-0.98	-1
4.45	12.1414141	95.7977567	-0.8985829	-0.8557143	-1.1	-1
4.46	as specified	91.5210060	-0.7303376	-0.8557143	-1.1	-1
4.46	3.505	66.672752	-0.94779892	-0.855372	-1.09956	-1

[95] R. Shaw, Strange attractor, chaotic behavior and information flow, *Zeitschrift fÃ¼r Naturforschung A*, **36**, 80–112, 1981 — C. Letellier, P. Dutertre, J. Reizner & G. Gouesbet, Evolution of multimodal map induced by an equivariant vector field, *Journal of Physics A*, **29**, 5359–5373, 1996.

[96] C. Letellier, T. Tsankov, G. Byrne & R. Gilmore, Large-scale structural reorganization of strange attractors, *Physical Review E*, **72**, 026212, 2005 — C. Letellier, G. F. V. Amaral & L. A. Aguirre, Insights into the algebraic structure of Lorenz-like systems using feedback circuit analysis and piecewise affine models, *Chaos*, **17**, 023104, 2007.

[97] O. E. Rössler, Horseshoe map in the Lorenz equation, *Physical Letters A*, **60** (5), 392–394, 1977.

A "strange" attractor with a complex topology has also been observed (Figure 4.44(g)). Its complexity comes from the central zone located between the two scrolls. It will be shown below that such a structure is related to a toroidal structure. An attractor (Figure 4.44(h)) similar to an attractor solution to a simple model for a pulsating star[98] was also found in the modified Chua circuit (4.19). This attractor has a very different structure from all the others already discussed. A topologically equivalent attractor produced by this pulsating star model was investigated in Letellier's Ph.D. Thesis.[99] The two scrolls are quite similar to the two scrolls of the common double-scroll attractor but the way in which they are linked is rather unusual. It looks like a Lorenz attractor whose central part was mirrored. Note that such a special topology seems to be only observed in a system with an inversion symmetry.

The last three attractors (Figure 4.44(j), 4.44(k), and 4.44(l)) are all related to the Rössler spiral attractor. The first ones (Figure 4.44(j)) are two symmetry-related spiral attractors. They may become a single symmetric chaotic attractor through a merging attractor crisis. The case of the attractors shown in Figure 4.44(k) looks like a two-fold cover of a spiral Rössler attractor.[100] It is thus a symmetric Rössler attractor with two foldings, one being the symmetric of the other under an inversion symmetry. A second example of such a two-fold cover was also obtained (Figure 4.44(l)), but with a different orientation in the state space compared to the attractor shown in Figure 4.44(k). In spite of this, the last two attractors are topologically equivalent. The richness of the dynamics produced by the Chua circuit could result from the fact that it is characterized by an universal template as discussed p. 236.

4.7 Toroidal Chaos

Using the Chua circuit (4.19), Chua and co-workers obtained a quasi-periodic regime (Figure 4.45(a)) whose Poincaré section is a regular closed loop (Figure 4.45(b)) as expected.[101] More surprisingly, they observed a folded torus, that is, a toroidal chaotic attractor (Figure 4.46). Toroidal chaos produced by three-dimensional autonomous system is quite rare, and only very few examples are known.[102] Varying the value of the capacitance C_1 allows to developed the toroidal chaotic regime

[98] M. Auvergne & A. Baglin, A dynamical instability as a driving mechanism for stellar oscillations, *Astronomy & Astrophysics*, **142**, 388–392, 1985.

[99] C. Letellier, *Caractérisation topologique et reconstruction des attracteurs étranges*, Ph.D. Thesis, University of Paris VIII, 1994.

[100] C. Letellier & R. Gilmore, Covering dynamical systems: Two-fold covers, *Physical Review E*, **63**, 16206, 2001.

[101] L. O. Chua, M. Komuro & T. Matsumoto, A universal circuit for studying and generating chaos — Part II: Strange attractors, *IEEE Transactions on Circuit and Systems*, **40** (10), 745–761, 1993.

[102] Bo Deng, Constructing homoclinic orbits and chaotic attractors, *International Journal of Bifurcation & Chaos*, **4** (4), 823–841, 1994 — D. Li, A three-scroll chaotic attractor, *Physics Letters A*, **372** (4), 387–393 2008 — C. Letellier & R. Gilmore, Poincaré sections for a new three-dimensional toroidal attractor, *Journal of Physics A*, **42**, 015101, 2009.

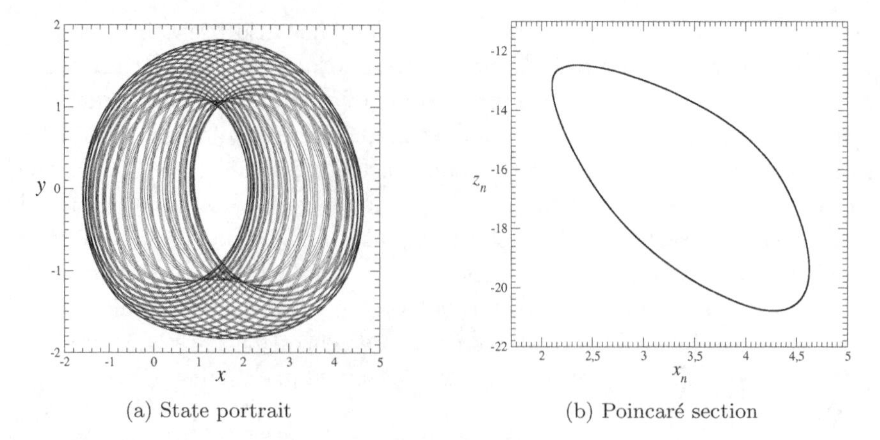

(a) State portrait

(b) Poincaré section

Figure 4.45 Quasi-periodic regime produced by Chua circuit (4.19). Parameter values: $C_1 = 0.0297$ μF, $C_2 = 0.3606$ μF, $G_a = 0.599$ mS, $G_b = 0.77$ mS, $R = -1/0.0007$ Ω, $R_0 = 13.4$ Ω, and $L = 7.682$ mH.

(Figure 4.46(b) and 4.46(c)). Just before a boundary crisis leaving a single singular point for attractor, the toroidal attractor (Figure 4.46(d)) has a structure reminiscent of the double-scroll attractor. When parameter α is decreased, another very strange toroidal structure is obtained (Figure 4.46(a)) just before a second boundary crisis. These types of toroidal chaotic attractors are not yet fully understood and remain to be more carefully investigated.

A "torus circuit" was investigated by Matsumoto and co-workers using the governing equations[103]

$$\begin{cases} \dot{x} = -\alpha f(y-x) \\ \dot{y} = -z - f(y-x) \\ \dot{z} = \beta z \end{cases} \tag{4.22}$$

where the piecewise-linear function reads as

$$f(u) = -au + \frac{a+b}{2}\left(|u+1| - |u-1|\right). \tag{4.23}$$

For some parameter values, a toroidal chaotic attractor was obtained (Figure 4.47). It was shown that three mechanisms responsible for the breakdown of a torus T^2 are realized in the torus circuit. They are[104]

i) a transition via a cascade of period-doubling bifurcations;
ii) an abrupt transition to chaos in the homoclinic region via saddle-node bifurcation of a limit cycle;
iii) a soft transition to chaos due to the loss of torus smoothness.

[103] T. Matsumoto, L. O. Chua & R. Tokunaga, Chaos via torus breakdown, *IEEE Transactions on Circuits and Systems*, **34** (3), 240–253, 1987.

[104] V. S. Anishchenko, M. A. Safanova & L. O. Chua, Confirmation of the Afraimovich-Shilnikov torus-breakdown theorem via a torus circuit, *IEEE Transactions on Circuit and Systems*, **40** (10), 792–800, 1993.

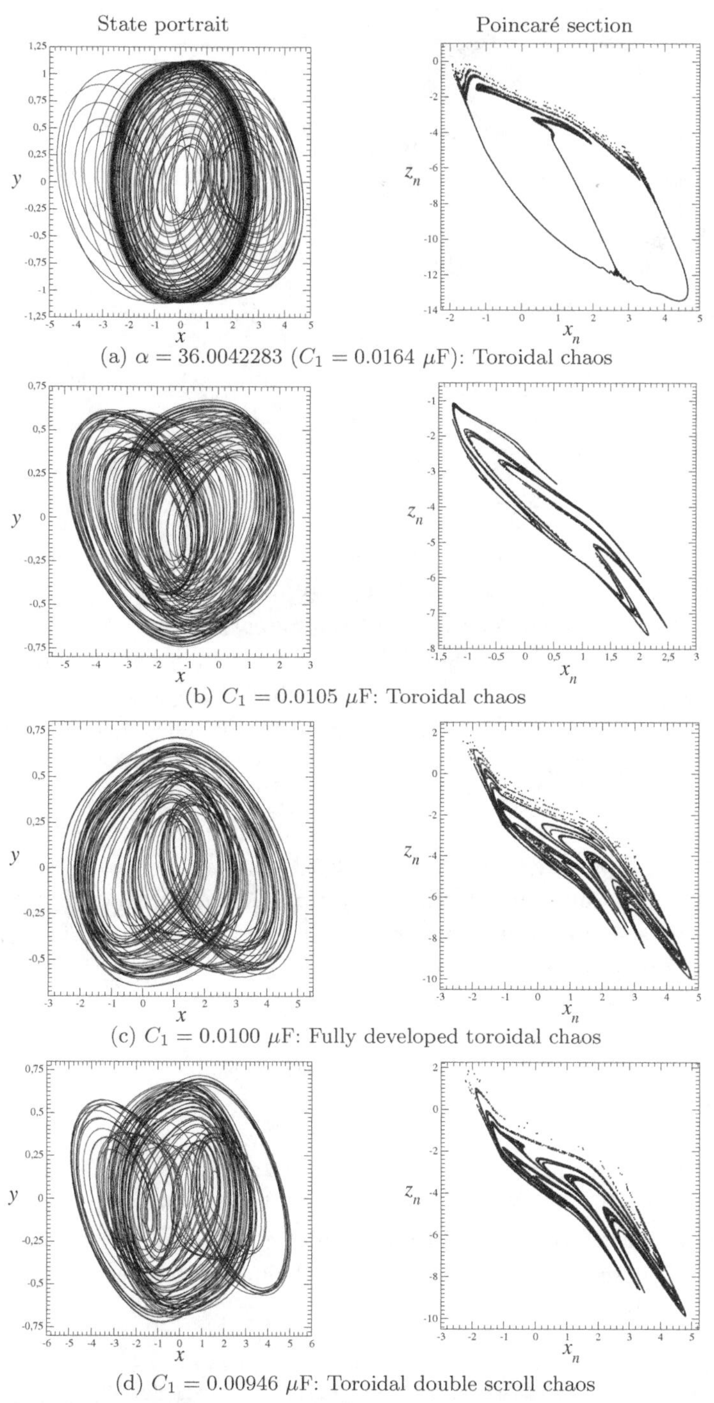

(a) $\alpha = 36.0042283$ ($C_1 = 0.0164$ μF): Toroidal chaos

(b) $C_1 = 0.0105$ μF: Toroidal chaos

(c) $C_1 = 0.0100$ μF: Fully developed toroidal chaos

(d) $C_1 = 0.00946$ μF: Toroidal double scroll chaos

Figure 4.46 Toroidal chaotic attractors solution to the Chua circuit (4.19). Parameter values: $C_2 = 0.3406$ μF, $G_a = 0.599$ mS, $G_b = 0.77$ mS, $R = -1/0.0007\Omega$, $R_0 = 11.4\Omega$, $L = 7.595$ mH and corresponding values of α, β, γ, a, b and κ are reported in Table 4.2.

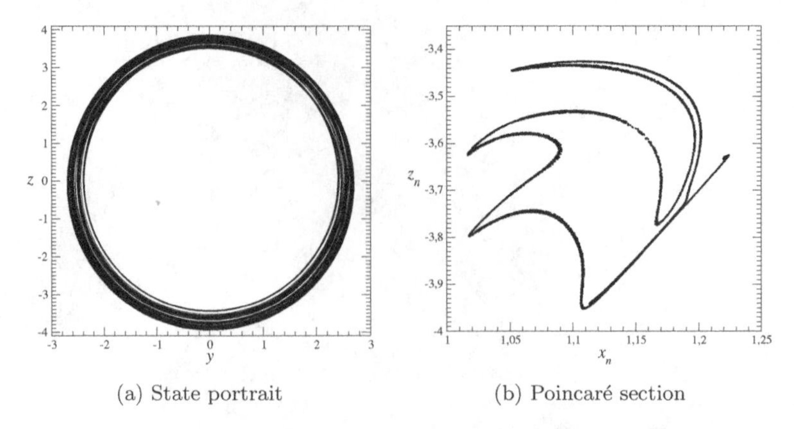

(a) State portrait (b) Poincaré section

Figure 4.47 Toroidal chaotic attractor produced by the "torus circuit" (4.22). Parameter values: $a = 0.07$, $b = 0.10$, $\alpha = 27.65$, and $\beta = 2.12$.

All these toroidal attractors are based on a torus T^2 structure. Higher-dimensional tori T^n ($n > 2$) obviously require higher-dimensional systems to produce them. If there is no explicit nontrivial example in Chua's works of such torus, they were mentioned in the book written with Thomas S. Parker when they introduced "higher-order Poincaré maps" (Section 2.3 of that book[105]) corresponding to section of Poincaré section. The idea was to reduce the dimension of the limit set to investigate by sampling $(n-1)$ times the trajectory up to recover a two-dimensional object. For instance, a torus T^3 characterized by three independent frequencies f_1, f_2, and f_3 would be investigated by using a second-order Poincaré map to perform a double sampling: the trajectory would be thus sampled at f_1 and f_2 simultaneously. While Parker and Chua provided a trivial example with a solution resulting from the sum of three sinusoids characterized by three incommensurable frequencies, let us exemplify this procedure with the three variables map[106]

$$\begin{cases} x_{k+1} = -ay_k^2 + z_k \\ y_{k+1} = x_k + b + cx_ky_k + dz_k \\ z_{k+1} = y_k \end{cases} \tag{4.24}$$

which corresponds to the first-order Poincaré map of a torus T^3. With a single plane projection — or a first-order Poincaré map — (Figure 4.48(a)), it is rather difficult to figure out that it corresponds to a toroidal chaos. But the toroidal structure characterized by an annular shape becomes obvious with a second-order Poincaré map computed by selecting points $x_k \in [-\epsilon; +\epsilon]$. The limit set is approached as $\epsilon \to 0$.

[105] T. S. Parker & L. O. Chua, *Practical numerical algorithms for chaotic systems*, Springer-Verlag, 1989.

[106] M. Klein, G. Baier & O. E. Rössler, From n-tori to hyperchaos, *Chaos, Solitons & Fractals*, **1** (2), 105–118, 1991.

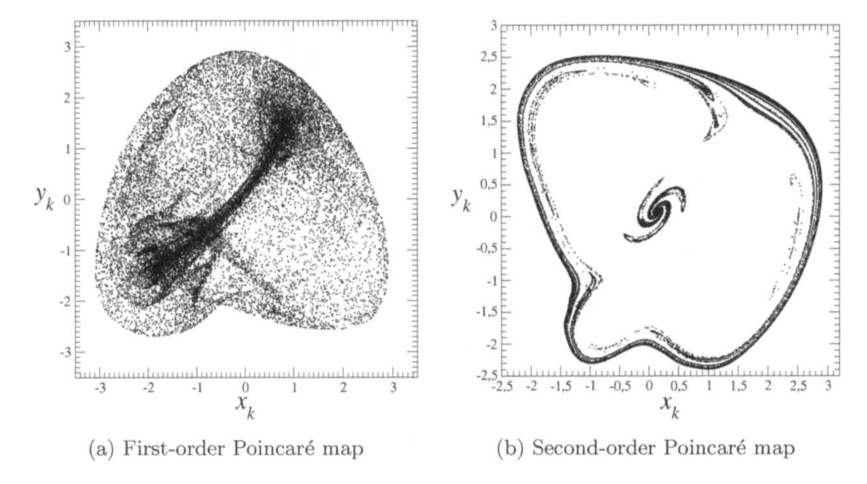

(a) First-order Poincaré map (b) Second-order Poincaré map

Figure 4.48 Toroidal chaos structured around a torus T^3 solution to map (4.24). Parameter values: $a = 0.28$, $b = c = 0.2$ and $d = 0.125$. The second-order Poincaré (b) map was obtained using $x_k \in [-\epsilon; +\epsilon]$ with $\epsilon = 0.005$.

The advantage of a higher-order Poincaré map is that it allows easier identification of torus T^k. But, as mentioned by Parker and Chua, "*the main drawback of the higher-order Poincaré map is that it requires an enormous amount of input data to produce a reasonable amount of output.* [...] *Another disadvantage is that, owing to the ϵ-neighborhood, the limit sets are fuzzy — a point becomes a segment and a circle becomes an annulus. This effect can be lessened by choosing a smaller value of ϵ, but this will increase the simulation time since more data points are required.*" Such a technique was for instance used to investigate non trivial toroidal chaos in a laser system.[107]

4.8 Conclusion

In the final analysis systems of three variables are correctly described by using templates that describe the different classes of chaotic behavior. Chaotic systems — originally considered as impossible to describe — can finally be described, at least when considered in their state spaces, where time is not explicitly present. It is not really necessary to understand the time evolution explicitly — in fact long term prediction is impossible — but it is possible to identify its behavior, to understand its structure. In the midst of the 1970s in a remarkable effort Rössler clearly identified the basic processes that produce chaotic behavior and synthesized these into a simple way to view this behavior. He opened the door to a really global approach to understanding chaotic behavior that did not depend on more quantitative classical methods.

[107] D. Amroun-Aliane, L. Pastur & C. Letellier, Defects in spatiotemporal diagrams and their relations to phase coherence and lack of observability, *Physical Review E*, **83**, 056212, 2011.

Chapter 5

Chemical Reactions

5.1 The Earliest Experiments

Chemical reactions are among the first phenomena for which chaotic behavior was observed. Most often, chemical reactions evolve in one direction in time: they progressively consume some species, the reactants, and produce others, the products. Nevertheless, there are some reactions that produce periodic oscillations in the chemical concentrations. One of the first oscillating chemical reactions was observed by Georg Bredig (1878–1956) and Andreas Antropoff (1868–1944) around 1906.[1] We should point out that reaction took place in a heterogeneous medium, which could explain why oscillations occurred. The first oscillating chemical reaction in a homogeneous solution was produced by William Bray and Asa Caulkins in 1917.[2] It was based on the decomposition of hydrogen peroxide H_2O_2 in an acid medium, catalyzed by an iodine/iodate combination I_2/IO_3^-. This reaction concerns the oxidation of iode in ionic acid

$$5H_2O_2 + I_2 = 2HIO_2 + 4H_2O$$

and the reduction of ionic acid in iode

$$5H_2O_2 + 2HIO_2 = 5O_2 + I_2 + 6H_2O\,.$$

Bray and Caulkins chose to investigate this redox couple since they hoped to be able to catalize the decomposition of oxygenated water. The oscillating nature of this reaction is clearly evident in Figure 5.1. The reaction took place in a closed reaction vessel, without the addition of reactants, so that the oscillations died out in this transient regime and the reaction moved to chemical equilibrium, a singular point. The possibility of decaying oscillations had been announced after a study in 1904 of a hypothetical autocatalytic reaction[3] — since at that time "*no reaction is known which follows the* [mentioned] *law* [...] *of damped oscillations*" — by Alfred Lotka

[1] G. Bredig & A. von Antropoff, Über Quecksilberperoxydat, *Zeitschrift für Elektrochemie*, **12**, 585–589, 1906.

[2] W. C. Bray, A Periodic Reaction in homogeneous solution and its relation to catalysis, *Journal of the American Chemical Society*, **43**, 1262–1267, 1921.

[3] A. J. Lotka, Contribution to the theory of periodic reactions, *Journal of Physical Chemistry*, **14**, 271–274, 1910.

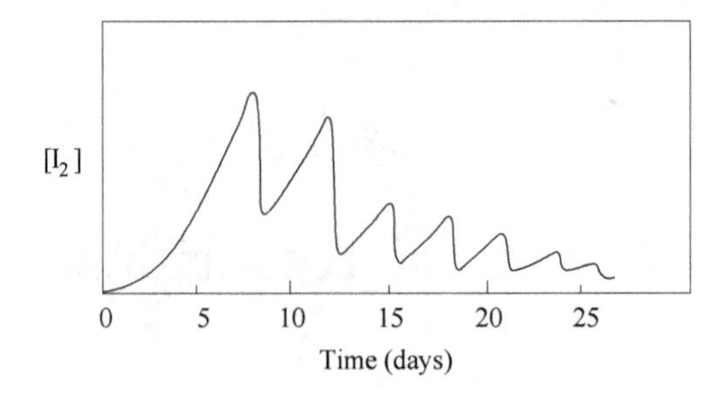

Figure 5.1 Evolution of the I_2 concentration for the oscillating chemical reaction conducted by Bray and Caulkins: the oscillations decay.

(1880–1949) and by Julius Hirniak.[4] Both studied the differential equations for the intermediary reactions and, after a mathematical analysis, defined the conditions under which an oscillating chemical reaction could be seen.

Before this experimental evidence of damped oscillations in chemical reactions, another work never quoted deserves a particular attention. It was performed by Henry Heathcote after a suggestion by Wolfang Ostwald (1883–943) to investigate dry passive iron obtained by washing with a series of reagents. These experiment seemed to be quite difficult to reproduce as noted by Heathcote: "*In view of the many contradicting results obtained not only by different early experimenters but by the same experimenter (who found that different rods of iron behaved differently and even the same rod did not always behave in the same way)*". Heathcote exhibited why chemical oscillations are of interest:[5]

> One is so accustomed to chemical action proceeding continuously from beginning to end, or from beginning till equilibrium is attained, that the mention of a chemical action which proceeds and then stops, then begins again, stops, begins again and so on, at one rivets attention. So long as reactions like this proceed as the result of external interference or some external process happening at the same time, the phenomenon is not remarkable. In connection with passive iron both kinds of variation have been observed and we shall classify them accordingly into pulsations proper when no external electric current is employed, and current oscillations when an external electric is used.

With the chemical cell shown in Figure 5.2, Heathcote gradually increased the applied electro-motrice force by moving the clip from plate to plate of the thermopile. At a certain plate, the current would fall to very nearly zero, then rise again and again fall, and so on. He thus observed sustained oscillations whose few examples are shown in Figure 5.2. The time series provided could lead to conclude to periodic oscillations but Heathcote remarked that

[4] J. Hirniak, Zür Frage der periodischen Reaktionen, *Zeitshrift für Physik und Chemie*, **75**, 675–680, 1911.

[5] H. Heathcote, The passifying, passivity, and actifying of iron, *Journal of the Society of Chemical Industry*, **26**, (16), 899–917, 1907.

in spite of the use of a stronger actifying solution and small anode area the periods are not perfectly constant. Possibly variations in temperature may have had something to do with this, and also the diffusion of the products near the anode during the active period.

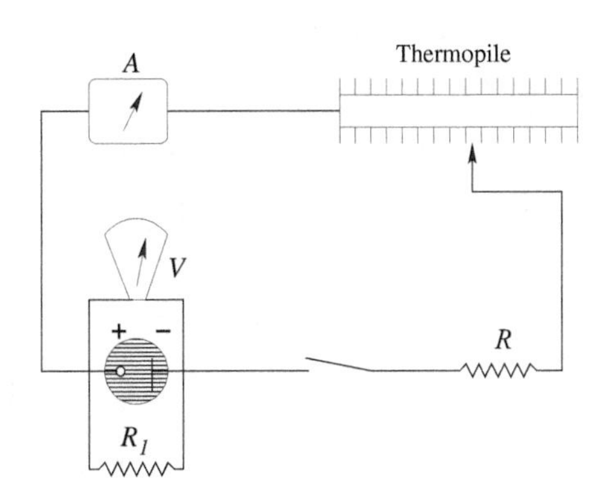

Figure 5.2 Two electrodes were placed in sulphuric acid. R and R_1 are variable resistances which were 0 and infinity, respectively. The resistance of the whole circuit was about 6.2 Ω, the electrolytic cell being about 4 Ω and the amperemeter 2 Ω. Both electrodes were of iron, the anode being much smaller, about 0.5 cm^2, and the temperature that of the air.

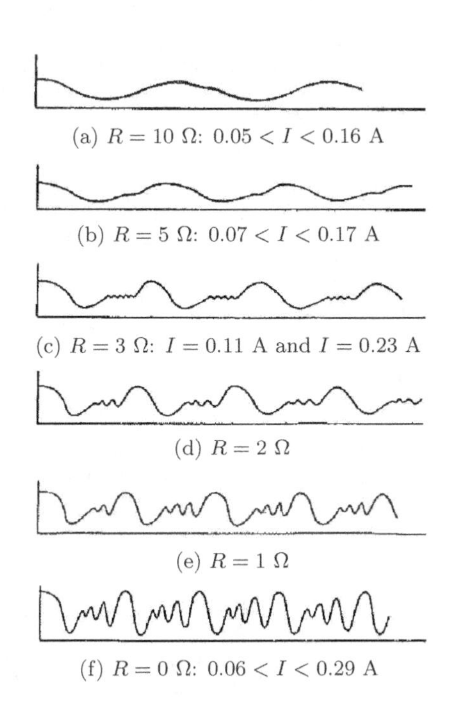

For Heathcote, the lack of periodicity in the oscillations was due to not sufficiently well controlled experimental conditions. The first model for self-sustained oscillating chemical reactions was proposed by Lotka in 1920. Using a convention that letters towards the end of the alphabet represented chemical species with variable concentrations and those toward the beginning of the alphabet represented those with constant concentrations (the reactor is open and the flow of reactants allows some of the concentrations to be held constant), Lotka proposed the model[6]

$$\left\{\begin{aligned} \mathrm{A} + \mathrm{X} &\stackrel{k_1}{\to} 2\mathrm{X} \\ \mathrm{X} + \mathrm{Y} &\stackrel{k_2}{\to} 2\mathrm{Y} \\ \mathrm{Y} &\stackrel{k_3}{\to} \mathrm{P} \end{aligned}\right.$$

where k_i are reaction rates. This set of reactions can be reduced to the set of ordinary differential equations

$$\left\{\begin{aligned} \dot{X} &= k_1 AX - k_2 XY \\ \dot{Y} &= k_2 XY - k_3 Y\,. \end{aligned}\right. \tag{5.1}$$

[6] A. J. Lotka, Undamped Oscillations derived from the law of mass action, *Journal of American Chemical Society*, **42**, 1595–1599, 1920.

This model produces sustained periodic oscillations (Figure 5.3), somewhat similar those for the ideal pendulum (Figure 1.1, p. 79). Lotka computed a plot similar to the one shown here. He followed this with a stability analysis *à la Poincaré*, and determined the nature of the singular points — a focus at $(X = 1, Y = 1)$ and a saddle at $(X = 0, Y = 0)$ around which periodic orbits are organized. Apparently, this chemical model remains without any experimental counterpart for a few decades.

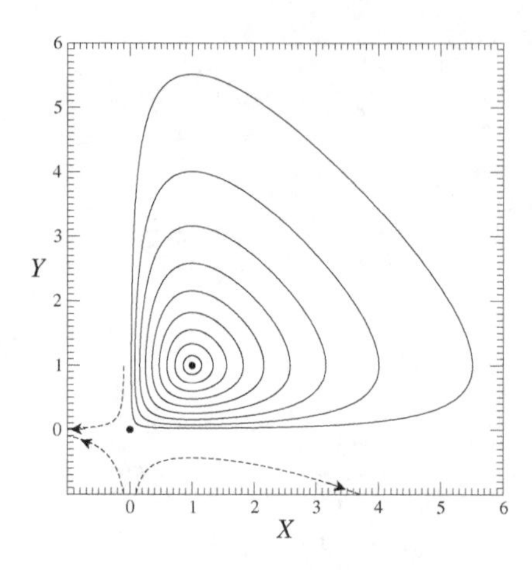

Figure 5.3 Oscillating behavior observed for the Lotka model (5.1) for oscillating chemical reactions. Several trajectories starting from different initial conditions are shown. Periodic orbits are in solid lines and trajectory ejected to infinity in dashed lines. Parameter values: $k_1 = k_2 = k_3 = A = 1$.

In 1950, M. G. Peard and C. F. Cullis, also investigating the reaction between hydrogen peroxide and iodic acid, observed damped or drifting oscillations[7] but sustained oscillations were still nonobserved in chemical reactions. This is only in the late 1950s that Boris Belousov (1930–1998) conducted a chemical experiments producing observed sustained oscillations in the concentrations:[8] his experiments were the first observations of such oscillations reported in chemical reaction without using an electric current. These oscillations were described as follows: "*the reaction described here is remarkable because during its occurrence there is a complex ordered sequence of oxidation-reduction processes, one which is periodically revealed by a temporary change in the colour of the entire reaction mixture.*"[9] In fact, the color of the mixture depends on the concentration of Ce^{3+}, Ce^{4+}, and citric acid $C_6O_7H_8$.

[7] M. G. Peard & C. F. Cullis, A periodic chemical reaction. The reaction between hydrogen peroxide and iodic acid, *Transactions of the Faraday Society*, **47**, 616–630, 1951.

[8] B. P. Belousov, Periodicheski deistvuyushchaya reaktsia i ee mekhanism (A periodic reaction and its mechanism), *Sbornik Referatov po Radiatsionni Meditsine*, Medgiz, Moscou, pp. 145–147, 1958.

[9] Quoted by A. Pechenkin, B. P. Belousov and his reaction, *Journal of Biosciences*, **34** (3), 365–371, 2009.

The whole mixture consists in these chemical species to which are added bromate and inactive pentabromacetone C_3OHBr_5. Belousov proposed the chain of reactions

$$\begin{aligned}
C_6O_7H_8 + Ce^{4+} &\longrightarrow C_5O_5H_6 + Ce^{3+} + CO_2 + H_2O \\
BrO_3^- + Ce^{3+} &\longrightarrow Ce^{4+} + Br^- \\
Br^- + 2H^+ + BrO_3^- &\longrightarrow HBrO + HBrO_2 \\
Br^- + H^+ + HBrO &\longrightarrow 2Br^- + 2H_2O \\
3Br^- + 3H^- + HBrO_2 &\longrightarrow 2Br_2 + 2H_2O \\
C_5O_5H_6 + 5Br_2 &\longrightarrow C_3OHBr_5 + 5Br^- + 2C0_2 + 5H^+
\end{aligned}$$

This is a somewhat complicated chain of chemical reactions: the oxidation of organic molecules by bromate ions BrO_3^-, oxidized by the redox pair Ce^{3+}/Ce^{4+}. This reaction can be reduced to[10]

$$3\ CH_2(COOH)_2 + 2\ HBr + HBrO_3 \longrightarrow 3\ CHBr(COOH)_2 + 3\ H_20.$$

Belouzov's observations remained without any response from the chemical society until Anatol Zhabotinsky (1938–2008) who confirmed the oscillating nature of this chemical reaction in 1964.[11] This reaction is now called the *Belousov-Zhabotinsky reaction.* The network of chemical reactions is somewhat complicated and involves a large number of intermediate reaction species.

In 1967, René Lefever, Grégoire Nicolis and Ilya Prigogine (1919–2003) proposed a two-variable model that generates sustained periodic oscillations.[12] Starting from an analysis of the Belousov-Zhabotinsky reaction, Richard Field, Endre Körös and Richard Noyes proposed in 1972 a set of three ordinary differential equations[13]

$$\begin{cases} \dot{x} = a(x + y - xy - bx^2) \\ \dot{y} = \dfrac{1}{a}(-y - xy + cz) \\ \dot{z} = d(x - z) \end{cases} \tag{5.2}$$

where x, y and z designate the concentrations in bromic acid $HBrO_2$, in Br^- ions and in Ce^{4+} ions.

This model is baptised "the Oregonator", in honor of the state of Oregon, where these three scientists were living. When their system of differential equations is numerically integrated, oscillating behavior (Figure 5.4(b)) resembling that of the Br^- ions (Figure 5.4(a)) is observed.[14] This system can be reduced to a set of two equations and, as a result, only periodic (as opposed to chaotic) behavior can occur.

[10] A. H. Zaikin & A. M. Zhabotinsky, Concentration wave propagation in two-dimensional liquid-phase self-oscillating system, *Nature*, **225**, 535–537, 1970.

[11] M. A. Zhabotinsky, Periodic Processes of the oxydation of malonic acid in solution, *Biofizika*, **9**, 306–311, 1964.

[12] R. Lefever, G. Nicolis & I. Prigogine, On the Occurrence of oscillations around the steady state in systems of chemical reactions far from equilibrium, *Journal of Chemical Physics*, **47** (3), 1045–1047, 1967.

[13] R. J. Field & R. M. Noyes, Oscillations in chemical systems — IV. Limit cycle behavior in a model of a real chemical reaction, *Journal of Chemical Physics*, **60** (5), 1877–1884, 1974.

[14] R. J. Field, E. Körös & R. M. Noyes, Oscillations in chemical systems — II. Through analysis of temporal oscillation in the Bromate-Cerium-Malonic acid system, *Journal of the American Chemical Society*, **94** (25), 8649–8664, 1972.

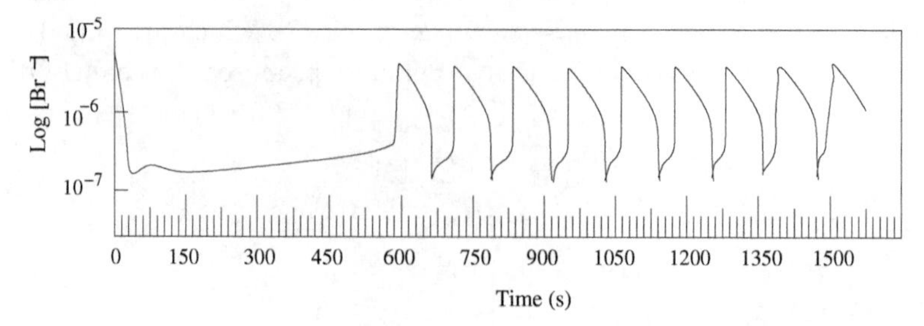

(a) Time series of the concentration in Br^- ions measured by Field, Körös and Noyes

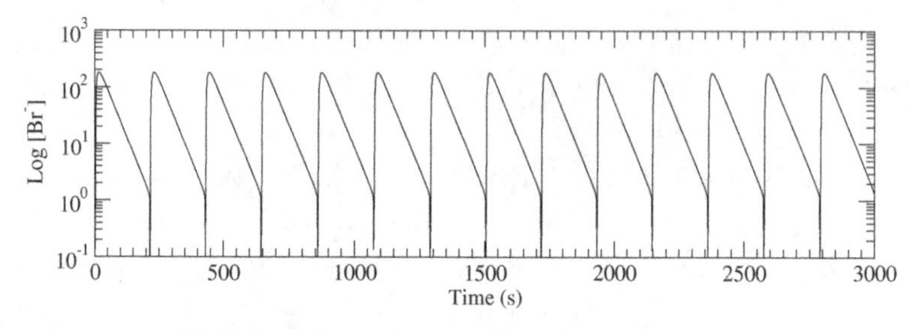

(b) Time series of the y-variable of the Oregonator

Figure 5.4 Comparison of the evolution of one of the Oregonator variables (b) with the Br^- concentration measured experimentally in the Belousov-Zhabotinsky reaction (a). Parameter values: $a = 77.27$, $b = 8.375 \cdot 10^{-6}$, $c = 1$ and $d = 0.161$.

5.2 Chaos in an Experimental BZ-Reaction

It was not until 1975 that the first observation of chaotic behavior in the Belousov-Zhabotinsky reaction took place. This was performed by the group led by John Hudson (1937–2016) from University of Virginia. Since there was no understanding of chaotic behavior at that time, these results were not published. In fact, all the work carried out in this field was on periodic oscillations. This changed only after the publication of Rössler's work on oscillating chemical reactions.[15] This work used sets of ordinary differential equations to describe hypothetical chemical reactions and proposed the use of computers for numerically integrating these equations to show chaotic behavior. Rössler also mentioned that the Belousov-Zhabotinsky reaction was a good candidate for finding chaotic behavior due to the observations of irregular oscillations in this reaction by Arthur Winfree.[16] On reexamining their old data Hudson and his colleagues had the satisfaction of discovering plots like those shown in Figure 5.5 that evidenced "*a time dependence, on average stable,*

[15] O. E. Rössler, Chaotic Behavior in simple reaction system, *Zeitschrift für Naturforsch A*, **31** (3-4), 259–264, 1976 — O. E. Rössler, Chemical Turbulence: chaos in a simple reaction-diffusion system, *Zeitschrift für Naturforsch A*, **31** (10), 1168–1172, 1976.

[16] A. Winfree, Scroll-Shaped Waves of chemical activity in three dimensions, *Science*, **181**, 937–939, 1973.

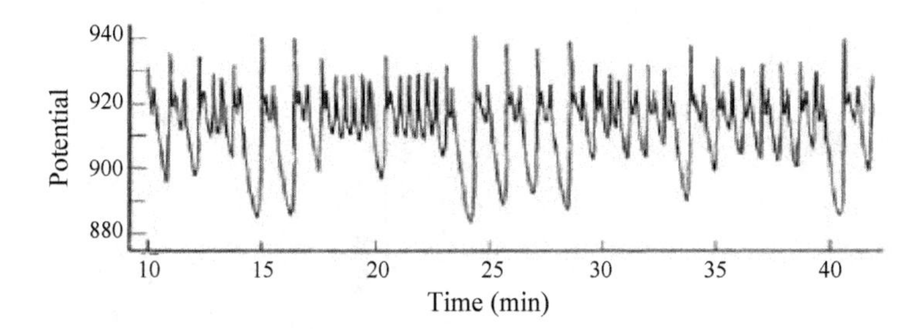

Figure 5.5 Time evolution of the potential across a platinum electrode inserted into the Belousov-Zhabotinsky reaction vessel. These were interpreted as chaotic oscillations by John Hudson and colleagues in 1977.

but not periodic".[17] Guided by Rössler's papers, they were able to explain their irregular oscillations.

Otto E. Rössler was aware that the Belousov-Zhabotinsky reaction was nothing else than a Bonhöffer-van der Pol chemical circuit[18] and was convinced, once he got his first chaotic model, that chaos was possible in the Belousov-Zhabotinsky-reaction. With Klaus Wegman, he thus conducted an experiments and found an aperiodic time series recorded in a Belousov-Zhabotinsky reaction.[19] Then due to his use to produce state portrait when he was performing his numerical simulations of chaotic systems on an analog computer, Rössler knew that more than a single measured variable was required: with Wegman, they therefore got a second one. They plotted the potential of a bromide ion sensitive electrode (ordinate) versus the electrochemical potential (abscissa) recorded in a well stirred Belousov-Zhabotinsky reaction under isothermal open flow conditions[20] to obtain a two-dimensional projection of the state portrait (Figure 5.6). These plots were the very first chaotic state portraits obtained from experimental data.

These early observations were followed by those of Jean-Claude Roux, Annie Rossi, S. Bachelart and Christian Vidal in 1980.[21] The principal difference between this latter work and the former one by Wegman and Rössler was that they "reconstructed" a three-dimensional state portrait from measurements of a single variable, the concentration in Ce^{4+} ions. Roux's team used derivative coordinates following a procedure adopted by Packard, Crutchfield, Farmer and Shaw, and that

---

[17] R. A. Schmitz, K. R. Graziani & J. L. Hudson, Experimental Evidence of chaotic states in the Belousov-Zhabotinsky reaction, *Journal of Chemical Physics*, **67** (7), 3040–3044, 1977.

[18] O. E. Rössler & D. Hoffmann, Repetitive hard bifurcation in a homogeneous reaction system, in *Analysis and Simulation of Biochemical Systems*, pp. 91–102, 1972.

[19] O. E. Rössler & K. Wegmann, Chaos in the Belousov-Zhabotinsky reaction, *Nature*, **271**, 89–90, 1978.

[20] K. Wegman & O. E. Rössler, Different kinds of chaotic oscillations in the Belousov-Zhabotinsky reaction, *Zeitchrift für Naturfoschung A*, **33**, 1179–1183, 1978.

[21] J.-C. Roux, A. Rossi, S. Bachelart & C. Vidal, Representation of a strange attractor from an experimental study of chemical turbulence, *Physics Letters A*, **77**, 391–393, 1980 — C. Vidal & J.-C. Roux, *Pour la Science*, **39**, 50, 1981.

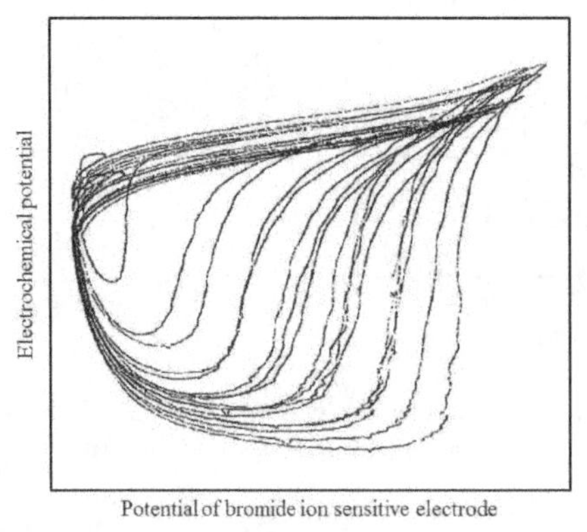

(a) Endogeneous chaos (without external noise)

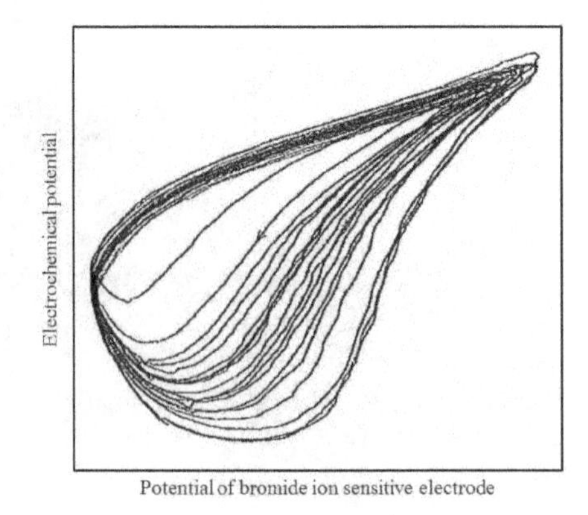

(b) Exogeneous chaos (with external noise)

Figure 5.6 Two different types of chaos observed by Wegmann and Rössler in a Belousov-Zhabotinsky reaction in 1978.

was submitted for publication at that time.[22] The principle was to "unfold" the time series by using delay coordinates, that is, by plotting the measured variable $x(t)$ versus the first derivative $\dot{x}$ and the second derivative $\ddot{x}$.[23] They were thus able to construct a trajectory such as the one shown in Figure 5.7(a). During the same year and also based on the work by Packard and his colleagues, John Hudson and Joe Mankin observed similar behavior, shown in Figure 5.7(b). In addition to a representation of the chaotic attractor, they constructed a first-return map to a Poincaré section and showed that it was parabolic as the maps drawn by Rössler for his chaotic attractors. This was a clear signature that the behavior was chaotic and similar to the chaotic behavior observed by Rössler in his numerical simulations.[24]

At about the same time, a representation of another chaotic attractor obtained by Harry Swinney's group from the University of Texas at Austin[25] (Figure 5.8(a)).

[22] N. H. Packard, J. P. Crutchfield, J. D. Farmer & R. S. Shaw, Geometry from a time series, *Physical Review Letters*, **45** (9), 712–716, 1980.

[23] This technique can be understood with the help of a circle of period $T_0 = \frac{2\pi}{\omega}$ drawn in a space with coordinates $x(t) = \cos(\omega t)$ and $y(t) = \sin(\omega t)$. Suppose that only the time series x is known, then the time series y can be obtained using the derivative of x since $\dot{x} = -\omega \sin \omega t$. Variable y is thus equal to $-\frac{\dot{x}}{\omega}$. A similar reasoning can be developed for delay coordinates. Variable y can be obtained from x since $\sin(\omega t) = \cos(\frac{\pi}{2} - \omega t)$ where $\frac{\pi}{2\omega}$ is the time τ corresponding to a delay. Since $T_0 = \frac{2\pi}{\omega}$, we thus have $\tau = \frac{T_0}{4}$. It therefore comes that $-x(t - \frac{T_0}{4}) = -\cos \omega(t - \tau) = \sin(\omega t) = y(t)$. The circle can be plotted by drawing $-x(t - \tau)$ versus $x(t)$. This approach which can be applied to any system was first suggested by David Ruelle in various seminars in American universities and then published by Packard and co-workers. The validity of this technique to any system was demonstrated by Floris Takens, Detecting strange attractors in turbulence, *Lecture Notes in Mathematics*, **898**, 366–381, 1981.

[24] J. L. Hudson & J. C. Mankin, Chaos in the Belousov-Zhabotinsky reaction, *Journal of Chemical Physics*, **74**, 6171–6177, 1981.

[25] J. S. Turner, J. C. Roux, W. D. McCormick & H. L. Swinney, Alternating Periodic and Chaotic Regimes in a chemical reaction — Experiment and theory, *Physics Letters A*, **85**, 9–12, 1981.

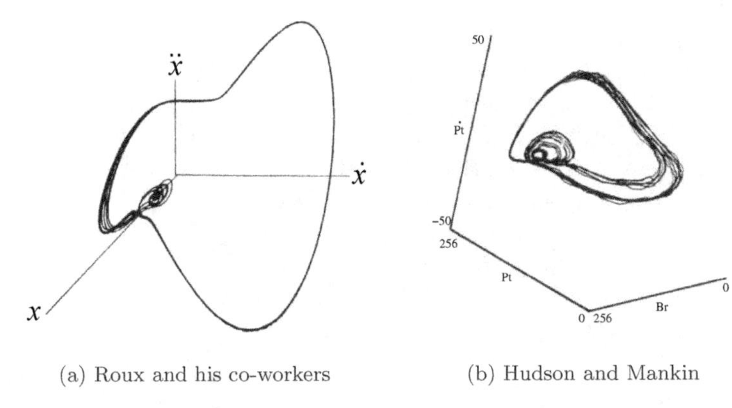

(a) Roux and his co-workers (b) Hudson and Mankin

Figure 5.7 Reconstructions of representative phase space trajectories for the Belousov-Zhabotinsky reaction obtained by two different groups in two different ways in 1981.

A template of this chaotic attractor (Figure 5.8(b)) was proposed by Gabriel Mindlin and Robert Gilmore:[26] they showed that it was a horseshoe template (Figure 5.8(b)). This means that the route to this chaotic attractor is a period-doubling cascade. It should be noted that they used a rather atypical set of coordinates for reconstructing the state space. They spanned the reconstructed space with the variables

$$\begin{cases} X(i) = \sum_{j<i} \mathrm{Ce}^{4+}(j) e^{-\frac{i-j}{\tau}} \\ Y(i) = \sum_{j<i} \mathrm{Ce}^{4+}(i) \\ Z(i) = \mathrm{Ce}^{4+}(i+1) + \mathrm{Ce}^{4+}(i-1) \,. \end{cases}$$

The integral variable X has the advantage to be less sensitive to noise contamination than the second derivative $\ddot{\mathrm{Ce}}^{4+}$ of the measured variable.

A multitude of behaviors typical of chaotic systems were also observed: intermittency, period-doubling, etc. One of these is very typical and was studied by Françoise Argoul:[27] the trajectory slowly winds away from the singular point surrounded by the attractor, only to be reinjected back to the neighborhood of the focus (the unstable manifold) and begins a new cycle (Figure 5.8(a)). This is called a homoclinic orbit: Poincaré had already discovered these at the heart of the three-body problem. This type of chaos is somewhat difficult to analyze (because there is no clear nonvisited domain surrounded by the attractor, thus preventing from a safe Poincaré section). Nevertheless, this is an important type of attractor because this is one of the situations where a mathematical proof that chaos exists can be

[26] G. B. Mindlin & R. Gilmore, Topological analysis and synthesis of chaotic time series, *Physica D*, **58**, 229–242, 1992.

[27] F. Argoul, A. Arnéodo & P. Richetti, Experimental evidence for homoclinic chaos in the Belousov-Zhabotinsky reaction, *Physics Letters A*, **120** (6), 269–275, 1987.

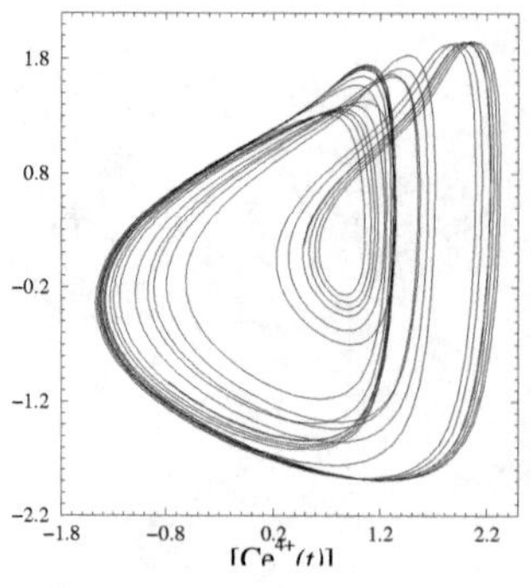

(a) Reconstructed state portrait

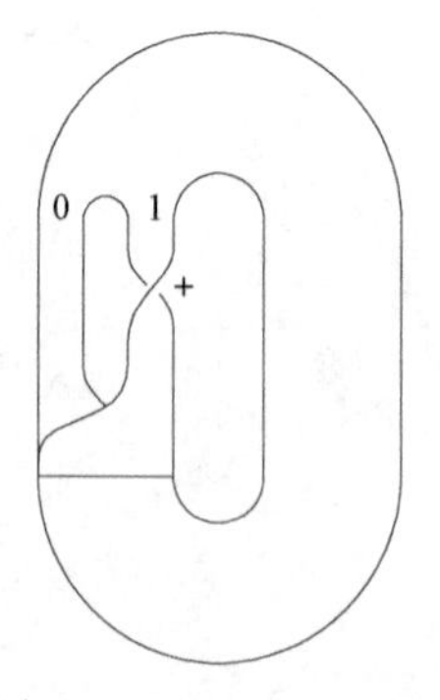

(b) Two-branch template

Figure 5.8 Chaotic attractor observed for the Belousov-Zhabotinsky reaction in 1981 by Swinney's group (a). The corresponding template proposed by Mindlin and Gilmore (1992).

carried out: the first was that of Poincaré. The second proof was proposed by Leonid Shil'nikov in the 1960s.[28]

The experimental data collected by Argoul and co-workers were used to reconstruct a state portrait (Figure 5.9(a)) using derivative coordinates. The first-return map to a Poincaré section (Figure 5.9(b)), made of 154 points, evidences two branches, one increasing and one decreasing. The template of this attractor had thus two branches as shown in Figure 5.9(c).[29]

As mentioned in Section 2.5.2 (p. 137), inverse problems are related to the possibility to get a set of differential equations, directly from the measured data, by using an algorithm: this is designated as *global modelling*.[30] One of the technique was developed with Gérard Gouesbet, Loïs Le Sceller and Jean Maquet.[31] The main principle is as follows. A tridimensional representation of the state portrait is required since three variables are needed to obtain chaotic behaviors. The concentration $[Ce^{4+}]$ and its successive first two derivatives $[\dot{Ce}^{4+}]$ and $[\ddot{Ce}^{4+}]$. Using the notations $X = [Ce^{4+}]$, $Y = \dot{X}$ and $Z = \ddot{X}$, the set of ordinary differential equations

$$\left\{ \begin{array}{l} \dot{X} = Y \\ \dot{Y} = Z \\ \dot{Z} = F(X, Y, Z) \end{array} \right.$$

[28] L. P. Shil'nikov, The existence of a denumerable set of periodic motions in four-dimensional space in an extended neighborhood of a saddle-focus, *Dokladi Akademia Nauk SSSR*, **1** (172), 54–58, 1967.

[29] C. Letellier, J. Maquet, H. Labro, L. Le Sceller, G. Gouesbet, F. Argoul & A. Arnéodo, Analyzing chaotic behaviour in a Belousov-Zhabotinskii reaction by using a global vector field reconstruction, *Journal of Physical Chemistry A*, **102**, 10265–10273, 1998.

[30] L. A. Aguirre & C. Letellier, Modeling nonlinear dynamics and chaos: A review, *Mathematical Problems in Engineering*, **2009**, 238960, 2009.

[31] G. Gouesbet & J. Maquet, Construction of phenomenological models from numerical scalar time series, *Physica D*, **58**, 202–215, 1992 — G. Gouesbet & C. Letellier, Global vector field reconstruction by using a multivariate polynomial L_2-approximation on nets, *Physical Review E*, **49** (6), 4955–4972, 1994.

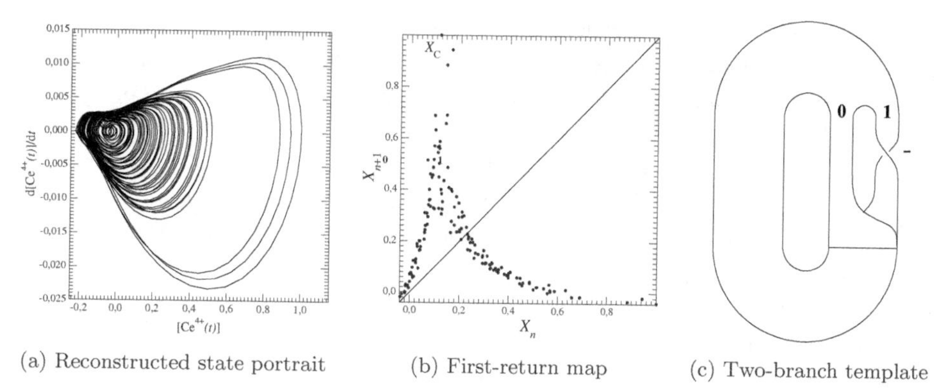

(a) Reconstructed state portrait (b) First-return map (c) Two-branch template

Figure 5.9 Homoclinic chaos produced by the Belousov-Zhabotinsky reaction conducted in 1987 by Argoul and co-workers. The first-return map to a Poincaré section (made of 154 points) of the attractor is plotted (b). This attractor is characterized by the two-branch template. Adapted from Letellier and co-workers (1998).

is obtained. The function $F(X, Y, Z)$ is the function, *a priori* unknown, to estimate: once $F(X, Y, Z)$ is known, then the set of differential equations governing the dynamics of the experiments is known. According to the global modelling technique retained, the function as the polynomial form

$$\begin{aligned} F(X, Y, Z) = K_0 + K_1 X + K_2 Y + K_3 Z + K_4 X^2 + K_5 XY \\ + K_6 XZ + K_7 Y^2 + K_8 YZ + K_9 Z^2 + ... \end{aligned}$$

All the problem is resumed in estimating cœfficients K_i of this polynomial. This is achieved using a least-square technique as introduced by Carl F. Gauss (1777–1855), that is, by searching the cœfficient set $\{K_i\}$ allowing to minimize the sum

$$\sum_{n=1}^{N} \left| \dot{Z}_n - F(X_n, Y_n, Z_n) \right|^2$$

where N is the number of points with coordinates (X_n, Y_n, Z_n) used to estimate the function F to which the derivative of Z is added — the third time derivative of the measured variable I. Getting a global model provides a strong proof for the existence of an underlying determinism, the most difficult of the properties required for chaos. The other properties — sensitivity to initial conditions, boundedness of the trajectory in the state space, and some recurrent properties (aperiodicity combined with boundedness is somewhat equivalent to this last property) — are far easier to demonstrate.

Applying the global modelling technique to the data measured in the Belousov–Zhabotinsky reaction led to the 56-term global model

$$\begin{cases} \dot{X} = Y \\ \dot{Y} = Z \\ \dot{Z} = \displaystyle\sum_{k=1}^{N_K} K_k X^l Y^m Z^n \end{cases} \tag{5.3}$$

where K_k are the model coefficients.[32] A numerical integration of this global model produces the chaotic attractor shown in Figure 5.10(a). A first-return map to a Poincaré section, made of 4380 points, reveals three branches (Figure 5.10(b)), as indicated by the template shown in Figure 5.10(c). Branches 0 and 1 of this template are organized in a way which is topologically equivalent to the organization of branches 0 and 1 extracted from the experimental data (Figure 5.9(b)). The model is therefore topologically validated. The fact that branch "3" was not seen in the experimental data may result from the number of data points in the Poincaré section (154) significantly smaller than the number of points (4380) used for characterizing the global model dynamics.

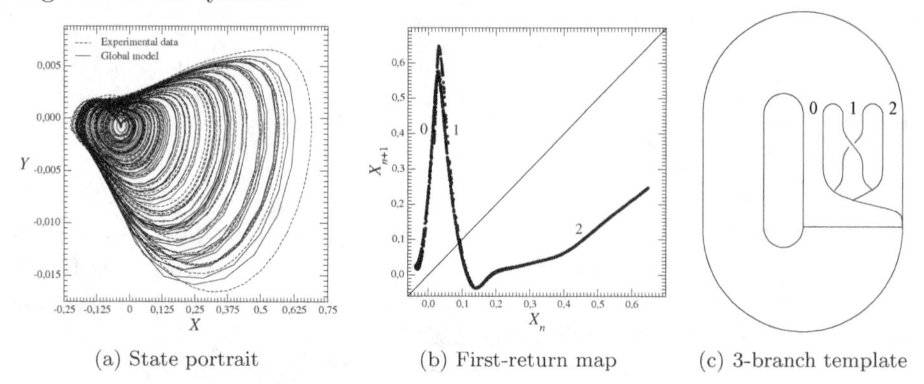

(a) State portrait (b) First-return map (c) 3-branch template

Figure 5.10 Homoclinic chaos produced by the global model extracted from the Belousov-Zhabotinsky reaction conducted by Argoul and co-workers. The first-return map to a Poincaré section (made of 4380 points) of the attractor is plotted (b). This attractor is characterized by a three-branch template. Adapted from Letellier and co-workers (1998).

The simple three-dimensional model

$$\begin{cases} \dot{x} = y \\ \dot{y} = z \\ \dot{z} = -\mu x - \nu y - z + x^2 - k_1 y^2 - k_2 xz - k_3 x^2 z \end{cases} \tag{5.4}$$

for describing the oscillations in the concentration of Ce^{4+} ions was proposed by Argoul and co-workers.[33] A numerical integration of this model (Figure 5.11(a)) produces a chaotic attractor whose template (Figure 5.10(b)) contains the three branches which were identified in the experimental data (Figure 5.10(a)).[34] This model also captures the main characteristics of the experimental dynamics. When the parameter μ is varied, there is a period-doubling cascade leading to chaos. A unimodal chaotic attractor is shown in Figure 5.12(a): notice that its shape has

[32]See Letellier *et al.*, 1998, for their numerical values.

[33]Argoul *et al.*, 1987. *Ibid.*

[34]C. Letellier, J. Maquet, H. Labro, L. Le Sceller, G. Gouesbet, F. Argoul & A. Arnéodo, Analyzing chaotic behaviour in a Belousov-Zhabotinskii reaction by using a global vector field reconstruction, *Journal of Physical Chemistry A*, **102**, 10265–10273, 1998.

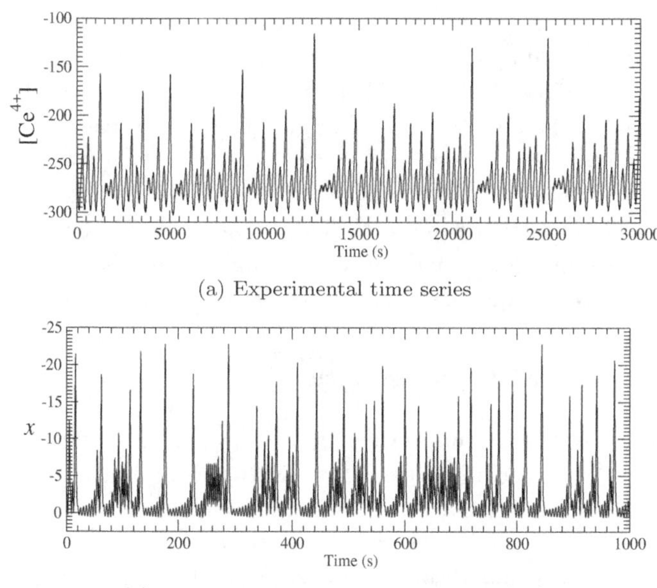

(a) Experimental time series

(b) Numerical simulations using model (5.4)

Figure 5.11 Comparison of the time evolution of the concentration of Ce^{4+} ions measured by Argoul and co-workers and the numerical integration of their three-variable model. The alternation between small and large amplitude oscillations, so typical of homoclinic chaos, is well reproduced qualitatively. Parameter values: $k_1 = 1.425$, $k_2 = -0.2$, $k_3 = 0.01$, $\nu = 1.3$, and $\mu = 1.38$.

some similarities with the attractor observed by Swinney and his colleagues (Figure 5.8(a)).

When μ is increased, a bimodal and then a three-modal chaos is observed (Figure 5.12(b)), that is, this is an attractor characterized by a first-return map with three and four branches, respectively. The first three branches are topologically

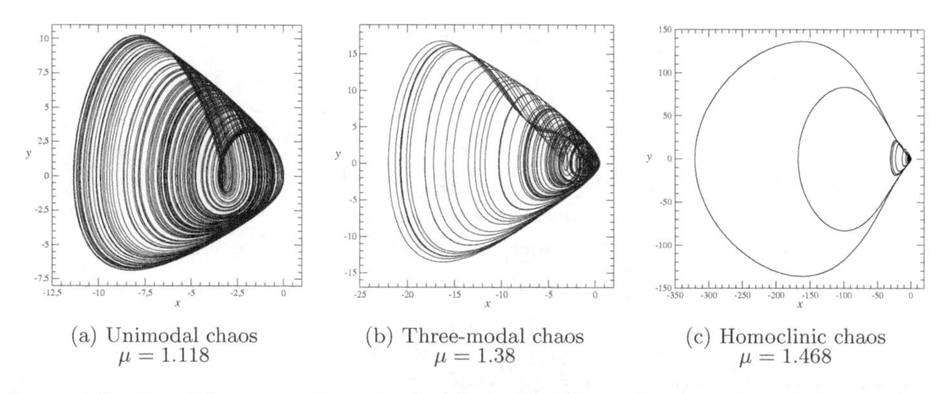

(a) Unimodal chaos $\mu = 1.118$

(b) Three-modal chaos $\mu = 1.38$

(c) Homoclinic chaos $\mu = 1.468$

Figure 5.12 Two different templates obtained from two different Belousov-Zhabotinsky reactions. The third template corresponds to the data produced by a global model extracted from the BZ-reaction near a homoclinic orbit. Other parameter values as in Figure 5.11.

equivalent to those observed in the global model (see the template shown in Figure 5.10(c)).[35] When the bifurcation parameter is still increased, a homoclinic configuration is observed (Figure 5.12(c)). There are small amplitude oscillations around the singular point — here located at the origin of the state space — that are interrupted with large amplitude oscillations: this is a typical signature of homoclinic chaos. In such a case, the orbit has an infinite period and there is an infinite number of branches in the template.[36] The chaotic nature of the oscillations in the Belousov-Zhabotinskii reaction are thus strongly established. Other interesting chaotic behaviors as toroidal chaos were investigated by Argoul and coworkers.[37]

5.3 Chaotic Copper Electrodissolution

Chaotic behaviors are also found in electrodissolution. Electrolysis is an electrochemical reaction that occurs between two electrodes in a cell. A total chemical reaction appears in this cell that is the sum of two independent chemical reactions that occur at the two electrodes: they both involve the transfer of electrons across a metal/solution interface and adsorption/desorption of matter at the electrode surface. Usually only one of these reactions is of interest: the corresponding electrode is called the *working electrode* and the other electrode is held at constant composition. The two potentials are usually measured with respect to a *reference electrode*. Since the reference electrode has a constant composition, its potential is constant. As a result, all potential variations that occur in the cell are due to the working electrode.

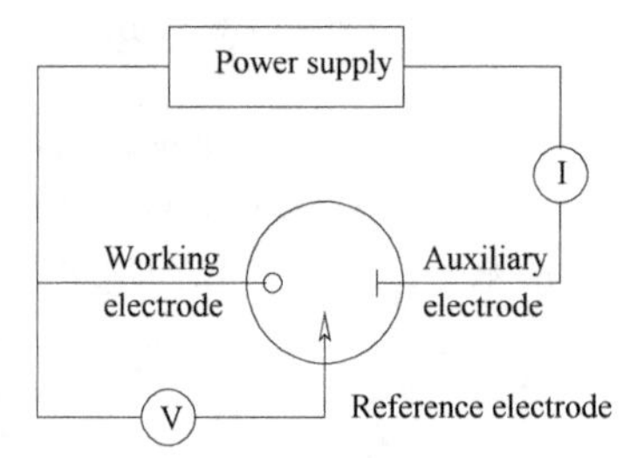

Figure 5.13 Schematic diagram of a cell with three electrodes.

A setup with three electrodes is frequently used (Figure 5.13). In such a configuration the auxiliary electrode can have arbitrary electrochemical properties without affecting the behavior of the working electrode; it is usually chosen so that it does not produce reactants that can migrate to the working electrode and, thus to

[35] Letellier *et al.*, 1998, *Ibid.*

[36] C. Letellier, *Caractérisation topologique et reconstruction des attracteurs étranges*, Ph.D. Thesis, Chapter 3, University of Paris VII, May 1994. The thesis is available at `http://atomosyd.net/spip.php?article1`.

[37] F. Argoul, A. Arnéodo, P. Richetti, J. C. Roux & H. L. Swinney, Chemical chaos: from hints to confirmation, *Accounts in Chemical Research*, **20** (12), 436–442, 1987.

produce unintended or parasitic reactions. The potential of the working electrode is controlled with respect to the reference electrode which is placed so that one end is close to the working electrode.

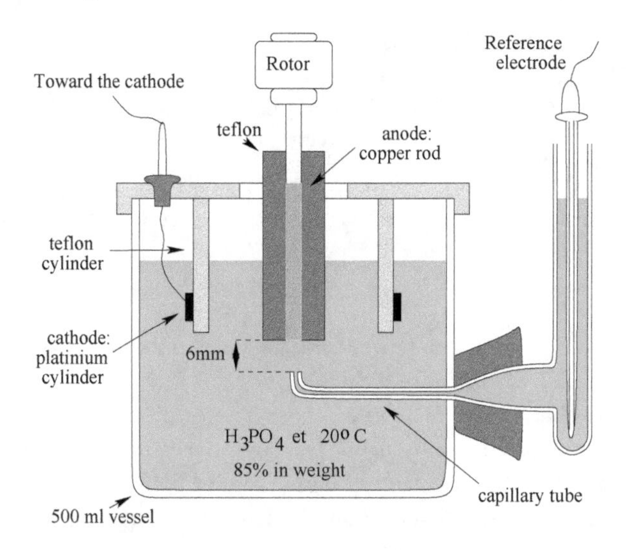

Figure 5.14 Schematic of the copper electrolysis experiment carried out by John Hudson and Zihao Fei.

Very accurate current measurements reveal oscillations. Copper electrodissolution in a solution of phosphoric acid (H_3PO_4) was studied by John Hudson's group at the University of Virginia in the United States.[38] The anode, a copper cylinder 8.26 mm in diameter inserted in a teflon cylinder 2 cm in diameter is rotated at a moderate speed ($\approx$ 700 rotations/minute) in an 85% (by mass) solution of phosphoric acid maintained at 20° by a heat bath (Figure 5.14): the rotation speed must be low enough to avoid creating turbulence but high enough to avoid reactants migrating too far. All these precautions are needed in order to get sufficiently accurate measurements of the time evolution of the current I.

A reference electrode is used to maintain the potential at 689 mV with the aid of a potentiometer. This is a three-electrode cell in a 500 ml vessel containing 250 ml of solution. The anode is the working electrode. The cathode, the auxiliary electrode, consists of a platinum ring whose diameter is larger than that of the teflon cylinder: it surrounds the anode and allows a uniform distribution of the current as well as the potential.

When they measured the current across the anode, John Hudson and Zihao Fei observed relatively large oscillations that could reach amplitudes as large as 15 mA while the average current was 40 mA (Figure 5.15). These oscillations have an irregular amplitude while their period is relatively constant. Further, the dynamics

[38] M. R. Bassett & J. L. Hudson, Quasi-periodicity and chaos during an electrochemical reaction, *The Journal of Physical Chemistry*, **93**, 2731–2737, 1989.

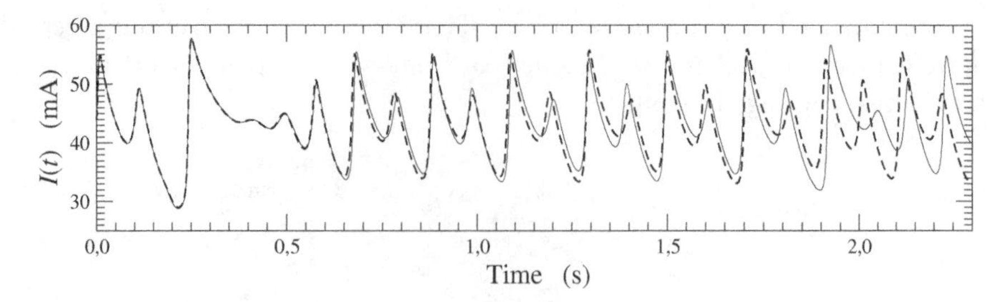

Figure 5.15 Time evolution of the anode current in the electrolysis of copper in phosphoric acid. The swift amplification of small perturbations on two trajectories with nearby initial conditions is also shown. This is a signature of chaotic behavior.

shows rapid growth of small perturbations, as encountered in the Lorenz system (compare Figure 5.15 with Figure 3.8).

Starting from the time evolution of the current I it is possible to construct a representation of the attractor by using the time derivative of the current, $\dot{I} = \frac{\mathrm{d}I}{\mathrm{d}t}$, which is another natural dynamical variable (Figure 5.16(a)).[39] A first-return map to a Poincaré section is smooth and unimodal (Figure 5.16(b)). The important point is its smooth nature, that is, that the maximum of this curve is differentiable. This is sufficient to guarantee that the dynamics in this electrodissolution experiment belongs to the same "chaos class" as that of the logistic map: as a result, a period-doubling cascade should be observable. In fact, Hudson's group did observe a period-doubling cascade by varying the potential (Figure 5.17).

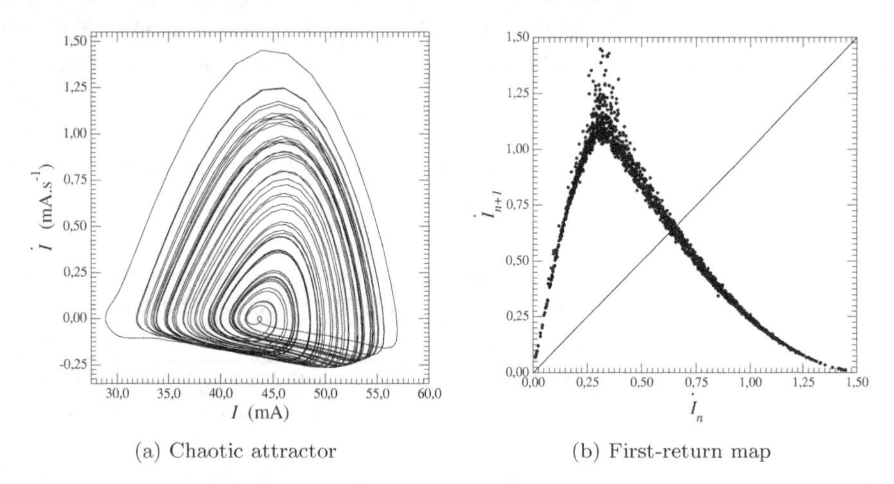

Figure 5.16 Chaotic attractor observed in the copper electrodissolution experiment. A smooth unimodal first-return map is seen: a period-doubling cascade should therefore be observed.

[39] The use of derivative coordinates to obtain a representation of the state space can be justified with the example of a circle defined by its coordinates $x(t) = \cos t$ and $y(t) = \sin t$. Assume that only the time series $x(t)$ is known, then $y(t) = -\frac{\mathrm{d}}{\mathrm{d}t}\cos t = -\dot{x}(t)$. Thus, plotting $\dot{x}$ versus x is equivalent as plotting $-y$ versus x.

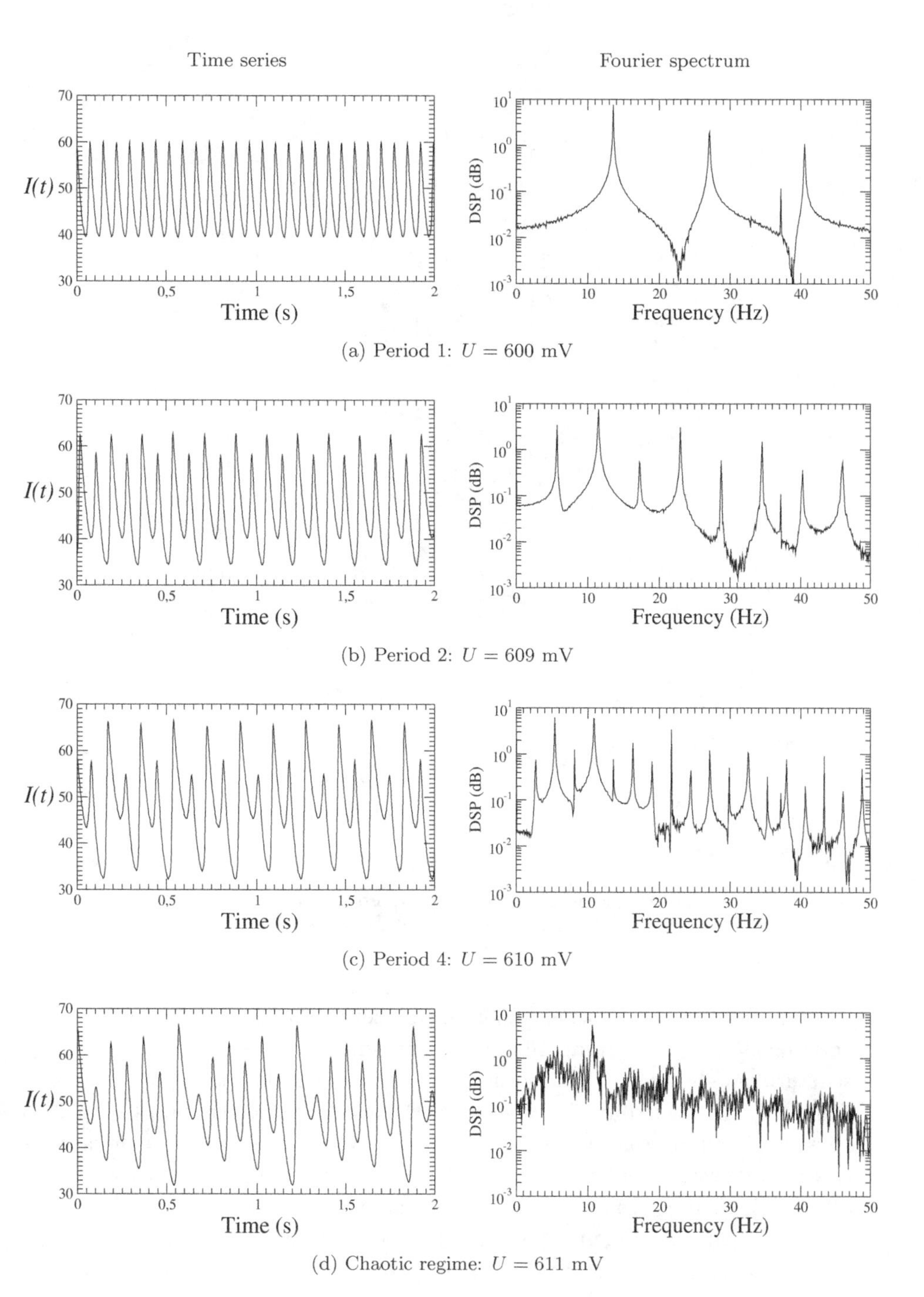

(a) Period 1: $U = 600$ mV

(b) Period 2: $U = 609$ mV

(c) Period 4: $U = 610$ mV

(d) Chaotic regime: $U = 611$ mV

Figure 5.17 Period-doubling cascade observed in the copper electrodissolution in phosphoric acid by Hudson's group. Data provided by Hudson and Fei.

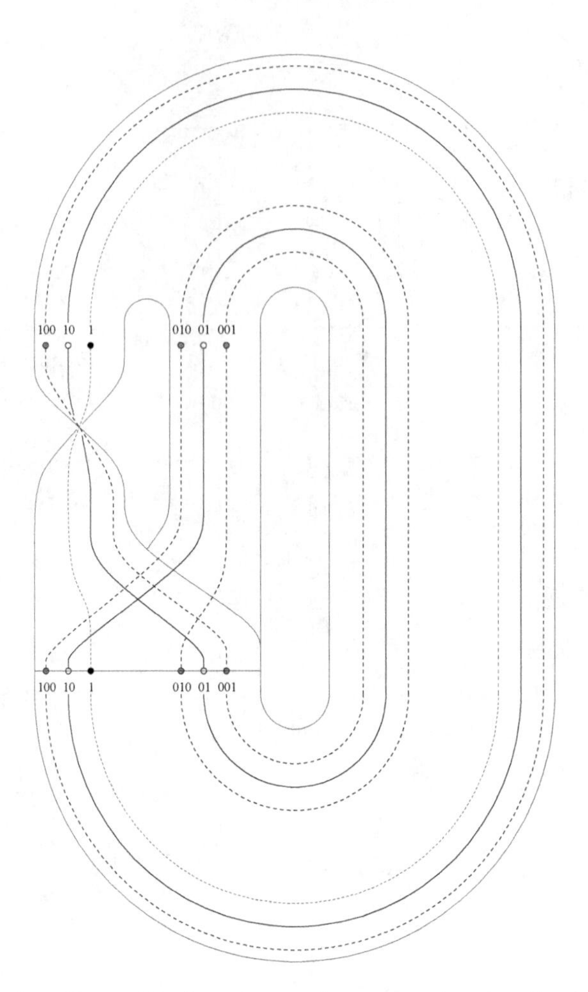

Figure 5.18 Periodic orbits predicted on the template proposed to describe the dynamics underlying the copper electrodissolution experiment. Shown are orbits (1), (10), and (100).

These observations provide experimental confirmation for the existence of chaotic behavior that is compatible with very simple theoretical models, that is, first-return map belonging to the class of the logistic map. It is thus possible to predict the organization of periodic orbits using the horseshoe map (Figure 4.23, p. 217) on the template that was proposed in Figure 5.18 and to compare these predictions with the organization of the periodic orbits extracted from the attractor (Figure 5.19).[40] This chaotic dynamics is a perfect example of experimental dynamics that presents a topological organization as predicted by the horseshoe map. Further, the period-doubling cascade has been observed experimentally. Thus, there exist

[40]C. Letellier, L. Le Sceller, P. Dutertre, G. Gouesbet, Z. Fei & J. L. Hudson, Topological characterization and global vector field reconstruction from an experimental electrochemical system, *Journal of Physical Chemistry*, **99**, 7016–7027, 1995.

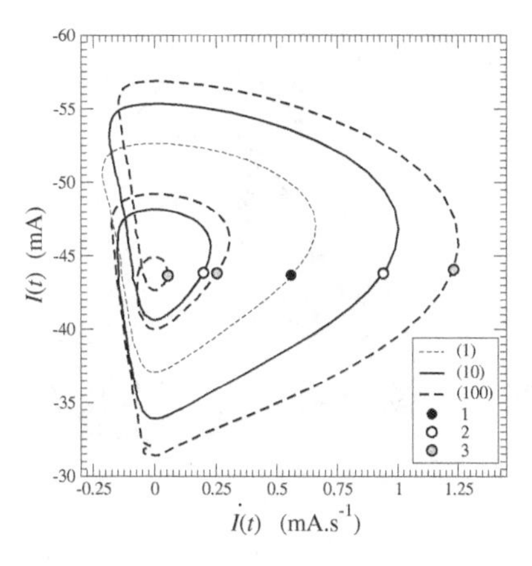

Figure 5.19 Periodic orbits extracted from the experimental data. Their relative organization is compared with that predicted from the template (Figure 5.18) from the orbits (1), (10), and (100). The orders of the points in the Poincaré section are identical.

experimental systems that show chaotic behavior that satisfies the universality properties discovered by Feigenbaum and, by Coullet and Tresser. The theory of chaos can really be used as a paradigm for the study of phenomena that are governed by a deterministic dynamics.

No three-variable models have been proposed to describe the copper electrodissolution but it is possible to apply a global modelling technique to these data. Starting from a state portrait for which one projection is shown in Figure 5.16(a), a model — a bit complicated as it involves a polynomial in three variables with 52 terms — was obtained.[41] When numerically integrated, this model produces the state portrait shown in Figure 5.20(a). A first-return map to a Poincaré section (Figure 5.20(b)) is quite similar as the experimental map (Figure 5.16(b)) — observe that the increasing branch is shorter — and it does not have the thickness of the latter. Indeed, this difference is due to the presence of an experimental noise — necessarily of a random nature that has no place in a deterministic model. To check that, a small-amplitude noise was added during the integration of the global model; the first-return map of the resulting dynamics is now very close to the observed one (compare the experimental map, Figure 5.16(b), with that of the noisy model, Figure 5.20(c)). The organization of the periodic orbits in the model attractor is the same as in the experimental attractor. That is, they are topologically described by the same template (Figure 5.18) as the experimental orbits (Figure 5.19).[42] The global model is here optimal since it is topologically equivalent to the attractor reconstructed from the experimental data.

[41] C. Letellier, L. Le Sceller, E. Maréchal, P. Dutertre, B. Maheu, G. Gouesbet, Z. Fei & J. L. Hudson, Global vector field reconstruction from a chaotic experimental signal in copper electrodissolution, *Physical Review E*, **51** (5), 4262–4266, 1995.

[42] C. Letellier, L. Le Sceller, P. Dutertre, G. Gouesbet, Z. Fei & J. L. Hudson, Topological characterization and global vector field reconstruction from an experimental electrochemical system, *Journal of Physical Chemistry*, **99**, 7016–7027, 1995.

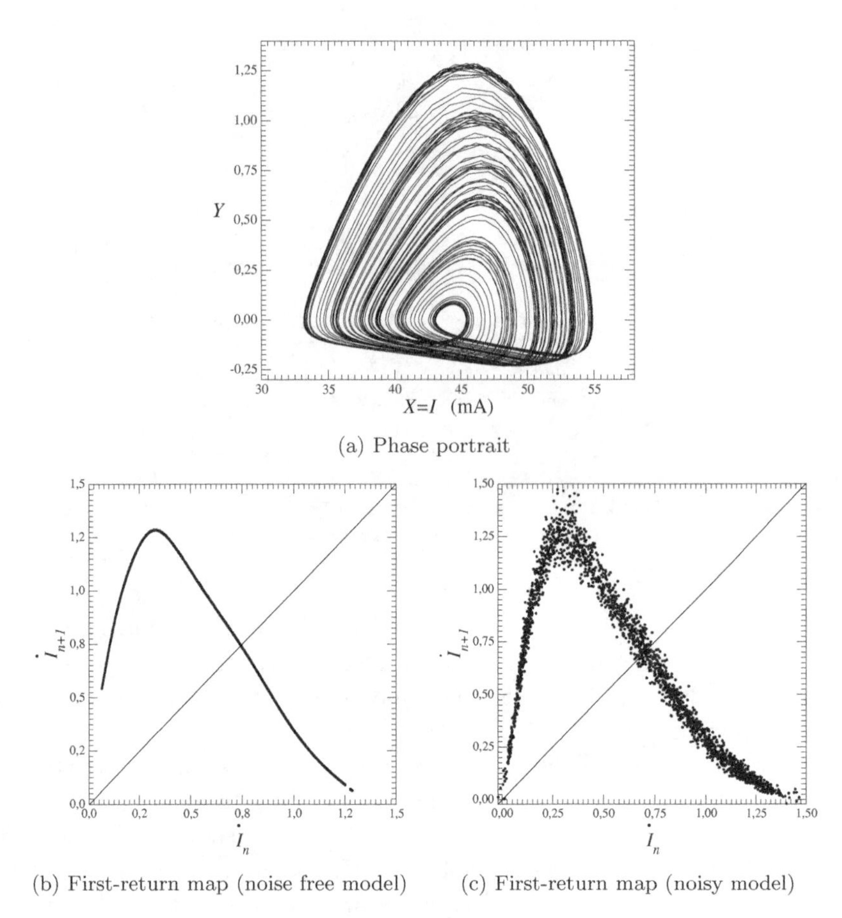

Figure 5.20 A solution to the global model obtained from the copper electrodissolution in phosphoric acid which behaves chaotically.

Finding a three-variable model shows that the copper electrodissolution in phosphoric acid is described by a chaotic dynamics of the lowest possible dimension, despite a strong sensitivity to initial conditions. This technique of *global modeling* presents the interesting potential for finding models of attractors depending on a small number of oscillations (here about 20). This turns out to be particularly important when only a small number of measurements are available, as we will see when we discuss solar activity (p. 287). We point out again that the model dynamics is always less developed than the experimental dynamics because of the presence of experimental/observational noise which is necessarily of a random nature and which, as a result, cannot be taken into account in a deterministic model.[43]

[43]C. Letellier, L. A. Aguirre & U. S. Freitas, Frequently asked questions about global modeling, *Chaos*, **19**, 023103, 2009.

5.4 Conclusion

Chemistry presents the advantage of providing experiments that may be governed by quite simple and low-dimensional processes. From that point of view, this is not surprising that chemistry is on the few fields which provided the early experimental evidences for chaos. Roughly, one century was needed to make the bridge between the first periodic oscillations and the first chaotic ones. As in the other domains, first the stability of periodic oscillations was investigated and, then, the emergence of the chaos theory, made possible the discovery of more complex behaviors. Today, there is no longer any doubt for the existence of chemical chaos. Chemistry helped to confirm that, indeed, the nonlinear dynamical system theory is useful for applied science.

Chapter 6

Population Evolution

6.1 Theories of Malthus and Verhulst

Ecology underwent a veritable explosion during the 19th century: the term *ecology* (from the Greek *oikos*, home, and *logos*, science) was introduced by Ernst Haeckel (1834–1919) in 1866 to designate the science devoted to the study of the relation between living organisms and their environment.[1] It appears that living organisms could live in an organized way in a given environment: population evolution exhibits structures that could be described, understood, and then reduced to mathematical models. Not only content to analyze the mechanisms that are responsible for the growth or reduction of a population, ecology adopted an evolutionary perspective as well, to consider populations and ecosystems on different time scales.

Each individual in a species is born, lives a certain time, and then dies. A population is therefore a dynamical system whose numbers depend on compensating phenomena: some individuals leave the system (mortality, emigration) while others join the system (birth, immigration). We provide an illustration of these to understand the dynamical processes that exist in predator-prey relations. Other phenomena such as competitive interactions, development of resistance to pesticides, ecological control of harmful animals, could also be studied.[2]

Regular observations often permit us to notice the relative stability of various populations: there exists a rough equilibrium between birth and death, between emigration and immigration. Sometimes populations grow rapidly, at other times they crash. Models of a single species are needed for laboratory studies where isolated populations are maintained under environmentally controlled conditions. These allow us to understand the real world effects that influence population dynamics. To begin these studies it is useful to consider the simple case of a population without emigration or immigration and for which the birth rate b and death rate d are constant. Let $N(t)$ be the population of the species at time t; the growth rate is equal to the difference between the birth and death rates and the migration rate. Since

[1] E. Haeckel, *Generale Morphologie der Organismen*, Berlin, 1866.

[2] B. M. Adams, H. T. Banks, J. E. Banks, J. D. Stark, Population dynamics models in plant-insect herbivore-pesticide interactions, *Mathematical Biosciences*, **196** (1), 39–64, 2005.

the number of births and deaths are proportional to the population at time t, the equation that describes how the population grows is

$$\dot{N}(t) = bN(t) - dN(t)$$

where b and d represent respectively the birth and death rates and $\dot{N}$ represents the rate at which the population changes. This equation has for solution

$$N(t) = N_0 e^{(b-d)t}$$

where N_0 represents the initial population. If there are more births than deaths ($b > d$) there is an exponential growth in the population; conversely, if $b < d$ there is a rapid extinction of the population. The difference $\mu = b - d$ between the birth and death rates is called the *intrinsic rate of demographic growth.*

The first models of this type were introduced in 1789 when Thomas Malthus (1766–1834), Anglican pastor, published his *Essay on the Population Principle.* Malthus had been preoccupied by the large number of poor peoples in England at the end of the 18th century: he estimated, on the basis of the data available to him at the time, that the basic cause for poverty was the inexorable growth of the human population following a geometric progression, doubling every 25 years in the absence of limiting factors: the population grew faster than the food supply, which only grew linearly. This resulted in a disequilibrium which weighted most heavily on the part of the population least able to defend itself.

Malthus introduced a postulate that forms the basis of the models that we study: "*population growth is necessarily limited by available resources.*" The major drawback to his analysis is that food production assumed to grow linearly was expected to limit the population explosion evolving in a geometric manner. In addition, Malthus introduced "obstacles" to population growth such as *moral constraints*, voluntary limits to procreation by chastity in late marriages since in his position as a minister he was not able to deal with contraceptive practices.

The exponential growth predicted by Malthus' model seemed unrealistic. Nevertheless, if one follows the human population, this could be debated (Figure 6.1). If the law of exponential growth does not accurately reproduce human population growth since 1650 (Figure 6.1), this law does describe the growth rate since 1900. This can be understood in the context that, starting from the 18th century epidemics and famines have become progressively rarer. Although recent observations on cereal crops confirm an arithmetic progression of yields since 1800, it is certain that technological progress and land clearing in and outside Europe have rendered obsolete the laws of subsistence that were valid in the 19th century.

However, at the end of the 18th and beginning of the 19th centuries no limiting factors had to be balance the exponential growth: but a food supply in excess could only lead to population growth to a level exceeding that allowed by resources. According to Pierre-François Verhulst (1804–1849):[3]

[3]P.-F. Verhulst (1838), Notice sur la loi que la population suit dans son accroissement, *Correspondance Mathématique et Physique de l'Observatoire de Bruxelles*, **4**, 113–121, 1838.

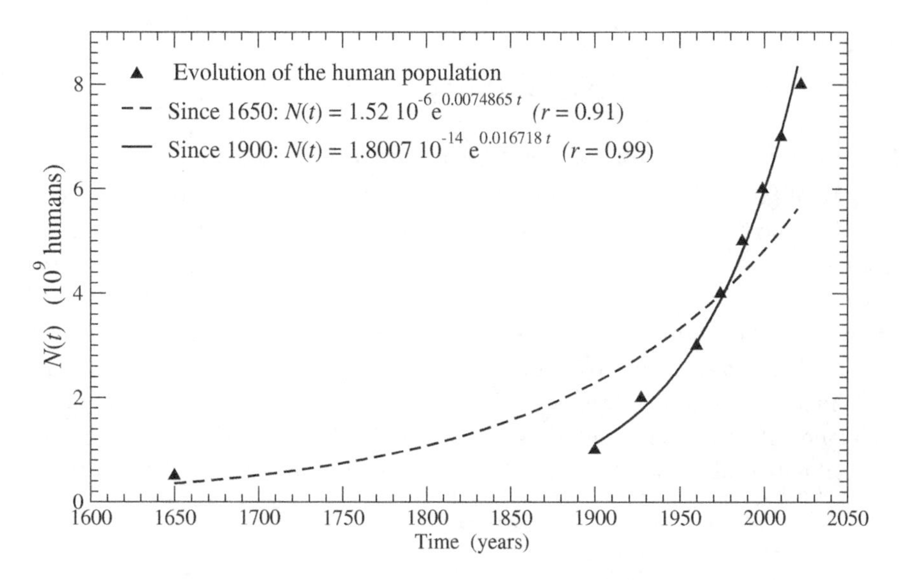

Figure 6.1 Evolution of the human population since about 1650. Apparently, the growth does not satisfy the exponential growth law. In fact, an exponential law does reproduce population growth particularly well starting at the beginning of the 20th century.

> One knows that the celebrated Malthus has established that the human population tends to grow geometrically, in such a way that it doubles in a certain time, for example every twenty five years. This proposition is unarguable, provided one neglects the problems related to finding resources while the population becomes urbanized to a certain degree, or the resources that the population needs while it is growing, even when it is just beginning, such as a greater division of labor, the existence of a reliable government and the means of defense that assures public peace, etc.
>
> [...] In our mature European societies, where the good lands have been cultivated for a long time, the work needed to increase the productivity of an already cultivated land is a project of diminishing returns; suppose that, during the first twenty five years one succeeded in doubling the yield, in the second period one might succeed in producing yet one third more. The expected increase in the population has thus a limit by the extent and the fertility of the land, and the population will tend, more and more, to become stationary.

Verhulst added the notion of inhibiting factors to Malthus' idea of exponential growth. Thus, a population could not grow exponentially, but is limited to some maximal value (Figure 6.2). Verhulst suggested that the rate of growth is not constant but rather depends on the size of the population. More precisely, he guessed that the growth rate depends on the difference between the maximum population that the land could support and its present value. In 1838 he proposed the equation

$$\dot{N}(t) = \mu N(t)\left(1 - \frac{N(t)}{\kappa}\right)$$

where the inhibiting factor $\mu\left(1 - \frac{N(t)}{\kappa}\right)$ is the mean birth rate per head that depends on $N(t)$: it limits the population when it became too large. Parameter κ designates the maximum number of individuals that can belong to a population in the environment where it leaves: this is the *biotic capacity.* This simple model is in fact a *logistic* function — name given by Verhulst — which is here used in a slightly different manner than those discussed in Chapter 1 from Part II. Even so, this model was too simple to describe the complexity of real situations. In fact, independent of initial conditions the population stabilized at the carrying capacity of the land. That is, the population rapidly adjusted itself to the maximum number of individuals that could live in the environment (Figure 6.2).

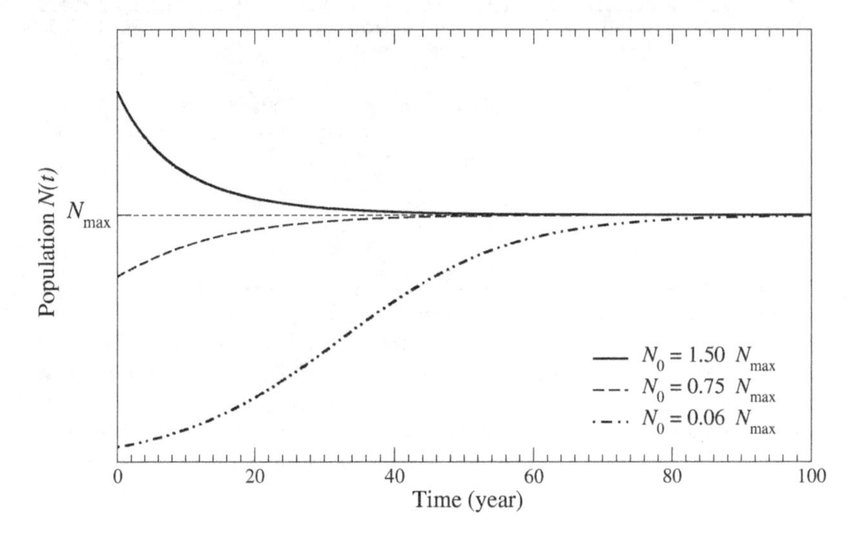

Figure 6.2 Evolution of populations under Verhulst's logistic function starting from different initial conditions (represented by N_0). The population stabilizes around the maximum value the land can support, independently of the initial conditions.

Verhulst came to a conclusion that certainly did not contradict Malthus:[4]

> Of the number of causes that influence population growth, we include our own human fecundity, the status of the land, the values of the nation that we treat, the civil and religious laws. Among the various causes that we cannot consider as accidental, they are generally due to the difficulty that as the population becomes larger and larger, it becomes more and more difficult to find unoccupied land.
>
> When one considers the calamities that lead to the continually growing exuberance of the population, and the inadequacies well evidenced today, of the

[4]P.-F. Verhulst, Recherches Mathématiques sur la loi d'accroissement de la population, *Mémoires de l'Académie Royale de Belgique*, **18** (1), 1–39, 1845.

methods tried by our contemparies to fix this problem, one cannot help but be astonished by a thought of Aristotle, presented in Plato's *Republic*: "*Perhaps someday it will become politically useful, to allow or restrain the number of births, based on the sterility or the death rate. It is the lack of foresight of governments on this essential point that is responsible for the misery of men in cities, for sedition, and for crimes, for which poverty is the mother.*[5]" This evil of which we speak has been put to the test by the ancients, since one of their better known moralists:[6] dared to praise the poor to abandon or to destroy their children, in the belief that to raise them into poverty and slavery: "*because, he said they cannot face the idea that they would leave poverty as their heritage, which they thought was the worst possible evil, like a cruel and terrible disease.*"

6.2 A Model with Two Species

During the 1920s, Raymond Pearl (1879–1940) and Lowell Reed (1886–1966) used a similar approach.[7] Pearl collaborated with the demographer and physicist Alfred Lotka, who we have already encountered in our study of chemical reactions. Lotka proposed differential equations to describe periodic population fluctuations in two species involved in a predator-prey relation:[8]

- A species of organism S_1, a plant species, say, deriving its nourishment from a source presented in such large access that the mass of the source may be considered constant during the period of time with which we are concerned.
- A species S_2, for example a herbivore animal species, feeding on S_1.

In this case, we have the following obvious relation:

Rate of increase of S_1 per unit of time	=	Mass of newly formed S_1 per unit of time
	–	Mass of S_1 destroyed by S_2 per unit of time
	–	Other dead or excretory matter eliminated from S_1 per unit of time

Rate of increase of S_2 per unit of time	=	Mass of newly formed S_1 unit time (derived from S_1 as food ingested)
	–	Mass of S_2 destroyed or eliminated per unit of time

[5] Aristotle, *Politics*, Book II, Chapter 4.
[6] Plutarque, *De Amore Prolis*, V.
[7] R. Pearl & L. J. Reed, On the Rate of growth of the population of the United States since 1790 and its mathematical representation, *Proceedings of the National Academy of Sciences* (USA), **6**, 275–288, 1920.
[8] A. J. Lotka, Analytical Note on certain rhythmic relations in organic systems, *Proceedings of the National Academy of Science*, **6**, 410–415, 1920.

These relations were translated into the pair of ordinary differential equations

$$\begin{cases} \dot{m}_1 = \mu_1 m_1 - k_1 m_1 m_2 \\ \dot{m}_2 = k_2 m_1 m_2 - \mu_2 m_1 \end{cases}$$

where m_1 and m_2 designate masses of S_1 and of S_2 at time t, respectively. Parameter μ_1 is related to the growth rate of vegetal species (preys) and parameter μ_2 to the death rate of the animal species. Parameters k_1 and k_2 correspond to the interactions between these two species. Note that the form of this model is similar to those of the *logistic* function in both equations. Terms $\mu_i m_i$ designate the growth rate of the species, and terms $k_i m_i m_j$ $(i \neq j)$ the destruction of the animal species. Since the system depends on two variables, only periodic behavior could be found (Figure 5.3). We point out that Lotka offered the observation that this type of system could well *play an important role in physiology* and quoted the cardiac rhythm as an example. Several years later, William Robin Thompson (1887–1972) described host-parasite models governed by differential equations with the same form as those of Lotka.[9]

A little while later, Vito Volterra (1860–1940) was motivated by the study of two species in competition, following discussions with his son-in-law Umberto d'Ancona[10] who had carried out a statistical analysis on species of fish in the Adriatic Sea. This study revealed that *a decrease in the catch favored the more voracious species.* In fact, he observed that *during the period 1915–1920, when the catch was smaller because of the war, there was an increase in the population of selacians*[11] *which are particularly voracious, feasting on other fish.* Volterra tried to describe the predator-prey relations and came up with a set of two equations,[12] for two interacting populations, that looked very similar to those of Lotka. One of the species corresponded to small fish, represented by the population S_1, and the other a larger fish, represented by the population S_2. It appeared that the larger fish ate the smaller fish and multiplied and, the population of the smaller fish decreased to the point where it was no longer possible to support the large population of the larger fish. As the population of the larger fish decreased, that of the smaller fish increased up to the point where the larger fish could begin feasting again, and so on.

A Soviet ecologist, Georgii Frantsevich Gause (1910–1986) in collaboration with Aleksandr Vitt (Andronov's colleague) tried to verify the Lotka-Volterra equations "experimentally".[13] To do that, he studied unicellular organisms, such as paramecia

[9]W. R. Thompson, La Théorie Mathématique de l'action des parasites entomophages, *Revue Générale des Sciences Pures et Appliquées*, **34**, 1923.

[10]U. d'Ancona, Dell'Influenza della stasi pescherecchia del periodo 1914–1918 sul patrimonio ittico dell' Alto Adriatico (On the influence of fish stocks in the Adriatic sea due to the interuption of fishering during the period 1914–1918), *Rendiconti Comitato Talassografico Italiano*, **126**, 95, 1926 and *The struggle for existence*, Brill, 1954.

[11]Class of fish containing sharks and rays.

[12]V. Volterra, Variazioni e fluttuazioni del numero d'individui in specie animali conviventi, *Memoria della Reale Accademia Nazionale dei Lincei*, **2**, 31–113, 1926.

[13]G. F. Gause & A. A. Witt, Vérifications expérimentales de la théorie mathématique de la lutte

or yeast cells. His conclusion was that "*experiments on two species in competition for the same ecological niche completely confirm Volterra's equations but as for the processes that occur when one species feeds on the other, the results disagree with the mathematical predictions.*" Following this, Gause stated his "principle of competitive exclusion" according which two species cannot permanently occupy the same ecological niche in the same place.

Up to the beginning of the 1970s, most ecologists implicitly believed that regulating factors, dependent on the population densities, served to maintain populations at constant levels, or at least allow them to vary cyclically. When irregular fluctuations were observed in populations, they were mostly attributed to unpredictable changes in the environment and, as a result, could not be predicted by deterministic models. By the end of the 1960s Colin Pennycuick, R. M. Compton and Linda Beckingham investigated the growth of a single population divided into age-groups with the aid of a "computer model".[14] For certain level of fecundity, they observed irregular oscillations (Figure 6.3) which they just described as "*alternating peaks of large and small amplitude.*"

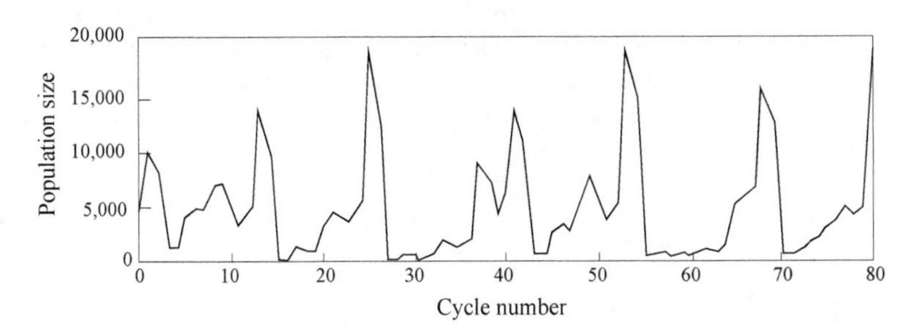

Figure 6.3 Time evolution of the population produced by the computer model by Pennycuick and co-workers (1968).

During the 1970s, George Oster (University of California, Berkeley), James Yorke (University of Maryland)[15] and Robert May (Imperial College, London)[16] began studying the Lotka-Volterra equations and the logistic map that we used in Chapter 1: they began to speak of aperiodic solutions, later of chaotic solutions. In 1975, John Beddington, C. A. Free and John Lawton proposed the predator-prey

pour la vie, *Actualités Scientifiques*, **277**, Hermann, Paris, 1935 — Behavior of mixed populations and the problem of natural selection, *American Naturalist*, **69**, 596–609, 1935.

[14]C. J. Pennycuick, R. M. Compton & L. Beckingham, A Computer model for simulating the growth of a population, or of two interacting populations, *Journal of Theoretical Biology*, **18**, 316–329, 1968.

[15]J. A. Yorke & W. N. Anderson, Predator-prey patterns, *Proceedings of the Natural Academy of Sciences*, **70**, 2069–2071, 1973.

[16]R. M. May, Time-delay versus stability in population models with two and three trophic levels, *Ecology*, **54** (2), 315–325, 1973.

model[17]

$$
\begin{cases}
H_{n+1} = H_n \, e^{r\left(1 - \frac{H_n}{\kappa}\right) - qP_n} \\
P_{n+1} = \alpha H_n \left(1 - e^{-qP_n}\right)
\end{cases}
\tag{6.1}
$$

where H_n designates the host population and P_n the parasitoïd population. This two-dimensional discrete map considers populations with non-overlapping generations and was based on Nicholson-Bailey host-parasite equations[18] to describe the interactions between a population of herbivorous arthropods — invertebrate animal having an exoskeleton — and their insect parasitoïds. They observed some chaotic behaviors as shown in Figure 6.4. The observation of chaotic behaviors in predator-prey model was a major breakthrough for ecologists, as Beddington and co-workers pointed out:

> The existence of high period cycles or chaotic behaviors in predator-prey models [...] may be of considerable importance in interpreting the patterns of fluctuation shown by many arthropod populations in the field, as this implies the possibility of long term co-existence between predator and prey within well-defined limits, but of a seemingly random nature. The temptation to ascribe such behavior to "environmental fluctuations" is obvious. Thus a recognition that such behavior may occur in an extremely simple, entirely deterministic predator-prey model is of considerable importance.

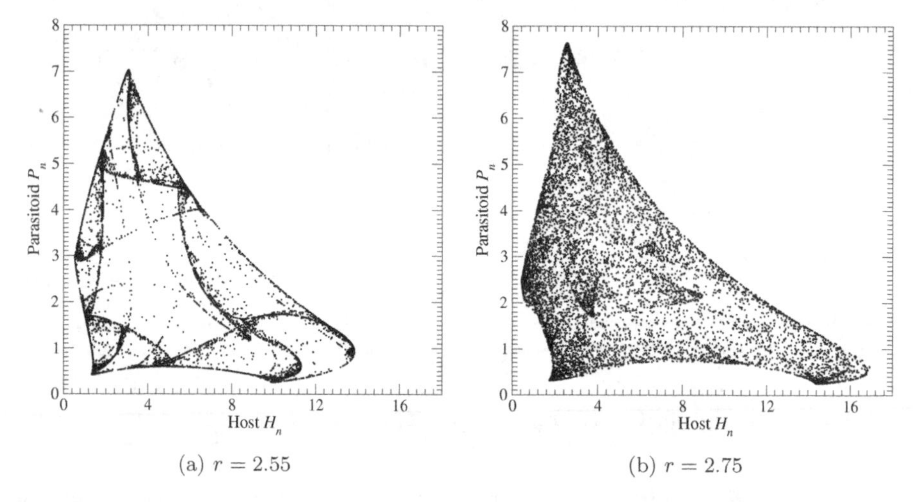

Figure 6.4 Chaotic behaviors observed in the two-dimensional map for arthropods and their parasitoïd insects as computed by Beddington and co-workers in 1975. Other parameter values: $\alpha = 1$, $\kappa = 10$, and $q = 0.5$.

---

[17] J. R. Beddington, C. A. Free & J. H. Lawton, Dynamic complexity in predator-prey models framed in difference equations, *Nature*, **255**, 58–60, 1975.

[18] A. J. Nicholson & V. A. Bailey, The balance of animal populations, *Proceedings of the Zoological Society of London*, **105** (3), 551–598, 1935.

During studies of fish populations in Canada or insect populations in Australia chaos had already been encountered, but as the objective of these studies had been to find constant or periodic population levels, these results had been set aside. Ecologists' interest in chaotic behavior only followed on the heels of the work of researchers such as Yorke and May, who had solid mathematical credentials. As John Guckenheimer and co-workers wrote in 1975:[19]

> Several authors have pointed out recently that even simple deterministic models can exhibit apparently chaotic behavior which is essentially indistinguishable from a random process. This blurs the distinction between deterministic and stochastic effects in models. The capacity of familiar dynamical systems to display complicated behavior has been known since Poincaré's discussion of "homoclinic points" in Hamiltonian systems. During the **last decade**, significant progress has been made toward understanding the nature of such complex behavior.

In retrospect, this is essentially what happened in celestial mechanics with George William Hill and Henri Poincaré, in meteorology with Edward Lorenz, in electronics with Balthazar van der Pol and Aleksandr Andronov, etc.

6.3 Models with Three Species

The first models of population evolution that were studied depended on only two species, following the example of the Lotka-Volterra model. As a result, the most complicated behavior that was seen was periodic, in conformity with the Poincaré-Bendixon theorem. After the first studies of the logistic map by Li, Yorke and May, and of a two-dimensional map by Beddington & Co, it was possible to imagine that populations could also evolve in a chaotic way. During an encounter with Otto Rössler and Robert May in 1979, Mickael Gilpin had the idea to study the Lotka-Volterra type model[20]

$$\left\{ \begin{array}{l} \dot{N}_1 = \mu_1 N_1 + \alpha_{11} N_1 N_1 + \alpha_{12} N_1 N_2 + \alpha_{13} N_1 N_3 \\ \dot{N}_2 = \mu_2 N_2 + \alpha_{21} N_2 N_1 + \alpha_{22} N_2 N_2 + \alpha_{23} N_2 N_3 \\ \dot{N}_3 = \mu_3 N_3 + \alpha_{31} N_3 N_1 + \alpha_{32} N_3 N_2 + \alpha_{33} N_3 N_3 \end{array} \right.$$

with three species. Gilpin found a chaotic attractor (Figure. 6.5(a)). Slightly earlier Richard Vance wrote down a model with one predator species and two prey species: he had observed behavior that he had called "quasi-cyclic".[21] Shortly afterwards other chaotic attractors were found with this set of equations but with different parameter values. One of them is shown in Figure 6.5(b).[22] It is characterized by

[19] J. Guckenheimer, G. F. Oster & A. Ipaktchi, Periodic solutions of a logistic difference equation, *Journal of Mathematical Biology*, **4**, 101–147, 1976.

[20] M. Gilpin, Spiral Chaos in a predator prey model, *The American Naturalist*, **113**, 306–308, 1979.

[21] R. R. Vance, Predation and resource partitioning in one predator-two prey model community, *The American Naturalist*, **112** 797–813, 1978.

[22] A. Arnéodo, P. Coullet & C. Tresser, Occurrence of strange attractors in three-dimensional Volterra equations, *Physics Letters A*, **79**, 259–263, 1980.

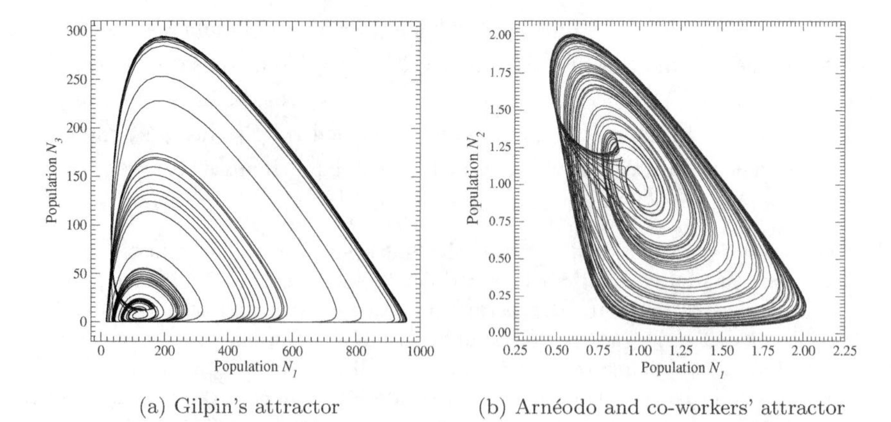

(a) Gilpin's attractor (b) Arnéodo and co-workers' attractor

Figure 6.5 Chaotic attractors solution to the Lotka-Volterra model with three species. Parameters values: (a) $\mu_1 = 1$, $\mu_2 = 1$, $\mu_3 = -1$, $\alpha_{11} = 0.001$, $\alpha_{12} = 0.001$, $\alpha_{13} = 0.01$, $\alpha_{21} = 0.0015$, $\alpha_{22} = 0.001$, $\alpha_{23} = 0.001$, $\alpha_{31} = -0.005$, $\alpha_{32} = -0.0005$, $\alpha_{33} = 0.0$, and (b) $\mu_1 = 1.1$, $\mu_2 = -0.5$, $\mu_3 = 1.75$, $\alpha_{11} = -0.5$, $\alpha_{12} = -0.5$, $\alpha_{13} = -0.1$, $\alpha_{21} = 0.5$, $\alpha_{22} = 0.1$, $\alpha_{23} = -0.1$, $\alpha_{31} = -1.55$, $\alpha_{32} = -0.1$ and $\alpha_{33} = -0.1$.

a smooth unimodal first-return map: as predicted by theory, this chaotic attractor emerged after a period-doubling cascade.

In fact, the Lotka-Volterra model for three species is too simple to reflect real population dynamics. For this reason, many ecologists do not believe that population species really undergo chaotic variations. For example, in such models the size of the population of hunters cannot be arbitrarily large because it is always proportional to the prey population. For these reasons, more realistic models of the food chain with two or three species are now being studied.

Consider for example a model proposed by R. K. Upadhyay, S. R. K. Jyengar & Vikas Rai (University of New Delhi, India): they include prey (rodents), specialized predators (snakes), and generalized predators (peacocks). By taking into account that the hunting abilities of the snakes and peacocks are limited, and the land cannot support an arbitrarily large rodent population, etc., the model

$$\left\{\begin{aligned} \dot{x} &= a_1 x - b_1 x^2 - \frac{xy}{x + d_0} && \text{(rodents)} \\ \dot{y} &= -a_2 y + 2\frac{xy}{x + d_1} - \frac{\omega_2 y z}{y + d_2} && \text{(snakes)} \\ \dot{z} &= c_0 z^2 - \frac{z^2}{y + d_3} && \text{(peacocks)} \end{aligned}\right. \tag{6.2}$$

is mathematically more complicated than the ones used by Lotka and Volterra.[23] The range of behaviors seen as the rodent reproduction rate a_1 increases is shown in the form of a bifurcation diagram (Figure 6.6). For a low reproduction rate the populations oscillate periodically. When the rate increases the oscillations have

[23]R. K. Upadhyay, S. R. K. Jyengar & V. Rai, Chaos: an ecological reality?, *International Journal of Bifurcation & Chaos*, **8** (6), 1325–1333, 1998.

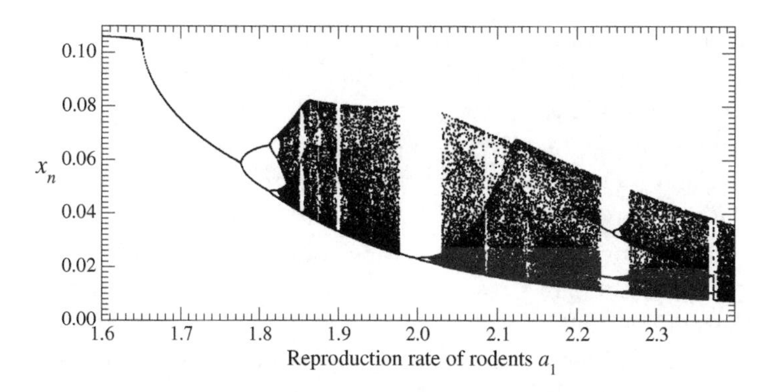

Figure 6.6 Bifurcation diagram for a realistic model of three species as a function of a reproduction rate. The variable x_n represents the rodent population each season. Parameter values: $a_2 = 1$, $b_1 = 0.06$, $c_0 = 0.03$, $d_0 = 10$, $d_1 = 10$, $d_2 = 10$, $d_3 = 20$, and $\omega_2 = 0.405$.

period 2 (the population oscillates between two values for the reproduction rate between $a_1 = 1.785$ and 1.805). Then the behavior switch for a period 4, then a period 8, a period 16, etc. As the reproduction rate increases: a period-doubling cascade takes place.

As any "chaotician" would expect, the first-return map for this attractor (Figure 6.7(b)) is a smooth unimodal map (Figure 6.7(a)), as always associated with a period-doubling cascade.

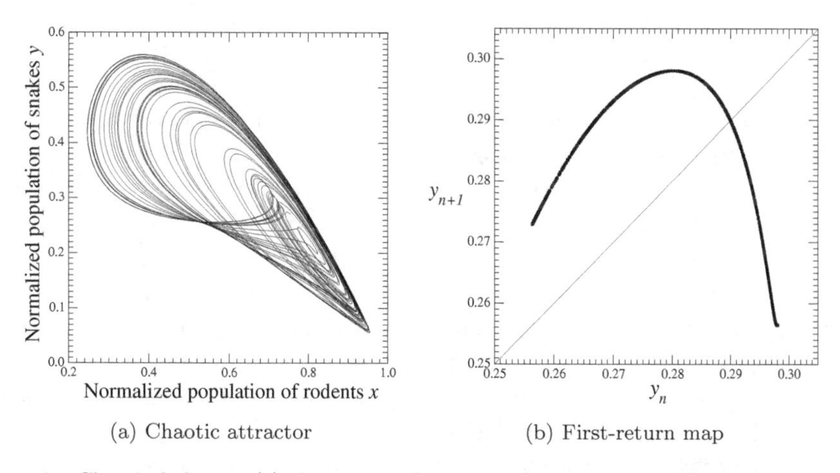

(a) Chaotic attractor

(b) First-return map

Figure 6.7 Chaotic behavior (a) that occurs for a reproduction rate of $a_1 = 1.93$. The first-return map (b) is a smooth unimodal map as typically seen after a period-doubling cascade. Other parameter values as in Figure 6.6.

Another type of behavior can also be observed: this type of behavior is called *intermittency*. If we set the rodent reproduction rate at 1.97740, the rodents seem to evolve periodically during a finite period of time.[24] This evolution is suddenly interrupted by chaotic oscillations during short time intervals, then it evolves in a seemingly periodic way once again (Figure 6.8). This peculiar type of oscillation was discovered in very simple models (Lorenz and Rössler systems, etc.) in 1979 by Yves Pomeau and Paul Manneville.[25] According to the classic line, ecologists believe that the short bursts of irregular oscillations (chaos) are due to unpredictable changes in the environment, following which the ecological system returns to its usual periodic behavior. As a result, "classical" ecologists try to find the environmental perturbations that are responsible for this behavior. With the theory of chaos this type of behavior could come about naturally as the result of the interactions among three species and no environmental changes are needed to explain them. In fact, ecologists are hoping to find a model that reproduces intermittent oscillations.

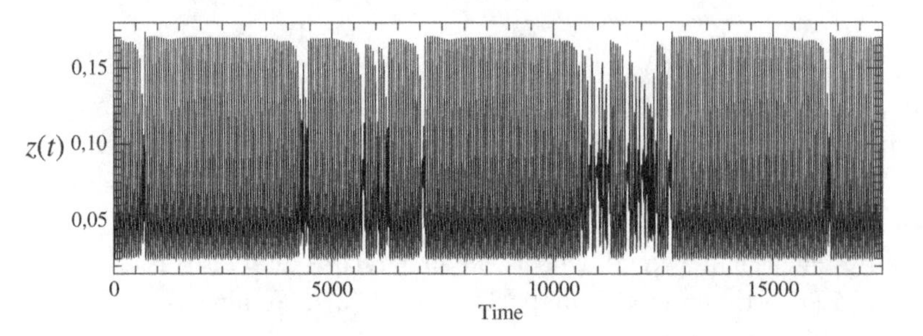

Figure 6.8 Intermittent behavior seen for $a_1 = 1.97740$. The laminar phases during which the behavior is almost exactly periodic are interrupted by chaotic bursts.

Another important property of ecological systems interests ecologists: bistability. This involves two simultaneously coexisting attractors in the state space. As a result, depending on the initial conditions, the population evolves to one or the other of the attractors. This shows that the same system can evolve in two different ways, even for the same parameter values (Figure 6.9). For example, an ecological system might evolve periodically over a number of years: then the trajectory falls on the periodic attractor. An epidemic hits one of the populations... what happens? If the system has only a single attractor, the system will resume its periodic behavior after a shorter or longer transient regime. On the other hand, if the system is bistable, it can very well happen that after the epidemic has passed, the system evolves to the other attractor after a longer or shorter transient regime, so that its evolution is completely different from the type of evolution that it had before the epidemic, despite the fact that no lasting change occurred in the environment. One can see that the theory of chaos can significantly change the analysis of evolving

[24]C. Letellier & M. A. Aziz-Alaoui, Analysis of the dynamics of a realistic ecological model, *Chaos, Solitons & Fractals*, **13**, 95–107, 2002.
[25]P. Manneville & Y. Pomeau, Intermittency and the Lorenz model, *Physics Letters A*, **57** (1), 2, 1979.

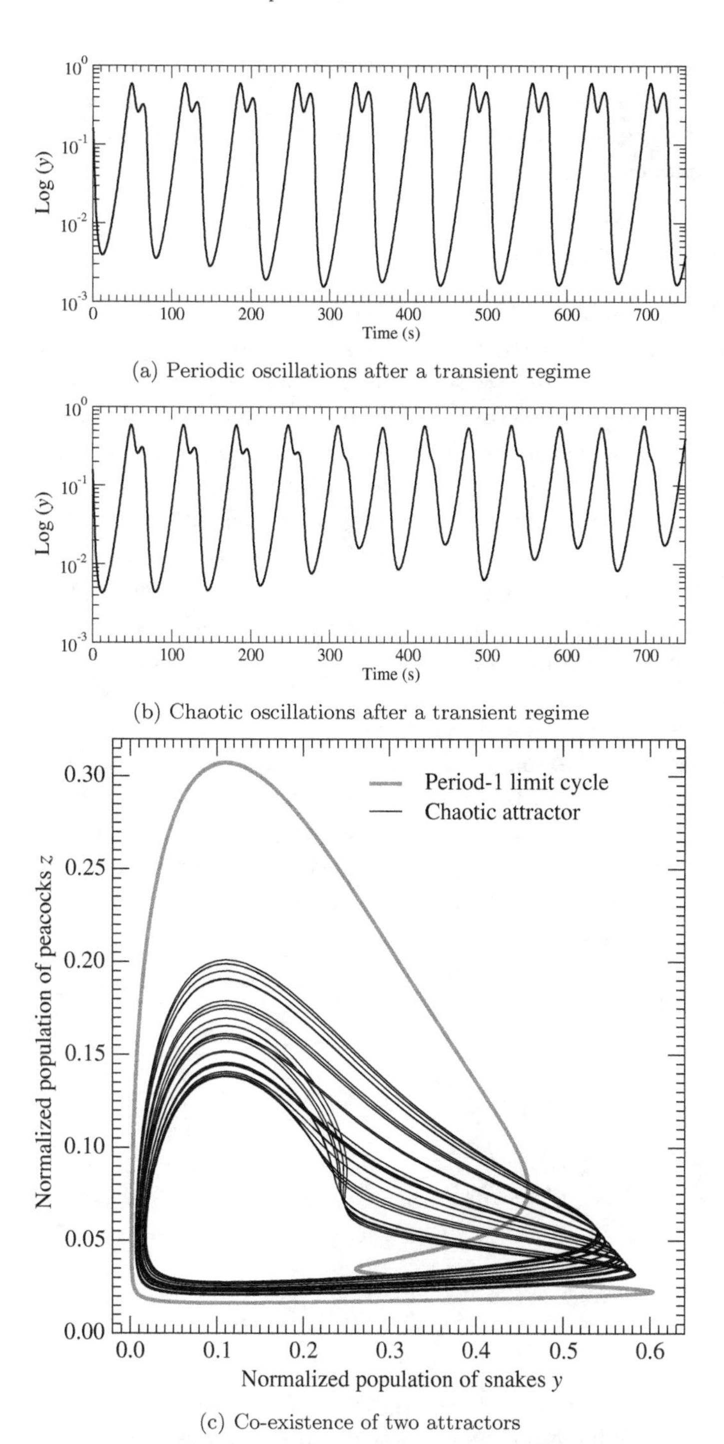

(a) Periodic oscillations after a transient regime

(b) Chaotic oscillations after a transient regime

(c) Co-existence of two attractors

Figure 6.9 Coexistence of two attractors, one periodic and the other chaotic, both solutions of the three species ecological model (6.2). A semi-logarithmic scale has been used (a and b) to provide a better representation of population fluctuations starting from two populations initially slightly different from each other.

populations; in this way one need not look for changes in the behavior that were produced by the environment, but rather to see if the existence of bistability could account for this change in behavior. The theory of chaos offers new interpretations of many phenomena.

6.4 Observational Evidence

Many studies have been carried out for more than a century on the evolution of evolutionary chains. Nevertheless, ecologists have great problems finding observational data of sufficient quality for convincingly showing chaotic evolution of real species. As a result, the possibility of chaotic evolution in food chains is even now still in debate. The reason for this is that, in order to prove the existence of chaos in ecosystems it is necessary to plot the trajectory in some state space, and this implies large, long data sets. To be specific, if we assume that it takes at least fifty oscillations sampled at the rate of about fifty points per oscillation, this means that if an animal that breeds once per year is being studied, it is necessary to record the population once every week for at least fifty years! As a result, only experiments on insects (which reproduce very rapidly) can realistically be carried out to identify chaotic tendencies.

The earliest evidence for fluctuations comes from records of the Hudson Bay Company regarding the populations of lynx and hares. This company bought and sold lynx furs. Their records (Figure 6.10) — studied by Charles Sutherland Elton and Mary Nicholson[26] — show that the number of animals fluctuates with a period of about nine years, so that about a dozen cycles were observed in the data during the century. The amplitude of these cycles varies significantly from year to year, as would be expected for a chaotic system.

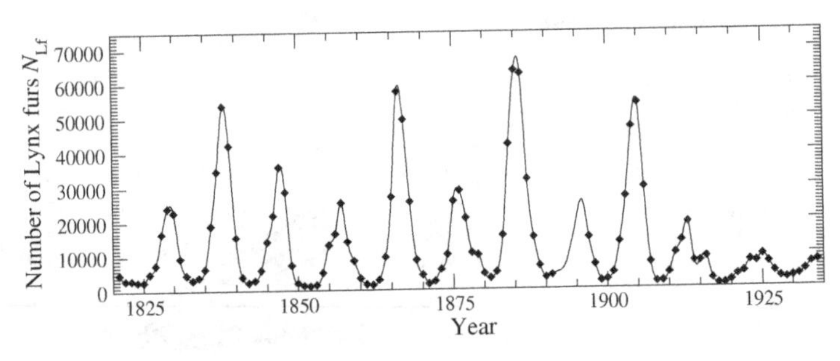

Figure 6.10 History of the number of lynx pelts sold in the different regions of Canada between 1821 and 1934.

As for our analysis of copper electrodissolution (Chapter 5), our goal was to find a set of ordinary differential equations that reproduce the dynamics responsible for

[26]C. Elton & M. Nicholson, The Ten-Year Cycle in numbers of the Lynx in Canada, *Journal of Animal Ecology*, **11**, 215–244, 1942.

the Elton-Nicholson data. We use derivative coordinates to reconstruct the state space trajectory (Figure 6.11(a)). The attractor that is obtained looks like a large ribbon around a singular point of saddle-node type. The small oscillations around this point are the signatures of folding responsible — dynamically speaking — for irregular fluctuations in the lynx population.

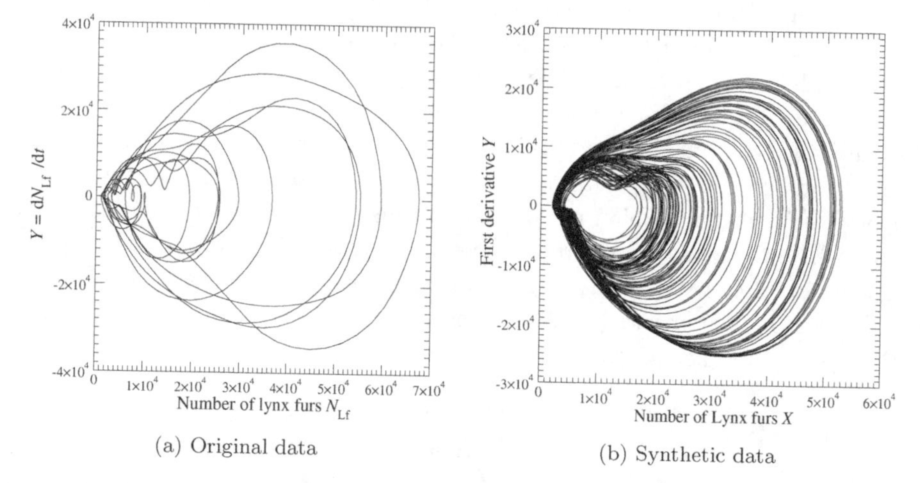

(a) Original data

(b) Synthetic data

Figure 6.11 Different state portraits for the lynx population (a) spanned by the records of the Hudson Bay Company and (b) produced by the four-dimensional global model obtained from those records.

Among the conclusions of Elton and Nicholson, we should point out that the lynx population depends not only on the hare population, since they also eat snowshoe rabbits, muskrats and salmon. Further, the lynx is not the chief predator: it is hunted by trappers![27] It is surprising that these factors are not taken into account in most of the studies of these data. The important point is that we need to model the interaction of more than three species to explain the variations in the lynx population in a realistic way. For this reason, with Jean Maquet we have sought, and found, a four-dimensional model — corresponding to four interacting species.[28]

To obtain a four-dimensional model in the form

$$\begin{cases} \dot{X} = Y \\ \dot{Y} = Z \\ \dot{Z} = W \\ \dot{W} = F(X, Y, Z, W), \end{cases}$$

where $X = N_{Lf}$ and for which the first four derivatives of the number of Lynx furs N_{Lf} must be computed to estimate the model function F. This work is limited by the available data (there are only 10 cycles). Unfortunately, the best model

[27] Martin S. Weinstein, Hares, Lynx, and Trappers, *The American Naturalist*, **111**, 806–808, 1977.
[28] J. Maquet & C. Letellier, Global models from the Canadian Lynx cycles as a first evidence for chaos in real ecosystems, *Journal of Mathematical Biology*, **55** (1), 21–39, 2007.

that was found is not completely stable. It was integrated for 420 cycles (this corresponds to about 4000 years) before the trajectory was ejected to infinity. This lack of stability could be a consequence of the fact that there is only one point per year, that is, roughly, ten points per oscillations. A data set is considered as good when it has about fifty points per oscillation;[29] such a requirement ensures a reliable computation of the successive time derivatives of the recorded time series. A first-return map on a Poincaré section shows three monotonic branches with a layered structure (Figure 6.12). The first increasing branch is nearly tangent to the diagonal: this is a signature of "lethargy" — long minima around zero — when there are very few lynx. In fact, this lethargy is related to the existence of a singular point of saddle-node type whose neighborhood is visited often. This is a common property of homoclinic orbit that gives rise to unstable periodic oscillations. With this property, the global model reproduces the aperiodic oscillations, an important dynamical characteristic in the original data (Figure 6.13). Once again, finding a global model by starting with observational data allows us to place chaotic nature in the midst of mathematical dynamics.

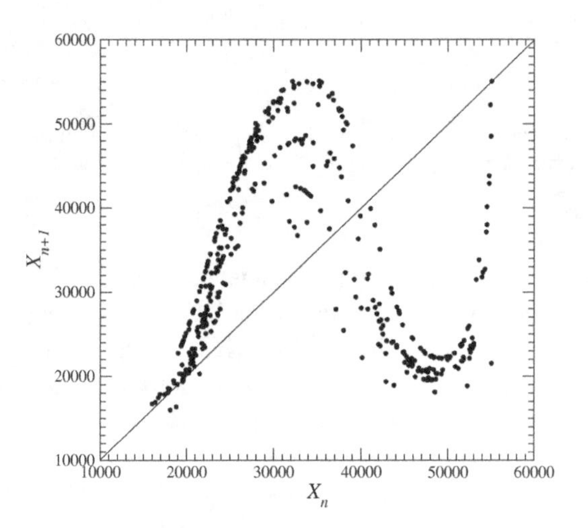

Figure 6.12 First return map on a Poincaré section for the metastable chaotic solution of the four-dimensional model based on data from the Hudson Bay Company.

Another study, dating from 1957, is due to the Australian Alexander Nicholson (1895–1969) dealing with flies on sheep (*Lucila Cuprina*) whose populations are important for Australian sheep raisers.[30] Over a period of two years, Nicholson studied these pests under controlled temperature and food supply conditions. The goal of this study was to analyze how this population evolved under the constraints

[29] C. Letellier, L. A. Aguirre & U. S. Freitas, Frequently asked questions about global modeling, *Chaos*, **19**, 023103, 2009.

[30] A. J. Nicholson, The Self-Adjustement of populations to change, *Cold Spring Harbor Symposia on Quantitative Biology*, **22**, 153–173, 1957.

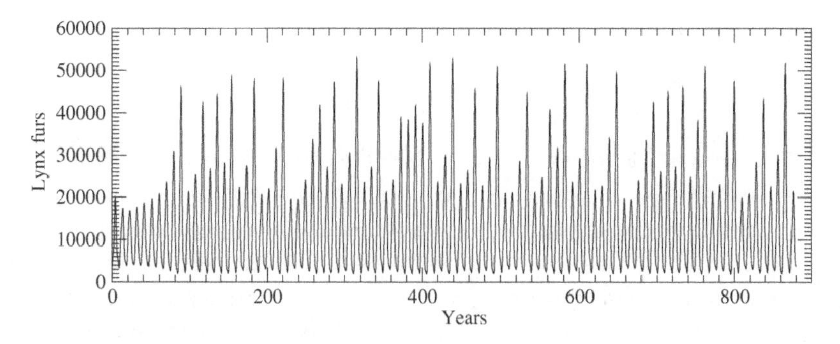

Figure 6.13 Evolution of the lynx population obtained by numerically integrating the global model. Lethargies — long passages near the minimum — are reproduced in a manner very close to that seen in the original data.

that could be imposed on the environment, then to apply those constraints and determine the survival capacity when they changed. Despite a constant environment, Nicholson observed repeated (apparently irregular) oscillations with a period of 35 to 40 days (Figure 6.14). However, the possibility of seeing chaotic oscillations with simple models was not yet known, so that Nicholson did no further research on his model.

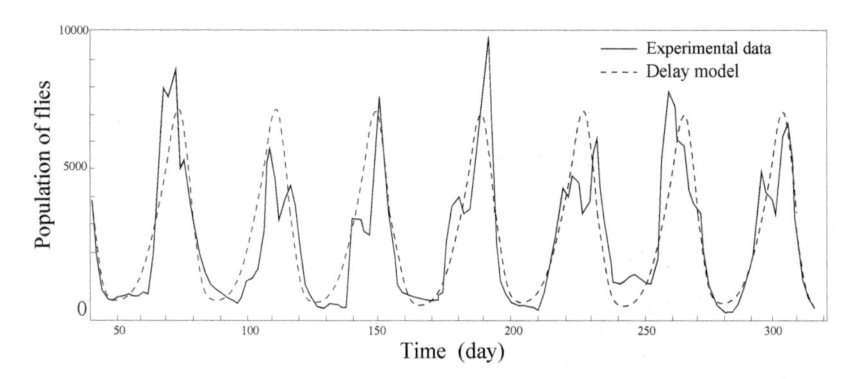

Figure 6.14 Evolution of the population of flies on sheep revealed by the studies of Alexander Nicholson (1957). The population is regulated by the food supply available to adult flies. These data are compared with the solution of the time-delay model investigated by Robert May (1971).

In this type of study a single species is investigated. If one uses the *logistic function* of Verhulst, the population stabilizes and no oscillations are seen (Figure 6.2). In fact, one of the deficiencies of this model is that the birth rate is considered as acting instantaneously and no account is taken of the time it takes for the newborn to mature. It was George Evelyn Hutchinson who in 1948 introduced a time delay

τ into the logistic function to get:[31]

$$\dot{N}(t) = \mu N(t) \left[1 - \frac{N(t-\tau)}{\kappa} \right] \tag{6.3}$$

where κ is the quantity of available food. The delay τ designates the duration needed by flies to become mature. At the beginning of the 1970s, Robert May[32] used this delay model to reproduce the population of flies on sheep seen by Nicholson. With the parameters that Nicholson used to describe his experiments, May found oscillations with a period of 40 days which corresponds reasonably well with the observations (Figure 6.14). However, the delay used was about nine days instead of the 14 days needed for flies to become mature. In addition, the fluctuations in the amplitudes of oscillations were not reproduced.

In 1980 William Gurney, Steve Blythe & Roger Nisbet reviewed this study. They proposed a new model based on the assumptions as follows:[33]

- adults die off at a rate proportional to their present numbers;
- the number of eggs laid depends only on the size of the adult population;
- all the eggs develop into sexually mature adults in exactly the same time;
- the probability that any given egg reaches maturity depends on the number of competitors of the same age: the larger the number of eggs, the smaller the probability that any egg reaches maturity.

The resulting model

$$\dot{N}(t) = P\, N(t-\tau)\, e^{-\frac{N(t-\tau)}{N_0}} - \delta N(t) \tag{6.4}$$

is a delay differential equation where P characterize the maximum number of eggs laid *per capita* moderated by the probability that any egg reaches maturity, N_0 is the value of the population at which reproduction rate is maximum, δ designates the death rate which does not depend on the population density and, τ is the maturation delay. This model has a form somewhat more complicated than the simple *logistic* model (6.3) with a delay.

When the parameters are fixed at values determined by Nicholson, the behavior is chaotic (Figure 6.15(c)). Just as for the observational data, the time evolution of the model shows a secondary oscillation superposed on the principle oscillation. The model of Gurney and his colleagues is quantitatively better than May's model. Even so, it remains difficult to conclude that the model produces a dynamics equivalent to that seen in the experiments in view of the small number of oscillations (seven cycles for a year's worth of observations — Figure 6.14). We should point out that

[31] G. E. Hutchinson, Circular Causal Systems in ecology, *Annals of the New York Academy of Sciences*, **50**, 221–246, 1948.

[32] R. M. May, *Stability and complexity in model ecosystems*, 2nd Edition, Princeton University Press, 1975, p. 96.

[33] W. S. C. Gurney, S. P. Blythe & R. M. Nisbet, Nicholson's Blowflies revisited, *Nature*, **287**, 17–21, 1980.

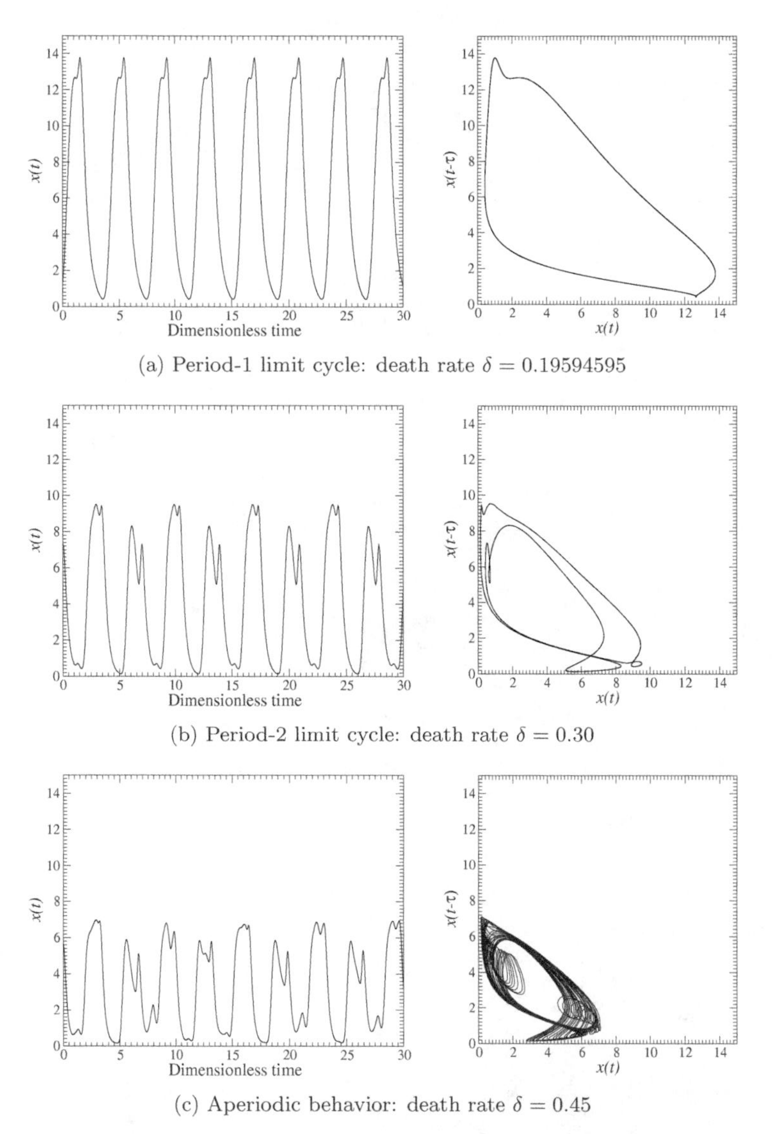

(a) Period-1 limit cycle: death rate $\delta = 0.19594595$

(b) Period-2 limit cycle: death rate $\delta = 0.30$

(c) Aperiodic behavior: death rate $\delta = 0.45$

Figure 6.15 Different behaviors produced by the model (6.4) of Gurney and his colleagues for different values of the death rate. A period-doubling cascade is seen when the death rate is progressively increased. Parameter values: $P = 8.883736$ and $\tau = 14.8$.

when the death rate is varied a period-doubling cascade is seen (Figure 6.15(a) and 6.15(b)).

Some ecologists now work in the paradigm of chaos theory; despite the observation of chaos in most realistic models, the absence of enough observational data still raises a certain timidity with regard to this new approach.

Chapter 7

Chaotic Stars

Astrophysics has not escaped chaotic behavior: for example, stars like our sun or variable stars exhibit oscillatory behavior that may eventually turn out to be chaotic. Since the end of the 19th century, Assyriologists have come to the cuneiform texts of the Babylonians, dating from two or three thousand years ago, report the discovery of stars whose luminosity is variable.[1] This hypothesis is supported by observations of a star in the constellation of Cetus the Whale in the eastern part of *Aquarius*. This star could become visible and very brilliant or *go out like a torch*; it could appear dark, yellow, or very red. This description applies accurately to the star *Mira Ceti*.[2] However, there is no reference to stellar variability in the catalog of Hipparcus (-130) or the *Almagest* of Ptolemy ($\simeq$ 138).[3] This absence extends through the star catalogue *Zij-i Sultani* of Ulugh Begh — his name means the great ruler — (1394–1449) dating from 1437.[4] It seems that the main reason for the absence of these phenomena in the scientific tracts is that dogma blinded observers. One of the foundational principles of Aristotle's physics was that change was not possible in the supralunary heavenly world, home of the celestial bodies and constituted of the quintessence, the divine, imperishable and inalterable matter. In the sublunary world, where nature consists of the four other elements (water, earth, air, and fire), that changes could occur. In fact, it seems that medieval scientists were unaware of a number of celestial events, for example the supernova in the *Crab nebula*, that occurred on 4 July 1054, was recorded by the Chinese but for which there is no European record. The Chinese called "*guest stars*" those appearing temporarily.[5]

---

[1] P. Jensen, *Die Kosmologie der Babylonier*, K. Trübner, Strasbourg, 1890.

[2] J. Schaumberger, in *Sternkunde und Sterndienst in Babel, Assyriologische, astronomische und astralmythologische Untersuchungen*, 1935.

[3] *Ptolemy's Almagest*, Translated and annotated by G. J. Toomer, Princeton University Press, 1998.

[4] Edited in Europe by Thomas Hyde (1636–1703) under the title *Tabulae longitudinis et latitudinis stellarum fixarum ex observatione Ulugbeighi*, Oxford.

[5] See Duncan Campbell, The Huntington Library's volume of the Yongle Encyclopaedia (Yongle Dadian): A bibliographical and historical note, *East Asian History*, **42**, 1–13, 2018.

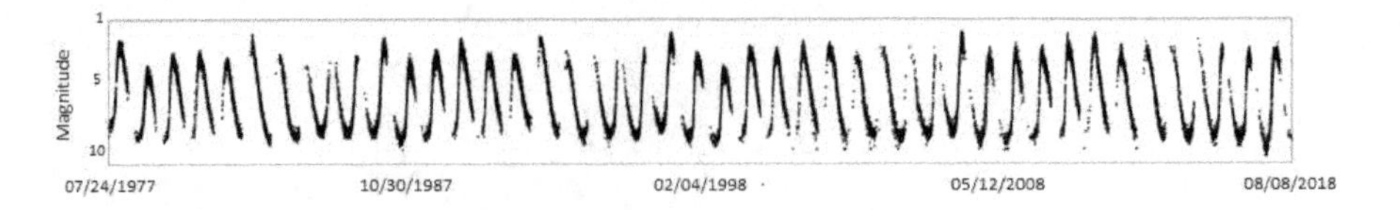

Figure 7.1 Visual light curve of Mira Ceti which is a red giant star whose variations in brightness are caused by changes in size. The star was first recorded in 1596 by David Fabricius, but the cyclic nature of the changes was not recognized until 1638. The name Mira was given to the star by Johannes Hevelius in 1662. Mira Ceti is located in the neck of the Whale. Made with the light curve generator provided by the American Association of Variable Star Observers (https://www.aavso.org).

7.1 The Solar Activity

7.1.1 *Early Observations*

In the heavens, there is another candidate for producing chaotic behavior: the sun. Indeed, in 1963, Lorenz wrote that "*we cannot say with any confidence what the phase of the sunspot cycle will be 100 years from now.*"[6] Sunspots result from the concentration of strong magnetic fields that pierce the solar photosphere and block the convection, inducing a "cold" spot at the solar surface. One consequence is the presence of dark spots on the solar surface. Most sunspots are too small to be seen with the unaided eye, but some of them are large enough to be seen without a telescope. Originally, the appearances of such spots were taken as omens of future events. Chinese astronomer-astrologers observed them two thousand years ago. Further, in one of the oldest Chinese books, the *Book of Changes*,[7] one may read

> A *dou* is seen in the sun, [and] a *mei* is seen in the sun.

In this context, the Chinese characters *dou* and *mei* mean "dark spot" and "obscuration." Other more or less elliptical allusions were mentioned in the Chinese and Korean courts when the emperor demanded astrological predictions. Contrary to this, in the Mediterranean basin, because of the supremacy of Aristotelian thought, any mention of such spots (imperfections) could only be considered as contrary to classical dogma.

One of the earliest drawings of sunspots can be found in the *Chronicon ex chronicis* of John of Worcester, one of many monks who wrote them.[8] The sunspots were drawn on Saturday, 8 December 1128 (Figure 7.2) and described as follows.

[6]E. Lorenz, The predictability of hydrodynamic flow, *Transactions of the New York Academy of Sciences*, **25** (4), 409–432, 1963.

[7]Zhou yi (Changes of Zhou) is a divination text written the 10th and 4th centuries BC. For a translation, see for instance, Richard J. Lynn, *The Classic of Changes*, Columbia University Press (New York), 1994.

[8]John of Worcester, *The Chronicle of John of Worcester*, Corpus Christi College, Oxford, MS 157, p. 380, 1128.

... from morning to evening, appeared something like two black circles within the disk of the sun, the one in the upper part being bigger, the other in the lower part smaller. As shown in the drawing.

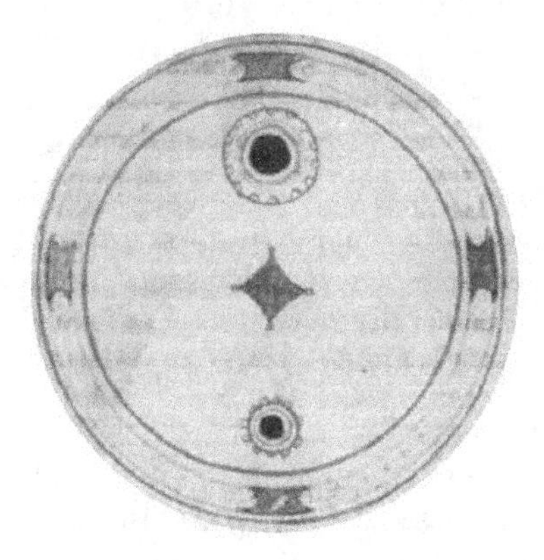

Figure 7.2 Representations of sunspots that occurred in December, 1128. It is remarkable that the penumbra around each spot is reproduced. (Adapted from R. W. Southern, *Medieval Humanism*, Harper & Row, 1970.)

With the invention of the astronomical lens (around 1609), several scientists began their study of sunspots: Johannes Fabricius (1587–1616 — son of David) in Holland, Thomas Harriot (1560–1621) in England, the Jesuit Christoph Scheiner (1573–1650) in Germany and Galileo (1564–1642) in Italy. Galileo recorded his first observations as follows.[9]

About eighteen months ago, while I looked at the sun in the lens a little before sunset, I saw several very dark spots; repeating this observation several evenings later, I saw that these spots moved, that they were not always the same as they had previously appeared or even placed in the same order; sometimes they were more numerous, sometimes less, and sometimes I did not see any at all.

[They are] in contact with the solar body, they are ceaselessly created and annihilated, some denser and darker, others less so; in general, they change shape from day to day and their outlines are very irregular; it happens sometimes that one group divides into two, in three or even more; and that others, separated at first, combine into a single group; finally, because of their universal and common motion, I have become convinced that it is the sun itself that rotates from the west to the east, that is, following the same revolution as all the planets, and that this all happens in about the same time as the lunar month.

It appears that Galilei dated these earliest observations to the month of January 1611. He remarked that these sunspots appeared in a well-defined zone on the solar disk. He observed the same spots many times: he was convinced that they occurred

[9]Galilei, Letter to Maffeo Barberini (2nd June 1612), in *Dialogues*, Herman, 379–380, 1997.

in the sun itself. The variation of their sizes near the center and the edges of the sun, where they disappeared, attracted his notice.

However, Harriot observed these phenomena even earlier than Galilei. Harriot recorded his observation on 18 December 1610.[10] Although he did not explicitly mention the sunspots, they are clearly shown in his sketch of the sun. Like Fabricius' father, but not like Galilei and Scheiner, Harriot observed the sun directly through his telescope. He drew more than 200 figures between 1610 and 1612. Harriot, unlike Galilei and Scheiner, drew no conclusions from his observations. Fabricius was the first to publish his results in 1611 and to correctly interpret the apparent movement of sunspots as due to the axial rotation of the sun:[11]

> ... these spots do not always preserve the same distances among themselves, nor do they traverse the solar disk with the same speed, but they move more rapidly near the center, slower near the sides. In addition, the form that they take near the middle, they lose near the edges. But I discovered the reason for this... In fact, it is reasonable to assume, from the observations, that the spots on the body of the sun — which is spherical, round, and solid — can not possibly have the same speed and the same form during the course of their displacement. In the middle of this globe, the spots move along a line more or less parallel to our view, but when they arrive at the edges, the move along a line oblique to our view...

Without a doubt Galilei and Scheiner were the most active in this field. In 1612 Scheiner published three letters to Mark Welser[12] (1558–1614) under the pseudonym Apelles (following the request of his superior to protect the Jesuit order from controversy).[13] Scheiner observed that the sunspots do not all move at the same speed.[14] In his *Rosa Ursina*, he concluded that according to Aristotelian dogma, since the sun is a solid, the spots could not occur on the solar surface. As a result, Scheiner believed they were small planets moving near the surface of the sun, since a gaseous sun was "*physically absurd.*" This opinion was refuted by Galilei in three letters in which he concluded that in fact the spots were indeed on the surface of the sun.[15] In the exchange that followed,[16] he also showed that some changes can arise in the

---

[10]Albert van Helden, Galileo and Scheiner on sunspots: A case study in the visual language of astronomy, *Proceedings of the American Philosophical Society*, **140** (3), 358–396, 1996.

[11]J. Fabricius, *De Maculis in sole observatis et apparente earum cum Sole conversione, Narratio*, 1611.

[12]Welser was a magistrate from Augsburg. He exchanged some scientific letters with Scheiner and Galilei.

[13]W. M. Mitchell, The history of the discovery of the solar spots, *Popular Astronomy*, **24**, 206–217, 1916.

[14]C. Scheiner, *Tres Epistolae de maculis solaribus scriptae ad marcum verserum*, 11 November 1611, published on January 1612.

[15]Galilei, *Istoria e dimostrazini intorno alle macchie solari e loro accidenti* also sent to Mark Welser on 1613.

[16]C. Scheiner was in Roma from 1624 to 1633 and played a quite important role in the procedure developed in 1632 against Galilei.

surface of the sun. These observations of sunspots allowed the introduction of ideas of *mutability*, *corruption*, and *generation of the supreme substance of the sky* and contributed to discrediting the distinction between the Aristotelian sublunary and supralunary realms.

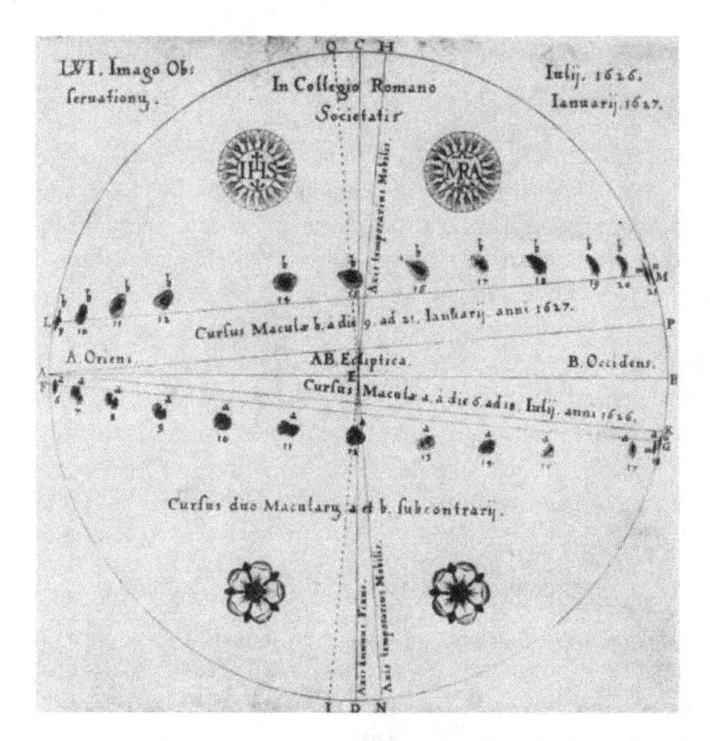

Figure 7.3 Representations of sunspots seen by Scheiner. He described the apparent path of two groups of sunspots across the solar disk separated by a six month interval (July 1626 and January 1627). Based on these observations, Scheiner concluded that the equatorial plane of the sun is inclined by 7° with respect to the ecliptic. This was repeated by Galilei in his *Dialogues.* The convergence of these sunspots towards the equator is here clearly shown. (Drawing by C. Scheiner, *Rosina Ursina*, p. 325, 1626–1630.)

After the foundation of the Paris Observatory in 1667, a systematic observation program was put into effect by Dominique Cassini (1625–1712) with Jean Picard (1620–1682) and Philippe La Hire (1640–1718). Under this program more than 8000 observations were made over the period of 70 years. In spite of all these observations, the authorities in astronomy did not see any periodicity nor regularity in the appearances of sunspots:

- Jacques Cassini at Paris: "*It is clear that, from what we just reported, there is no certain rule in* [sunspot] *formation, neither in their numbers nor in their figures;*"[17]

[17] J. Cassini, *Éléments d'astronomie*, Imprimerie Royale (Paris), 1740.

- Pierre-Charles Le Monnier (1715–1799) at Paris: "*It seems that* [sunspots] *does not follow any rule in their appearances*;"[18]
- Roger Long (1680–1770) at Cambridge: "*Solar spots observe no regularity in their shape, magnitude, number, or in the time of their appearance or continuance*;"[19]
- Joseph-Jérôme Lalande at Paris: "*Appearances of solar spots are not regular at all.*"[20]

In 1826 the amateur astronomer Samuel Heinrich Schwabe (1789–1875) was looking for a planet in orbit between the sun and Mercury; this search was motivated by an anomalous advance in the perihelion of Mercury that could not be explained within the context of classical celestial mechanics. Among the many illustrious astronomers who searched for this hypothetical planet, one counts Urbain Le Verrier. Among many others, Schwabe began his search by making a precise map of sunspots to avoid mistaking these for the mystery planet. Thus began a meticulous observation of the positions of the sunspots. In 1843, after 17 years of observations, he failed to discover any planet interior to Mercury's orbit but he did discover the increase and decrease in the average number of spots visible on the surface of the sun, with a period that Schwabe estimated to be ten years.[21] Seven years later he returned to this problem with 24 consecutive years of observations, shown in Figure 7.4. According to Humboldt, he wrote:[22]

> The numbers in the following table leave no doubt that, at least from the year between 1826 to 1850, the occurrence of spots has been so far characterized by periods of ten years, that its maxima have fallen in the years 1828, 1837, and 1848, and its minima in the years 1833 and 1843. I had no opportunity of acquainting myself with the older observations in a continued series, but I willingly concur in this opinion that this period may itself be further characterized by variability.

Taking Schwabe's discovery seriously, Johann Rudolph Wolf (1816–1893), director of the Zurich Observatory, undertook a reconstruction of data before 1850 in order to verify, or test, Schwabe's hypothesis. In order to normalize observations taken by different astronomers using a variety of techniques, Wolf introduced the *relative number of sunspots* at the solar surface defined as

$$N_s = k\,(N_t + 10 \times N_g)$$

[18]P.-C. Le Monnier, *Institutions Astronomiques ou Leçons élémentaires d'astronomie*, H.-L. & J. Guérin (Paris), 1746. Augmented translation of J. Keill, *Introductio ad veram astronomium*, Oxford, 1718.

[19]R. Long, *Astronomy*, Cambridge, 1764.

[20]J.-J. Lalande, *Traité d'Astronomie*, Vol. 3, Veuve Desaint (Paris), 1771.

[21]S. H. Schwabe, Sonnenbeobachtungen im Jahre 1843, *Astronomische Nachrichten*, **21** (15), 233–236, 1843.

[22]Manuscript by S. H. Schwabe quoted by A. von Humboldt, *Cosmos — A sketch of a physical description of the universe*, IV, Harper & Brothers (New York), p. 85, 1866.

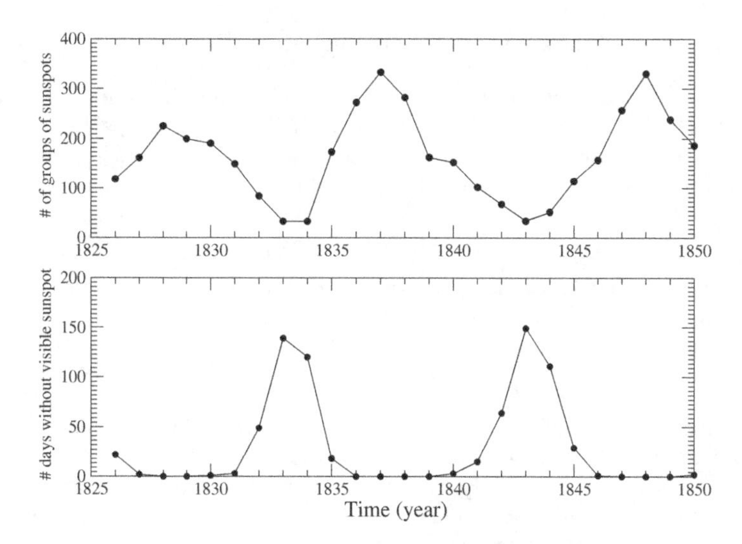

Figure 7.4 Graphical representation of the data collected by Samuel Heinrich Schwabe up to 1850 and reported in the *Cosmos* written by Alexander von Humboldt (1866).

where N_t is the number of individual sunspots, N_g is the number of groups of sunspots (which contain on average 10 sunspots), and k is a normalization constant ("fudge factor") that varies from one observer to another (by definition, $k = 1$ for Wolf's observations). Sunspot groups were introduced because it is often difficult to resolve individual sunspots within a cluster of sunspots. Wolf succeeded in reconstructing a relatively believable variation in the number of sunspots back to 1755. The cycle that developed between 1755–1766 is taken by convention as cycle 1, the others are counted from there. Cycle 23 began January 1, 2000. The 20 or so solar cycles known today are studied quantitatively thanks to the Wolf index (Figure 7.5).[23] Note that the period of these cycles varies between 8 and 14 years. The amplitude of these cycles also varies from a minimum of 48 in 1816 to a maximum of 190 in 1957.

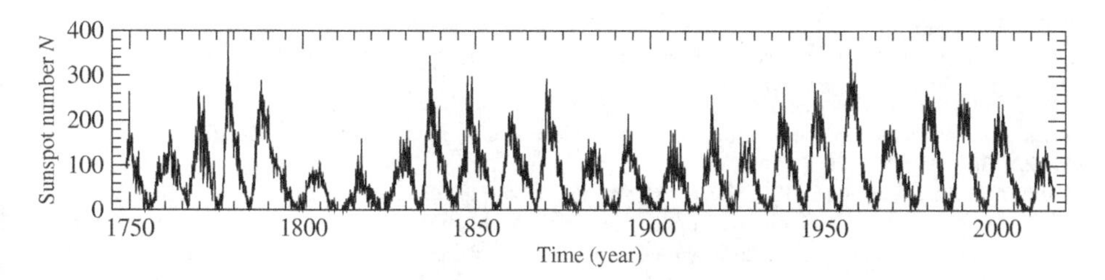

Figure 7.5 Evolution of the monthly averaged number of sunspots on the solar disk visible from the earth. Data before 1850 were collected and processed by Wolf.

[23]The data here used can be downloaded from `http://science.msfc.nasa.gov`.

Wolf reached the following significant conclusions:[24]

> I have combed through at least 400 volumes to find all the observations of sunspots since their discovery. [...] My memoir is divided into six parts, as follows:
>
> In the first chapter I showed, that based on 16 different epoches marked by the minimum and the maximum of sunspots, that the average sunspot period can be fixed at
>
> $$11.111 \pm 0.038 \text{ years,}$$
>
> so that nine periods is just about equivalent to one century.
>
> In the second chapter I showed that in each century the years
>
> 0.00 11.11 22.22 33.33 44.44 55.56 66.67 77.78 88.89
>
> correspond to solar minima. The interval between the minimum and the maximum is variable; the average is about five years.
>
> The fourth chapter establishes remarkable analogies between sunspots and variable stars, from which one could presume that there is a remarkable connection between these two surprising phenomena.
>
> In the fifth chapter I demonstrated that my period of 11.111 years coincides more exactly with the period of $10\ \frac{1}{3}$ years for the variations in the magnetic declination, established by M. Lamont.[25] The magnetic variations even follow the sunspot variations, not only for their regularity, but also for all their small irregularities, and I believe that this last remark should suffice to prove definitely that this relation is important.
>
> The sixth chapter contains is devoted to a comparison between the solar period and the meteorological record contained in the Zurich chronicles for the years 1000–1800. The result is that (conforming to the ideas of W. Herschel) the years when the sunspots are more numerous are generally drier and more fertile than the others; the others, on the contrary, are stormier and more humid. The aurora borealis and earthquakes recorded in this chronicle, occur in a striking manner in the years of sunspots.

At the beginning of the 19th century William Herschel[26] (1738–1822) took up a hypothesis due originally to Alexander Wilson (1792–1871) and dating from 1744 according to which the sunspots were holes in the luminous solar atmosphere,[27] offering a view of the solar surface, which was much cooler.[28] At the beginning of the 19th century, astronomers were increasingly intrigued by the fact that the

[24] R. Wolf, Sur le Retour périodique de minimums de taches solaires ; concordance entre ces périodes et les variations de déclinaisons magnétiques, *Comptes-Rendus de l'Académie des Sciences* (Paris), **35** (19), 704–705, 1852.

[25] Johann von Lamont (1805–1879), *Astronomie und Erdmagnetismus*, Stuttgart, 1851.

[26] W. Herschel, Observations tending to investigate the nature of the sun, in order to find the causes or symptoms of its variable emission of light and heat, with remarks on the use that may possibly be drawn from solar observations, *Philosophical Transactions of the Royal Society of London*, **91**, 265–318, 1801.

[27] A. Wilson, Observations on the solar spots, *Philosophical Transactions of the Royal Society*, **64**, 1–30, 1774.

[28] Note that this is in good agreement with the Aristotelician viewpoint that planets are surrounded by a sphere of fire which produces their light!

determination of the solar rotation rate obtained by tracking the sunspots varied between 25 and 28 days. This difference, though small, was significantly larger than uncertainties due to the measurements of the best astronomers. The explanation came in 1858 by Richard Carrington (1826–1875) in England,[29] followed closely by Gustav Spörer (1822–1895).[30] On the one hand, the latitude at which the sunspots are most frequently observed decreases systematically from slightly less than 40 degrees to 5 degrees during the course of one cycle. On the other hand, sunspots located at higher latitudes move more slowly than those located at lower latitudes. As Fabricius had observed, Carrington deduced the *differential* rotation of the sun. This was a very strong argument in favor of the gaseous nature of the sun. In this way, variations in the determination of the rotational velocity of the sun were explained.

7.1.2 *The Physics of the Sun*

In fact, the sun is a large gas sphere that can be divided into three parts (Figure 7.6) as follows.

(1) The core (about 25% of the solar radius) is the site of thermonuclear reactions which unleash a great deal of energy. The interior temperature, which determines the rate of nuclear burning, is such that at the present time the rate of energy production is practically constant.
(2) The radiative zone (about 70% of the solar radius) surrounds the core: energy released in the core passes through this zone by radiation.
(3) The convective zone (about 5% of the solar radius) is a zone where the transport of energy is carried out by convective processes that are more or less turbulent. Hot gas — from the interior — rises towards the exterior where it cools and emits photons — sunlight — then returns to the interior.

In fact, the gas in the sun consists of electrons and ions, that is, charged particles. Violent gas movements entrain magnetic fields created by moving charged particles. The magnetic field can block convection in the convective zone: there is no longer release of energy and the temperature can drop 2000 K degrees below that of the surface, where the average temperature is about 6000 K. These "cold" spots look like dark spots at the solar surface: these are the sunspots.

In 1908 George Ellery Hale (1868–1938), of the Mount Wilson Observatory in California, discovered that sunspots were the sites of intense magnetic fields and measured the field strengths with a spectrograph of his own invention:[31] the magnetic field was detected by the doubling and tripling (splitting) of rare spectral lines

[29] R. C. Carrington, On the distribution on the solar spots in latitude since the beginning of the year 1854, *Monthly Notices of the Royal Astronomical Society*, **19**, 1–3, 1858.
[30] G. Spörer, Beobachtungen von Sonnenflecken in den Jahren 1885 bis 1893, *Publikationen des Astrophysikalischen Observatoriums zu Potsdam*, **10** (1), 144, 1894.
[31] G. E. Hale, On the probable existence of a magnetic field in sunspots, *The Astrophysical Journal*, **28**, 315–343, 1908.

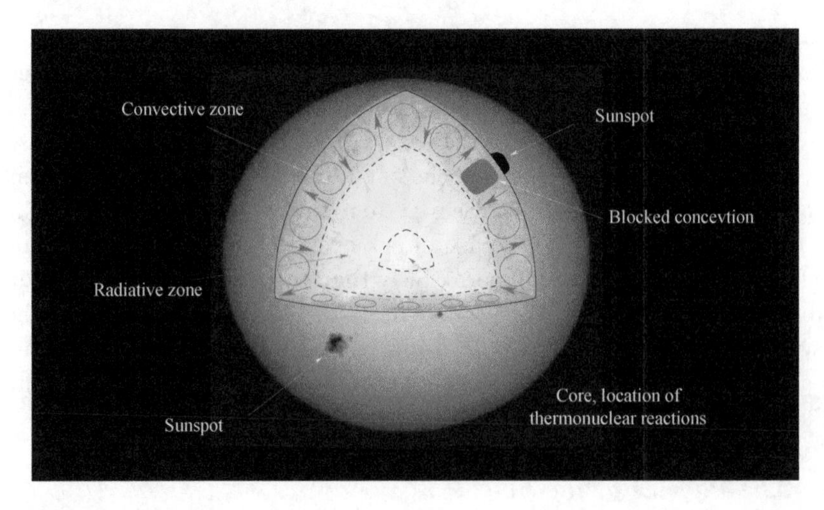

Figure 7.6 The sun consists of a core, location of thermonuclear reactions, where hydrogen burns to helium. The energy produced is conveyed towards the surface of the sun by radiation in the radiative zone. Finally, convection occurs in the thin peripheral shell. Sunspots result from the blocking of convection by intense magnetic fields.

(Zeeman effect). The magnetic field measured in this way is very strong: of the order of 3000 gauss (5000 times stronger than the Earth's magnetic field). These strong fields are considered to be responsible for the suppression of convective motion. There is a strong correlation between the number of sunspots and the solar activity. Thus, a minimum activity is associated with an absence of sunspots (Figure 7.7(a)): movements are not sufficiently violent to produce magnetic fields that are strong enough to block convective motion. The maximum activity produces numerous convective blockages and, as a result, a large number of sunspots (Figure 7.7(b)).

Another of Hale's discoveries was to observe that the sunspots occur most often in east-west oriented pairs. These pairs form dipoles as follows.[32]

> Sun-spots frequently occur in pairs, the principal members of which may be several degrees apart. [...]
>
> The most significant characteristic of these binary spot-groups lies in the fact that the two principal members, whether single or multiple, are almost invariably of opposite polarity. [...] The two smaller spots are of the same polarity, but opposite to that of the largest spot. [...]
>
> We find that there are apparently two "spheres of influence" of opposite polarity which meet near the centre of the group. The first of these is dominated by the large preceding spot, while the other comprises the oppositely directed magnetic fields of the two following spots. [...] The tendency toward bipolar structure is so strongly marked that hardly more than 10 per cent of all spots observed are wholly free from it. In the case of spots which are apparently single, some

[32] G. E. Hale, F. Ellerman, S. B. Nicholson & A. H. Joy, The magnetic polarity of sun-spots, *The Astrophysical Journal*, **49**, 153–178, 1919.

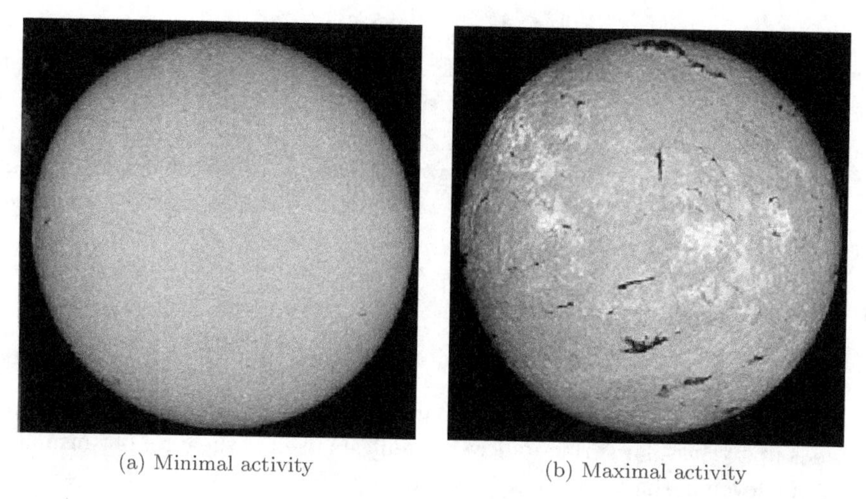

(a) Minimal activity (b) Maximal activity

Figure 7.7 Relation between the level of solar activity and the number of sunspots. Adapted from National Solar Observatory, AURA, NSF.

traces of asymmetry, more or less suggestive of the structure of bipolar groups, can usually be detected. Sometimes such evidence of asymmetry is afforded by faculae following or preceding the spot. [...]

After the sun-spot minimum, which occurred in December 1912, we found, to our surprise, that the polarity of the members of bipolar groups was opposite to that observed before the minimum. This sudden change was so remarkable that it was feared some observational error had been made. The results have been checked repeatedly by different observers, however, and in all cases the conclusion had been the same.

Thus, more than sixty percent of sunspots occur in binary pairs whose members, simple or multiple, have opposite magnetic polarity. The bipolar structure of these groups is inverted during each solar cycle. This is a property that we must take into account.

7.1.3 *A Model for the Solar Cycle*

Two questions naturally arise about solar activity:

(1) Is it possible to predict in advance the evolution of the next cycle?
(2) What is the nature of the underlying dynamics? In other words, is this behavior the result of a chaotic behavior governed by a small number of degrees of freedom, or is it the result of a system with a so large number of degrees of freedom that it appears as a random process?

The magnetic field variations at the heart of bright stars below the principal sequence (Figure 7.28) depend on the rotational velocity of the star. During its "life", the rotation rate of a star typically decreases, forcing a decrease in its magnetic field and, as a result in its activity. Magnetic field oscillations are observed in stars that have lived half as long as the sun, that is, while they are relatively inactive. In the case of the sun, there are sunspot cycles with a period of eleven years that undergo long term modulations.

The spatial structure of the magnetic field is known for the sun from the work of Hale, but it is not so well-known for other stars. The solar magnetic field, which emerges from sunspots and from active regions, is antisymmetric with respect to the equator and reverses itself after each cycle. It is generally accepted that the magnetic field is produced by a solar dynamo at the bottom of the convective zone: it extends up to the solar surface where it manifests itself in the form of sunspots and faculae, and even in the outer solar atmosphere.[33] The modulation of the solar cycle is aperiodic and could have a deterministic origin. Unfortunately, the available data are not sufficiently accurate to determine with common signal analysis whether they are governed by a deterministic chaotic process or a random one. An alternative is to find a set of differential or discrete equations that reproduce accurately the dynamics underlying the data, as performed in chemistry (see pages 255 and 263).

Before attempting a global model, let us discuss a model that captures the main physics of the dynamo action while preserving the correct spatial symmetries observed in the solar magnetic field. Since the slow modulation of the solar cycle could be explained as low frequency oscillations between the dipole and quadrupole components of the toroidal magnetic field, the model is based on the interaction between these two components, designated by z_1 and z_2, respectively. The velocity of the magnetic field can be described by a symmetric component v and an antisymmetric one w: these two components interact according to a Lorentz force. This system is six-dimensional since z_1 and z_2 are complex components ($\bar{z}_i$ is the complex conjugated of z_i). The model — proposed by Edgar Knobloch and his colleagues — consists of the four ordinary differential equations[34]

$$\left\{ \begin{array}{l} \dot{z}_1 = [\mu + \sigma + i\omega_1 + a(|z_1|^2 + |z_2|^2) + b|z_2|^2 + \epsilon v + \delta v^2] z_1 + \beta w z_2 \\ \dot{z}_2 = [\mu + i\omega_2 + a'(|z_2|^2 + |z_1|^2) + b'|z_1|^2 + (\epsilon' v + \delta' v^2)] z_2 + \beta' w z_1 \\ \dot{v} = -\tau_1 v + e_1(|z_1|^2 + |z_2|^2) \\ \dot{w} = -\tau_2 w + e_2(z_1 \bar{z}_2 + z_2 \bar{z}_1) \end{array} \right. \tag{7.1}$$

where $\mu + \sigma$ and μ are the growth rate of dipolar and quadrupolar modes, respectively; ω_1 and ω_2 are their frequencies, respectively. For certain parameter values, the behavior produced by this model is quasiperiodic: the general aspect of the

[33] S. K. Solanki, B. Inhester & M. Schüssler, The solar magnetic field, *Reports on Progress in Physics*, **69**, 563–668, 2006.

[34] E. Knobloch & A. S. Landsberg, A new model for the solar cycle, *Monthly Notices of the Royal Astronomical Society*, **278**, 294–302, 1996 — E. Knobloch, S. M. Tobias & N. O. Weiss, Modulation and symmetry changes in stellar dynamos, *Monthly Notices of the Royal Astronomical Society*, **297** (4), 1123–1138, 1998.

simulated time series (Figure 7.8) is somewhat similar to the observed sunspot time series (Figure 7.5).

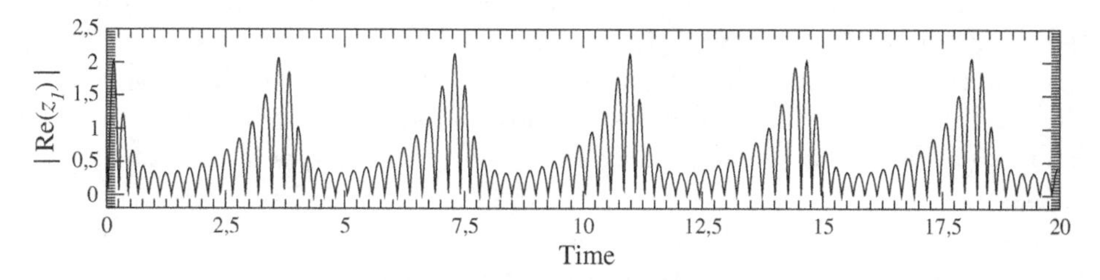

Figure 7.8 Time evolution of the dipolar component in the model of Knobloch and his colleagues. The behavior is quasiperiodic. Parameter values: $\mu = 0.63$, $a = 0.5 - 0.5i$, $a' = 0.38 - 0.38$, $b = -1.8$, $b' = -2.2$, $\omega_1 = 12.5108$, $\omega_2 = 12.51081$, $\sigma = -0.37$, $\beta = 1.39 - 1.25i$, $\beta' = 0.43 - 0.43i$, $\delta = -0.965 + 0.965i$, $\delta = -1 + i$, $\epsilon = 1.1 - 1.1i$, $\tau_1 = 1$, $\tau_2 = 1.1$, $e_1 = 1.31$, and $e_2 = 2$.

The quasi-periodic nature of this behavior can be revealed by an annular Poincaré section that provides a non-ambiguous signature of the toroidal structure of the state portrait. For the parameter values used in Figure 7.8, a numerical integration shows that the anti-symmetric velocity w tends to zero and that the antisymmetric mode z_2 is smaller by four orders of magnitude than the symmetric one. The model could be well-approximated to a three-dimensional system, that is, working in the three-dimensional space $\mathbb{R}^3(z_1, v)$. The toroidal structure is already well-evidenced in the two plane projection of the state space (Figure 7.9(a) and 7.9(b)). The chosen Poincaré section

$$\mathcal{P} \equiv \left\{ (\mathrm{Re}(z_1)_k, v_k) \in \mathbb{R}^2 \mid \mathrm{Im}\,(z_1)_k = 0 \right\} \tag{7.2}$$

has the expected regular annular structure (Figure 7.9(c)), thus confirming the quasi-periodic nature of the behavior.

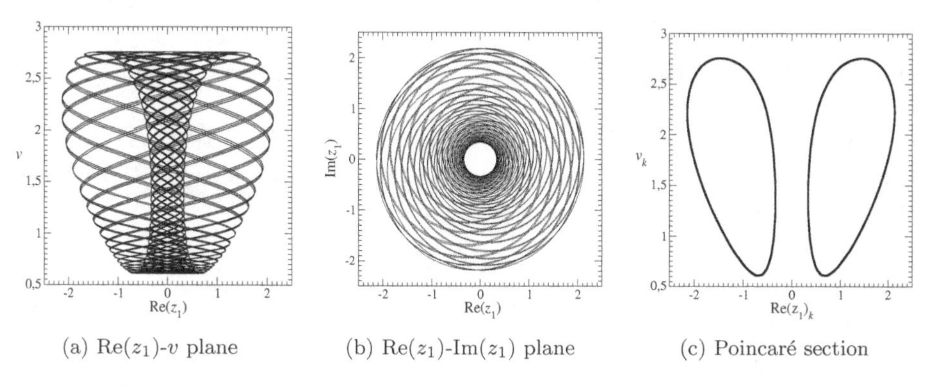

(a) $\mathrm{Re}(z_1)$-v plane (b) $\mathrm{Re}(z_1)$-$\mathrm{Im}(z_1)$ plane (c) Poincaré section

Figure 7.9 Quasi-periodic behavior produced by the model for the solar activity. The Poincaré section reveals an annular structure characteristic of a torus. Same parameter values as in Figure 7.8.

There are many possible routes to chaos issued from a quasi-periodic behavior.[35] One of them is observed when the surface of the torus starts to be folded. As we saw p. 208, a folding is necessarily associated with a stretching and a squeezing of the surface on which the trajectories are developed. Stretching induces a sensitivity to initial conditions and squeezing mixes the trajectories: the two main ingredients for chaos are thus produced. A route to chaos *via* the emergence of some folding on the toroidal surface was suggested by James Curry and James Yorke using a two-dimensional map.[36] The model (7.1) for the solar cycle is, by construction, well designed for quasi-periodic behavior since it results from two complex variables, one frequency being associated with each of them. When parameter μ is increased, the regular annular structure is folded (Figure 7.10(a) and 7.10(b)), leading to a torus with a complex structure, characteristic of toroidal chaos (Figure 7.10(c)).

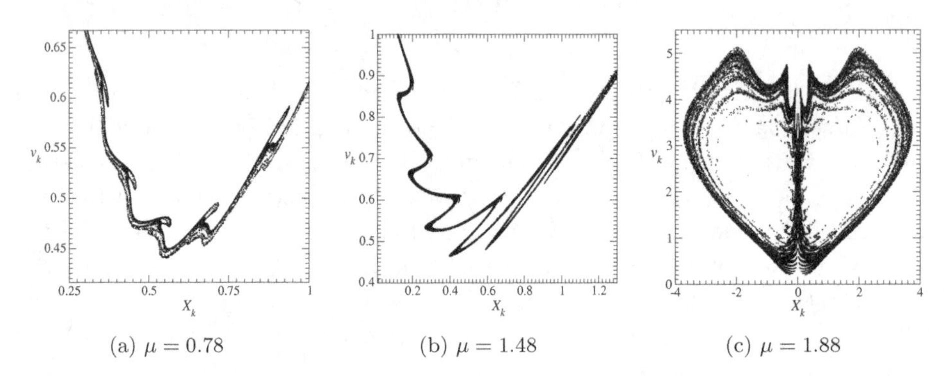

(a) $\mu = 0.78$ (b) $\mu = 1.48$ (c) $\mu = 1.88$

Figure 7.10 From a quasi-periodic behavior to a toroidal chaos *via* a Curry-Yorke scenario. Other parameter values as in Figure 7.8. The emergence of the folding is evidenced by blow-ups (a and b), leading to a foliated toroidal structure confirming the presence of toroidal chaos.

By using the main properties of the solar magnetic field, it was thus possible to produce a time series (Figure 7.11) presenting irregular peaks as observed in the sunspot numbers, that is, with a significant cycle-to-cycle variability in amplitude and in duration.

This system has nontrivial symmetry properties. In the six-dimensional space $\mathbb{R}^6(\text{Re }(z_1), \text{Im }(z_2), \text{Re }(z_2), \text{Im }(z_1), v, w)$, the model (7.1) obeys to the relationships

$$\Gamma \cdot \boldsymbol{f}(\boldsymbol{x}) = \boldsymbol{f}(\Gamma \cdot \boldsymbol{x}) \tag{7.3}$$

[35] See for instance, Z. T. Zhusubaliyev & E. Mosekilde, Novel routes to chaos through torus breakdown in non-invertible maps, *Physica D*, **238** (5), 589–602, 2009.

[36] J. H. Curry & J. A. Yorke, A transition from Hopf bifurcation to chaos: computer experiments with maps on $\mathbb{R}^2$, *Lecture Notes in Mathematics*, **668**, 48–66, 1978.

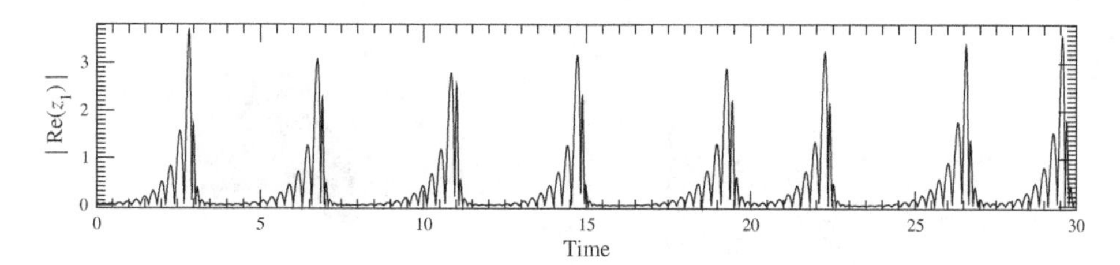

Figure 7.11 Toroidal chaos observed in the dipole component of the model (7.1). All parameter values as in Figure 7.8 but $\mu = 1.88$.

where $\boldsymbol{f}$ is the six-dimensional vector field, $\boldsymbol{x}$ the state vector and

$$\Gamma = \begin{bmatrix} -1 & 0 & 0 & 0 & 0 & 0 \\ 0 & -1 & 0 & 0 & 0 & 0 \\ 0 & 0 & -1 & 0 & 0 & 0 \\ 0 & 0 & 0 & -1 & 0 & 0 \\ 0 & 0 & 0 & 0 & 1 & 0 \\ 0 & 0 & 0 & 0 & 0 & 1 \end{bmatrix} \tag{7.4}$$

is the matrix defining the rotation under which the dynamics is left invariant. This is an order-2 symmetry since $\Gamma^2 = \mathbb{I}$, where $\mathbb{I}$ is the identity matrix. This is a discrete symmetry since it is possible to find an integer power of Γ to obtain the identity. Since this system is based on complex variables that are necessarily associated with a rotation as shown in Figure 7.10(b), there is also a continuous rotation symmetry in this model. As introduced by Rick Miranda and Emily Stone, it is possible to modd out an order-2 rotation symmetry using some appropriate coordinate transformation to obtain a so-called *image* of the dynamics without any residual symmetry.[37]

The relationships between the original attractor and its image were intensively investigated with Robert Gilmore.[38] The case of continuous symmetry is more difficult to hand. A possible solution that is simple to implement consists in reconstructing a space from an invariant coordinate.[39] In the present case, the space spanned by the successive derivatives of the variable v can be conveniently used. The v-$\dot{v}$ plane projection (Figure 7.12(a)) provides a representation of the chaotic attractor where the toroidal structure is obviously modded out and suggesting an attractor whose structure could share some properties with the Rössler attractor (see p. 206). A first-return map to the Poincaré section

$$\mathcal{P}' \equiv \left\{ (v_k, \ddot{v}_k) \in \mathbb{R}^2 \mid \dot{v}_k = 0, \ddot{v}_k < 0 \right\} \tag{7.5}$$

[37] R. Miranda & E. Stone, The proto-Lorenz system, *Physics Letters A*, **178**, 105–113, 1993.

[38] C. Letellier & R. Gilmore, Covering dynamical systems: Two-fold covers, *Physical Review E*, **63**, 016206, 2001 — R. Gilmore & C. Letellier, *The symmetry of chaos*, Oxford University Press, 2007 — C. Letellier & R. Gilmore, Symmetry groups for 3D dynamical systems, *Journal of Physics A*, **40** (21), 5597–5620, 2007.

[39] C. Letellier, Modding out a continuous rotation symmetry for disentangling a laser dynamics, *International Journal of Bifurcation & Chaos*, **13** (6), 1573–1577, 2003.

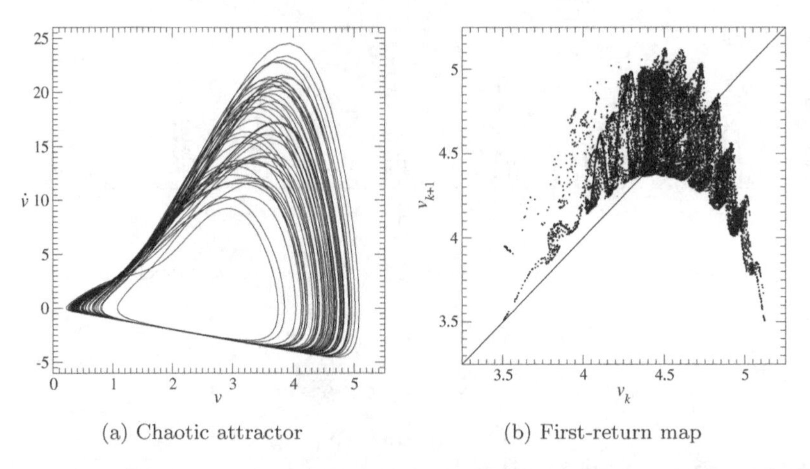

(a) Chaotic attractor (b) First-return map

Figure 7.12 Chaotic behavior of a model of solar activity. The first-return map reveals a rather complicated structure: nevertheless the presence of a structure argues in favor of a chaotic behavior, although more complex than the previously discussed ones. All parameter values as in Figure 7.8 but $\mu = 1.88$.

reveals a rather thick map (Figure 7.12(b)), most likely a signature of the six-dimensional nature of the underlying dynamics. Nevertheless, the global shape can be interpreted as a thick unimodal map.

A bifurcation diagram is computed in the Poincaré section $\mathcal{P}'$ *versus* the parameter μ which contributes to the growth rate of the two modes for the magnetic field; when μ increases, the antisymmetric mode z_2 becomes more influent on the dynamics. As we saw with the description of the Curry-Yorke route to chaos, the growth of this second mode interacting with the first one is at the origin of the chaotic behavior. The bifurcation diagram (Figure 7.13(a)) mainly reveals that the amplitude and its variability increase with μ. One region of this diagram deserves further investigations: this is the interval $\mu \in [1.544; 1.5535]$ where a cascade of period-doubling bifurcations is observed (Figure 7.13(b)). It can be shown that the symmetry must be broken for having a period-doubling bifurcation.[40] In this interval, two attractors coexist in the state space, one being the symmetric of the other under the order-2 rotation Γ (Figure 7.14(a) and 7.14(b)).

This route to chaos leads to a chaotic attractor which is characterized by a rather foliated map (Figure 7.14(c)). Such a complex structure directly results from the high-dimensionality of the system, such a feature being impossible in a three-dimensional space. This is another argument in favor of a dynamics that takes place in a space whose dimension is, at least, equal to four. The model (7.1) allows us to seriously consider that the dynamics responsible for solar activity is of a deterministic nature, at least if it results from dynamo effects as considered by Knobloch and his coworkers.

[40]C. Letellier, P. Dutertre, J. Reizner & G. Gouesbet, Evolution of multimodal map induced by an equivariant vector field, *Journal of Physics A*, **29**, 5359–5373, 1996.

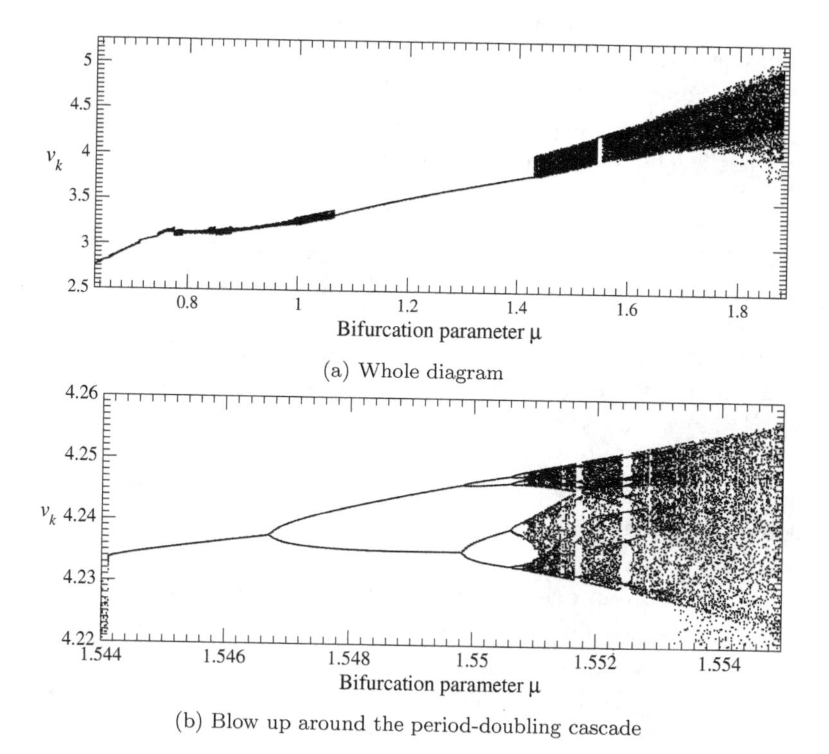

(a) Whole diagram

(b) Blow up around the period-doubling cascade

Figure 7.13 Bifurcation diagram *versus* the parameter μ in the model (7.1) for the solar cycle. Other parameter values as in Figure 7.8.

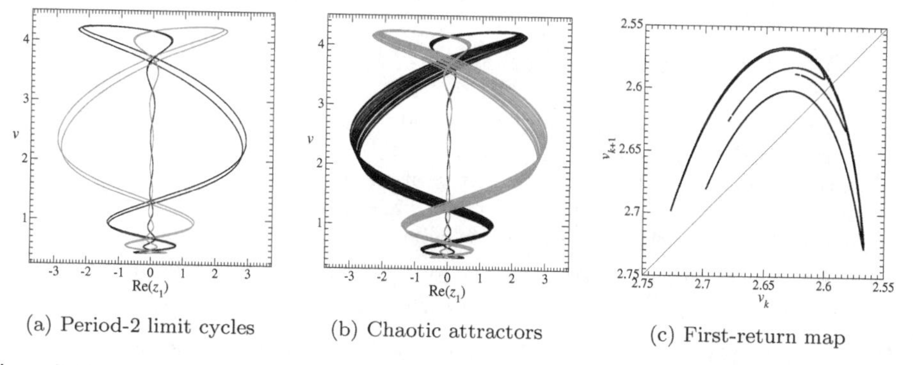

(a) Period-2 limit cycles (b) Chaotic attractors (c) First-return map

Figure 7.14 Two attractors co-exist in the state space when the period-doubling cascade is observed. All parameter values as in Figure 7.8 but $\mu = 1.553$. Two symmetric sets of initial conditions are used to obtain the two attractors.

7.1.4 *A Global Model from the Sunspot Numbers*

The time series of the sunspot numbers presents an almost constant period, but large amplitude variations. These variations in the sunspot numbers reflect the fact that the solar magnetic field significantly affects this behavior, and does that over relatively short time intervals: this indicates that the sunspots are in fact produced by the sun itself. The solar dynamo model ought to explain

(1) the eleven year sunspot cycle,
(2) Hale's polarity law according to which the magnetic field reverses itself between cycles, so that it has a 22 year periodicity.

After 300 years of observations, 23 cycles of data are available (Figure 7.5): this is far from being different for identifying the signature of chaotic dynamics using classical analysis techniques. Nevertheless, we have shown that this is almost adequate for global modeling technique (see Section 5.3, p. 258). Unfortunately, data before 1850 have been reconstructed by Wolf and suggest an underlying dynamics quite different from that suggested by later data.[41]

Since we are primarily interested in long term variations in the solar dynamics, that is, fluctuations from one cycle to another, we prefer to use monthly average sunspot numbers, especially since daily averages present high frequency noise. A state portrait (Figure 7.37) reconstructed using delay coordinates taking $N(t)$ and $N(t+\tau)$, where $N(t)$ is the Wolf index and τ is a time delay that was fixed at 15 months. The attractor (Figure 7.15(a)) still shows fluctuations at frequencies much higher than the eleven year cycle: in addition, the attractor lacks strong structure. We assume that this is due to a stochastic component in the data and we apply a smoothing method (Figure 7.15(b)).[42] This filtering process does not significantly affect the long term dynamics but greatly simplifies the analysis of the available data.

In 1953, Ronald Bracewell remarked that[43]

> Very numerous attempts have been made to analyse the series, with little success. It does not appear to contain a truly periodic term, as do tides and weather records. [...] Very little regularity of any kind has been found. [...] The range and accuracy of forecasting would presumably improved if some hypothesis could be found which would give rise to series resembling the sunspot series.
>
> According to Hale's well-known discovery, based on observations of the magnetic polarities of sunspots, the sunspot cycle lasts twenty-two, not eleven, years.

[41] M. Carbonell, R. Oliver & J. L. Ballester, A Search for chaotic behavior in solar activity, *Astronomy & Astrophysics*, **290**, 983–994, 1994.

[42] A smoothing consists to fit a smoothed curve in the neighborhood of a set of experimental data points in order to evidence a "general" tendency: this allows to avoid some counting errors of sunspot numbers. The eyes and the hand are doing this in a very efficient manner. But there exists few numerical algorithms to reduce these fluctuations. Here a low-pass filtering using a fast-Fourier transform was applied.

[43] R. N. Bracewell, The Sunspot number series, *Nature*, **171**, 649–650, 1953.

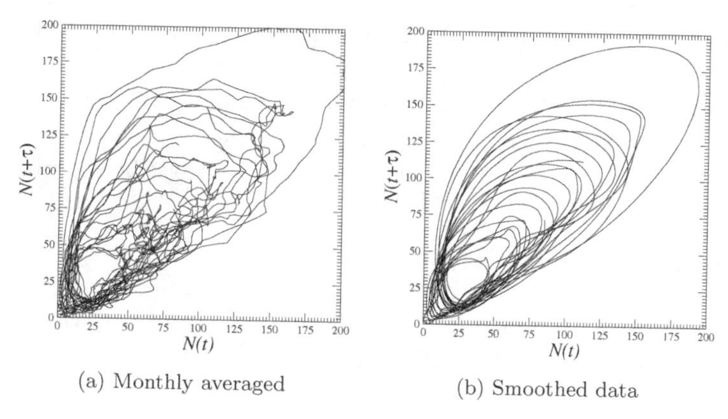

(a) Monthly averaged (b) Smoothed data

Figure 7.15 Attractors reconstructed using delay coordinates $N(t)$ and $N(t+\tau)$ where the time delay τ is 15 months. Notice that all 23 cycles observed since 1749 are presented here.

For this, Bracewell desired to introduce an inversion of the solar magnetic field to agree with Hale's observations. In place of a period of 11 years as shown in Figure 7.5, the period of the sunspot cycles would then be 22 years: he therefore proposed to alternately plot the sunspot cycles, positive and negative, as represented in Figure 7.16.

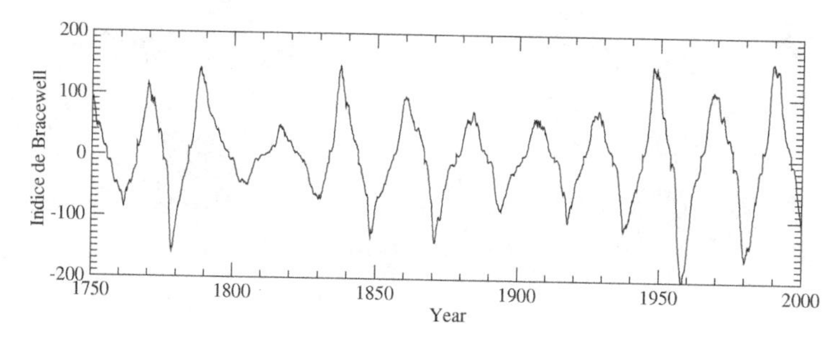

Figure 7.16 Evolution of the number of sunspots (Wolf index), taking account of the magnetic field inversions after each cycle, as suggested by Bracewell.

As Bracewell himself pointed out, there is a discontinuity problem as follows.

> The two curves of Figure 7.5 and 7.16 look at least equally regular. In particular, the curve [shown in Figure 7.16] does not exhibit obvious discontinuities at the zeros, apart from the gaps due to the above-mentioned deviations of the minima from zero. It has attractive features, such as symmetry about its mean value, and a mean value which is practically zero (less than 1 per cent of mean maximum).

Unfortunately, discontinuities like this prohibit the development of differential equations using global modeling methods. As a result, it is useful to introduce symmetry properties to model the magnetic field inversion but without introducing discontinuities.

To do this, recall that the Lorenz system has a symmetry consisting of a rotation by π radians about the z-axis. That is, the attractor is invariant under the change of variables $(x, y, z) \mapsto (-x, -y, z)$: this rotation is described by the matrix

$$\Gamma_{\mathcal{R}_z} = \begin{bmatrix} -1 & 0 & 0 \\ 0 & -1 & 0 \\ 0 & 0 & 1 \end{bmatrix} . \tag{7.6}$$

By using the change of variables

$$\Psi = \left| \begin{array}{l} u = \text{Re } (x+iy)^2 = x^2 - y^2 \\ v = \text{Im } (x+iy)^2 = 2xy \\ w = z \end{array} \right. \tag{7.7}$$

where $i = \sqrt{-1}$ (variable z is unchanged since it corresponds to the rotation axis), it is possible to construct a representation of this attractor without symmetry.[44] The chaotic attractor without symmetry (Figure 7.17, right), that is, the image of the left attractor shown in Figure 7.17, is almost dynamically equivalent to the original attractor with symmetry (Figure 7.17, left).

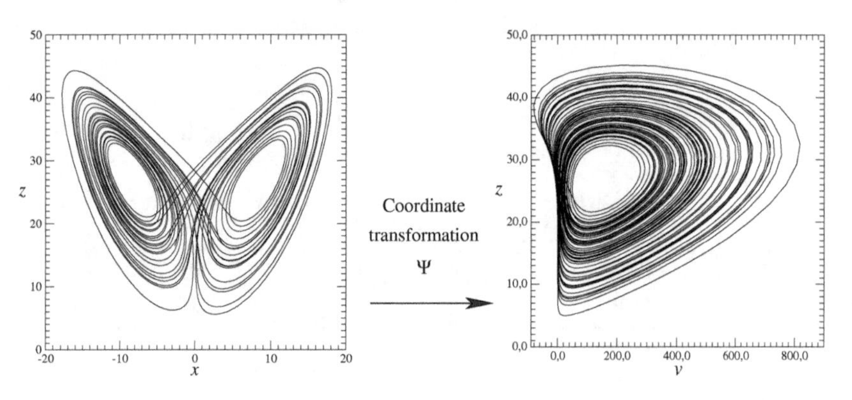

Figure 7.17 The Lorenz attractor with symmetry (left) can be mapped to a representation without symmetry (right) by a simple change of coordinates. This has the effect of folding the left and right wings together.

This is reversible. If we can remove symmetries, we can just as well introduce symmetries. To do this it suffices to invert the change of coordinates. In this way, by applying the inverse transformation we can map the Rössler attractor (without symmetry) to a version of this attractor with rotation symmetry around the z-axis (Figure 7.18). The folding characteristic of the Rössler attractor is now found twice over in the "symmetrized" Rössler attractor: the folding occurs symmetrically in the two parts of the attractor related by rotations about the z-axis.

[44] C. Letellier & R. Gilmore, Covering dynamical systems: Two-fold covers, *Physical Review E*, **63**, 16206, 2001 — R. Gilmore & C. Letellier, *The symmetry of chaos*, Oxford University Press, 2007.

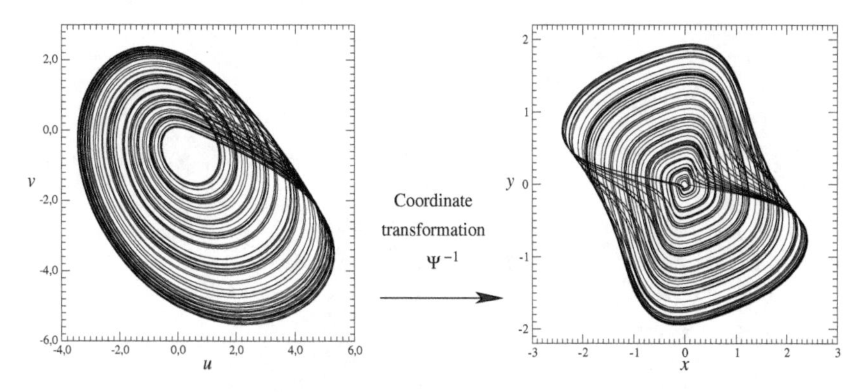

Figure 7.18 One can construct an attractor with rotation symmetry by an inverse change of coordinates. Two folding episodes are now found in the symmetric attractor.

Further, there is a new parameter that is introduced by this inverse coordinate transformation: this is the location of the rotation (symmetry) axis with respect to the attractor that has no symmetry.[45] For the case shown in Figure 7.18, this axis is placed at the center of the attractor (at the location of the singular point). But this axis can be placed elsewhere. In fact, when this axis is located outside the attractor without symmetry (Figure 7.19(a)), the coordinate transformation produces two disjoint chaotic attractors, both identical to the original (Figure 7.19(b)). In this case, a trajectory exists in one of the two attractors and never leaves that attractor. In other words, a magnetic field assumes a polarization and never changes that polarization: an inversion never occurs. Note that this case corresponds in fact to the Bracewell index, because inverting the cycle at each minimum corresponds to placing the rotation axis outside the attractor reconstructed from the sunspot data (Figure 7.15(b)), and "forcing" the trajectory to switch from one of the two symmetric attractors to the other at each minimum: this is the discontinuity mentioned by Bracewell.

When the rotation axis is placed in such a way that it "crosses" the attractor, a single symmetric attractor is found (Figure 7.19(c)). In this case, magnetic field inversions do take place but they occur in a chaotic way: in other words, irregularly in time. This does not correspond at all to the property of the solar magnetic field. When the rotation axis is located inside the attractor, in a zone not visited by any trajectories, the symmetric attractor (Figure 7.19(d)) presents an inversion of the magnetic field at each cycle: this actually corresponds to the solar dynamics. Consequently, the adequate inverse change of coordinates applied to the attractor reconstructed from the Wolf index corresponds to a rotation axis placed in its interior. The resulting attractor is shown in Figure 7.19(d).

[45]C. Letellier, J. Maquet, L. A. Aguirre & R. Gilmore, Evidence for low dimensional chaos in the sunspot cycles, *Astronomy & Astrophysics*, **449**, 379–387, 2006.

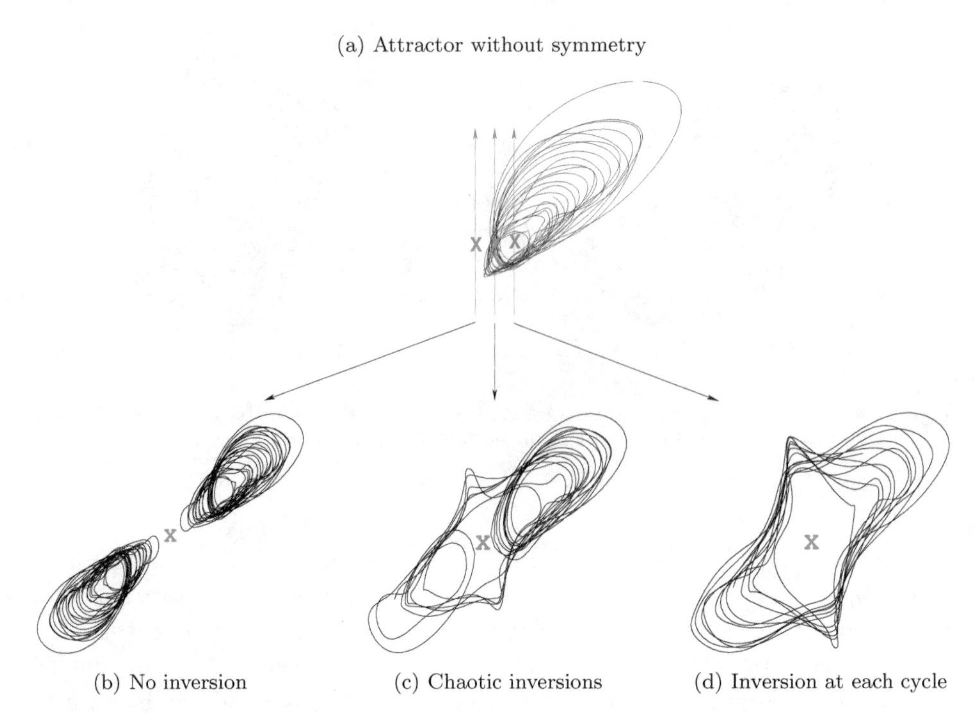

Figure 7.19 Depending on the position of the rotation axis (indicated by a cross) with respect to the attractor without symmetry, three types of attractors with a rotation symmetry can be found. The sign of the dynamical variables describing the attractor with rotation symmetry is inverted after each eleven year cycle only in case (d), that is to say, only when the rotation axis is located inside the attractor without symmetry. In the other cases, the signs alternate either irregularly (c) or not at all (b).

This preprocessing of the data is interesting because it allows the trajectory to remain sufficiently far from the origin (where the variables assume values close to zero and where, as a result, they are very sensitive to noise and measurement uncertainties). Beginning with the first five cycles after 1850 — data before then were reconstructed by Wolf and are not reliable — a set of ordinary differential equations using the same methods that we previously applied to the time evolution of the current during the electrolysis of copper in phosphoric acid (Section 5.3, p. 258). A set of three ordinary differential equations has the form of the global model (5.3) — see p. 255 — but its function F is too complicated to be reproduced here. This model is sufficient to describe the dynamics responsible for the long-term evolution of sunspots.[46] The chaotic attractor that is produced by this model is compared in Figure 7.20 with the fifty years of data — from 1850 to 1900 — that were used for this global modelling procedure. The attractor has a structure that closely follows the observational data. Regrettably, the available data set is too short to allow a complete topological characterization of the attractor.

[46] L. A. Aguirre, C. Letellier & J. Maquet, Forecasting the time series of sunspot numbers, *Solar Physics*, **241**, 103, 2008.

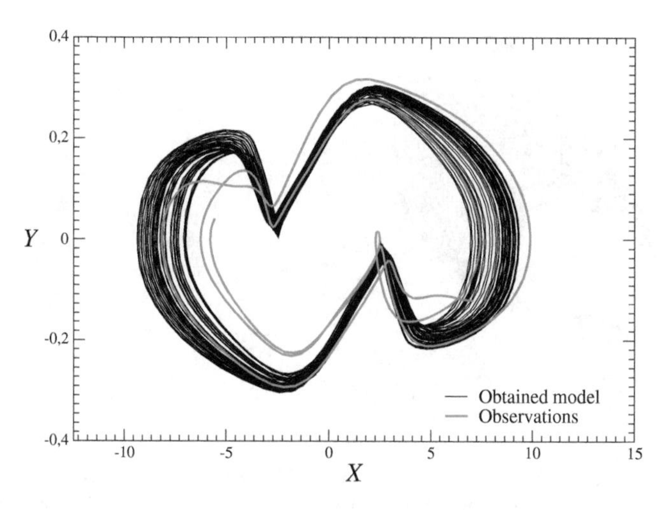

Figure 7.20 Chaotic attractor obtained from a three-variable global model, starting from "symmetrized" sunspot data.

The global model can be numerically integrated for times much longer than the 23 cycles between 1750 and 2000. The "numerical data" can be used for a finer characterization of the dynamics. The image of attractor — the attractor without symmetry — produced by the global model for (Figure 7.21(a)) has the same branched manifold as the Rössler attractor. In particular, the first-return map to a Poincaré section is a smooth unimodal map (Figure 7.21(b)). As a result, the idea of using the Rössler system as a paradigm for studying solar activity[47] is therefore justified.

The global model does not completely reproduce the observed dynamics. In particular, large oscillations are not reproduced by this model. This frequently happens for models obtained using a global modelling procedure.[48] Fluctuations resulting from high-dimensional dynamics, appearing as random, cannot be reproduced by low dimensional deterministic models. In constructing the model, noise is filtered out and, as a result, the model dynamics is simpler and less developed than the observational one. With such a model, we understand that the long term dynamics underlying solar activity is deterministic and of low dimension. This dynamics may be affected by additional processes as those investigated with the model (7.1) proposed by Knobloch and coworkers but are not taken into account in the global model: they can have quantitatively significant effects.

---

[47]K. Jinno, S. Xu, R. Berndtson, A. Kawaruma & M. Matsumoto, Prediction of sunspots, using reconstructed chaotic system equations, *Journal of Geophysical Researches*, **100** (A8), 14773–14781, 1995 — M. Kremliovsly, Can we understand time scales of solar activity?, *Solar Physics*, **151**, 351–370, 1994.

[48]C. Letellier, L. A. Aguirre & U. S. Freitas, Frequently asked questions about global modeling, *Chaos*, **19**, 023103, 2009.

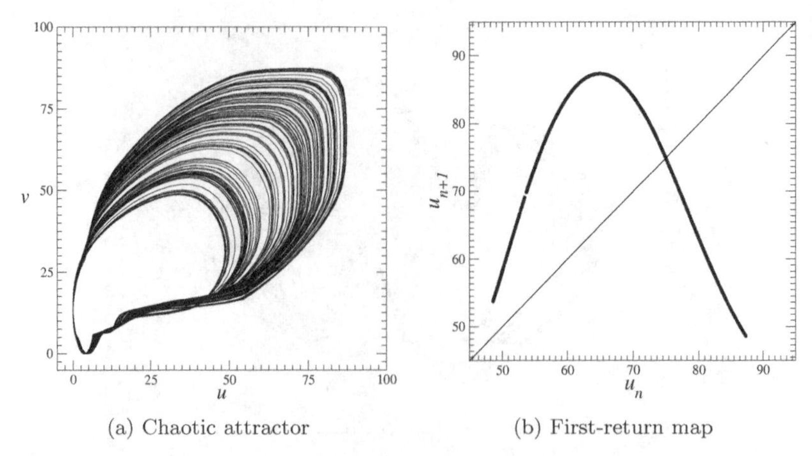

(a) Chaotic attractor (b) First-return map

Figure 7.21 (a) Attractor associated with three ordinary differential equations obtained after changing coordinates to remove the rotation symmetry. (b) A smooth unimodal first-return map confirms the relation with the Rössler system.

Difference equations were also obtained by Luis A. Aguirre. These equations were used for prediction.[49] These equations are rather helpful for making prediction because they take information (in the data) up to a given time and they map such information (predict) in the future. Of course, the newly predicted value can be injected into the model to predict even further, and so on. In particular, our model takes information spread over the last 44 months and predicts 4 months into the future. A key point in our experience is that both modeling and prediction of the sunspot time series has been greatly facilitated if performed in the transformed (symmetrical) space rather than directly on the original space. After performing analysis and prediction in the transformed space, the results should be mapped back to the original space. Prediction results (performed in 2006) are shown in Figure 7.22.

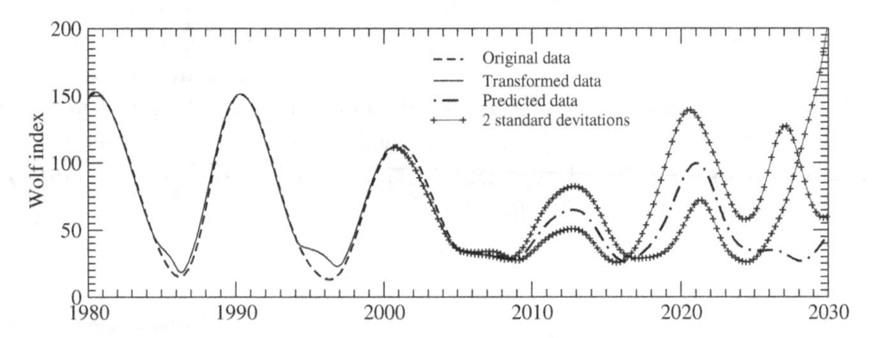

Figure 7.22 This plot shows the original sunspot numbers with dashed line up to 2005. From 2005, the predictions transformed back to the original space are shown.

[49] L. A. Aguirre, C. Letellier & J. Maquet, Forecasting the time series of sunspot numbers, *Solar Physics*, **249** (1), 103–120, 2008.

On June 5, 2012, the current prediction by the NASA for the next sunspot cycle maximum gave a smoothed sunspot number maximum of about 60 in the Spring of 2013.[50] With our global model, we proposed two different predictions (performed in slightly different ways) they were a peak at about 65 in September or October 2012, or a peak at about 87 in between June and December of 2013. The maxima was finally observed in April 2014 with a peak at 81.8. We therefore quite correctly predicted the amplitude (87 *versus* 82) but we slightly anticipated the occurrence of that maximum (June to December *versus* April 2014, that is, a relative error between 2.7 and 6.7%). The fact that the solar cycle 24 was unusually long and weak[51] could explain why our prediction anticipated its maximum. The data we had in 2005 when we made this prediction did not allow us to identify the unusually long minimum with which this cycle started. In spite of this, we predicted rather accurately its amplitude, thus confirming the reliability of our deterministic model and, consequently, evidencing that there is indeed a deterministic component underlying the solar cycle.

7.2 Variable Stars

7.2.1 *Early Observations*

It was only toward the end of the 16th century that variations in the luminosity of certain stars was no longer be attributed to observational limitations. For instance, in a letter to Tycho Brahe (1546–1601), David Fabricius (1564–1617) reported that the luminosity of a star in the neck of the whale (the star Mira Ceti) (Figure 7.1) changed from a maximum luminosity to complete invisibility over a period of two months:[52]

> While I was observing with my instruments I noticed, toward the south of the Whale constellation, an unusual star that I had never before seen in that place at that magnitude. When I looked at it more carefully and determined its position, I was struck by the idea that a new comet had appeared. I compared this star with my celestial globe, and then consulted the star catalog Prussian Tables[53] to see if a star of this magnitude had possibly been recorded there. But I did not find anything similar at this position, least of all with the observed magnitude [...] This star is of the second magnitude, [...] reddening like Mars [...] After the 21 August I could no longer observe its position with my instruments, because I could no longer discern any difference with my preceding observations. Nevertheless,

[50] http://solarscience.msfc.nasa.gov/predict.shtml.

[51] S. Basu, The peculiar solar cycle 24 — where do we stand?, *Journal of Physics: Conference Series*, **440**, 012001, 2013.

[52] D. Fabricius, Letter to Tycho Brahe (August 3, 1596), Observationes quas misit mihi Dominus David Fabricius, in *Tychonis Brahe Dani opera omnia*, ed. J. L. E. Dreyer & E. Nystrom, XIII, 114–115.

[53] Erasmus Reinhold, *Prutenicætabulæcoelestium motuum*, 1551.

> I did see this star again several times during the first days of September, but it became smaller almost every day.

In his last letter to Johannes Kepler, Fabricius reported a new observation of his star:[54]

> On February 5 observing the incoming conjunction of Jupiter and Venus [occurred on March 26], I have seen an unusual star in Cetus. Measuring with the sphere the distances, I have seen that they were showing the place of the star I have noted on the [celestial] sphere, which I observed in August and September [15]96, and which I have not seen since that epoch. Wonderful thing! I witness to God to have seen and observed twice in so different times and, what is to be noticed, Jupiter was almost in the same place of that one of [15]96. I can't enough contemplate the admirable Work of God, and see here, my Kepler, that my [star] among new stars and comets is real, it is not created *ex novo*, but they are sometimes deprived of the light, and nevertheless they complete in this way their motions. When actually God wants to show to us something that is beyond the [normal] order mean, he enlightens these invisible bodies, letting them to appear and to move in public. I think that I have not wrongly argued regarding those bodies of ether. At the end of February up to now I have seen [it], [but] now I could not observe because of the Moonlight.

Mira Ceti is indeed a variable star. In 1638 Jan Fokkens (Jean-Phocyclides) Holwarda (1618–1651) determined the periodicity (11 months) of the oscillations in the light curve of this star.[55] Then Ismaël Bouillaud (1605–1694) determined its period quite accurately to 333 days.[56] In the 1960s, the period of Mira Ceti was considered to be equal to 331.96 days.[57] Nevertheless, it should be noticed that this period received different mean values, depending on the data used.[58] Since the amplitude of these oscillations are not constant (Figure 7.1), fluctuations in the period are quite expected as for chaotic behaviors. In fact, Friedrich Argelander (1799–1875), from the Bonn Observatory, investigated in details various variable stars[59] and proposed to describe the period of the nth oscillation in the light curve

[54]D. Fabricius, Letter to Kepler on 12 March 1609, quoted in J. Kepler, *De Stella Nova in Pede Serpentarii*, 1606 and as translated in C. Sigismondi, D. Hoffleit & R. Coccioli, Long-term behavior of Mira Ceti maxima, *Journal of the American Association of Variable Star Observers*, **30**, 31–43, 2001.

[55]Johann Helvetius (1611–1687) named it *Mira* — which means *Miraculous* — in his *Historiola Mirae Stellae* dated on 1662.

[56]I. Bouillaud, *Ad astronomos monita duo*, Paris, 1667.

[57]P. N. Kholopov, *General catalogue of variable stars*, 4th edition, Moscow Nauka Publishing House, 1985.

[58]D. Hoffeit, History of the discovery of Mira stars, *Journal of the American Association of Variable Star Observers*, **25**, 115–136, 1997.

[59]F. W. A. Argelander, Beobachtungen und Rechnungen über Veränderliche Sterne, *Astronomische Beobachtungen auf der Sternwarte zu Bonn*, **7**, 315–518, 1869.

of Mira Ceti according to[60]

$$
\begin{aligned}
P(t) = 331.3363n + 10.5 \sin\left(\frac{360}{11}n + 86.383\right) + 18.2 \sin\left(\frac{450}{11}n + 231.7\right) \\
+33.9 \sin\left(\frac{450}{22}n + 170.316\right) + 65.3 \sin\left(\frac{150}{11}n + 6.616\right)
\end{aligned}
\tag{7.8}
$$

where t is the time expressed in day since September 6th, 1751 and the phase in degree. The mean period $\overline{P}$ obtained with Argelander's formula is 331.27 day. Using this formula, the fluctuations in the period of Mira Ceti can be computed (Figure 7.23): since resulting from the combination of sinusoids, this is either periodic or quasi-periodic. In the present case, there is a period of 260 cycles (about 240 years). Neither the quality of observation nor the duration over which the visual light curve of Mira Ceti is continuously known would allow to check whether those oscillations are periodic, quasi-periodic, or chaotic.

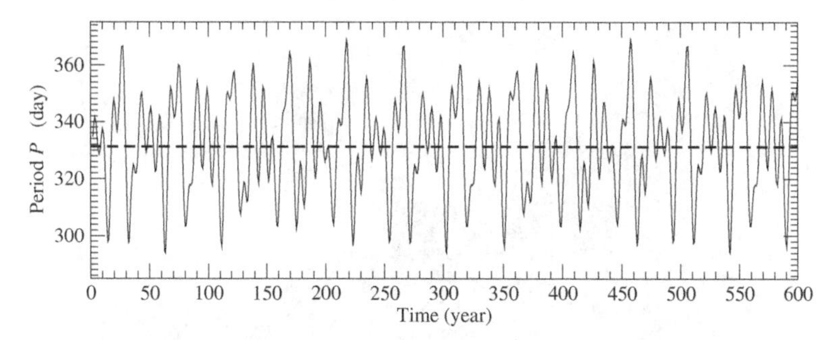

Figure 7.23 Maxima of the visual light curve for the Mira Ceti produced by the formula (7.8) of Argelander. Time $t = 0$ on September 6th, 1751.

Another variable star, *Algol* in the constellation Perseus (β Persei), was identified between 1667 and 1670 by Geminiano Montanari (1639–1710) of the University of Padua.[61] Algol takes its name from *Ra's al-Ghul* which means *demon's head* as shown in Ulugh Begh's *Catalog of the Fixed Stars* (Figure 7.24): due to its variability it was considered as the evil, contrary to the devine that is eternal and unchangeable. This discovery of Montanari was described by Agostino Fabri:[62]

> Sir Montanari [...] remarked, to the consternation of all those who believe that celestial bodies are forever and always the same that, several years ago, certain fixed stars had disappeared from the heavens, in particular two of the second magnitude; that he observed others become brighter, and others less bright, and mentioned that he happened from time to time some changes.

[60]As reported in A. von Humboldt, *Cosmos — A sketch of a physical description of the universe*, **3**, p. 169, Harper and Brothers, New York, 1852.

[61]G. Montarani, *Della Sparizione d'alcune stelle*, in Prose de' Signosi Accademici Gelati, Bologne, p. 388, 1671.

[62]A. Fabri, *Tacuino Astronomico dello Studio di Bologna per l'anno 1674*, Bologna, 1674, p. 6. Translated with the help of Girolamo Ramunni.

Figure 7.24 Constellation of Perseus carrying the inscription *"Image of Perseus as seen in the heavens"*. The "head of the demon" shows the star Algol. Detail from Ulugh Begh's chart of the Fixed Stars (1437).

At this time the influence of Aristotle was still so pervasive that it was difficult to believe that there were things in the heavens that could fluctuate but Argelander, who was specialized in the study of variable stars, was perfectly aware of the difficulties related to the lack of sufficient data, as one of his letters shows:[63]

M. de Vico had announced to the academy[64] that a star in the celestial chart

[63] From a letter by M. Argelander, head of the observatory in Bonn (communicated by M. Mauvais), *Comptes-Rendus de l'Académie des Sciences* (Paris), **26**, 108, 1848.
[64] M. de Vico, *Comptes-Rendus de l'Académie des Sciences* (Paris), **25**, 394, 1847.

at 22nd hours could no longer be found in the sky. M. Argelander, whose observations had served as the foundations for this star chart, wrote today to explain this error.

It belongs, without doubt, to a group of two small stars of the 9th magnitude which is found on the chart at 22 h 51 min 22 s right ascension, and 6°25' southern declination. There is only a single star at this location. M. Argelander had observed this single star several times with a net-micrometer, from Steinheil, which only gives locations to the nearest minute. Two of the observations gave sufficient differences between them to believe that they came from two different stars; but in reviewing the original observations, M. Argelander is certain that they belong to one and the same star which is certainly there in the heavens. [...]

M. Argelander has already brought the attention of astronomers to different phenomena that his studies of this star have revealed several times: in this way, he noticed the variability of several stars. Today he announces two new ones: the star ζ Geminorum[65] and the star ϵ Aurigae. The first has been recognized as a variable star by [Johann Schmidt (1825–1884)], adjoint astronomer at the Observatory of Bonn; M. Argelander himself has determined its period, which is 10 days 3 hours and 40 minutes.

As for the star [ϵ Aurigae], which was recognized as a variable star by [Eduard] Heis [(1806–1877)] from Aachen, M. Argelander has not yet been able to measure its period *with precision*; but it appears to be about 250 days.

The ϵ Aurigae belongs to a binary system and has a rather complicated light curve (Figure 7.25),[66] with a main component with a period of 27.12 years associated with its eclipse by its companion, and there is a second period at about 164 days which corresponds to the seasonal observations.[67] The pulsating nature of ϵ Aurigae is still questioned.

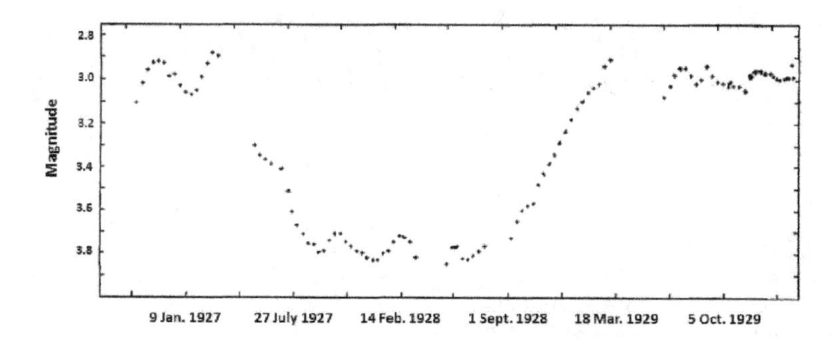

Figure 7.25 Light magnitude of the ϵ Aurigae during the eclipse of 1928–1930. (Adapted from Gyldenkerne, 1970.)

[65] A variable star of the Cepheid type.

[66] K. Gyldenkerne, The light and colour variation of Epsilon Aurigae, *Vistas in Astronomy*, **12**, 199–216, 1970.

[67] J. L. Hopkins & R. E. Stencel, Precision UBVJH single channel photometry of Epsilon Aurigae in the *Proceedings of the 26th Annual Symposium on Telescope Science*, held by the Society for Astronomical Sciences in May 22–24, 2007 at Big Bear, CA, p. 37, 2007.

In July 1686, Gottfried Kirch (1639–1710), of the Berlin Observatory, observed the star χ Cygni.[68] Later, he confirmed the variability in its light curve.[69] As we saw, Argelander understood that the variations in stars could be irregular. Thus, he proposed a description of the variations in the light magnitude of star χ Cygni with a main period T_0 (408 days as today confirmed) combined with two other periods, one equal to $100\,T_0$, the other to $8.5\,T_0$. According to our modern, though classic, terminology, the variations in the star χ Cygni could be described by a linear coupling of three oscillators of which one beats at period T_0, the second with a period $8.5\,T_0$, and the third with a period $100\,T_0$. That is to say the luminosity behaves like the sum $x(t)$ of the three cosines

$$x(t) = A + A_0 \cos(2\pi f_0 t) + A_1 \cos(2\pi f_1 t) + A_2 \cos(2\pi f_2 t) \tag{7.9}$$

where the three frequencies f_i are different. A signal of this type is shown in Figure 7.26. If this type of oscillations is accepted for some variable stars, the mechanism leading to this type of oscillation remains yet unknown.

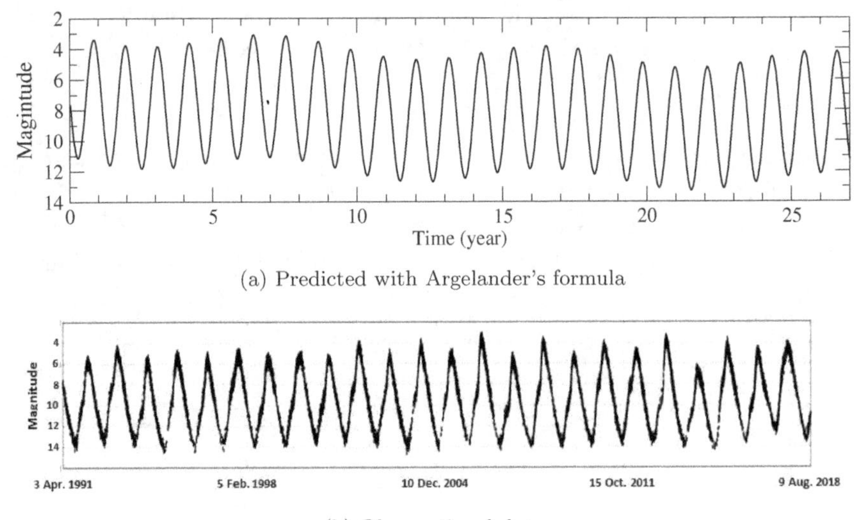

(a) Predicted with Argelander's formula

(b) Observational data

Figure 7.26 Evolution of the luminosity of the star χ Cygni (a) modeled by the linear coupling of three oscillators characterized by the periods T_0, $T_1 = 8.5\,T_0$, and $T_2 = 100\,T_0$, respectively (other parameter values: $A = 7$, $A_0 = 4$, $A_1 = 0.6$, and $A_2 = 1.8$; the initial phases are set to 0) and (b) produced with the light curve generator provided by the American Association of Variable Star Observer (`www.aavso.org`).

[68] G. Kirch, Stellae in Cygno Fixae, alternis temporibus visae et invisae, vicissitudines Lipsiae observatae a Godofredo Kirchio, *Acta Eruditorum*, **6**, 647–648, 1687.

[69] G. Kirch, D. Gothofredi Kirchii Astronomi & Observatoris Praestantissimi, & Societatis Regiae Berolinensis Dum Vixit Socii, De Varia Apparentia Stellae Novae in Collo Cygni Narratio: è Miscellaneis Berolinensibus anno MDCCX Editis Desumpta. pag. 208, *Philosophical Transactions of the Royal Society*, **29**, 226–228, 1714–1716.

In fact the light curve (Figure 7.26(a)) produced with Argelander's formula (7.9) is too regular, compared to the observational data shown in Figure 7.26(b). There is a clear irregularity in the latter but there are not sufficient data for checking whether there is a determinism underlying the light curve or not. In order to provide another view of the variability of the oscillations in the light of the χ Cygni, the period of oscillations is computed from the available observational data and shown in Figure 7.27.[70] If the mean period is at about 408 days, there is a huge cycle-to-cycle variability. The available data are rather insufficient to determine with certainty the actual nature of the underlying dynamics. It is indeed rather difficult to be conclusive with astrophysical data.

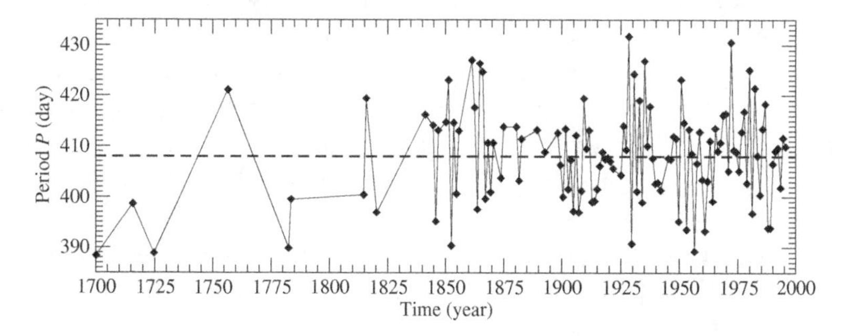

Figure 7.27 Period of the oscillations in the light magnitude of the χ Cygni. From the data reported by Sterken *et al.*, 1999.

Table 7.1 Characteristics of the stars discussed in this chapter. Since some stars belong to a multiple system, the number N of stars the system has is reported. When $N > 1$, only the characteristics of the main star are reported. Mass M, luminosity L and radius R are expressed in terms of the solar characteristics $M_\odot = 1.9885 \cdot 10^{30}$ kg, $L_\odot = 3.828 \cdot 10^{26}$ W, and $R_\odot = 696 \cdot 10^6$ m, respectively. All these stars are pulsating ones but β Persei and ϵ Aurigae are eclipsing. ϵ Aurigae has two clear periods, the very long one is due to its eclipsing nature, the short one being due to the seasonal observations.

Name	Type	N	Period (days)	Mass ($M_\odot$)	Luminosity ($L_\odot$)	Radius ($R_\odot$)
β Persei	Main sequence	3	irregular	3.17	182	2.73
Mira Ceti	Giant red	1	331.96	1.18	8.4 – 9.36	541
χ Cygni	Supergiant red	1	408.7	2.1	6.0 – 9.0	737
ϵ Aurigae	Supergiant	2	9890 (1st) 164 (2nd)	2.2 – 15	37.875	3.9
ζ Geminorum	Cepheid	1	10	7.7	2.9	86.2

[70]C. Sterken, E. Broens & C. Koen, On the period history of χ Cygni, *Astronomy & Astrophysics*, **342**, 167–172, 1999.

The first attempt to consider pulsating celestial objects was performed by August Ritter (1826–1908) from Aachen who considered gazeous mass.[71] Decisive contributions were provided at the beginning of the 20th century with the works of Harlow Shapley (1885–1972) and Henry Russel (1877–1957) who linked light variations of different stars to intrinsic processes.[72] Since then, several types of variable stars have been identified: rotating stars, erupting stars, and pulsating stars. Rotating stars have large regions of their photospheres that are hotter or cooler than average. Since the star is rotating, the luminosity changes as the photosphere viewable along our line of sight changes. Eruptive stars are characterized by sudden, erratic variations in their luminosity over short time scales.

Variable stars correspond to well-defined characteristics. To better understand stars, astrophysicists employ a Hertzsprung-Russel diagram, named after Ejnar Hertzsprung (1873–1967), then at Potsdam, and Henry Russel, of Princeton University, who tried to distinguish different types of stars by tracing a relationship between the mean luminosity L and the surface temperature T. In such a diagram, the points representing stars do not appear at random but rather occur along several bands describing stellar evolution. Most of the stars fall along the diagonal line called the principal sequence (Figure 7.28). Stars along this branch are in a stable period of their evolution and the burning of hydrogen in their cores is essentially constant. Stars not occurring along the principal sequence fall above this line: these are the *giants* and the *red supergiants* which have large luminosities but low temperatures (Mira Ceti). Finally, there are stars with low luminosity and high temperatures that occupy a region below the principal sequence: these are called *white dwarfs*.

Among stars with fluctuating light curve, cepheids (ζ Geminorum) were viewed for long as a binary system, that is, one main star with a smaller companion. While investigating stars from the Magellanic cloud, Henrietta Leavitt (1868–1921) remarked that "*the brighter variable* [stars] *have the longer periods.*"[73] With Edward Pickering (1846–1919), Leavitt determined accurately the period of 25 variable stars in the small Magellanic cloud and discovered a simple relationship between the luminosity (photographic magnitude) and the period of oscillations (Figure 7.29).[74] Processing their data with a modern graphical tool, one may obtain the relation

$$M = 15.56 - 0.88 \log P\,. \tag{7.10}$$

[71]A. Ritter, Untersuchungen über die Höhe der Atmosphäre und die Constitution gasförmiger Weltkörper, *Annalen der Physik*, **244** (9), 157–183, 1879.

[72]E. Hertzprung, Über die Sterne der Unterabteilung c und ac nach der Spektralklassifikation von Antonia C. Maury, *Astronomische Nachrichten*, **179** (24), 373–380, 1908 — E. Hertzprung, Bemerkungen zur Spektralklassifikation der gelben Sterne, *Astronomische Nachrichten*, **208** (18), 265–272, 1918 — H. N. Russell, Relations between the spectra and other characteristics of the stars, *Popular Astronomy*, **22**, 275–294, 1914.

[73]H. S. Leavitt, 1777 variables in the Magellanic clouds, *Annals of Harvard College Observatory*, **60** (4), 87–108, 1908.

[74]H. S. Leavitt & C. E. Pickering, Periods of 25 variable stars in the small Magellanic cloud, *Harvard College Observatory Circular*, **173**, 1–3, 1912.

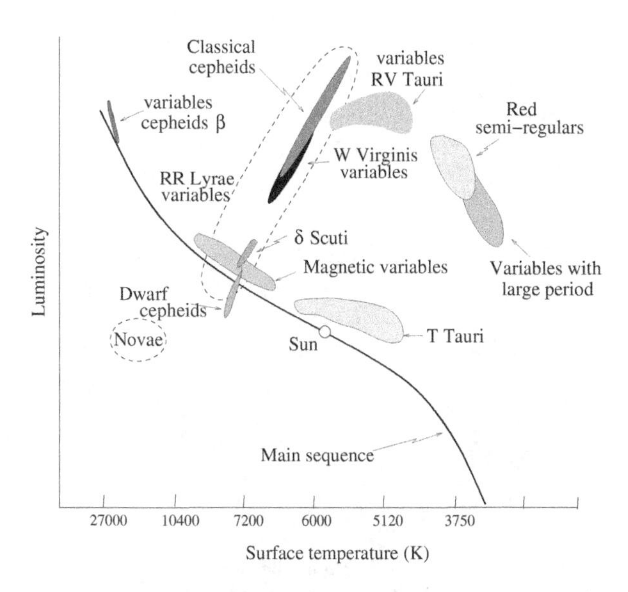

Figure 7.28 Domains describing several types of stars on a Hertzsprung-Russel diagram. Note the instability band where the classical variable cepheids are found.

Such a formula was further investigated by Ejnar Hertzsprung.[75] Since the luminosity is necessarily an intrinsic property of stars, the period must be inherent to the stars too. Thus, variable light curve can be produced by isolated stars due to fluctuations of some of their physical properties.

Pulsating stars may present oscillations with a nearly constant period (ζ Geminorum) as well as oscillations whose periods are irregular as observed in the SS Cygni (Figure 7.30). In both cases, the light curve strongly deviates from a sinusoïd and shows extremely abrupt changes. In the latter case, "*the amplitude is nearly constant in spite of the fact that the durations of the cycles are very unequal*".[76] The oscillations were compared to the relaxation oscillations with an explicit reference to van der Pol by Adriaan Wesselink (1909–1995).[77] Such an analogy led Arthur Eddington to develop a model for pulsating stars made of three shells: i) the core of the star with a temperature above 100,000°C where the thermonuclear reactions produce the energy, ii) an intermediary region and iii) the exterior shell with a temperature below 40,000°C with a poor capacity for storing heat.[78] Eddington, although never explicitly written, had clearly in mind relaxation oscillation and

[75]E. Hertzsprung, Über die räumliche Verteilung der Veränderlichen vom δ Cephei-Typus, *Astronomische Nachrichten*, **196**, 201, 1913.

[76]T. E. Sterne, L. Campbell & H. Shapley, Properties of the light curve of SS Cygni, *Annals of the Astronomical Observatory of Harvard College*, **90** (6), 189–206, 1940.

[77]A. J. Wesselink, Stellar variability and relaxation oscillations, *Astrophysical Journal*, **89**, 659–668, 1939.

[78]A. S. Eddington, On the cause of Cepheid pulsation, *Monthly Notices of the Royal Astronomical Society*, **101**, 182–194, 1941.

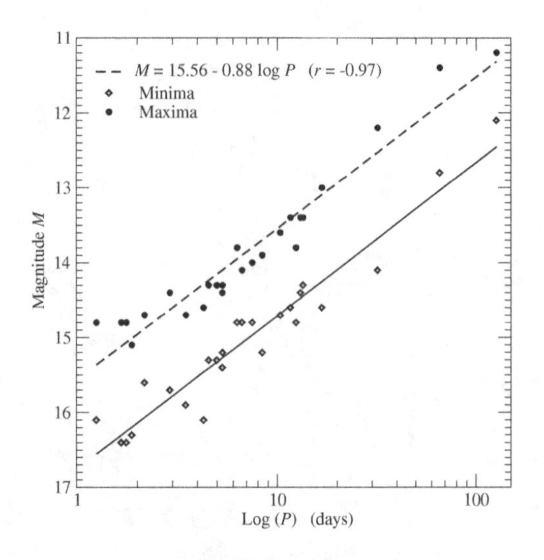

Figure 7.29 Relationship between the period and the magnitude — a quantity which measures the luminosity of stars — for some variable stars in the small Magellanic cloud. From the data published by Henrietta Leavitt in 1912.

electronic valve, since he designated his model as a valve. As for oscillating electronic circuit for which a negative resistance is required for producing relaxation oscillations, Eddington considered the possibility for a "*negative dissipation of energy.*" He also understood that a particular tiny range of physical conditions for which the production of energy is nearly equal to the its dissipation. These conditions are quite similar to the conditions required for sustained oscillations in electric valves (see p. 89).

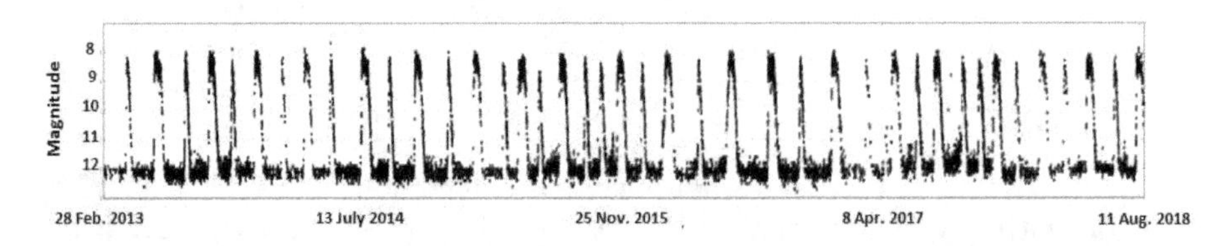

Figure 7.30 Light curve of the SS Cygni discovered in 1896 by Louisa D. Wells working for Pickering as Henrietta Leavitt. Although the amplitude of its oscillations is nearly constant, their periods are quite irregular. (Produced with the light curve generator provided by the American Association of Variable Star Observers (`https://www.aavso.org`).)

In fact, a negative dissipation occurs when the opacity to the transport of energy increases with compression (when the star decreases in size), stopping the "leak" of energy during compression and increasing it during expansion. This was explained with a peripheral zone of He^+ critical ionization by Sergei Zhevakin (1916–2001): 15% (by number of atoms) of helium in the envelope of pulsating stars would be sufficient to have a valve mechanism for sustained oscillations.[79] As Fred Hoyle (1915–2001) and Raymond Lyttleton (1911–1995) did with another type of model,[80] Zhevakin obtained a relation between physical characteristics of the star (luminosity or density ρ) and the period P of oscillations. Hoyle and Lyttleton used the relation

$$P\sqrt{\rho} = \frac{P}{\sqrt{\dfrac{3M}{4\pi R^3}}} = K \tag{7.11}$$

where K is a constant to determine. Using the data for few stars as reported in Table 7.2 (the radii of the cepheids are those reported by Ripepi *et al.*[81]), we obtained $K = 0.0168 \pm 0.0025$. Using the period and the radius, the relation (7.11) can be used to assess the mass of the star.

Table 7.2 Characteristic of few pulsating stars. The observed periods as reported by Hoyle and Lyttleton (1943), the computed periods with the relation (7.11) (using $K = 0.0168$), and the relative errors ϵ are reported to assess the precision of such a relation.

Name	Mass	Radius	Observed P	Predicted P	ϵ	Type
RR Lyrae	$0.65M_\odot$	$5.35R_\odot$	0.57 days	0.53 days	7.4 %	RR Lyrae
α Ursae minoris	$5.4M_\odot$	$37.5R_\odot$	3.97 days	3.40 days	14.4 %	supergiant
δ Cephei	$4.5M_\odot$	$52.8.5R_\odot{}^*$	5.37 days	6.22 days	15.8 %	cepheid
η Aquilae	$5.7M_\odot$	$56.6R_\odot{}^*$	7.18 days	6.13 days	14.6 %	cepheid
ζ Geminorum	$7.7M_\odot$	$86.2R_\odot{}^*$	10.15 days	9.92 days	2.3 %	cepheid
Mira Ceti	$1.18M_\odot$	$541R_\odot$	331.96 days	398.3 days	20.0 %	red giant
χ Cygni	$2.1M_\odot$	$737R_\odot$	408.7 days	474.7 days	16.2 %	red giant

After the discovery of the correlation between variations in the radial velocity and that of the luminosity, the luminosity variations are now considered as consequences of radial oscillations resulting from processes internal to stars. This understanding has been confirmed in the case of the star Betelgeuse, from the Arab *ibt al-Jarzab — shoulder of the giant* — which was identified as a variable with a period of 2050 days in 1835 by John Herschel (1792–1871).[82] The first measurement of the diameter of this star was made by Albert Michelson (1852–1931) and Francis Pease (1881–1938) in December 1920.[83] Following this, periodic variations in the

[79] S. A. Zhevakin, Physical basis of the pulsation theory of variable stars, *Annual Review of Astronomy and Astrophysics*, **1**, 367–400, 1963.

[80] F. Hoyle & R. A. Lyttleton, The theory of Cepheid variables and novæ, *Monthly Notices of the Royal Astronomical Society*, **103**, 21–37, 1943.

[81] V. Ripepi, F. Barone, L. Milano & G. Russo, Cepheid radii and the CORS method revisited, *Astronomy & Astrophysics*, **318**, 797–804, 1997.

[82] J. F. W. Herschel, On the variability and periodical nature of the star α Orionis, *Memoirs of the Royal Astronomical Society*, **11**, 269–278, 1940.

[83] A. A. Michelson & F. G. Pease, Measurement of the diameter of α-Orionis by the interferometer, *Proceedings of the National Academy of Science*, **7**, 143–146, 1921. They obtained a radius equal to 277 $R_\odot$; today it is measured at 887 $R_\odot$. See M. M. Dolan, G. J. Mathew, D. D. Lam, N. Q. Lan, G. J. Herczeg & D. S. P. Dearborn, Evolutionary tracks for Betelgeuse, *Astrophysical Journal*, **819**, 7, 2016.

diameter were measured. These oscillations are now explained in terms of the competition between gravitational forces and radiation pressure due to thermonuclear reactions in the interior of the star.

7.2.2 Hydrodynamical Models

One of the motivations for developing a model for pulsating stars was to explain the asymmetry of radial velocity curves measured in Cepheids. Starting from an "Eddington valve", Wasley Krogdahl (1919–2009) of the Dearborn Observatory developed a dissipative model involving higher-order terms.[84] He then reduced his model to the second order differential equation

$$\ddot{x} = -x + \frac{2}{3}\lambda x^2 + \frac{14}{27}\lambda^2 x^3 + \mu\left(1 - x^2\right)\dot{x} + \frac{2}{3}\lambda(1 - \lambda x)\dot{x}^2$$

where x designates the luminosity. Note that this equation reduces to the van der Pol equation (see p. 105) when $\lambda = 0$. This equation can be rewritten under the form of the two ordinary differential equations

$$\begin{cases} \dot{x} = y \\ \dot{y} = +\mu\left(1 - x^2\right)y - x + \frac{2}{3}\lambda x^2 + \frac{14}{27}\lambda^2 x^3 + \frac{2}{3}\lambda(1 - \lambda x)y^2. \end{cases} \tag{7.12}$$

The corresponding state space is therefore two-dimensional. The solutions produced by this model can only be periodic, according to the Poincaré-Bendixson theorem. Consequently, the luminosity curve produced by Krogdahl's model is necessarily periodic and cannot explain the irregularities in the period of oscillations observed in some pulsating stars. Nevertheless, it may explain the asymmetry observed in the radial velocity curve as shown in Figure 7.31.

If one consider that the light observed from a pulsating star is roughly as the square of its radius, the Krogdahl equation (7.12) can be used to produce a simulated light curve as shown in Figure 7.32): apart the lack of the cycle-to-cycle variability, this curve is not so different than the light curve produced by a star like the Mira Ceti (Figure 7.1). This simple model could serve as a justification for seing the oscillations produced by pulsating stars as relaxation oscillations as suggested by Wesselink.

To overcome the limitations of the model proposed in 1955 by Krogdahl, Derek W. Moore (1931–2008) and Edward Spiegel introduced in 1966 a model able to explain the physical origins of the irregularities seen in pulsating stars. To do this, they modeled a small mass of compressible fluid immersed in a horizontally stratified fluid: a gravitational force toward the center of the star and an "elastic" restoring force were applied. This small fluid mass interacted with the ambient fluid through radiative transfer, and could move into a convective zone in a star such as our sun (as explained later). Their model is a third order differential equation

$$\dddot{x} = -\ddot{x} - (T - R + Rx^2)\dot{x} - Tx$$

[84] W. Krodgahl, Stellar pulsation as limit-cycle phenomenon, *Astrophysical Journal*, **122**, 43–51, 1955.

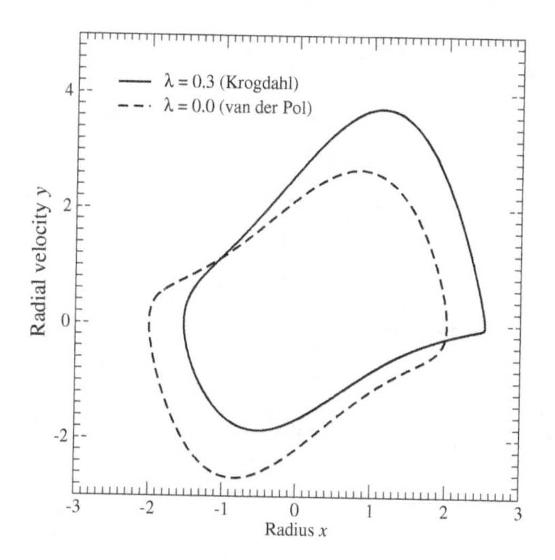

Figure 7.31 Solution of the equation proposed by Krogdahl for the asymmetry observed in the oscillations of pulsating stars. The case of $\lambda = 0$ — thus a solution to the van der Pol equation — is also plotted for comparison. Parameter value: $\mu = 1$.

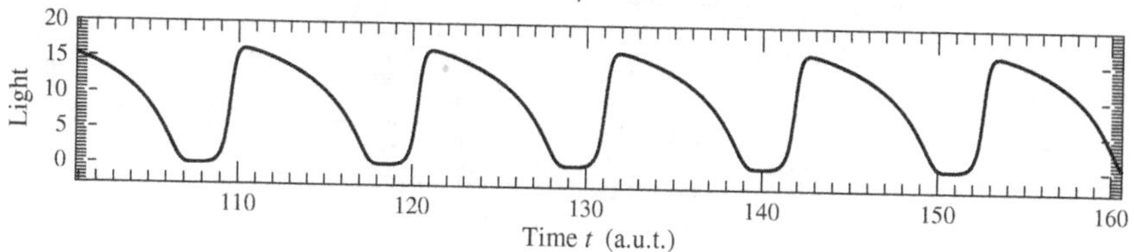

Figure 7.32 Evolution of x^2 as produced by the Krogdahl equation (7.12) as a synthetic curve for the light observed in a pulsating star. Parameter values: $\mu = 1$ and $\lambda = 0.3$.

which can be rewritten as

$$\begin{cases} \dot{x} = y \\ \dot{y} = z \\ \dot{z} = -z - (T - R + Rx^2)y - Tx \end{cases} \tag{7.13}$$

using the coordinate transformation $(x, \dot{x}, \ddot{x}) \rightarrow (x, y, z)$.[85] As such, three variables are necessary to completely define the state of that model. The three-dimensional nature of the state space allows the possibility that the star could evolve chaotically. Numerical integration of these equations produces irregular behavior typical of variable stars (compare for instance the evolution of $|x|$ in Figure 7.33(b) with the light curve of the SS Cygni shown in Figure 7.30). Moore and Spiegel described their solutions as aperiodic, that is to say, they used a terminology identical to that used by Lorenz three years earlier. The similarity between the behavior of the solution to the Moore-Spiegel equations and the solutions of the equations proposed by Lorenz in 1963 (Figure 3.8, p. 175) is remarkable. This is the fourth chaotic system dating from the 1960s that we have encountered (along with the Duffing

[85] D. W. Moore and E. A. Spiegel, A thermally excited nonlinear oscillator, *Astrophysical Journal*, **143** (3), 871–887, 1966.

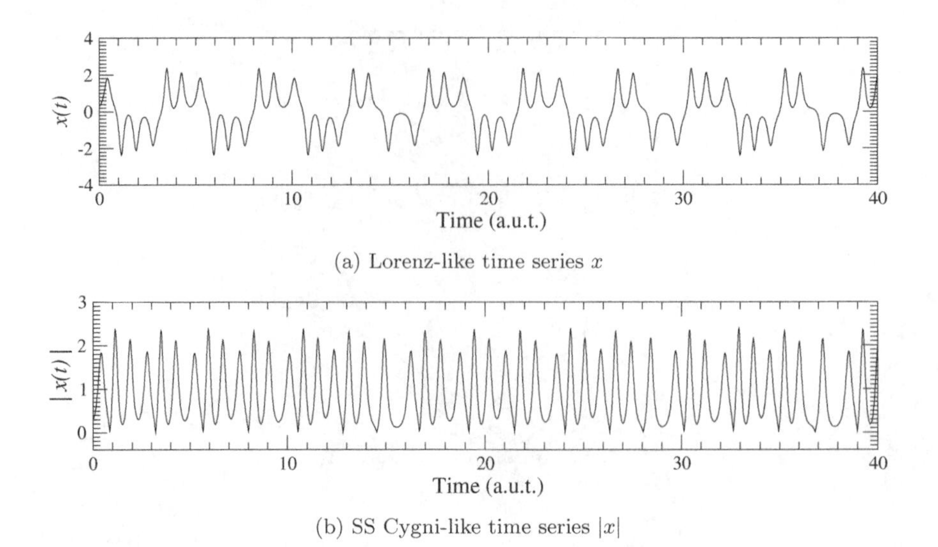

(a) Lorenz-like time series x

(b) SS Cygni-like time series $|x|$

Figure 7.33 Chaotic time evolution of the mass centroid of the small fluid mass produced by Moore and Spiegel's model. Parameter values: $R = 100$ and $T = 26$.

system studied by Ueda — see p. 125) and the laser model studied by Grasiuk and Oraevsky — see p. 169). With this model, Moore and Spiegel showed that realistic physical processes that occur in stellar evolution could lead to irregular oscillations such as those that are observed in cepheid stars.

A representation of the trajectory in a plane of the state space (Figure 7.34) allows to better understand the chaotic nature of the behavior: the trajectory never passes through a point that it has already passed through, while it outlines a clearly deterministic structure. Moore and Spiegel were not aware, as Lorenz was, of Poincaré's work; this would have permitted them to use the state space as Lorenz had done; similarly, as also for Grasiuk and Oraevsky, they were not able to identify any particular properties of the time series produced by their model. Just as for the Lorenz system, the behavior observed by Moore and Spiegel is sensitive to initial conditions and allows very rapid amplification of small perturbations. For carefully chosen parameter values, their model exhibits a period-doubling cascade.[86]

The Moore-Spiegel model does not provide a precise description of a star: as a result Michel Auvergne and Annie Baglin, then at the Nice Observatory, developed in 1985 a zonal model of a pulsating star.[87] This model is devoted to the physical processes arising in the ionization zone introduced by Eddington: this zone is bounded, in its centre, by an inert core and by a radiative atmosphere as its periphery. The governing equations of these fluids were written, taking account of

[86] C. Letellier & J.-M. Malasoma, Universalities in the chaotic generalized Moore & Spiegel equations, *Chaos, Solitons & Fractals*, **69**, 40–49, 2014.
[87] M. Auvergne & A. Baglin, A dynamical instability as a driving mechanism for stellar oscillations, *Astronomy & Astrophysics*, **142**, 388–392, 1985.

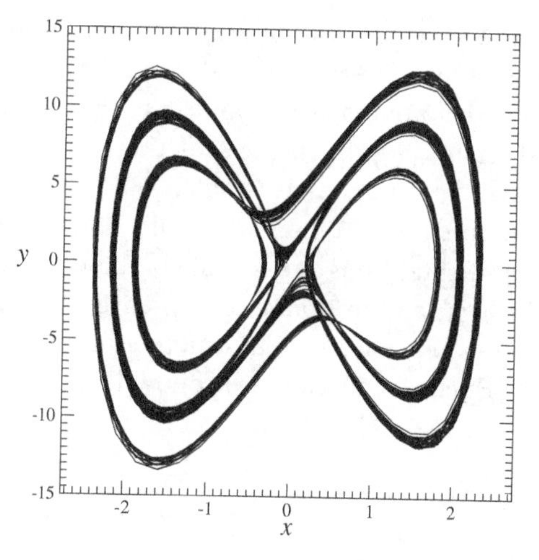

Figure 7.34 Projection of a solution to the Moore and Spiegel equations onto a plane in the state space. A chaotic attractor is observed.

most of the thermodynamic properties of a star. Auvergne and Baglin reduced the differential equations governing the pressure P, the radius R, the luminosity L and the temperature T to the single third-degree differential equations

$$\dddot{x} + \ddot{x} \left[\alpha + \beta x^2 \left(1 - \gamma \frac{\ddot{x}}{x} \right)^2 \right] \dot{x} + \delta x = 0 \tag{7.14}$$

which approximates the one-zone description of the star and where $x = \frac{\delta R}{R}$ is the relative radial displacement. Using the coordinate transformation $(x, \dot{x}, \ddot{x}) \mapsto (x, y, z)$, the set of three ordinary differential equations

$$\begin{cases} \dot{x} = y \\ \dot{y} = z \\ \dot{z} = -z - \left[\alpha + \beta x^2 \left(1 - \gamma \frac{z}{x} \right)^2 \right] y - \delta x \end{cases} \tag{7.15}$$

is obtained. The third equation of the model (7.15) and of the Moore-Spiegel model (7.13) can be both rewritten under the form

$$\dot{z} = -z - \left[\alpha + \beta x^2 f(z) \right] y - \delta x \tag{7.16}$$

where $f(z) = \left(1 - \gamma \frac{z}{x} \right)^2$ and $f(z) = 1$, respectively. These two models only differ by a nonlinearity which does not play a crucial role: consequently, the behaviors obtained with these models are very similar.

In 1987, Robert Buchler (1942–2012) — University of Florida, Gainsville — and Marie-José Goupil began from a more fundamental point of view, similar to that used by Lorenz. This approach considers that the complicated sets of partial differential equations that describe stellar hydrodynamics and heat transport could be replaced, in principle, by much simpler sets of ordinary differential equations. These simpler equations describe the time evolution of the amplitudes of a small number of linear modes of the system. These are called *amplitude equations*. There are two conditions under which this approach is applicable. First, that the nonlinearities are weak, and second, that the growth rates of the modes can be separated into three groups: the stable, the marginally stable, and the unstable. These groups correspond respectively to stable, marginally stable, and unstable directions in the state space. When these conditions are satisfied, the dynamics can be projected from state space (which is infinite dimensional, since the fundamental equations describing the stellar dynamics are partial differential equations) into a very low dimensional subspace. Buchler and Goupil proposed the set of three ordinary differential equations

$$\begin{cases} \dot{x} = y \\ \dot{y} = 2\xi y - (\mu + 1)x + Kx^2 + sz + Lxy \\ \dot{z} = 2(\eta + x)z \end{cases} \tag{7.17}$$

for describing the behavior of the envelope of pulsating supergiant stars.[88]

Two attractors produced by this model are shown in Figure 7.35. During the lifetime of the star, its characteristics change and, as a result, its behavior also changes. For example, for one value of the parameter η of the model, the attractor can be characterized by a smooth unimodal first-return map (Figure 7.35(a)): in this case the route to chaos follows a period-doubling cascade. When the η-value is slightly increased, a periodic window is seen (Figure 7.36). After a limit cycle of period 4, the first-return map exhibits three monotonic branches (Figure 7.35(b)). As a result, the bifurcation diagram is similar to that observed in the Rössler system or the logistic map. An important difference appears at $\eta \simeq 6$; the period-doubling cascade is not developed beyond the first bifurcation: rather, an inverse bifurcation occurs. Such a pattern is designated as a "period-doubling bubble".[89] This never occurs in the bifurcation diagram for the logistic map (see Figure 4.31, p. 226). With this simple model, it is shown that supergiant may oscillate chaotically.

To construct a more realistic model, Buchler's team developed a model for the variable W Virginis — a prototype for a subclass of cepheids pulsating with a period between 10 and 20 days. Cepheids are pulsating stars whose oscillations result from the existence of a region where the helium or the hydrogen ionization reduces the opacity of the atmosphere, thus allowing a better heat escape. When the radius decreases, the stellar atmosphere becomes denser and more opaque; there is an increase in the temperature and in the pressure that contribute to an increase in the radius which reduces the density and the opacity of the stellar atmosphere. The pressure and the temperature decrease, reducing the radius, and so on. In Cepheids, these oscillations in the size and the brightness are associated with a

[88] J. R. Buchler & M. J. Goupil, A mechanism for the irregular variability of supergiant stars, *Astronomy & Astrophysics*, **190**, 137–147, 1988.

[89] J. C. Alexander, A period-doubling bubble in the dynamics of two coupled oscillators, *Lecture Notes in Biomathematics*, **66**, 208–220, 1986.

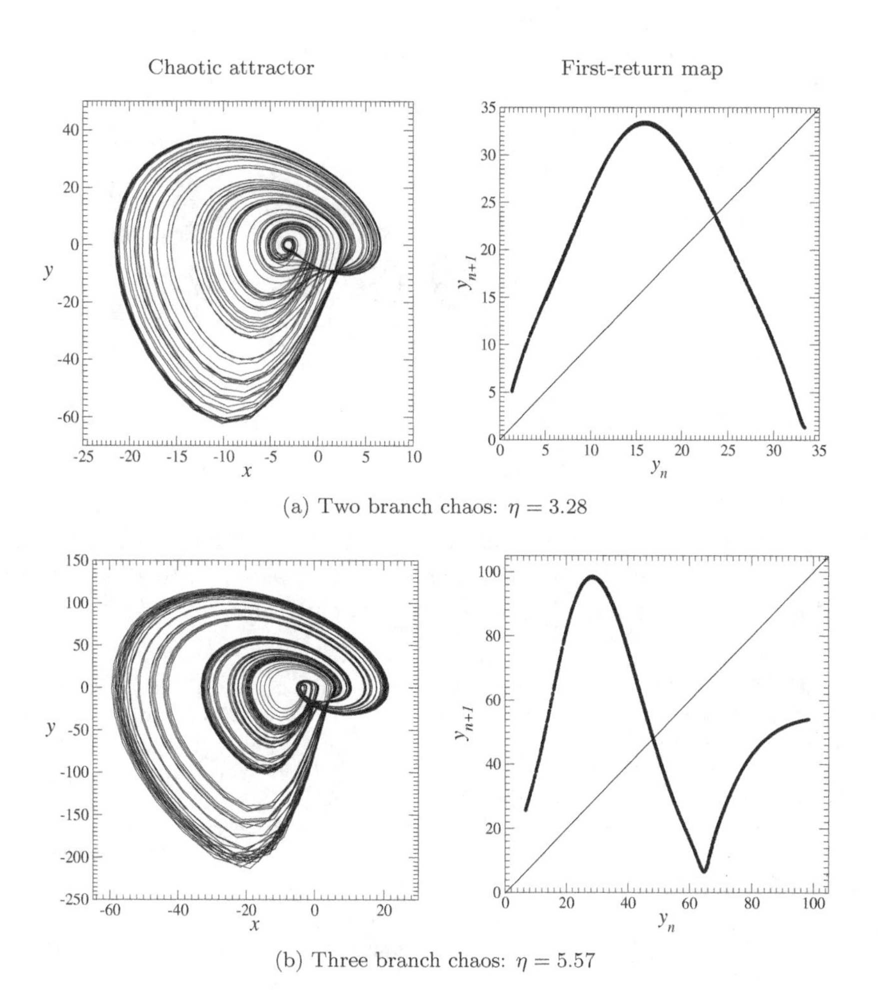

(a) Two branch chaos: $\eta = 3.28$

(b) Three branch chaos: $\eta = 5.57$

Figure 7.35 Two different chaotic behaviors for a model of variable supergiant stars. Other parameter values: $\xi = -1$; $\mu = 6$; $K = 0,05$; $s = -1$ and $L = 0$.

stable period and amplitude: one of their characteristics is a given relation between luminosity and period as discovered by Leavitt. Population II cepheids have a metal deficiency[90] because they were formed during an earlier time of the universe. Population II cepheids are divided in three subclasses according to their period P.[91] The RR Lyrae-like stars are quite similar to the population II cepheids but are much less luminous and their period is shorted; they are not strictly characterized

[90] G. Wallerstein, The Cepheids of population II and related stars, *Publications of the Astronomical Society of the Pacific*, **114**, 689–699, 2002.

[91] The threshold values reported in Table 7.3 are those provided by I. Soszyński, A. Udalski, P. Pietrukowicz, M. K. Szymański, M. Kubiak, G. Pietrzyński, L. Wyrzykowski, K. Ulaczyk, R. Poleski & S. Kozlowski, The Optical Gravitational Lensing Experiment — The OGLE-III catalog of variable stars. XIV Classical and type II Cepheids in the galactic bulge, *Acta Astronomica*, **61**, 285–301, 2011.

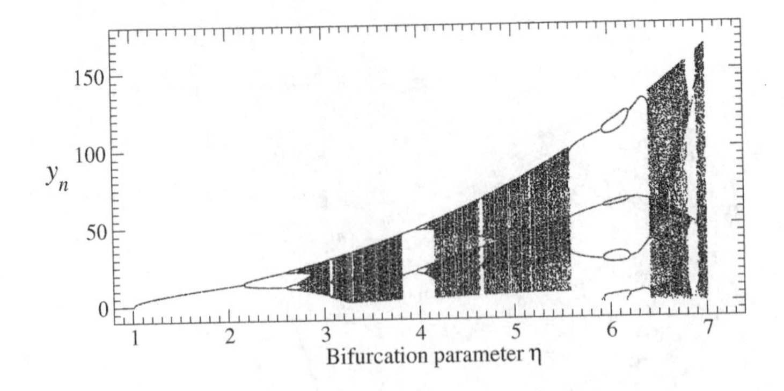

Figure 7.36 Bifurcation diagram for a model of variable supergiant stars.

by a period-luminosity relationship. The Mira-like stars have the particularity to be carbon or oxygen rich compared to the other pulsating stars; this could be the origin of the large cycle-to-cycle variability observed in their period. Some characteristics of the different types of variable stars are reported in Table 7.3.

Table 7.3 Classification of some types of variable stars using their composition, their mass M and their period P. A typical population I cepheid is the star ζ Geminorum.

Cepheid		RR Lyrae	Mira
Population I	Population II		
metal rich	metal poor	—	carbon/oxygen rich
$4M_\odot < M < 20M_\odot$	$M \approx 0.5M_\odot$	$M \leq M_\odot$	—
—	$1 < P \leq 5$ days BL Herculis $5 < P \leq 20$ days W Virginis $P > 20$ days RT Tauri	$P < 1$ day	variable

Among these types of variables, Géza Kovács (Konkoly Observatory, Budapest) and Robert Buchler proposed a hydrodynamical model for a W Virginis star, described with 60 concentric spherical shells.[92] The star was characterized by $M = 0.6M_\odot$, $L = 500L_\odot$, and its period was about 13.5 days. Hydrodynamic as well as nuclear processes were taken into account in each shell, and the shell edges were modeled. The chemical composition of the star belongs to the main characteristic to define a star; it was chosen as follows:

$$\begin{cases} \text{Abundance of Hydrogen H} & : X = 74.5\% \\ \text{Abundance of Helium He} & : Y = 25.0\% \\ \text{Abundance of heavy elements} & : Z = 0.5\% \end{cases}$$

[92] J. R. Buchler & G. Kovács, Period-doubling bifurcations and chaos in W Virginis models, *Astrophysical Journal Letters*, **320**, L57–L62, 1987 — G. Kovács & J. R. Buchler, Regular and irregular non linear pulsation in population II Cepheid models, *Astrophysical Journal*, **334**, 971–994, 1988.

In order to use the same kind of data that what would be observed by an astrophysicist, the luminosity L, the radius R, and the radial velocity V_R were recorded from the 58th shell, located at the surface of the star. In the case here considered, the temperature within that shell was $T = 5200$ K (the sun as a surface temperature $T_\odot = 5780$ K). In fact, depending on the effective temperature, the oscillations are either periodic or chaotic. Starting from the time evolution of the radius R of the star, a state portrait was reconstructed by using delay coordinates (Figure 7.37(b)): it reveals a chaotic attractor that is characterized by a smooth unimodal first-return map to a Poincaré section (Figure 7.37(c)). The foliated structure of this first-return map indicates a slightly more complicated behavior than the previous model, perhaps due to a low dissipation rate (Figure 7.35).

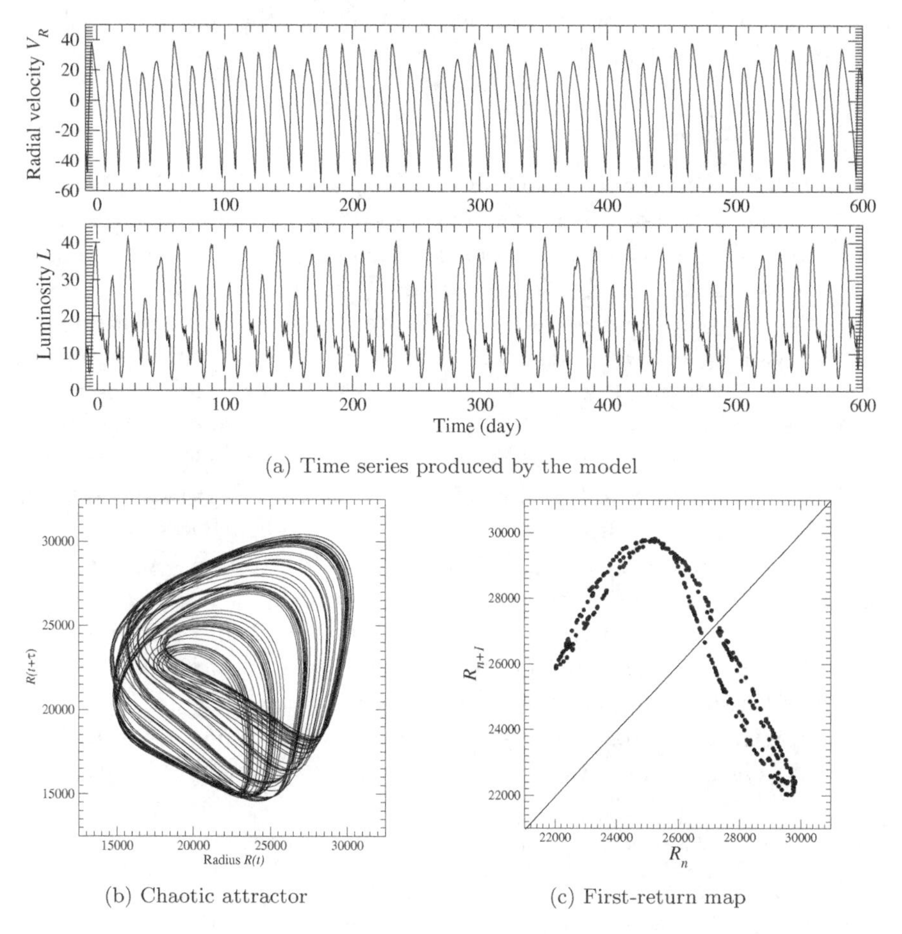

Figure 7.37 (a) Evolution of the radial velocity V_R and the luminosity L of the W Virginis according to the 60-shell model developed by Kovács and Buchler. The smooth unimodal first return map (c) is a signature of the chaotic nature of the oscillations in this cepheid. Parameter values: $X = 74.5\%$, $Z = 0.5\%$, $T = 5200$ K, $M = 0.6 M_\odot$, and $L = 500 L_\odot$. (Adapted from Letellier *et al.*, 1996.)

As the temperature of the star increases, Kovács and Buchler remarked that the oscillations changed. For $5425 \le T < 6200$ K, the oscillation have a constant amplitude. For $5350 \le T < 5400$ K, the amplitude oscillate between two values: a period-2 limit cycle is observed. When the temperature is decreased to 5300 K, a period-4 limit cycle is observed, then a period-8, and so on. This is a period-doubling cascade as expected from the smooth unimodal first-return map (Figure 7.37(c)). When the temperature is less than 5200 K, the evolution of the radius and the luminosity of the star becomes chaotic (Figure 7.37(a)). It was showed that the topology of this attractor (Figure 7.37(b)) is that of the Rössler attractor with the addition of a global torsion:[93] the template is similar to that shown in Figure 4.26 (p. 220), but with a half-twist along the right hand part. From the viewpoint of this model, the chaotic nature of cepheid pulsations has been demonstrated. In other words, assuming the correctness of the physics built into this model, the pulsations of such variable cepheid are chaotic.

7.2.3 *Observational Data*

In spite of all this, it remains to find observational proof that stellar pulsations are chaotic. Finding such a proof starting from observations is much more delicate than starting from "simple" integrations of model equations. In fact, obtaining good observational data is difficult due to atmospheric perturbations and to the distance between the star and the observers. To this we throw in the difficulty produced by the earth's rotation, which makes it difficult to collect continuous observations from the same observatory. It is thus useful to arrange a concerted observational program using observatories distributed in longitude for minimizing observational dropouts due to the earth's rotation. As a result, sites at Mauna Kea (Hawaii), MacDonald Observatory (Texas, US), Ceno Tololo (Chili), Itajuba (Brazil), La Palma (Canary Islands), Haute-Provence (France), the Sutherland Observatory (South Africa), Kavaliu (South India), and Siding Springs (Australia) were organized to obtain a set of data over 231 hours, with data recorded at 10 second intervals.[94] One of the stars recorded was the white dwarf PG 1159-035 located in the Virgo constellation: it was discovered in 1979.[95] This type of star is located at the extremity of the instability band of the Hertzsprung-Russel diagram (Figure 7.28). A white dwarf has a hydrogen-deficient atmosphere which is dominated by helium, carbon and oxygen.[96] Such atmosphere is very hot ($75,000 < T < 120,000$ K) and

[93] C. Letellier, G. Gouesbet, F. Soufi, J. R. Buchler & Z. Kolláth, Chaos in variable stars: topological analysis of W Vir model pulsations, *Chaos*, **6** (3), 466–476, 1996.

[94] R. E. Nather, D. E. Winget, J. C. Clemens, C. J. Hansen & B. P. Hine, The Whole Earth Telescope: a new astronomical instrument, *Astrophysical Journal*, **361**, 309–361, 1990.

[95] J. T. McGraw, S. G. Starrfield, J. Liebert & R. F. Green, PG 1159-035: A new, hot, non-DA pulsating degenerate, in *White dwarfs and variable degenerate stars*, IAU Colloquium #53, ed. H. M. van Horn & V. Weidemann (University of Rochester Press), pp. 377–381, 1979.

[96] K. Werner & F. Herwig, The elemental abundances in bare planetary nebula central stars and the shell burning in AGB stars, *Publications of the Astronomical Society of the Pacific* **118**, 183–204, 2006.

the helium fusion is possibly reignited.[97] In fact, a white dwarf is in a state that will turn soon to the end of its life because its fuel will be almost totally gone. It passes the rest of its life radiating away what remains of its energy. The modulations of this energy flux produce variations in its luminosity.

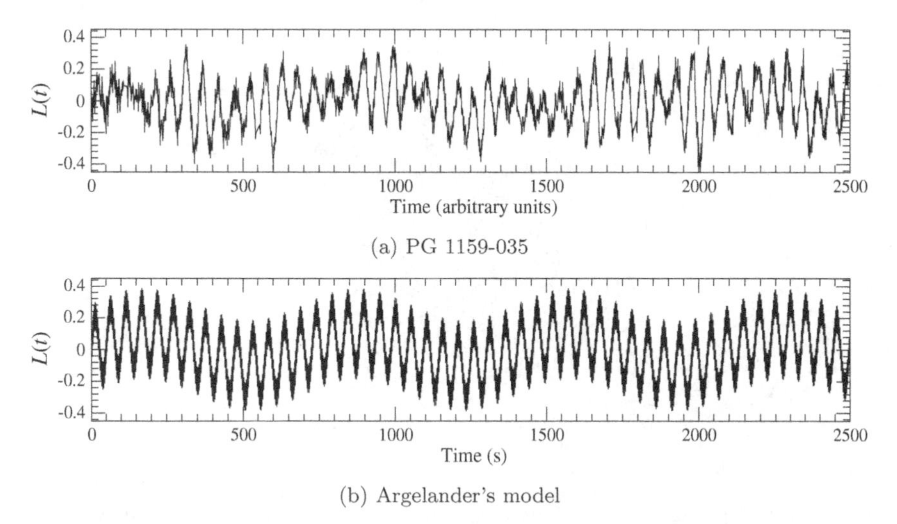

(a) PG 1159-035

(b) Argelander's model

Figure 7.38 Lightcurve of the white dwarf PG 1159-035 that is located at the bottom of the instability band in the Hertzsprung-Russel diagram. These oscillations are variable in both amplitude and frequency. Star parameters: $M = 0.59M_\odot$, $R = 0.00254R_\odot$, $L = 200L_\odot$, and $T = 136,000$ K. The synthetic curve (b) is produced with Argelander's model (7.9) with the parameters as follows. $T_0 = 700$ s, $T_1 = 52$ s, $T_2 = 3$ s, $A = 0$, $A_0 = 0.1$, $A_1 = 0.2$, and $A_2 = 0.1$; the initial phases are set to 0.

The white dwarf PG 1159-035 is nearly three time the size of the earth and is located about 1400 light years from the earth: its light curve is shown in Figure 7.38.[98] At first sight, the evolution of the luminosity shows similarities with the behavior produced by the three oscillator model proposed by Argelander (Figure 7.38(b)). However, the observations are somewhat noisy. In general, in astrophysics, the quantity measured is the luminosity of the star or, ultimately, its radial velocity. The relative quality of the observations depends on various measurement difficulties at the different observatories. One such difficulty is the darkness of the sky, which must be subtracted from the observed stellar luminosity. Another comes from earth's atmospheric perturbations which could modify the apparent stellar luminosity. Other major error sources include noise due to photon statistics, scintillations

[97]T. Nagel & K. Werner, Detection of non-radial g-mode pulsations in the newly discovered PG 1159 star HE 1429-1209, *Astronomy & Astrophysics*, **426**, L45-L48, 2004.

[98]These data were described by J. C. Clemens, Whole Earth Telescope observation of the white dwarf star PG 1159-035, for a competition to predict the future of time series. This was organized by the Santa Fe Institute. See the proceedings *Time Series Prediction: Forecasting the future and understanding the past*, Edited by A. S. Weigend and N. A. Gershenfield, Santa Fe Institute XV, Addison-Wesley, 1994. These data were at disposal at the address `ftp.santafe.edu`.

due to atmospheric fluctuations or turbulent cells acting as lenses to either concentrate or disperse light, creating modifications in the apparent luminosity. Finally, a temporal correction must be made to take into account the changes in the relative position of the sun and the moon during the period of observation.

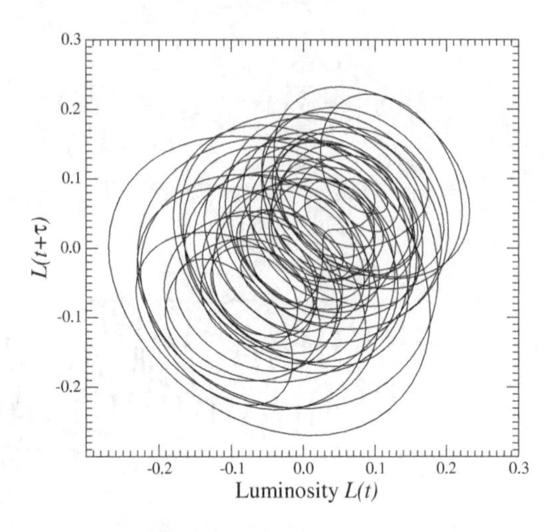

Figure 7.39 State portrait starting from luminosity measurements of the white dwarf PG 1159-035.

The observational state portrait (Figure 7.39) leaves us underwhelmed. The presence of cycles is clear, but the amplitude fluctuations do not imply an attractor as well structured as that produced by the model for the W Virginis. Once again, the insufficient quality of the data (small signal-to-noise ratio) does not allow us to make a clear statement about the nature of the observed irregularities. These dynamic behaviors illustrate the kinds of difficulties that the theory of chaos faces in its attempt to extend its domain of application into astrophysics.

7.3 Conclusion

In this chapter we have made an excursion into the world of astrophysics, studying variable stars. The dynamics underlying these phenomena is by nature deterministic — or, more exactly, the dynamics has a deterministic component — that leads to relatively simple chaotic behavior. Their identification is particularly problematic in view of the quality of the available data, despite recordings of increasingly high precision on the part of astrophysicists. Nature, because it involves a large number of interactions among a large number of components, is not always as simple as we would like to see it. Getting evidence from observations requires more and more sophisticated techniques to record good data.

Chapter 8

Chaos in Biology and Biomedicine

A dynamical system is a system that evolves as a function of time. Accordingly, all living systems are dynamical systems. Further, homeostasis is a fundamental property of the living and can be regarded as a propensity to maintain the living system within a particular dynamical domain. For example, a homeostatic dynamical system often works like a thermostat. Thus, a biological system remains within a certain dynamical range by self-regulating phenomena that can be considered in two ways. On the one hand, the system acts to modify the environment (like heating regulated by the thermostat modifies temperature) by controlling reactions that slow in order to stop some process. On the other hand, every change in the environment stimulates an appropriate adaption of the living system. Homeostatis is defined by the existence of specific regulatory mechanisms that maintain processes within a given dynamical regime.

Examples of chaotic dynamics in the fields of biology and biomedicine remain difficult to find for reasons that are, ultimately, similar to those encountered in ecology and astrophysics: it is very difficult to find experimental data that allow a direct application of the tools borrowed to the theory of chaos. In this Chapter we will present some examples as biological systems or models that do behave chaotically and how the techniques developed for analyzing chaotic behaviors can be used to discriminate patients from control subjects, while investigating the cardio-respiratory system. Some applications in oncology will be also discussed.

8.1 Glycolysis Oscillations

The relation between structure and function of proteins is an idea at the heart of understanding biological phenomena and regulatory processes. In this context, the structure and function of enzymes plays a fundamental role in cellular mechanisms. Enzymes, whose role is very specific, act on a substrate through a very small number of reactions to synthesize a new product. The reactions can be summarized as

$$\text{Enzyme} + \text{Substrate} \rightleftarrows \begin{array}{c}\text{Intermediate}\\ \text{products}\end{array} \rightleftarrows \text{Enzyme} + \text{Product}.$$

The intermediate products, which can be numerous, can be thought of as an enzyme-substrate complex. The synthesis of glycose falls into this category. In 1957, Lou Duysens and Jan Amesz showed that the synthesis of one of the components of glycose exhibited damped oscillations.[1] In 1964 Amal Ghosh and Britton Chance identified the source of these oscillations:[2] this is in a reaction involving phosphofructokinase. In 1968 Evgeny Sel'kov proposed the model[3]

$$\begin{cases} \dot{x} = 1 - xy^2 \\ \dot{y} = \alpha y\,(xy - 1) \end{cases}$$

where α is the affinity between the enzyme and the product. Variables x and y designate concentrations of substrate and of reaction product, respectively. This model reproduces the self-sustained oscillations of phosphofructokinase. It is based on a single substrate and a single reaction product where the enzyme is inhibitated by the substrate and activated by the product as it is for the phosphofructokinase. Depending on the value of the affinity α between the enzyme and the product, Sel'kov found decaying oscillations (Figure 8.1(a)) or self-sustained oscillations (Figure 8.1(b)). Other more realistic models were then proposed, but since they all depended on two variables, the most complex behavior they could exhibit was periodic oscillations, in light of the Poincaré-Bendixon theorem.

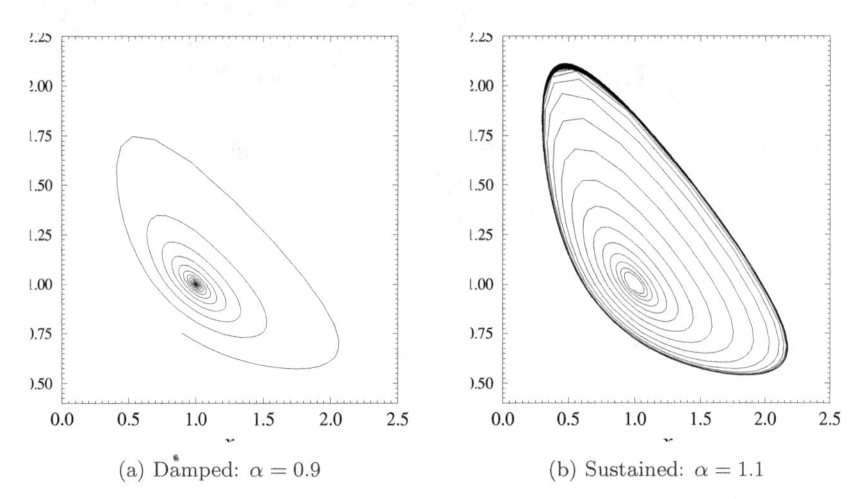

(a) Damped: $\alpha = 0.9$ (b) Sustained: $\alpha = 1.1$

Figure 8.1 Solutions of Sel'kov's model for describing oscillations in the glycolysis reaction.

[1] L. Duysens & J. Amesz, Fluorescence Spectrophotometry of reduced phosphopyridine nucleotide in intact cells in the near-ultraviolet and visible region, *Biochimica et Biophysica Acta*, **24**, 19–26, 1957.

[2] A. K. Gosh & B. Chance, Oscillations of glycolytic intermediates in yeast cells, *Biochemistry and Biophysics Research Communications*, **16**, 174–181, 1964.

[3] E. E. Sel'kov, Self-Oscillations in glycolysis: a simple model, *European Journal of Biochemistry*, **4**, 79–86, 1968.

In order to find models able to produce chaotic behavior, Olivier Decroly and Albert Goldbeter (University of Bruxelles) proposed the model[4]

$$\begin{cases} \dot{x} = V - \sigma_1\, \phi_1(x,y) \\ \dot{y} = q_1\, \sigma_1\, \phi_1(x,y) - \sigma_2\, \phi_2(y,z) \\ \dot{z} = q_2\, \sigma_2\, \phi_2(y,z) - K_s z \end{cases}$$

for this reaction chain involving three variables (Figure 8.2): variables x, y and z designate dimensionless concentrations of substrate S and products P_1 and P_2, respectively. The substrate S, under the action of a first enzyme E_1, furnishes a product P_1. This product serves as the substrate for a second enzyme E_2 that produces product P_2. At each step there is a reverse action of the product P_i on the enzyme E_i; the more the product, the more active the enzyme is. Finally, the reaction is governed by the rate constant K_s for the product P_2. Each of the two enzymes behaves like phosphofructokinase. Parameters σ_1 and σ_2 are the maximum dimensionless reaction rates between the two enzymes E_1 and E_2; these rates depend on functions

$$\begin{cases} \phi_1(x,y) = \dfrac{x\,(1+x)\,(1+y)^2}{L_1 + (1+x)^2\,(1+y)^2} \\ \phi_2(y,z) = \dfrac{y\,(1+z)^2}{L_2 + (1+z)^2}\,. \end{cases}$$

Parameter V corresponds to the dimensionless rate of injection of the substrate and K_s is the rate with which the final product is removed.

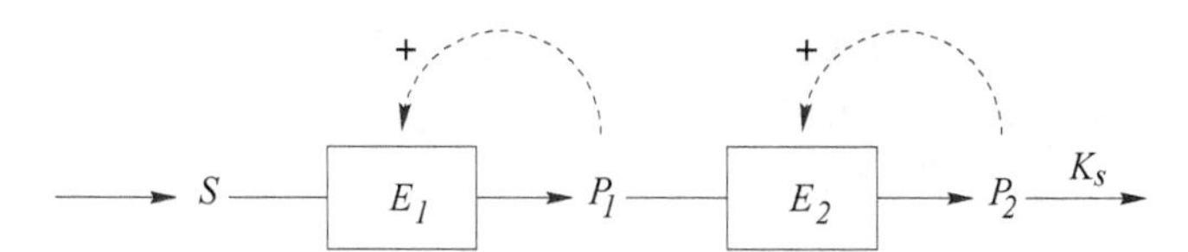

Figure 8.2 Schematic representation of the three-variable model for the coupling of two exzymatic reactions (after Decroly and Goldbeter, 1982).

Decroly and Goldbeter's model has a number of different kinds of solutions. The bifurcation diagram for this model shows a period-doubling cascade (Figure 8.3). Periodic windows are also seen. These typical behaviors, already seen several times, indicate that, on the one hand, this attractor ought to have a smooth unimodal first-return map (Figure 8.4) and on the other, that intermittencies might occur. Further, bistability is observed: under small change in the initial conditions two different types of asymptotic behavior are seen (Figure 8.5): one showing oscillations about a large mean value, the other showing oscillations about a small mean value.

[4]O. Decroly & A. Goldbeter, Biorhythmicity, chaos and other patterns of temporal self-organization in a multiply regulated biochemical systems, *Proceedings of the National Academy of Science* (USA), **79**, 6917–6921, 1982.

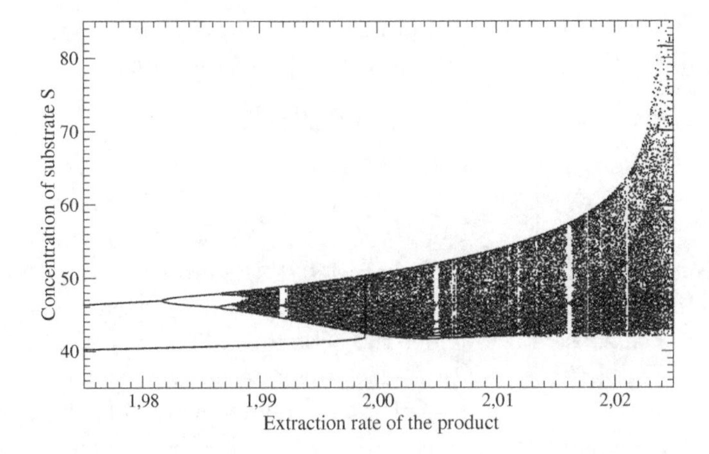

Figure 8.3 Bifurcation diagram of Decroly and Goldbeter's three-variable biochemical model. Bistability occurs for the control parameter value K_s between 1.975 and 1.999. Parameter values: $\sigma_1 = 10\ \mathrm{s}^{-1}$, $\sigma_2 = 10\ \mathrm{s}^{-1}$, $q_1 = 50$, $q_2 = 0.02$, $L_1 = 5 \cdot 10^8$, $L_2 = 100$, and $V = 0.45\ \mathrm{s}^{-1}$.

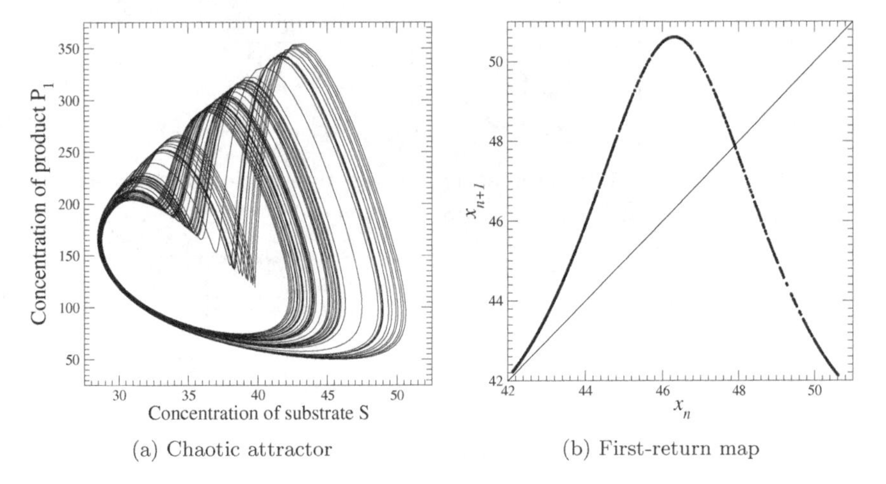

(a) Chaotic attractor (b) First-return map

Figure 8.4 Chaotic behavior observed following the period-doubling cascade characterized by a smooth unimodal first-return map. Parameter values: $K_s = 2$ and the others are as in Figure 8.3.

The state portrait shows the co-existence of two periodic orbits. From the experimental point of view, this shows that if an identical series of experiments is carried out, either oscillations around weak concentrations or oscillations around strong concentrations will occur, depending on the initial conditions. Since these are very difficult to control experimentally, biologists will have a difficult time predicting which oscillating regime will be observed in an experiment.

The chaotic behavior found in this model of reaction chains does not correspond exactly to the behavior found in experiments carried out by a group in Copenhagen

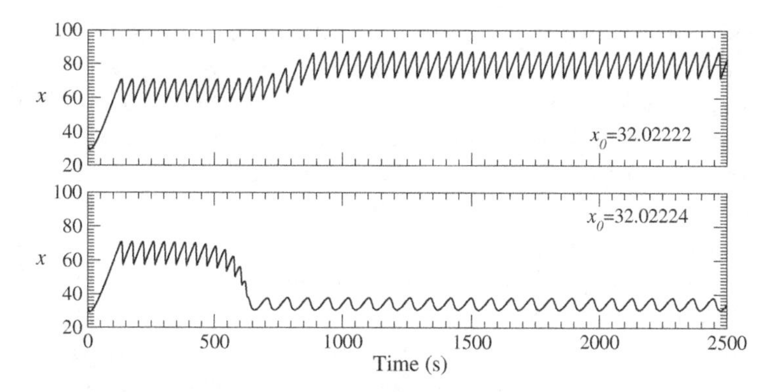

Figure 8.5 Bistability seen for the chain of biochemical reactions (K_s = 1.80). Two stable periodic orbits exist in the state space. Depending on the initial conditions, transient regimes relax to one or the other of these orbits.

in 1997 (Figure 8.6).[5] Goldbeter's model preceded the experiment by 15 years. As in ecology, there are very few experimental proofs of chaotic behavior observed in biological systems. It is a real problem to measure the time evolution of a biological system because it is necessary to monitor very small quantities without disturbing the system (Uncertainty Principle!). Nevertheless, the fact that realistic models predict such behavior should guide the analysis of experimental data to come, and, little by little, should change the attitude of biologists to complex phenomena which can emerge from rather simple systems.

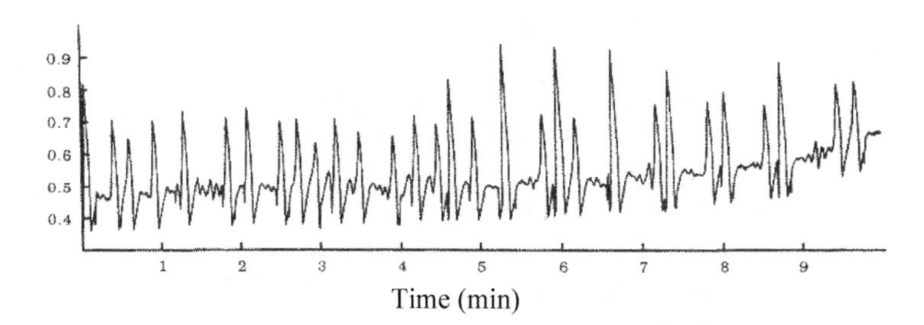

Figure 8.6 Time dependence of absorption mainly due to NADH: aperiodic behavior is clear... and chaos cannot be far. (Adapted from Nielsen and coworkers, 1997.)

8.2 Fluctuations in Hematopoiesis

Oscillation behavior can also be seen in our very own bodies. For example, the regulation of hematopoiesis, that is to say, the formation of the components of

[5] K. Nielsen, P. Graae Sorensen & F. Hyme, Chaos in glycolysis, *Journal of Theoretical Biology*, **186**, 303–306, 1997.

blood, can show this behavior. White blood cells, red blood cells and platelets, are produced by the bone marrow from which these components pass into the blood. When the oxygen concentration in the blood decreases a substance is released that, in its turn, causes the release into the blood of other substances produced by the bone marrow. In this sense there is a back reaction between the blood and the bone marrow.[6] Under certain conditions this back reaction can cause concentration oscillations in the blood components. This is what happens in the disease called leukemia.[7] Leukemia is a localized cancer in which the cells lose their aptosis ability, that is, to self-destruct at the conclusion of their useful lifetime. Because of this modification in the lifetime of cells, that is, in the characteristic time for hematopoiesis, an aperiodic oscillating behavior may occur in the white blood cell count in blood (Figure 8.7(a)).

At the end of the 1970s Leon Glass and Mickael Mackey proposed a delay differential model for the oscillations observed in a 12 year old white female complaining of vague aches and pains.[8] When the peripheral leukocyte (white blood cells) count was at its peak, "the patient suffered from headaches, mild malaise, and her spleen was enlarged." This leukocyte count was oscillating between 4000 and 130,000 cells/mm^3 approximately every 72 days. Glass and Mackey assumed that the population of mature cells (x) circulating in the blood was homogeneous, and that the cells were produced at a rate proportional to their concentration, that is, at a rate γx where the parameter γ is expressed in day^{-1}. After a reduction of the cell concentration in the blood, it takes about six days until the release of new mature cells from the bone marrow to make up this difference. They assumed that the flow of new cells into the blood at time t depended on the concentration at a previous time, that is, $(t-\tau)$, where τ is the delay. Such assumptions lead to the delay-differential equation

$$\dot{x}(t) = \frac{\mu a^h x(t-\tau)}{a^h + x^h(t-\tau)} - \gamma x(t) \tag{8.1}$$

where x is the cell concentration. As the delay is progressively increased from six days — period-1 limit cycle — to nineteen days (Figure 8.7(d)), the model (8.1) shows a period-doubling cascade, following which the behavior is chaotic. The period-doubling bifurcation between the period-1 (Figure 8.7(b)) and the period-2 (Figure 8.7(c)) limit cycles occurs with a delay τ at about 13 days.

Among normal adults, the white blood cell concentrations are either constant or show medium-amplitude oscillations with a period between 14 and 24 days. For patients suffering from chronic leukemia, the fluctuations are large and the period

[6] L. Glass & M. C. Mackey, Oscillations and chaos in physiological control systems, *Science*, **197**, 287–289, 1977.

[7] G. Chikkappa, G. Borner, H. Burlington, A. D. Chanana, E. P. Cronkite, S. Ohl, M. Pavelec & J. S. Robertson, Periodic oscillation of blood leukocytes, platelets, and reticulocytes in a patient with chronic myelocytic leukemia, *Blood*, **47**, 1023–1030, 1976.

[8] R. A. Gatti, W. A. Robinson, A. S. Deinard, M. Nesbit, J. J. McCullough, M. Ballow & R. A. Good, Cyclic leukocytosis in chronic myelogenous leukemia: New perspectives on pathogenesis and therapy, *Blood*, **41**, 771–782, 1973.

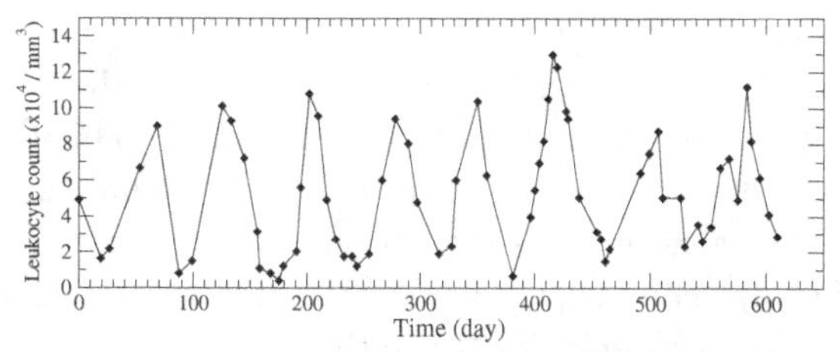

(a) Peripheral leukocyte count in the blood of a 12 year old girl with chronic myelogenous leukemia. The pseudo-period of oscillations is about 72 days (drawn from Gatti and coworkers' data, 1973).

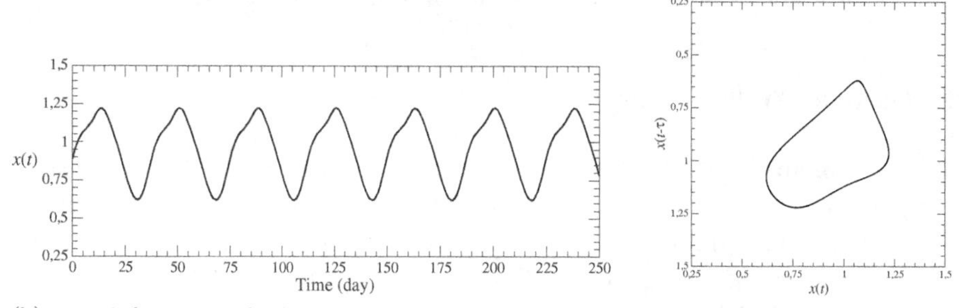

(b) $\tau = 12$ days: period-1 limit cycle with a pseudo-period equal to about 30 days.

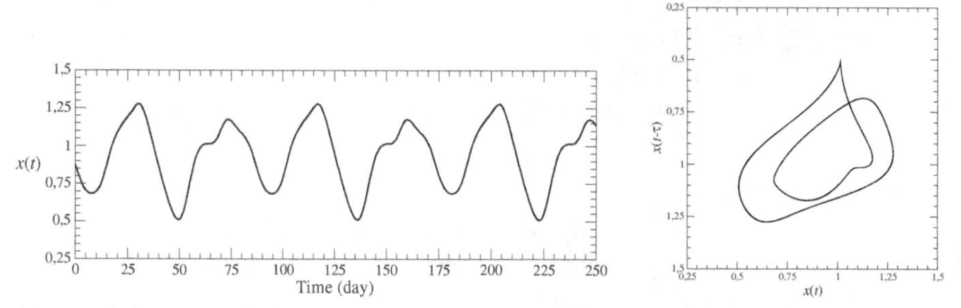

(c) $\tau = 14$ days: period-2 limit cycle with a pseudo-period equal to about 43 days.

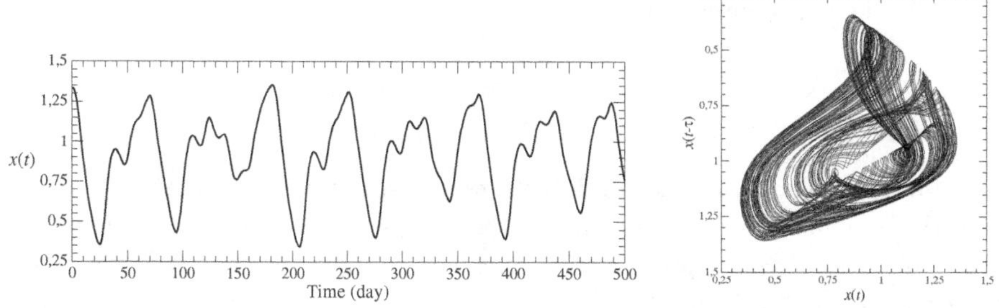

(d) $\tau = 19$ days: the behavior is chaotic. The pseudo-period of oscillations has increased to about 70 days.

Figure 8.7 Solutions for a model of hematopoiesis. The aperiodic behavior seen in a sick girl (a) can be reproduced by a simple model due to Mackey and Glass. The behavior can be periodic (b) or chaotic (c), depending on the maturation delay τ. Parameter values of model (8.1): $\gamma = 0.1$ days^{-1}, $a = 1$, $\mu = 0.2$ day^{-1}, and $h = 10$. The model is integrated with a time step $\delta t = 1$ day.

can vary from 30 to 70 days, depending on the individual. For a large number of them, cell production increases significantly, pointing to an increase in the delay. Long period oscillations appear in the absence of clinical intervention. This large variability could result from a series of bifurcations such as the period-doubling cascade. To understand in detail the origins of these oscillations could allow to have better methods for clinical treatments. For this, models such as that of model (8.1) provide possible scenarii to trigger some pathologies. Even though the model reproduces aperiodic behavior (Figure 8.7(d)) of the observations (Figure 8.7(a)), there are still significant quantitative differences. This means that certain hematopoiesis processes have not been properly taken into account in this model...

8.3 Cardiac Arrhythmias

The area of biomedicine where the measurements are the most advanced from the dynamical point of view is most certainly in cardiology. In fact the heart is a dynamical system, and its vibrating nature has interested "dynamicists" from very early on. The first ones were van der Pol and van der Mark,[9] who modeled cardiac activity. Van der Pol made a presentation in Paris in 1928 at the invitation of the Society of the Friends of the T.S.F, the French Society of Electricians, and the Biological Society. There Balthazar van der Pol pointed out the close relation between relaxation oscillations and the electrical potential of the heart. He started by describing the properties that define relaxation oscillations as follows.

(1) nonsinusoidal form;
(2) frequency determined by a relaxation time (time constant);
(3) great ease with which synchronization occurs under the influence of an external electromagnetic periodic source;
(4) as a result, the frequency can be subjected to large variations, by contrast the amplitude is absolutely constant.

Then he stated that

> Heartbeats are relaxation oscillations, which explains the properties of cardiac rhythms and its anomalies (system with three degrees of freedom). [It is therefore possible to give] a description of an electric model that shows, by means of relaxation oscillations of neon tubes, the rhythmic properties of normal and abnormal hearts. The activity of each part of the heart corresponds to the illumination of neon tubes.

[9]B. van der Pol & J. van der Mark, Le Battement du cœur considéré comme oscillation et un modèle électrique du cœur, *L'onde électrique*, **7**, 365–392, 1928.

Just as Alfred Lotka had established a connection between very different natural systems (chemical reactions and population oscillations), van der Pol created a bridge between electric circuits and cardiac activity, explaining the complete generality of this approach in terms of dynamical systems.

8.3.1 *The Beginnings of Electrophysiology*

Medical studies involving electrical signals only began in the 18th century when Jean Antoine Nollet (1700–1770) studied static current discharges for treatment purposes[10] and when Jean Jalabert (1712–1768) treated paralysis and contractions using electrical signals. A cardiac electrical simulation was described in 1774 by the reverend William Hawes (1736–1808):[11]

> A Mr. Squires, of Wardour Street, Soho lived opposite the house from which a three year old girl, Catherine Sophia Greenhill had fallen from the first storey window on 16th July 1774. After the attending apothecary had declared that nothing could be done for the child Mr. Squires, with the consent of the parents very humanely tried the effects of electricity. At least twenty minutes had elapsed before he could apply the shock, which he gave to various parts of the body without any apparent success; but at length, upon transmitting a few shocks through the thorax, he perceived a small pulsation: soon after the child began to sigh, and to breathe, though with great difficulty.

This was also described by Charles Kite (1768–1811) and it is probably the very first occasion of cardiac defibrillation.[12] Another relevant contribution was taken by Luigi Galvani (1737–1798) who carried out many experiments relating electrical forces with the movements of muscles, and which lead to theories of animal electricity.[13] Then, in 1780, while he was dissecting a frog, he noticed that when he accidentally touched a nerve in the frog's foot with his stainless steel scalpel (practically a machine for collecting static electricity), he observed that the foot moved. He later discovered that when the frogs legs were arranged on a glass slide and covered with a metal foil, they reacted when an electrical charge was applied to the upper part of the frog's vertibral column. Six years later he got an unexpected result: frog's legs contracted even when they were isolated as long as their nerves remained grounded and an electric generator produced a charge. Eleven years later Galvani produced a theory according to which an electric fluid was secreted by the

[10] J. A. Nollet, Conjectures sur les causes de l'électricité des corps, *Mémoires de l'Académie Royale des Sciences*, 1745.

[11] W. Hawes, *Transactions of the Royal Humane Society* (London), Annual report 1774, pp. 31–32, 1775. Reproduced in `http://www.ecglibrary.com/ecghist.html`.

[12] C. Kite, *An Essay on the recovery of the apparently dead* (1788), C. Dilly, London. 1791.

[13] L. Galvani, *De Viribus Electricitatis in motu musculari commentarius*, 1791. Published in 1792 at Modène, translated in German by Mayer (Prague, 1793) and published as a Ostwald's classical volumes (Leipzig, 1894). See also *Dell' uso e dell' attività dell' arco conduttore nelle contrazioni de' muscoli*, 1794 and *Memorie sulla elettricità animale*, 1797.

brain, conducted along the nerves, and stored in the muscles. He also showed that when the nerve and the muscle touched two different metals (for example, copper and iron) in contact with each other, muscular contraction followed, even without connection to a static electricity source: he assumed that there was a difference in potential between the frog's leg and the iron wire, and that the frog's leg contained electricity.

The electric fluid hypothesis immediately stirred up discussion and provoked the criticism of Allesandro Volta (1745–1827) who was unable to accept the idea that electricity could be produced by living tissues. Then in 1842 Carlo Matteucci (1811–1868) described the action of a muscle potential and how the muscle could contract when its nerve was in contact with a second muscle in an excited state. He showed that a potential difference exists between the interior and surface of a muscle (called a rest current). He found the earliest evidence of the electrical nature of the nerve pulse. In addition, he observed that in the frog, each heartbeat was accompanied by an electrical current.[14] In 1849 Emil Du Bois-Reymond (1818–1896) discovered action currents and, by measuring currents in contracting muscles, constructed the first electromyograph in 1851.[15] At the same time William Duchenne de Boulogne (1806–1875) show that once could electrically excite the nerves and the muscles at certain specific points on the skin (motor points).[16] He showed this in particular for facial expressions:[17] few of his photographs are reproduced in Figure 8.8. In 1872 he related similar facts to those related by Mr. Squires.[18]

Figure 8.8 Duchenne de Boulogne used photographs in his research. The old man is under almost total facial anesthesia so that he would not feel much pain from the electrical stimulations. (*Les Mécanismes des expressions faciales humaines*, Jules Renard, 1862.)

[14]C. Matteucci, Sur un Phénomène physiologique produit par les muscles en contraction, *Annales de Chimie Physique*, **6**, 339–341, 1842 — *Traité des phénomènes électro-physiologique des animaux*, Paris, 1844 and *Lezioni sui fenomeni fisico-chimici dei corpi viventi*, 2nd ed., Pisa, 1846.

[15]E. Du Bois-Reymond, *Researches on animal electricity*, 1848–1884.

[16]G. Duchenne de Boulogne, *Physiologie des Mouvements*, 1867.

[17]G. Duchenne de Boulogne, *Le Mécanisme des expressions faciales humaines*, Paris: Jules Renard, 1862.

[18]G. B. Duchenne, *De l'Electrisation localisée et de son application.à la pathologie et la thérapeutique par courants induits et par courants galvaniques interrompus et continus*, 3rd Ed., Paris, J.B. Baillière & fils, 1872.

Hermann Helmholtz (1821–1894) measured the conduction speed in the median nerve of the frog in 1850. Strange behavior of the ventricles — later called ventrical fibrillations — were described by Moritz Hoffa during experiments in which strong electrical currents were produced near the hearts of dogs and cats. In particular, he showed that a single electrical shock could produce a fibrillation.[19] Robert Remak (1815–1865) studied the length of a contraction under the effect of a galvanic current on a degenerate muscle.[20] Rudolph von Kölliker (1817–1905) and Heinrich Müller (1801–1858) confirmed that an electric current accompanied each heartbeat by connecting the leads of a galvanometer across a heart, from the base to the top of a ventricle. They also repeated the nerve-muscle configuration used by Matteucci to the ventrical, and observed that a contraction of the muscle occurred just before the ventricular systole, and then a smaller contraction appeared just after the systole.[21] These two phases were recorded by John Burden Sanderson and Frederick Page by measuring the electric current in a heart with a capillary electrometer.[22]

In 1876 Gabriel Lippmann (1845–1921) invented a capillary electrometer — consisting of a thin glass tube containing mercury immersed in sulfuric acid. The displacement of the mercury meniscus was proportional to the variations in the electric potential and was observed using a microscope. This galvanometer was later improved by Jacques Arsene d'Arsonval (1851–1940) and Marcel Deprez (1843–1918).[23] Etienne-Jules Marey (1830–1904) used this electrometer to record the electrical activity in the heart of a frog.[24] Nevertheless, electrocardiograms could only be obtained from a heart removed from the body. It was not until 1876 that Auguste Désiré Waller (1856–1922) recorded the first human electrocardiogram.[25] William Bayliss and Edward Starling connected the terminals to the right hand and on the skin above the heart of the subject, and showed that a three-phase variation accompanied each heartbeat.[26] In addition they observed a delay of 0.13

[19] M. Hoffa & C. Ludwig, Einige neue Versuche über Herzbewegung, *Zeitschrift Rationelle Medizin*, **9**, 107–144, 1850.

[20] R. Remak, *Über metodische Electrisierung gelähmter Muskeln*, 1855.

[21] A. von Kölliker & H. Muller, Nachweis der negativen Schwankung des Muskelstroms am naturlich sich kontrahierenden Herzen. *Verhandlungen der Physikalisch-Medizinischen Gesellschaft in Würzburg*, **6**, 528–533 and 1869–1870, 1856.

[22] J. Burden Sanderson, Experimental Results relating to the rhythmical and excitatory motions of the ventricle of the frog, *Proceedings of the Royal Society of London*, **27**, 410–414, 1878 and J. Burden Sanderson and F. Page, On the Electrical Phenomena of the excitatory process in the heart of the tortoise, as investigated photographically, *Journal of Physiology* (London) **4**, 327–338 1884.

[23] J. A. d'Arsonval & M. Deprez, Galvanomère Apériodique, *Comptes-Rendus de l'Académie des Sciences* (Paris), **94**, 1347–1350, 1882.

[24] E. J. Marey, Des Variations électriques des muscles et du cœur en particulier étudiées au moyen de l'électromètre de M. Lippman, *Comptes-Rendus de l'Académie des Sciences* (Paris), **82**, 975–977, 1876.

[25] A. D. Waller, A demonstration on man of electromotive changes accompanying the heart's beat, *Journal of Physiology*, **8**, 229–234 and 327–338, 1884.

[26] W. M. Bayliss & E. H. Starling, On the electrical variations of the heart in man, *Journal of Physiology* (London), **13**, lviii–lix, 1891.

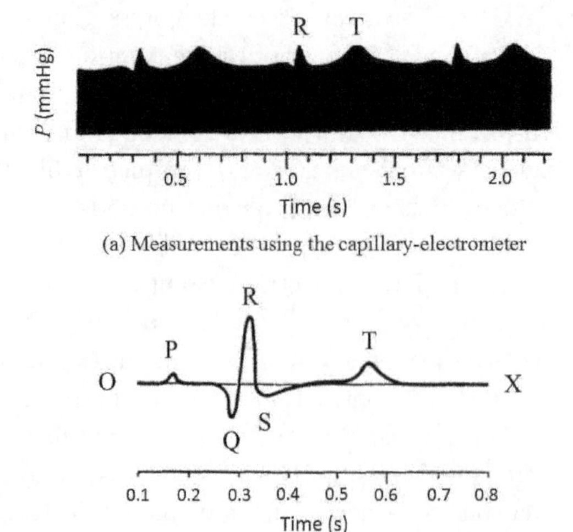

(a) Measurements using the capillary-electrometer

(b) Einthoven's corrected curve

Figure 8.9 Electrocardiagram measured by Einthoven in 1903. The choice of the letters PQRST is a simple mathematical convention using the letters of the second half of the alphabet. In fact, Einthoven always began his diagrams with the letter O to mark the time axis in his diagrams. P is simply the letter following O. The two graphs above are adapted from those inserted in the paper published by Einthoven in 1903.

seconds between the atrial stimulation and the ventricular depolarization.[27] In 1893 Willem Einthoven (1860–1927) used the term electrocardiogram following the lead of Waller.[28] In 1895 Einthoven identified five different deflections that he named P, Q, R, S, and T during the course of a heartbeat (Figure 8.9).[29]

In 1903 Willem Einthoven published the first recording of an electrocardiogram in human.[30] In the same article he presented descriptions and photographs of patients undergoing electrocardiography. He also described arrhythmias such as premature ventricular beats, ventricular bigeminy or the complete cessation of the heartbeat. But it was not until 1908 that Einthoven was able to show the clinical possibility of this method by measuring simultaneously the beats of the carotid and the electrocardiogram of a normal man, as well as several electrocardiograms

[27]W. M. Bayliss & E. H. Starling, On the electromotive phenomena of the mammalian heart, *Proceedings of the Royal Society of London*, **50**, 211–214, 1892.

[28]W. Einthoven, Nieuwe Methoden voor clinisch onderzoek, *Nederlands Tijdschr Geneeskunde*, **29** (2), 263–286, 1893.

[29]W. Einthoven, Über die Form des menschlichen Electrocardiogramms, *Archiv für die gesamte Psychologie*, **60**, 101–123, 1895.

[30]W. Einthoven, Die galvanometrische Registrirung des menschlichen Elektrokardiogramms, zugleich eine Beurtheilung der Anwendung des Capillar-Elektrometers in der Physiologie, *Archiv für die Gesammte Physiologie des Menschen und der Thiere*, **99**, 473, 1903 — English translation W. Einthoven, The galvanometric registration of the human electrocardiogam, likewise a review of the use of the capillary-electrometer in physiology, *Annals of Noninvasive Electrocardiology*, **2** (1), 93–93, 1997.

Figure 8.10 Einthoven's galvanometer, in 1901, produced relatively sensitive electrocardiograms, but it required almost 600 kilograms of stuff and also required the subject to place his hands and feet in water basins in order to increase bodily conduction. (After P. D. Lamson, *The Heart Rhythms*, Williams & Wilkins Company, 1921, pp. 21–22.)

related with different pathologies. If electrocardiograms were becoming reasonable tools, the technology enabling them remained difficult (Figure 8.10).

8.3.2 *The Heart — An Electric Machine*

The heart is a muscle whose function is to assure the circulation of blood in vessels and to maintain, with the aid of vascular plasticity, an intravascular pressure sufficient to furnish the forces necessary for the exchange of material between capillaries and interstitial liquids. Its normal function consists of a regular succession of contractions, called *systoles*, and relaxations, called *diastoles*. This harmonious behavior is guaranteed thanks to four fundamental properties of cardiac muscle, or myocardium: excitability, contractability, conductivity, and spontaneous rhythms.

- Myocardiac excitability follows the law of "all or nothing". The smallest possible stimulation unleashes a maximal contraction. This is opposite to what happens for skeletal muscles, where the intensity of the contraction is not changed by variations in the intensity of the stimulus. Further, the refractory period (duration of the relaxation), which corresponds to the absence of excitability that immediately follows the excitation, is longer than for ordinary muscles. Any second stimulation too close to the primary has no effect, so that it is not possible to have a fusion of successive contractions: heart muscle cannot be under tetany.
- Myocardiac contractibility develops the force necessary to send blood through the body. Besides its rhythmic character, the contraction is much longer than

for voluntary muscles. The rhythmic nature of the contractions constitutes the last very particular property of cardiac muscles.

- The automatic and rhythmic nature of the heartbeat are guaranteed by a specific muscular tissue: the *nodal tissue*, situated at the heart of the cardiac muscle and consisting of several anatomically defined components, which assure the automatic nature of the heartbeat.

Among living creatures, the relation between the mean cardiac frequency f_c and the body mass can be reduced to[31]

$$f_c = 241\, m^{-0.25} \,,$$

thus varying from about 30 bpm for massive elephant ($m \approx 5000$ kg) to about 1000 bpm for light canarie ($m \approx 0.020$ kg) (Figure 8.11). It is remarkable that almost the same "allometric" formula

$$f_v = 53.5\, m^{-0.26}$$

is obtained for the ventilatory frequency. When the ratio of the cardiac frequency over the ventilatory frequency is computed, we get

$$\frac{f_c}{f_v} = \frac{241 \ m^{-0.25}}{53.5 \ m^{-0.26}} = 5.4\, m^{-0.01} \,,$$

that is, a very weak dependency of this ratio on the body mass since $m^{0.01} \approx 1$ (it varies from 1,09 for elephants to 0,96 for canaries).

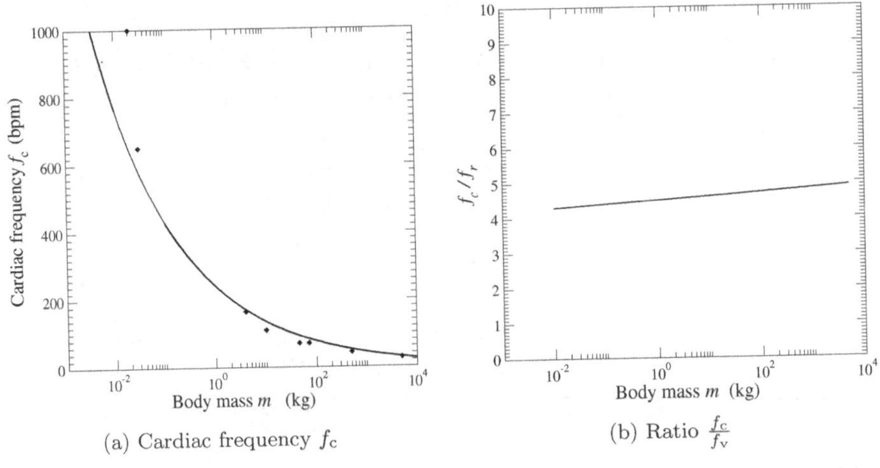

(a) Cardiac frequency f_c

(b) Ratio $\frac{f_c}{f_v}$

Figure 8.11 Allomeric relationships between the cardiac frequency and the body mass (a) and, between the ratio $\frac{f_c}{f_v}$ and the body mass (b). The cardiac frequency is given in beat-per-minute (bpm). Observational data for elephants, horses, men, sheeps, dogs, rabbits, mices and canaries are reported. Do not forget that all these values are subject dependent.

---

[31] W. R. Stahl, Scaling of respiratory variables in mammals, *Journal of Applied Physiology*, **22**, 453–460, 1967.

The *sinus node*, originally described in 1907,[32] is the dominant pacemaker in the heart (Figure 8.12). It is located in the wall of the right atrium close to the superior vena cava. The sinus node corresponds to the integrated activity of pacemaker cells in a compact region. These cells depolarize and produce action potentials almost synchronously by mutual entrainment.[33] The contraction wave is born there with a rapid rhythm that is slowed down by the nerves of the vagal system. If the sinus excitation is suppressed, the auriculo-ventricular node can substitute for it, but with a slower rhythm.

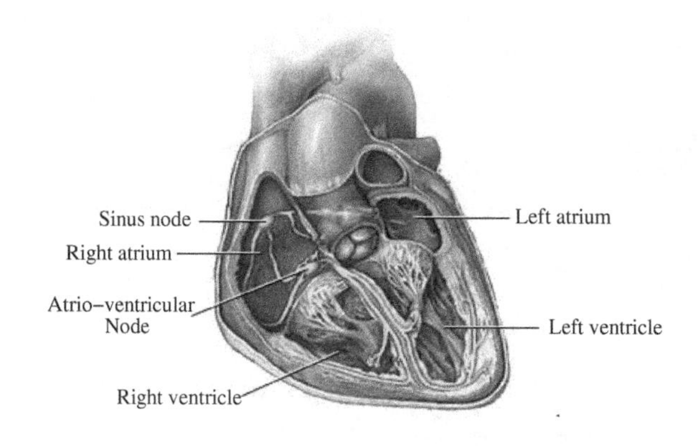

Figure 8.12 Electrical conduction system in the heart.

Cardiac automation is explained by the occurrence and maintenance of fluctuations in the membrane polarization of cells in the nodal tissue. These drive a local spontaneous depolarization in a rhythmic fashion, which in its turn drives a response propagated to the myocardiac cells. Temperature variations affect the rhythm of the sinus node. This was understood by Elias Cyon who made the first observations on the effects of temperature on isolated hearts:[34] the heart rate increases with temperature, reaching a maximum that depends on the heart chosen. Beyond the maximum related to the temperature of a fever, the heart rate rapidly decreases. He assumed that the heart was governed by an exciting system that produced a stimulus and by a regulating system (inhibitor), that modified the rhythmic transitions due to motor nerves in the heart.

[32] A. Keith & M. Flack, The form and nature of the muscular connections between the primary divisions of the vertebrate heart, *Journal of Anatomy, and Physiology*, **41**, 172–189, 1907.
[33] A. T. Winfree, *The geometry of biological time*, Springer-Verlag, 1980 — J. Jalife, Mutual entrainement and electrical coupling as mechanisms for synchronous firing of rabbit sino-atrial pacemaker cells, *Journal of Physiology*, **356**, 221–243, 1984.
[34] E. Cyon, Über den Einfluss der Temperaturänderungen auf Zahl, Dauer und Stärke der Herzschläge, *Berichte über die Verhandlungen der Königlich Sächsischen Gesellschaft der Wissenschaften zu Leipzig. Mathematisch-Physiche Classe*, **18**, 256–306, 1866.

The heart is thus a complex electrical system that emits different electric waves which fall into three groups (Figure 8.13):

- the P wave, associated with auriculo-myocardial contraction, unleashed by the sinus node;
- the QRS complex that corresponds to the propagation of an excitatory wave towards the two ventricles and preceding the ventricular systole;
- the T wave corresponding to the repolarization of the myocardian ventricle.

Among these waves we mention the PR segment that corresponds to the auriculo-ventricular conduction, and the ST segment that corresponds to the ventricular systole during the course of which the ventricles depolarize: the ventricular systole corresponds to the contraction of the heart that pumps blood into the arteries.

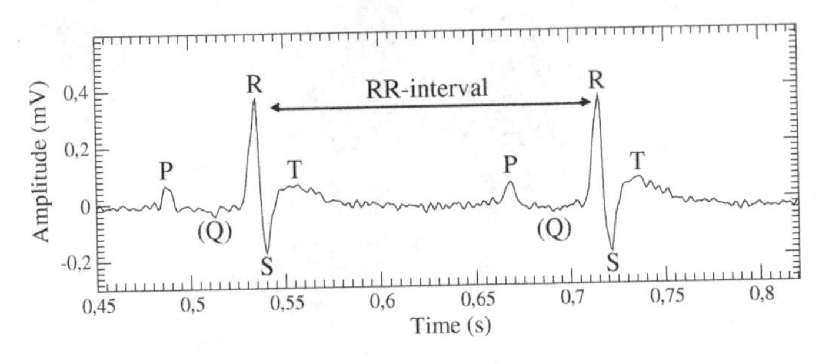

Figure 8.13 Different waves identified in an electrocardiogram of a rat following the terminology introduced by Einthoven. The ventricular systole occurs between the S wave and the T wave. The refractory period, which protects the normal heart from premature beating, corresponds to the segment TP. In the rat, the Q wave is hardly seen.

8.3.3 *Electrocardiograms and Arrhythmias*

Let us start with electrocardiograms measured in rats subjected to a light cycle of twelve hours per day. A telemetry system was surgically implanted in a manner that avoided stress on these animals and especially had no effect on the cardiac rhythm (Figure 8.14). By the use of telemetry it is possible to obtain electrocardiograms without otherwise constraining the rats and with a minimum of external perturbations. It is not possible for a human to remain uninfluenced by external sources such as television, with other humans, etc., exchanges that necessarily affect his cardiac activity because of emotions, etc.

Measured in this way, an electrocardiogram of a typical healthy rat is pretty regular, in period as well as amplitude (Figure 8.15). Even so, arrhythmias can occur even in healthy individuals. These appear as irregularities in the heartbeat rhythms. In a healthy individual these do not occur often and are inconsequential. They have a tendency to increase with age — particularly the extrasystoles of which we speak more later. Nevertheless, it sometimes happens that bad ventricular

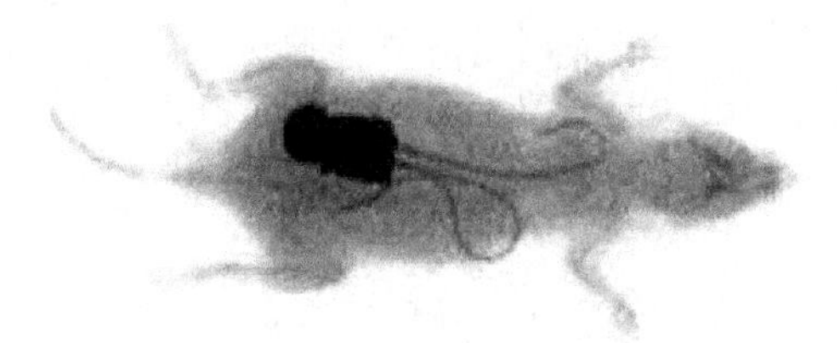

Figure 8.14 X-ray of an "instrumented" rat with radio emitter and electrodes (the two long wires) for recording electrocardiagrams.

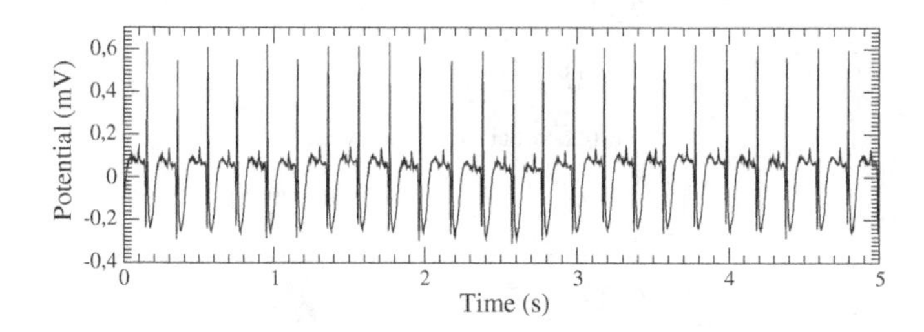

Figure 8.15 Typical electrocardiogram of a healthy rat. Relaxation oscillations of the electric potential are regular in both rhythm and amplitude.

arrhythmias such as ventricular tachycardia or ventricular fibrillation develop and lead to heart attacks and even sudden death. This occurs frequently in patients that have experienced a myocardia infarctus. As a result, the detection of such arrhythmias is quite important.

Typically, three pathologies are often encountered:

(1) Bradycardia which is indicated by a slowing down of the cardiac rhythm (Figure 8.16(a)).
(2) Tachycardia which is associated with an acceleration of the cardiac rhythm. The most frequent mechanism is associated with a dysfunction of the atrio-ventricular node which is indicated by a premature beat, followed by a short refractory period and finally by a long refractory period (Figure 8.16(b)).
(3) The extrasystoles correspond to a complex premature ectopic beat: the beats are called *ectopic* because they are generated outside the usual area of cardiac excitation which is the nodal tissue. In this case the succession of regular QRS waves is interrupted by bursts of unusual QRS complexes. These bursts can have either the same polarization as the normal QRS complex (Figure 8.16(c)) or the opposite polarization (Figure 8.16(d)).

The extrasystoles can lead to bursts that repeat. In the case shown in (Figure 8.16(c)), the extrasystoles occur every other beat: they are bigeminy. In the second example of extrasystoles (Figure 8.16(d)) they occur every fifth beat: they are

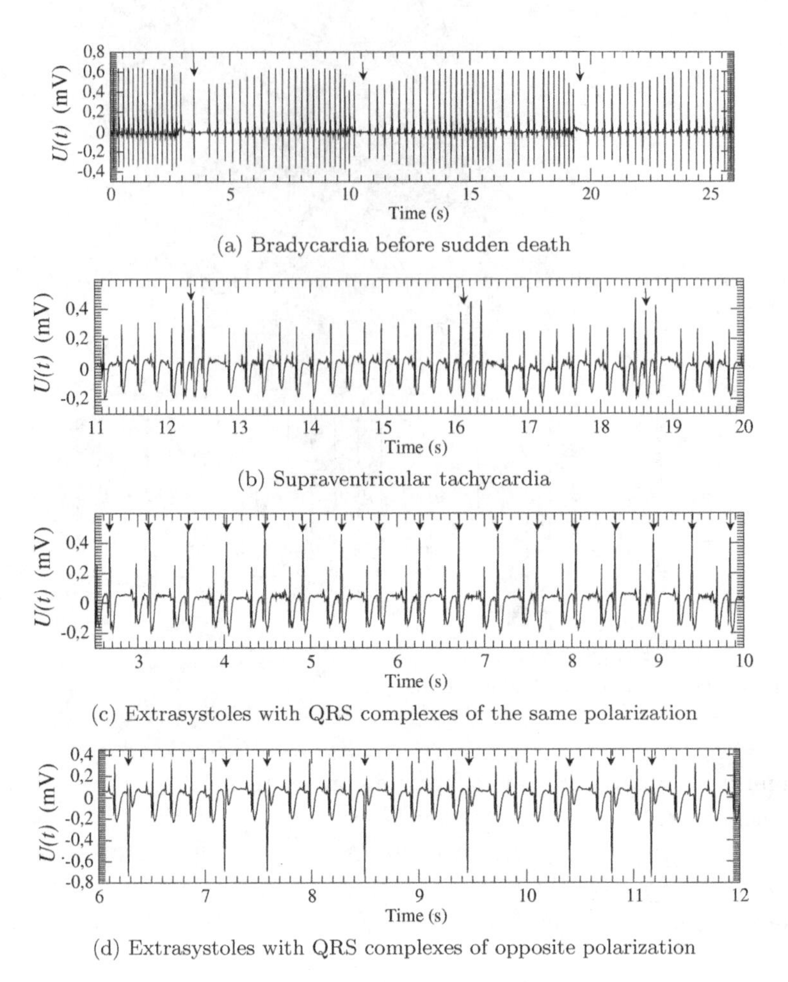

(a) Bradycardia before sudden death

(b) Supraventricular tachycardia

(c) Extrasystoles with QRS complexes of the same polarization

(d) Extrasystoles with QRS complexes of opposite polarization

Figure 8.16 Different types of arrhythmias observed in different rats. Arrows indicate abnormal beats.

quinquageminy. It is possible to have tri-geminy, quadrigeminy, etc., with complexes of either the same or opposite polarization.

It is possible to construct state space trajectories using delay coordinates obtained from these electrocardiagrams (Figure 8.17). Taking all possible precautions for recording these electrocardiagrams — the rats are placed in environments without sound or visual perturbations, and are not subject to stresses caused by the recording because of the use of telemetry — only small fluctuations are observed in the state portraits obtained from healthy rats (Figure 8.17(a)): they look like "slightly noisy" limit cycles. In fact, there is a weak variation in the cardiac rhythm due to ventilation and to muscular activity which is always present in healthy rats. This variability is usually weak from one heartbeat to another, and results from regulation by the sinus node: this is called *sinus variability*.

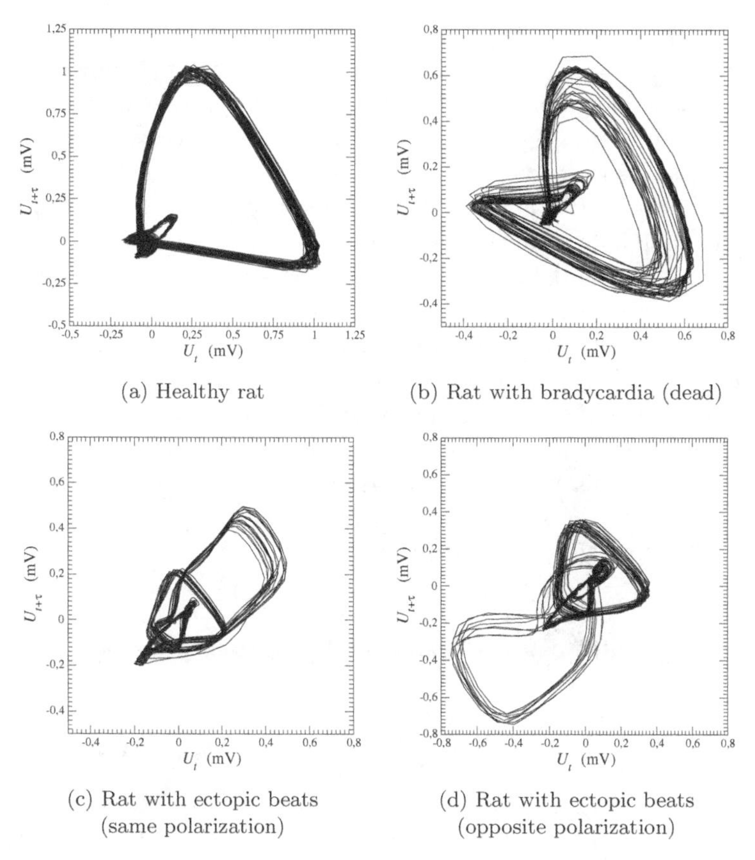

(a) Healthy rat

(b) Rat with bradycardia (dead)

(c) Rat with ectopic beats (same polarization)

(d) Rat with ectopic beats (opposite polarization)

Figure 8.17 Typical state portraits reconstructed from rat electrocardiograms (electric potential U) using delay coordinates ($\tau = 9$ ms). For healthy rats (a), the large loops correspond to QRS complexes and the small loops correspond to P waves. Bradycardia modifies the form of the QRS complex (b) and the extrasystoles show up as a second series of large loops, above right in (c) while the polarization of the abnormal complexes is the same as the normal QRS complexes, and below left in (d) when the polarization is opposite.

More generally, cardiac variability increases in the presence of arrhythmias. This is shown by state space trajectories that fluctuate greatly between heartbeats (compare the case of the healthy rat with the three others in Figure 8.17). Further, the structure of the state space portrait is different, revealing different morphologies in the electric wave, with larger than normal amplitudes associated with the normal QRS complexes: these are premature beats with either the same polarization (Figure 8.17(c)) or the opposite polarization (Figure 8.17(d)). Note that bigeminy (Figure 8.17(c)) is not so easily distinguished from quadrigemeny (except for the polarization, which plays no role in the extrasystole periodicity). In fact, if the state portrait can provide some information about the wave morphology, a more compact representation is also useful for the study of arrhythmias.

Usually, when we wish to interpret a state portrait we introduce a first-return map to a Poincaré section. In the present case a Poincaré section can be defined by the maximum value of each loop describing the QRS complex (Figure 8.17(a)). This amounts to determining the time interval between successive R waves: cardiologists call these RR intervals (Figure 8.13). In this way an electrocardiagram can be transformed into a succession of RR intervals — now called *tachograms* — such as that shown in Figure 8.18. For a healthy rat, most of the RR intervals occur about a mean value with only a slight dispersion about this value. For a healthy rat the first-return map is essentially an ellipse along the straight line through the origin: $RR_{n+1} = RR_n$ (this line is called a *bisecting* line). In short, the variability from one beat to another is very weak: this is the sinus variability. We point out that there is no evidence of any type of smooth unimodal structure in this first-return map: this is just a "cloud" of points meaning that the underlying determinism is hardly observable. As a result, it is a delicate issue whether to describe cardiac dynamics as chaotic or not in this case as we will discuss below.

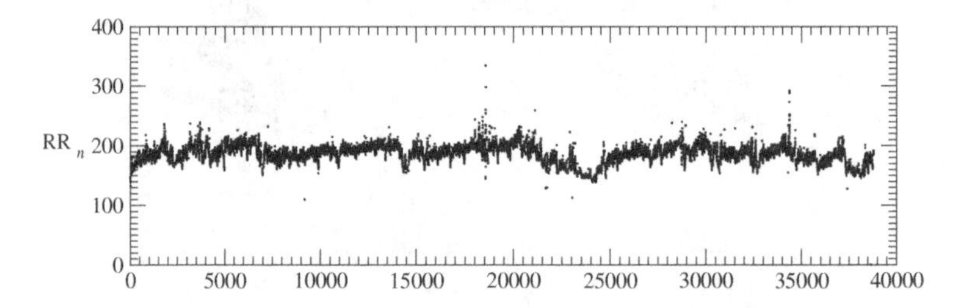

Figure 8.18 Tachogram for a healthy rat. The beat interval has a mean value of 188 ms with small dispersion. The length of a beat changes little from one beat to the next. Even so, a weak variation is seen: this is the sinus variability, due to movements of the animal.

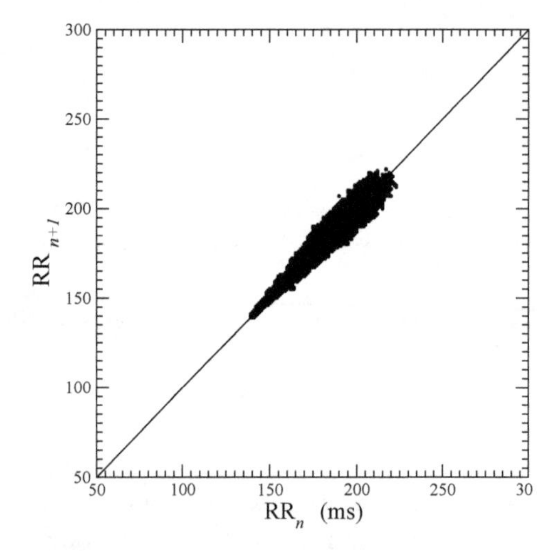

Figure 8.19 First-return map built from the RR intervals measured in a healthy rat.

8.3.4 *Analysis of some Heart Rate Variability*

There is an intersubject heart rate variability (Figure 8.20), related to the individuality of the cardio-respiratory system. There is also an intra-subject variability, often designated, for short, by heart rate variability. Heart activity results from an electrical conduction system starting from the sinoatrial node up to the atrioventricular node which stimulates the myocardium. Variation in the beat-to-beat interval is a physiological phenomenon and is performed through different levels of regulation. Cardiodynamics is largely under the control of the autonomic nervous system,[35] with a parasympathetic influence via the vagus nerve and the release of acetylcholine that slows the rate, and a sympathetic influence via β-adrenegic receptors that accelerates the pace. Accelerations and decelerations of the heart rate thus result from two different physiological processes.

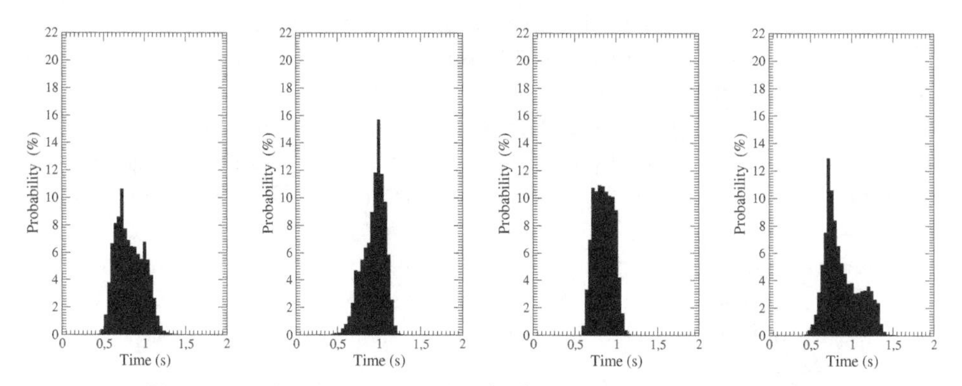

Figure 8.20 Heart rate variability for four different control subjects.

The sino-atrial (sinus) node receives different inputs from the sympathetic and the parasympathetic nervous system that aids in the control of most of body's internal organs with short time scale actions and long time scale actions (as salivation, lacrimation, urination, digestion), respectively. Humoral factors and respirations may also affect the heart rate. Among the factors inducing variations of the heart rate, one may mention baroreflex, thermoregulation, hormones, sleep-wake cycle, meals, physical activity, and stress. A certain variability is thus expected in healthy subjects.

Consequently, heart rate variability analysis is often investigated in adults to assess their mortality risk in patients affected by heart diseases.[36] Most of the routine analysis are based on RR-intervals and a Poincaré map, that is, a first-return

[35] Task force of the European Society of Cardiology and the North American Society of Pacing and Electrophysiology, Heart rate variability. Standards of measurement, physiological interpretation, and clinical use, *Circulation*, **93**, 1043–1065, 1996.

[36] R. E. Kleiner, J. P. Miller, J. T. Bigger & A. J. Moss, Decreased heart rate variability and its association with increased mortality after acute myocardial infection, *American Journal of Cardiology*, **59**, 256–262, 1987.

map to normal RR-intervals (arrhythmias are removed to only investigate the sinus activity), is included in the final report. Such a map for healthy adults looks like the map shown in the case of a control rat (Figure 8.19). Many works have been devoted for identifying chaos from heart rate by using such maps. Most of them used geometric arguments as correlation dimension or Lyapunov exponents[37] which are consistent with a deterministic chaotic behavior. But they cannot be conclusive. Surrogate data analysis,[38] that is, using data which are processed to blur any causality in them but preserving some statistical characteristics, can be used to reveal an underlying nonlinear process or, when combined with a global modelling technique, to detect a deterministic component.[39] But this is not enough to have a definite answer for identifying a chaotic behavior.[40] Chaos means "*fluctuations produced by deterministic rules that nevertheless lead to irregular, long-term unpredictable, dynamics.*"[41] Therefore, prior to asserting that a dynamics is chaotic, there should be clear evidence that deterministic equations govern the dynamics. Up-to-now, no fully deterministic model can reliably reproduce the dynamics underlying heart variability measured in patient.

Presented with the simple question "*Is the normal heart rate chaotic?*", a recent controversial topic proposed by Leon Glass[42] is thus the best illustration that this question — already addressed in 1989[43] — is still open today. Some contributions have concluded to the fact that physiological mechanisms that underlie cardiac dynamics variability result from cellular stochastic processes,[44] from ventilation influence,[45] and from the interaction of many feedback loops on the cardiovascular system.[46] From the clinical point of view, it is not necessarily relevant to ask such

---

[37] J. E. Skinner, C. Carpeggiani, C. E. Landisman & K. W. Fulton, Correlation dimension of heart beat intervals is reduced in conscious pigs by myocardial ischemia, *Circulation Research*, **68**, 966–976, 1991 — S. Guzzetti, M. G. Signorini, C. Cogliati, S. Mezzetti, A. Porta, S. Cerutti & A. Malliani, Non-linear dynamics and chaotic indices in heart rate variability of normal subjects and heart-transplanted patients, *Cardiovascular Research*, **31**, 441–446, 1996.

[38] J. Theiler, A. Logtin, S. Eubank, B. Galdrikian & J. D. Farmer, Testing for nonlinearity in time series: the method of surrogate data, *Physica D*, **58**, 77–94, 1992.

[39] M. E. D. Gomes, A. V. P. Souza, H. N. Guimarães & L. A. Aguirre, Investigation of determinism in heart rate variability, *Chaos*, **10** (2), 398–410, 2000.

[40] J. K. Kanters, N. H. Holstein-Rathlou & E. Agner, Lack of evidence for low-dimensional chaos in heart rate variability, *Journal of Cardiovascular Electrophysiology*, **5**, 591–601, 1994 — M. Costa, I. R. Pimentel, T. Santiago, P. Sarreira, J. Melo & E. Ducla-Soares, No evidence of chaos in the heart rate variability of normal and cardiac transplant human subjects, *Journal of Cardiovascular Electrophysiology*, **10**, 1305–1357, 1999.

[41] L. Glass, Chaos and heart rate variability, *Journal of Cardiovascular Electrophysiology*, **10**, 1358–1360, 1999.

[42] L. Glass, Introduction to controversial topics in nonlinear science: Is the normal heart rate chaotic?, *Chaos*, **19**, 028501, 2009.

[43] R. Pool, Is it healthy to be chaotic?, *Science*, **243**, 604–607, 1989.

[44] J. Q. Zhang, A. V. Holden, O. Monfredi, M. R. Boyett & H. Zhang, Stochastic vagal modulation of cardiac pacemaking may lead to an erroneous identification of cardiac chaos, *Chaos*, **19**, 028509, 2009.

[45] N. Wessel, M. Riedl & J. Kurths, Is the normal heart rate " chaotic" due to respiration, *Chaos*, **19**, 028508, 2009.

[46] J. Alvarez-Ramirez, E. Rodriguez & J.C. Echeverria, Delays in the human heartbeat dynamics,

a question. It is more important to focus on the medical issue and to answer to physicians' questions. For instance, the objective can be to use tools borrowed to the nonlinear dynamical system theory to discriminate control subjects from patients. For instance patient with congestive heart failure may present a first-return map computed from the RR-intervals (arrhythmia included) with a rich structure (Figure 8.21(a)) which is not observed in control subjects.

The first question to address is to choose the best variable to investigate the heart dynamics. Commonly, the dynamical analysis starts with a first-return map to RR-intervals as shown in Figure 8.21(a). The central ellipse along the first-bisecting line results from long term variability. Points distant from the bisecting line are associated with large beat-to-beat variability, that is, arrhythmias. Few main clouds of points may be identified but their boundaries are blurred by the long term variability. Premature ventricular complexes are in general eliminated from the data for only analyzing fluctuations in the normal sinus rhythm. But removing arrhythmia necessarily breaks the causality chain and the underlying determinism can no longer be seriously questioned. Moreover, keeping arrhythmia is particularly relevant for patients with congestive heart failure as we will show.

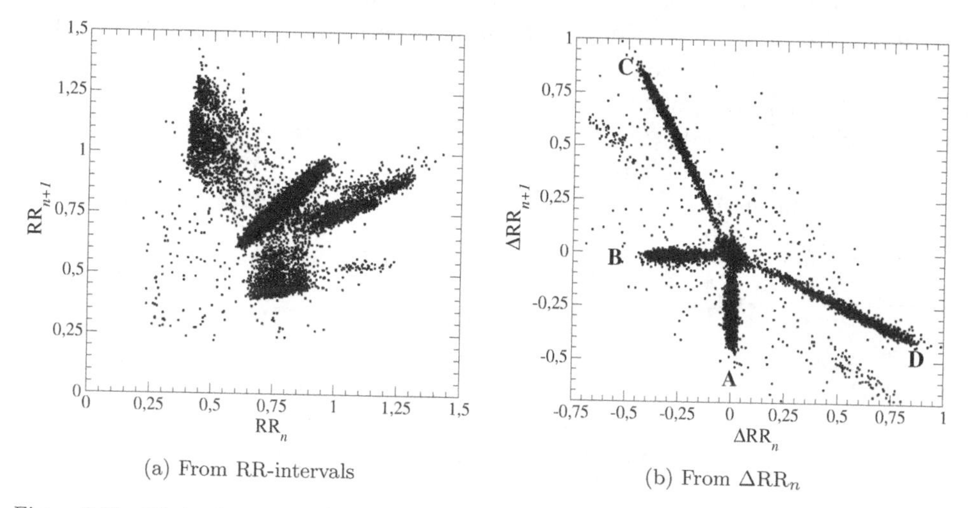

(a) From RR-intervals

(b) From ΔRR_n

Figure 8.21 First-return maps for a patient with congestive heart failure. Computing the first-return map from ΔRR_n removes any long term drift in the data due to the para-sympathetic activity.

In order to remove any long term drift, the dynamics is thus investigated using the variation between two successive RR-intervals, that is, $\Delta RR_n = RR_{n+1} - RR_n$.[47] A first-return map to ΔRR_n (Figure 8.21(b)) presents a cloud of points centered at

Chaos, **19**, 028502, 2009.

[47] E. Fresnel, E. Yacoub, U. Freitas, A. Kerfourn, V. Messager, E. Mallet, J.-F. Muir & C. Letellier, An easy-to-use technique to characterize cardiodynamics from first-return maps on ΔRR-intervals, *Chaos*, **25** (8), 083111, 2015.

the origin (associated with low variability) as well as four other clouds of points, all of them spread over segment with a well defined orientation. A symbolic dynamics is introduced by splitting the intervals visited by the ΔRR_n in three domains according to a threshold τ according to

$$\sigma_n = \begin{vmatrix} 0 & & \Delta\text{RR}_n \leq -\tau \\ 1 & \text{if} & -\tau < \Delta\text{RR}_n < +\tau \\ 2 & & \Delta\text{RR}_n \geq -\tau\,, \end{vmatrix} \tag{8.2}$$

where symbol 1 represents small variations due to the sinus rhythm ($|\Delta\text{RR}_n| < \tau$), symbol 0 the more than τ decreasing of RR intervals and symbol 2 the more than τ increasing of successive RR intervals. Symbols 0 and 2 are typically associated with arrhythmias. Since the heart variability is age-dependent,[48] the threshold τ is determined according to[49]

$$\tau(a) = 89 - 0.60a \tag{8.3}$$

where a is the patient age in years and τ is the threshold in milliseconds.

It is possible to quantify how these arrhythmias affect the cardiac dynamics by using an entropy. Entropies are often used to characterize the complexity underlying dynamical processes. Shannon entropy was introduced by Claude Shannon to characterize the information rate contained in a message.[50] A message containing a single word repeated many times does not carry too much information. Contrary to this, when new words are used, the information is enriched. This is similar for a certain number of successive symbols chosen among 0, 1 and 2 in our case.[51] To characterize the cardiodynamics complexity, we thus computed a Shannon entropy defined according to

$$\tilde{S}_h = \sum_{n=0}^{N_p^{N_q}-1} -P_n \log P_n\,, \tag{8.4}$$

where P_n is the realization probability of the nth possible symbolic sequence.[52] Typically, the entropy for a period-1 regime is equal to zero since there is no information produced from an event to the next one. Contrary to this, the entropy

---

[48] H. Tanaka, K. D. Monahan & D. R. Seals, Age-predicted maximal heart rate revisited, *Journal of the American College of Cardiology*, **37**, 153–156, 2001 — T. J. Ingall, J. G. McLeod & P. C. O'Brien, The effect of ageing on autonomic nervous system function, *Australian and New Zealand Journal of Medicine*, **20**, 570–577, 1990 — K. Umetani, D. H. Singer, R. McCraty & M. Atkinson, Twenty-four hour time domain heart rate variability and heart rate: Relations to age and gender over nine decades, *Journal of the American College of Cardiology*, **31**, 593–601, 1998.

[49] Fresnel *et al.*, 2015, *Ibid.*

[50] C. E. Shannon, A mathematical theory of communication, *Bell System Technical Journal*, **27**, 379–423 & 623–656, 1948.

[51] We retained the $N_q = 6$-symbol sequences, written with the $N_p = 3$ different symbols {0,1,2}. This leads to $N_p^{N_q} = 3^6 = 729$ possible sequences. Our statistics is correctly defined since we have about 100,000 RR intervals in a tachogram over 24 hours.

[52] The entropy is normalized by the largest entropy which can be obtained with equiprobable sequences, that is $S_{\max} == N_q \log N_p = 6 \log 3 = 6.59$.

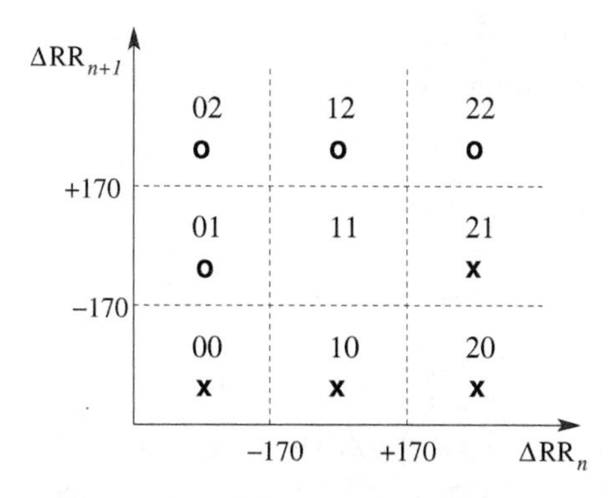

Figure 8.22 Split of the first-return map in 9 panels, according to the threshold τ. Decelerations $\circ$ and accelerations $\times$ of the heart rate are indicated.

of a system whose all possible sequences are equiprobable is maximum. A relative entropy close to 1 thus implies a cardiac dynamics with many arrhythmias. A sinus node ruled dynamics will be associated with a preponderance of small variations (symbols "1") and characterized by an entropy close to 0. The sole presence of symbols "1" would be associated with a poor variability and could be interpreted as a deterioration of the heart adaptation against effort and could be therefore pathological. A dynamics with only fast isolated variations in the cardiac rhythm should have a relative Shannon entropy between 0.2 and 0.3. Such entropy is known to be robust against artefacts.[53]

The threshold τ splits the first-return map in 9 panels (Figure 8.22), each of them being characterized by a probability of visits η_{ij}. The central domain, designated by "11", corresponds to the short term cardiac activity. Domains 00, 10, 20 and 21 correspond to acceleration in the heart rate, whereas domains 01, 02, 12 and 22 correspond to deceleration in the heart rate. The asymmetry coefficient

$$\alpha = \frac{1}{4}\left[\frac{\eta_{00}}{\eta_{22}} + \frac{\eta_{01}}{\eta_{21}} + \frac{\eta_{02}}{\eta_{20}} + \frac{\eta_{10}}{\eta_{12}}\right]$$

allows us to characterize the (un)balance between acceleration and deceleration in the heart rate.[54] A coefficient α about 1 represents a well-balanced cardiac dynamics, $\alpha < 1$ represents a tendency to fast decelerations and $\alpha > 1$ represents a tendency to fast accelerations in the heart rate.

One of the arrhythmias associated with a significant acceleration of the heart rate is extrasystole. It is associated with a premature contraction (inducing the acceleration) which is not triggered by the sinus node but by another cardiac tissue area. They thus occur randomly. This beat prematured by a delay δt is followed by a prolonged beat that offsets the anticipation in order to re-synchronize the heart

[53] D. E. Lake, J. S. Richman, M. P. Griffin & J. R. Moorman, Sample entropy analysis of neonatal heart rate variability, *American Journal of Physiology*, **283**, R789–R797, 2002.
[54] Fresnel *et al.*, 2015, *Ibid.*

activity with the sinus clock.[55] The second beat lasts $T + \delta t$ where T is the average length of a beat. The RR intervals take the following successive values

"...T T T T-δt T+δt T T T...",

and the ΔRR are worth

"...0 0 -δt +2δt -δt 0 0...".

An extrasystole is therefore encoded "...1 1 0 2 0 1 1...".

The presence of arrhythmias changes the first-return map structure, by introducing specific segments in the ΔRR_{n+1}-ΔRR_n plane, each of them forming a specific angle θ with the horizontal segment.[56] These four segments are associated with isolated extrasystoles. When successive extrasystoles are observed, two additional segments can be distinguished in first-return map (Figure 8.23(b)).[57] The corresponding symbolic sequence is "...1 1 0 $(20)^p$ 1 1...", where p is the number of successive extrasystoles: sequence " 20" is thus repeated p times.

When an isolated deceleration of the heart rate occurs as a long RR interval, the heart may return to the sinus activity during the next beat. In that case, the successive RR intervals take the value

"...T T T T+δt T T T..." ,

and the corresponding ΔRR are

"...0 0 +δt -δt 0 0..." .

The associated symbolic sequence is thus "...1 1 2 0 1 1...". In that case, the first-return map is structured by three segments.[58] (Figure 8.24) There is no particular constraint on the value of the delay δt which is thus distributed on a quite large range. The application thus presents an obvious triangular shape (Figure 8.24).

We used the normalized Shannon entropy S_h and the asymmetry coefficient α, to discriminate different types of patients. The Shannon entropy allows to distinguish wide variabilities ($S_h > 0.30$) from reduced variabilities ($S_h < 0.10$), whereas extreme values of the asymmetry coefficient α indicate an unbalance between accelerations and decelerations of the heart rate. Disparities between the control subjects, patients with atrial fibrillations and patients with congestive heart failures are clearly enlightened in such a map. The relative Shannon entropy is low ($\overline{S_h} = 0.03$) for normal subjects, greater ($\overline{S_h} = 0.08$) for patients affected by congestive heart failure, and significantly greater ($\overline{S_h} = 0.74$) for patients affected by atrial fibrillation and whose first-return maps are widely developed.

[55] R. Langendorf, Ventricular premature systoles with postponed compensatory pause, *American Heart Journal*, **46** (3), 401–404, 1953.

[56] Points in the first-return map corresponding to isolated extrasystole are located along four distinctly oriented segments (Figure 8.23): segment A ($\theta = \frac{3\pi}{2}$), segment B ($\theta = \pi$), segment C ($\theta \approx \frac{2\pi}{3}$), and segment D ($\theta \approx \frac{11\pi}{6}$).

[57] They are segment E ($\theta = \frac{3\pi}{4}$) and segment F ($\theta = \frac{7\pi}{4}$).

[58] The three segments are H ($\theta = \frac{\pi}{2}$), segment I ($\theta = \frac{5\pi}{6}$) and segment J ($\theta = \pi$).

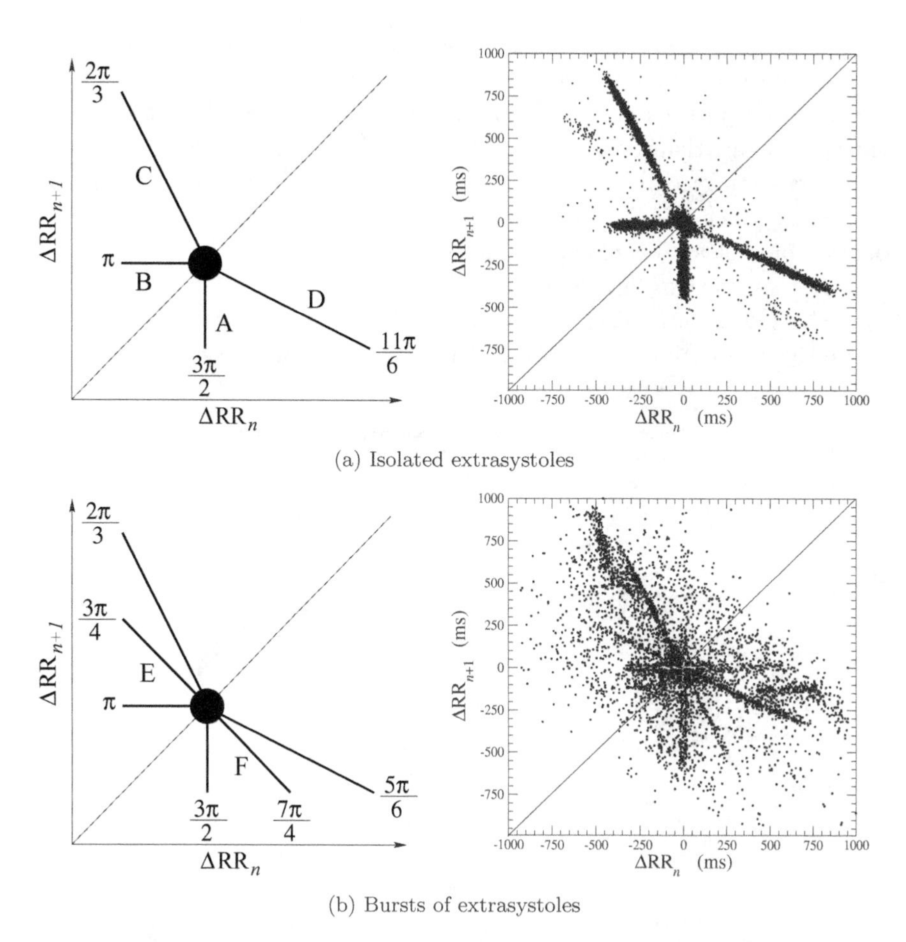

Figure 8.23 Typical structures of first-return maps when isolated (a) and successive (b) extrasystoles are observed in patient with congestive heart failure.

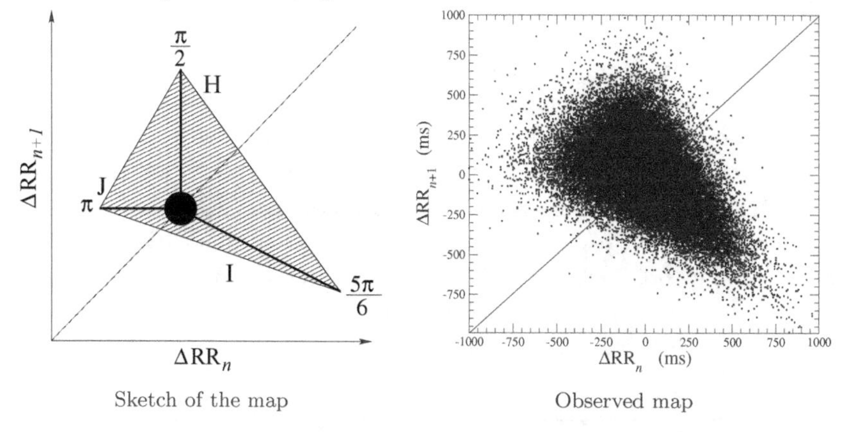

Figure 8.24 First-return map with a triangular shape when isolated decelerations are observed in a patient with atrial fibrillation.

The asymmetry coefficient α is less than 1 ($\overline{\alpha} = 0.37$) for healthy subjects, that is, a reversion to a standard variability (resting state like) which is slower than the answer to a physical effort. The averaged asymmetry coefficient ($\overline{\alpha} = 1.92$) is significantly higher than 1 for patients affected by congestive heart failure. For these patients first-return maps present specific segments characterizing the presence of extrasystoles which accelerate the heart rate. Finally, patients affected by atrial fibrillation present an α coefficient close to 1 ($\overline{\alpha} = 0.98$) meaning that arrhythmias are frequent and various (accelerating as well as decelerating the heart rate) (Figure 8.24(c)). The asymmetry coefficient can therefore help to identify patients affected by congestive heart failure from healthy subjects. An asymmetry was also evidenced in the sole sinus heart rate.[59]

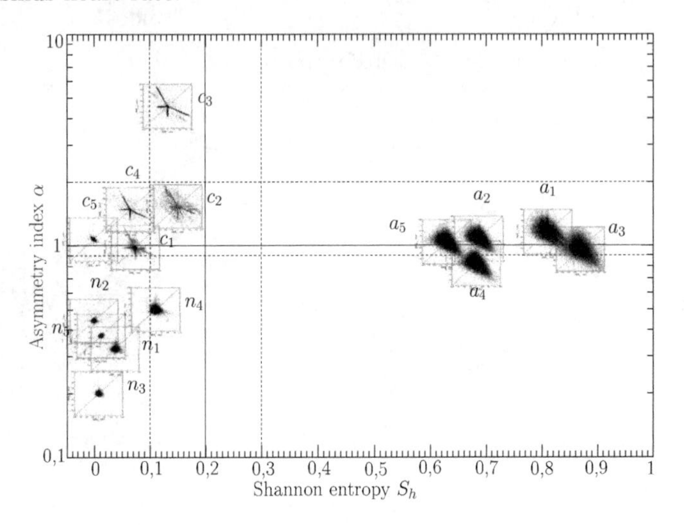

Figure 8.25 Discriminating map based on relative Shannon entropy S_h and asymmetry coefficient α, with the 15 patients. A semi-logarithmic scale is used. $n_i \equiv$ normal subject. $a_i \equiv$ patient with atrial fibrillation and $c_i \equiv$ patients with congestive heart failure.

We can also draw a map by plotting S_h versus α (Figure 8.25) and, where the first-return maps are grouped according to their structures. Structures at the upper left corner correspond to a large asymmetry coefficient. The corresponding first-return maps present points which are organized along specific oriented segments which are characteristic of the presence of extrasystoles and heart rate accelerations. These patients present a small Shannon entropy indicating a weak sinus variability. The five patients matching to these criteria have congestive heart failure. Otherwise, first-return maps with a triangular shape are at the right area of the graph where the Shannon entropy has large values revealing a complex dynamics.

[59] U. Lee & S. Kim, Event and time-scale characteristics of heart-rate dynamics, *Physical Review E*, **71**, 061917, 2005 — P. Guzik, J. Piskorski, T. Krauze, A. Wykretowicz & H. Wysocki, Heart rate asymmetry by Poincaré plots of RR intervals, *Biomedizinische Technik*, **51** (4), 272–275, 2006 — J. Piskorskil & P. Guzik, Geometry of the Poincaré plot of RR intervals and its asymmetry in healthy adults, *Physiological Measurements*, **28**, 287–300, 2007.

The asymmetry coefficient is close to 1: it indicates a balance between accelerations and decelerations in the heart rate, due to a wide variety of arrhythmias. This area of the map gathers the patients suffering from atrial fibrillation. Finally, control subjects are aggregated at the lower left corner of the map. They present a small Shannon entropy due to the small rate of arrhythmias and, a small asymmetry coefficient indicating a preponderance of symbols 2. The main dynamical properties of the cardiodynamics in different classes of subjects are summarized in Table 8.1.

Table 8.1 Indicative dynamical properties of the cardiodynamics in different classes of subjects.

	Normal	Congestive heart failure	Atrial fibrillation
Shape of the map	Centered rounded cloud	With well-defined segments	Triangular
Entropy	$S_{\rm h} < 0.10$	$0.05 < S_{\rm h} < 0.30$	$S_{\rm h} > 0.80$
Asymmetry	$0.7 < \alpha < 1.25$	$\alpha > 1.25$	$0.95 < \alpha < 1.20$

These different structures of first-return maps can be also observed in newborns hospitalized for cardio-respiratory alerts. Heart rate variability among the newborns is quite important as indicated by the average relative Shannon entropy ($\overline{S_h} = 0.28$), close to the limit value ($S_h = 0.30$) beyond which variability is considered to be substantial. The average asymmetry coefficient is greater than 1 ($\overline{\alpha} = 1.18$). The "recovery" mechanism of the cardiac activity does not seem to be as effective in these newborns as compared to the adults previously studied, since the asymmetry coefficient is slightly greater. In fact the cardiovascular system of the newborns is different from that of the adults: similar stimuli may not affect the adult or produce less abrupt changes. The servomechanism in adult could be more damped than in newborn, thus explaining that adults tend to respond with overshoot and reverberations, a feature clearly observed in newborns.[60]

As an example, newborn 3 is a two month old boy, born by caesarean section due to a placenta previa bleeding.[61] He was hospitalized with a bronchiolitis. The electrocardiogram revealed cardiac arrhythmias. His cardiac frequency ($\overline{f_3} = 171$) is close to a sustained tachycardia and his relative Shannon entropy ($S_h = 0.37$) is larger than the normal value. The first-return map from ΔRR reveals four oriented segments that are characteristic of isolated extrasystoles (Figure 8.26(a)). The large asymmetry coefficient ($\alpha = 3.55$) indicates predominant accelerations in the heart rate. This newborn was treated with corticoids and Ventolin, whose adverse effects frequently include tachycardia and, rarely the apparition of cardiac arrhythmias

[60] C. Vallbona, M. M. Desmond, A. J. Rudolph, L. F. Pap, R. M. Hill, R. R. Franklin & J. Rush, Cardiodynamic studies in the newborn. II Regulation of the heart rate, *Biology of the Neonates*, **5**, 159–199, 1963.
[61] Fresnel *et al.*, 2015, *Ibid.*

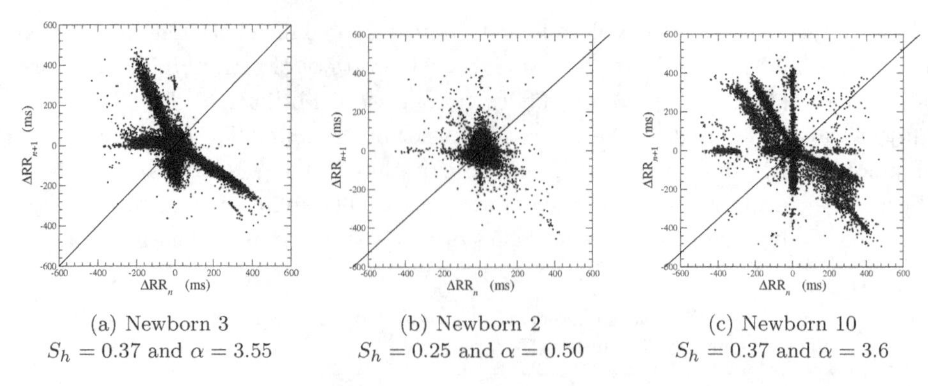

(a) Newborn 3
$S_h = 0.37$ and $\alpha = 3.55$

(b) Newborn 2
$S_h = 0.25$ and $\alpha = 0.50$

(c) Newborn 10
$S_h = 0.37$ and $\alpha = 3.6$

Figure 8.26 First-return maps computed from ΔRR recorded in newborns hospitalized for cardio-respiratory alerts. Newborn 3 present isolated extrasystoles and newborn 10 present bursts of extrasystoles.

such as supraventricular tachycardia or extrasystoles. Drugs could have induced the arrhythmias observed in this newborn.

Newborn 2 is a five month old girl, hospitalized with a H_1N_1 flu and a bronchiolitis with respiratory syncytial virus. Her pulmonary affections were also treated with corticoids and Ventolin. Contrary to what was observed in newborn 3, this newborn does not present any sign of cardiac arrhythmias: both cardiac frequency and Shannon entropy ($\overline{f_3} = 138$ bpm, $S_{\rm h} = 0.25$) are common and, points in the first-return map (Figure 8.26(b)) are aggregated in the central area. The asymmetry coefficient ($\alpha = 0.50$) is less than 1, in line with the "recovery" mechanism of the cardiac activity. This newborn is thus an example for which drugs did not induce cardiac arrhythmias. It is thus impossible to know whether and to what extent drugs are involved in the apparition of cardiac arrhythmias.

Newborn 10 is a one month old girl, hospitalized for an apparent life threatening event with hypotonia. The electrocardiogram showed a QT interval prolongation. Her cardiac frequency ($\overline{f_{10}} = 150$ bpm) is normal and her Shannon entropy ($S_{\rm h} = 0.33$) is quite large. Bursts of extrasystoles are observed in this newborn as revealed by the characteristic oriented segments (Figure 8.26(c)). The asymmetry coefficient for this newborn ($\alpha = 2.34$) is very large and reinforces the diagnostic of dominant accelerations in the heart rate. This newborn has smoking parents and tobacco is known for promoting the development of cardiac arrhythmias;[62] so it may have induced the apparition of extrasystoles in that case.

Using nonlinear dynamics to investigate the cardiac variability may lead to a better characterization of the complex phenomena involved. Our nonlinear analysis is based on noninvasive measurements, and allows to obtain information on the global heart status of patients. The assignment of a symbolic dynamics to the ΔRR allows to discriminate various grades of cardiac variability. The most

[62] A. D'Alessandro, I. Boeckelmann, M. Hammwhöner & A. Goette, Nicotine, cigarette smoking and cardiac arrhythmia: an overview, *European Journal of Preventive Cardiology*, **19** (3), 297–305, 2012.

discriminating analysis consists in combining the Shannon entropy S_h, and the asymmetry coefficient α. Thus, the statistical quantities we developed for the global cardiac dynamics showed to provide a strong discrimination power allowing us to distinguish control from pathological infants and adults.

8.4 Patient Breathing with a Noninvasive Mechanical Ventilation

8.4.1 *Early Techniques for Mechanical Ventilation*

Noninvasive mechanical ventilation is now the standard of care in acute respiratory failure due to chronic obstructive pulmonary disease.[63] In fact, mechanical ventilation was originally developed for acute respiratory failure. The idea to assist mechanically the ventilation is quite old since John Dalziel, a Scottish physician, already proposed an apparatus he described as follows[64]

> an air-tight box, large enough to contain the person to be experimented on (the head and the neck expected), in a sitting posture, and a pair of circular bellows inside, which were used as a forcing air-pump. The bellows were worked from without by a piston a rod, and the air which at every stroke they discharged was prevented by a valve from returning. In the side of the box were too small windows; one for the admission of light, the other for allowing an attendant to inspect the surface of the body during the experiment.

The early "massive" development of mechanical ventilation were due to poliomyelitis epidemic in the first half of the 20th century. The most feared outcome of this disease was paralysis of respiratory muscles that rapidly led to death from anoxia.[65] While his brother Cecil and a young physiologist, Louis Shaw were studying various aspects of respiratory physiology in cats with the help of a body plethysmograph, Philip Drinker (1894–1972) placed a curarized cat in the plethysmograph and succeeded in ventilating it with a hand-held syringe connected to the interior of the box. Once they had demonstrated that they could support a paralyzed animal for hours, Drinker and Shaw proceeded to construct an adult-sized respirator. The tank was built by a local tinsmith, and a pair of vacuum cleaner blowers and the necessary valving were salvaged from the laboratory's shop. The first successful mechanical ventilation was performed in 1928. In 1931, a severe poliomyelitis epidemic killed 4,138 people (12.2 percent of the reported cases).[66] The demand for Drinkler ventilators (Figure 8.27) thus increased a lot. This technique helped to save many patients. Drinker's ventilators were intensively used up to the end of 1950s.

[63] Q. S. Quon, W. Q. Gan & D. D. Sin, Contemporary management of acute exacerbations of COPD: a systematic review and meta analysis, *Chest*, **133** (3), 756–766, 2008.
[64] J. Dalziel, On sleep, and an apparatus for promoting artificial respiration, *Report of the 8th Meeting of the British Association for the Advancement of Science*, **7**, J. Murray (Ed.), London, 1839.
[65] P. A. Drinker & C. F. McKhann, The iron lung: First practical means of respiratory support, *Journal of the American Medical Association*, **255** (11), 1476–1480, 1986.
[66] Encyclopedia of Plague and Pestilence: From ancient times to the present, George Kohn (ed.), 3rd Edition, Facts on File, 2008.

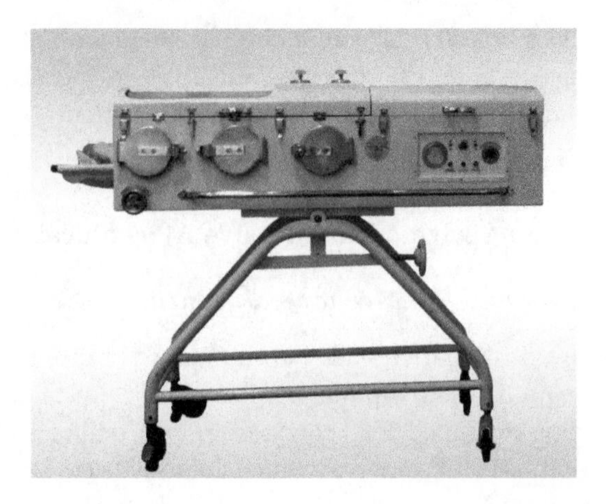

Figure 8.27 A Drinkler ventilator for babies. Collection of the Musée Flaubert et d'histoire de la médecine, Rouen.

In fact, one of the very first machines used to mechanically ventilate patients was certainly the "Pulmotor" (Figure 8.28) manufactured by the Dräger Company (Lubeck, Germany) since 1907. It was the first device for mechanical ventilation that could deliver gas and/or air at specific volumes. It was designated to resuscitate the victims of mine disasters, and then became used for victims of smoke inhalation by firemen. In the pulmotor oxygen from a cylinder flowed through a reducing valve and then through an injector to a face mask under a sufficient pressure to inflate the lungs. As soon as the lungs were filled sufficiently to resist further distension, the pressure tripped a valve, reversed the direction of flow and sucked out a part of the contents of the lungs, after which the direction of flow was again automatically reversed. In spite of this, not only the pulmotor but also the principle of suck and blow artificial respiration were condemned,[67] mainly because "*the expiration forced by negative pressure is unnatural and injurious.*"[68] In particular, large negative pressures tend to produce emphysema.[69] The second reason for this reject was that, "*instead of operating at a rate approximating that of normal breathing, such apparatus was responding to any obstructions in the throat, or to relapse of the tongue when the patient was on the back, and thus sucking and blowing phases so rapidly that no appreciable movement of the lung was induced.*" All these devices, among many others, were used for noninvasive mechanical ventilation. The Pulmotor and the E&J Resuscitator were working with positive inspiratory pressure

[67]Third Resuscitation Commission, *Science*, **48**, 563, 1918.

[68]Y. Henderson & J. McCullough Turner, Artificial respiration and inhalation: the principle determining the efficiency of various methods, *Journal of the American Medical Association*, **116** (14), 1508–1515, 1941.

[69]Breathing machines and their use in treatment, report of the Respirators (poliomyelitis) committee Medical Research Council (Great Britain), *Special report series*, **237**, London, H. M. Stationery Office, 1940.

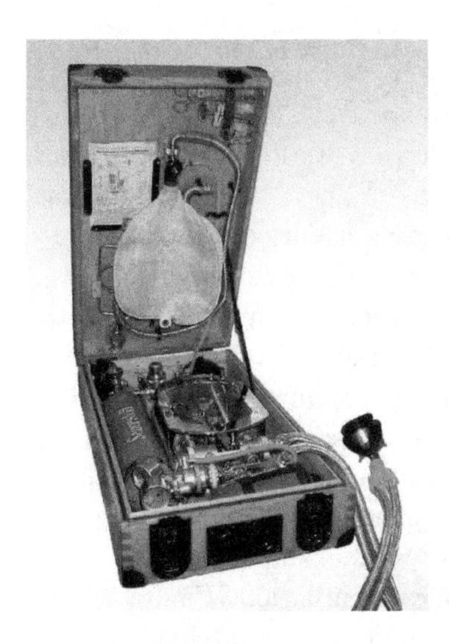

Figure 8.28 A pulmotor "resuscitator" manufactured by the Dräger Company. Adapted from the website *Histoire de l'Anesthésie et de la Respiration.*

but they were criticized, mostly due to the negative expiratory pressure they used. Drinker's mechanical ventilator, with a principle quite similar to the principle of Dalziel's apparatus, were working with a negative inspiratory pressure and a positive expiratory pressure applied to the thorax. They were much appreciated by clinicians because the expiration was more physiological than the expiration driven by Pulmotor-like machines. Drinker's mechanical ventilator was far more physiological, particularly when improvements of this device lead to discard the forced expiration.[70]

During the poliomyelitis epidemic in Copenhaguen (1952), some patients with severe respiratory complications were not successfully treated with mechanical ventilator and subsequently died. An anaesthesist, Bjørn Ibsen (1915–2007) demonstrated in a patient how sufficient ventilation could be administered through a tracheotomy, once secretions were sucked.[71] The ventilation was performed manually by squeezing a rubber bag attached to a tracheotomy tube. They solved the logistical problem with a roster of 200 medical students who operated in relays. This was the beginning of invasive mechanical ventilation with positive inspiratory pressure through tracheotomy. Today, due to the relevant development of noninvasive mechanical ventilation, invasive ventilation tends now to be reserved to extremely acute cases.

[70]Ibid. Henderson, 1941.

[71]B. Ibsen, The anæsthetist's viewpoint on the treatment of respiratory complications in poliomyelitis during the epidemic in Copenhagen, 1952, *Proceedings of the Royal Society of Medicine*, **47** (1), 72–74, 1954.

8.4.2 *Lack of Synchronization between the Patient and His Device*

In 1941, Yandell Henderson and J. McCullough Turner reported some asynchrony events they observed while they were tracing to resuscitate dogs from coma after breathing carbon monoxyde.[72] They showed that it was not possible to resuscitate these dogs with the E&J resuscitator (working more or less according to the principle of the pulmotor), while the attempts were successful when dogs were treated with manual artificial respiration and inhalation of carbon dioxyde and oxygen. As soon as the risk of immediate death was past and the animal was feebly breathing, mechanical artificial ventilation was started. But in large majority of case, Henderson and Turner observed conflict instead of cooperation (Figure 8.29), and the rate of natural breathing and the rate at which the apparatus operated were entirely different. The frequency of the apparatus was thus three times larger than the normal breathing rate. Such example of discordance between natural breathing and the artificial mechanical ventilation (Figure 8.29) is perhaps one of the very first recordings of asynchrony events in mechanical ventilation.

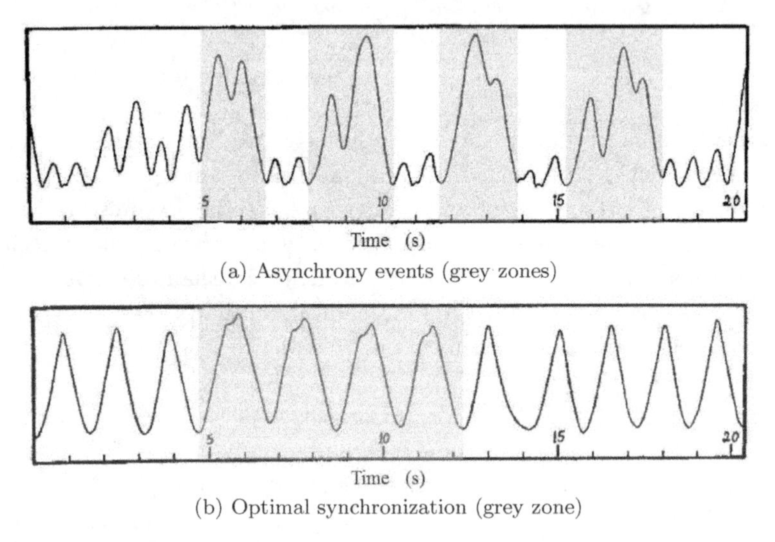

(a) Asynchrony events (grey zones)

(b) Optimal synchronization (grey zone)

Figure 8.29 Time series of the ventilation of two dogs by means of a body plethysmograph during treatment with the E&J resuscitator administering carbon dioxyde and oxygen. The grey zones in case of asynchrony events (a) indicate the natural breathings while the small oscillations result from the conflicting action of the apparatus. In case of optimal synchronization (b) indicate cooperation between natural breathings and the E&J resuscitators that Henderson and Turner were able to obtained. Adapted from Henderson and Turner, 1941.

In fact, in noninvasive mechanical ventilation, the dynamical system under study is made of the patient and his ventilator. Patient's breathing rhythm leads to consider patient as an oscillator. The device delivers pressure cycles (when the

[72] Yandell & McCullough Turner, 1941, *Ibid.*

pressure is the controlled variable) made of high pressure phases that are supposed to occur during patient's inspirations and low pressure phase during expirations. The device is therefore an oscillator too. When the patient has still some abilities to breath by himself and has sufficient strength to trigger the pressure rise to the high pressure $P_{\rm h}$, the patient drives the ventilator from the phase point of view. In turns, the ventilator provides support to increase the inspired volume. These two oscillators are therefore bidirectionally coupled, but in an asymmetric way. We have thus to distinguish patient's breathing cycle from the pressure cycles delivered by the ventilator. As we saw, these two oscillators are not always phase synchronized. Many reasons can lead to such asynchrony events: bad ventilator settings, poor inspiring power, patient fighting against his ventilator, etc.[73]

The difficulty in assessing the quality of synchronization is that, in common ventilatory circuit, only the pressure and the airflow in the circuit are measured; if the pressure directly offers an observability of the pressure cycle, this is not so simple for patient's breathing cycles. The airflow is the result of the combination between patient's breathing cycles with the pressure cycles: this leads to a third cycle that we will designate as the ventilatory cycle. From the variables measured in the ventilation circuit, there is no direct access to the sole breathing cycle. In clinical studies, the breathing cycles can be assessed by measured the esophageal pressure, the movement of the thoracic cage and of the abdomen (using belts) or a susternal electromyogram (see an example in Figure 8.30).

When the two oscillators are phase synchronized, the ventilator triggers a pressure rise when the patient produces his inspiratory effort; then, when the patient starts to expire, the pressure release is triggered. Within a pressure cycle, there are two switches, the pressure rise and the pressure release, as during breathing cycle there are two phases, inspiration and expiration. The lack of synchronization can be mainly quantified with the delay $\delta_{\rm h}$ between the beginning of the inspiratory effort and the initiation of the pressure rise, and the delay $\delta_{\rm l}$ between the end of inspiration and the triggering of the pressure release (Figure 8.31).[74]

Clinically speaking, there are three main asynchrony events: nontriggered, self-triggered, and double-triggered cycles.[75] The first one is very uncomfortable for the patient since it corresponds to an inspiratory effort that does not trigger the pressure rise (Figure 8.32(a)): the patient thus breathes only with the low pressure, that is, more or less as it would breathe without any assistance. The problem is in fact that the patient does not breathe as he expected, thus creating a frustration. The second asynchrony event occurs when a pressure cycle is triggered when when there is no inspiratory effort, that is, during patient's expiration (Figure 8.32(b)). Commonly,

[73]S. Nava, A. Carlucci & P. Ceriana, Patient-ventilator interaction during noninvasive ventilation: practical assessment and theoretical basis, *Breathe*, **5** (4) 323–333, 2009.
[74]E. Fresnel, J.-F. Muir & C. Letellier, Performances of domiciliary ventilators compared by using a parametric procedure, *EPJ Nonlinear Biomedical Physics*, **4**, 6, 2016.
[75]A. Carlucci, L. Pisani, P. Ceriana, A. Malovini & S. Nava, Patient-ventilator asynchronies: may the respiratory mechanics play a role?, *Critical Care*, **17**, R54, 2013.

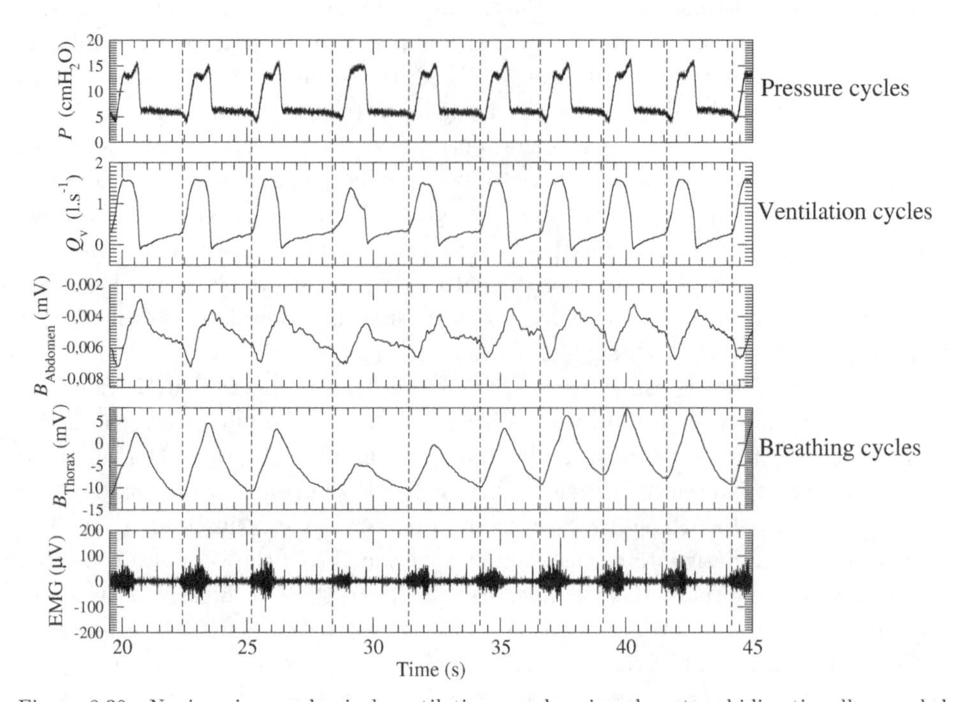

Figure 8.30 Noninvasive mechanical ventilation can be viewed as two bidirectionally coupled oscillators. The patient produces the breathing cycle (well observed with belt signals or an EMG) and the ventilator delivers pressure cycles (monitored with the pressure). The combination of these two types of cycles is investigated using the airflow. Data provided by Manel Luján Torne, Universitat Autònoma de Barcelona.

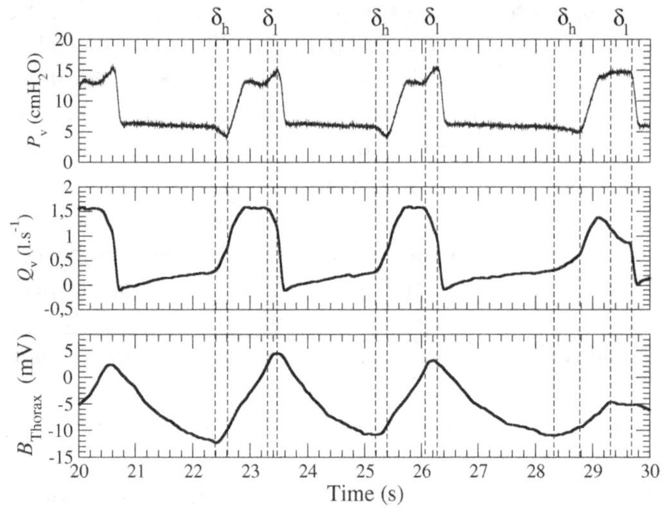

Figure 8.31 Lack of phase synchronization between patient's breathing cycles and the pressure cycles delivered by the ventilator. Two delays, δ_{h} and δ_{l}, are used to assess the quality of synchronization. From data provided by Manel Luján Torne, Universitat Autònoma de Barcelona.

such a cycle is shorter than the "normal" ones since the condition for a pressure release is quickly observed. This is a source of discomfort because the patient receives air when he wants to expire. The third asynchrony event corresponds to a double-triggered cycle: the ventilator triggers two pressure cycles during a single inspiration (Figure 8.32(c)). In each of these cases, there is a strong lack of synchronization since the number of cycles is not the same for the two oscillators (the ventilator and the patient).

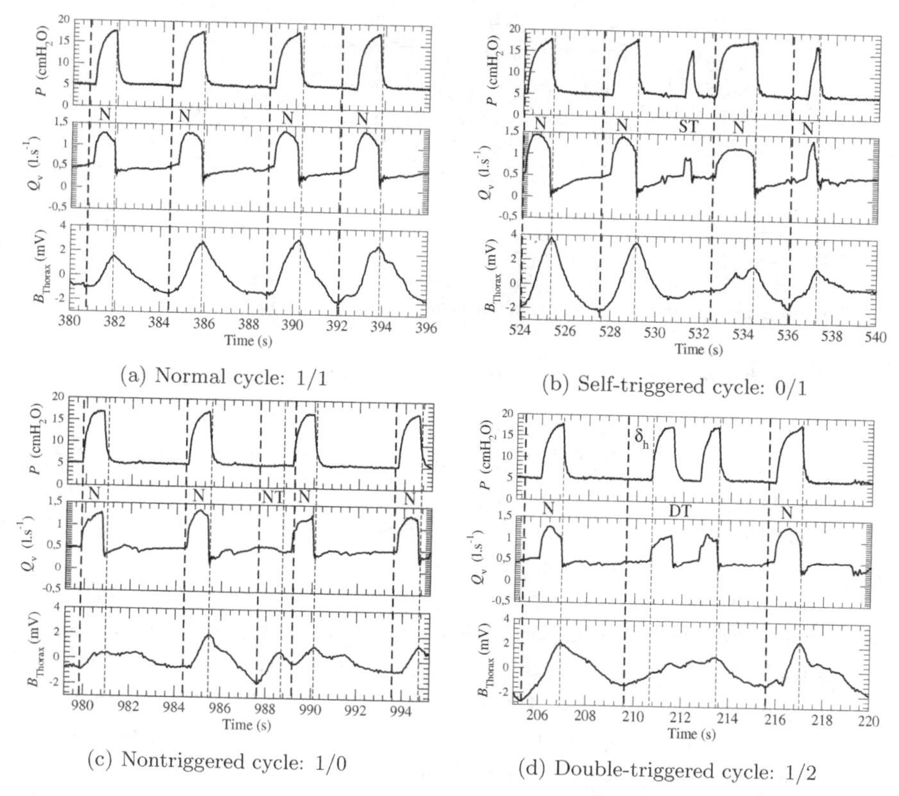

(a) Normal cycle: 1/1

(b) Self-triggered cycle: 0/1

(c) Nontriggered cycle: 1/0

(d) Double-triggered cycle: 1/2

Figure 8.32 Different types of ventilatory cycles in noninvasive mechanical ventilation. The thoracic belt is here used to detect the muscular contraction of the thorax during patient's inspiratory effort. The pressure cycle is associated with the ventilator. The airflow corresponds to a combination of the two preceding cycles. Case of a woman with an obstructive lung disease — typically she has difficulty to exhale all the air from her lungs — who is ventilated with a high pressure $P_\text{h} = 18$ cmH_2O and a low pressure $P_\text{l} = 5$ cmH_2O. During the asynchrony event, the ratio between the number of breathing cycles and the number of pressure cycles is reported. From data provided by Manel Luján Torne, Universitat Autònoma de Barcelona, Spain.

A less important asynchrony event is related to the delay δ_l with which the pressure release is triggered: when it is positive, this release is delayed and, contrary to this, it is advanced when it is negative. An example of advanced pressure release (Apr) is shown in Figure 8.33.

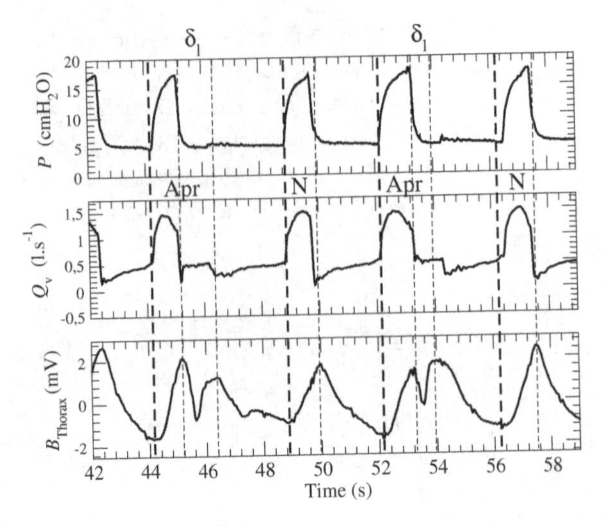

Figure 8.33 Lack of phase synchronization between patient's breathing cycles and the pressure cycles delivered by the ventilator: case of an advanced pressure release. The pressure is release to the low value before the end of patient's inspiration. Same patient as in Figure 8.32.

8.4.3 *Breathing Variability under Mechanical Ventilation*

Thus, in spite of significant improvements, physicians still have to solve some problems with noninvasive mechanical ventilation due to a lack of synchronization between patient's breathing cycles and machine cycles. It is shown that the asynchrony events have an impact on patient's discomfort and may lead to a lack of compliance,[76] longer treatment,[77] and to weaning failure.[78] It is thus of great practical importance to better understand the interactions of a conscious patient under noninvasive mechanical ventilation. Most often the "pressure support" mode of ventilation is used:[79] the patient drives the ventilator in triggering the switch from the lower (during expiration) to the higher (during inspiration) level of pressure; in turn, the ventilator supplies an airflow which helps the patient to increase his tidal volume. The dynamical features of this coupled system reveal aspects of the patient breathing effort and are influenced by the ventilator settings. One of the

[76] A. Carlucci, L. Pisani, P. Ceriana, A. Malovini & S. Nava, Patient-ventilator asynchronies: may the respiratory mechanics play a role?, *Critical Care*, **17** (2), R54, 2013.

[77] L. Blanch, A. Villagra, B. Sales, J. Montanya, U. Lucangelo, M. Luján, O. GarcÃa-Esquirol, E. Chacón, A. Estruga, J. C. Oliva, A. Hernández-Abadia, G. M. Albaiceta, E. Fernández-Mondejar, R. Fernández, J. Lopez-Aguilar, J. Villar, G. Murias & R. M. Kacmarek, Asynchronies during mechanical ventilation are associated with mortality, *Intensive Care Medecine*, **41** (4), 633–641, 2015.

[78] D. C. Chao, D. J. Scheinhorn & M. Stearn-Hassenpflug, Patient-ventilator trigger asynchrony in prolonged mechanical ventilation, *Chest*, **112** (6), 1592–1599, 1997.

[79] A. Jubran, W. B. Van de Graaff & M. J. Tobin, Variability of patient-ventilator interaction with pressure support ventilation in patients with chronic obstructive pulmonary disease, *American Journal of Respiratory and Critical Care Medicine*, **152**, 129–136, 1995 — B. Fauroux, C. Boffa, I. Desguerre, B. Estournet & H. Trang, Long term noninvasive mechanical ventilation for children at home: a national survey, *Pediatric Pulmonology*, **35**, 119–125, 2003.

goals in this field is to learn how to interpret the time series of the airflow and the pressure measured by the ventilator to detect asynchrony events in order to assess the quality of ventilation.[80] As pointed out by Mangin and colleagues "*characterizations of ventilatory chaos could also provide a respiratory drive monitoring tool, to detect drive changes indicative of loading variations and therefore to identify and monitor patient ventilator asynchrony.*"[81] They found from estimates of correlation dimension, Lyapunov exponents and by noise titration[82] that the data measured from patients under mechanical ventilation were chaotic. But these findings cannot be conclusive without discussing the presence of an underlying determinism as we saw in the previous section (p. 354).

Noninvasive mechanical ventilation is commonly applied to patients with chronic respiratory failures. In such a case, this assistance is applied at home during night using the pressure support mode with its two levels of pressure. The pressure level in the ventilatory circuit is controlled by the ventilator. Patient's inspiratory effort triggers the pressure rise from the low pressure P_l with which the patient expires to the high pressure P_h with which the patients inspires. Commonly, $P_l < P_h$ at least by around 5 cmH_2O. Unfortunately, the synchrony between patient's breathing cycle and the pressure cycle is not always optimal. As we saw in Figure 8.32 the most painful asynchrony event is when patient's inspiratory effort does not trigger the pressure rise.[83] Since it has been recognized for a long time that diseased patients present a smaller inspiratory power than healthy subjects[84] (Figure 8.34), when his inspiratory power becomes too weak, the patient can no longer trigger his ventilator. This failure may be greatly amplified when there are nonintentional

[80] K. Pehrsson, J. Olofson, S. Larsson & M. Sullivan, Quality of life of patients treated by home mechanical ventilation due to restrictive ventilatory disorders, *Respiratory Medicine*, **88** (1), 21–26, 1994 — P. Navalesi, F. Fanfulla, P. Frigerio, C. Gregoretti & S. Nava, Physiologic evaluation of noninvasive mechanical ventilation delivered with three types of masks in patients with chronic hypercapnic respiratory failure, *Critical Care Medicine*, **28** (6), 1785–1790, 2000 — B. Fauroux, N. Hart & F. Lofaso, Non invasive mechanical ventilation in cystic fibrosis: physiological effects and monitoring, *Monaldi Archives in Chest Disease*, **57** (5–6), 268–272, 2002 — H. Rabarimanantsoa, L. Achour, C. Letellier, A. Cuvelier & J.-F. Muir, Recurrence plots and Shannon entropy for a dynamical analysis of asynchronisms in noninvasive mechanical ventilation, *Chaos*, **17**, 013115, 2007.

[81] L. Mangin, M.-N. Fiamma, C. Straus, J.-P. Derenne, M. Zelter, C. Clerici & T. Similowski, Source of human ventilatory chaos: Lessons from switching controlled mechanical ventilation to inspiratory pressure support in critically ill patients, *Respiratory Physiology & Neurobiology*, **161**, 189–196, 2008.

[82] M. Barahona & C.-S. Poon, Detection of nonlinear dynamics in short, noisy time series, *Nature*, **381**, 215–217, 1996 — U. S. Freitas, C. Letellier & L. A. Aguirre, Failure for distinguishing colored noise from chaos by the "Noise titration" technique, *Physical Review E*, **79**, 035201R, 2009.

[83] A.-W. Thille & L. Brochard, Interactions patient-ventilateur, *Reanimation*, **16** (1), 13–19, 2007.

[84] J. Hutchinson, Contributions to vital statistics, obtained by means of a pneumatic apparatus for valuing the respiratory powers with relation to health, *Journal of the Statistical Society of London*, **7** (3), 193–212, 1844.

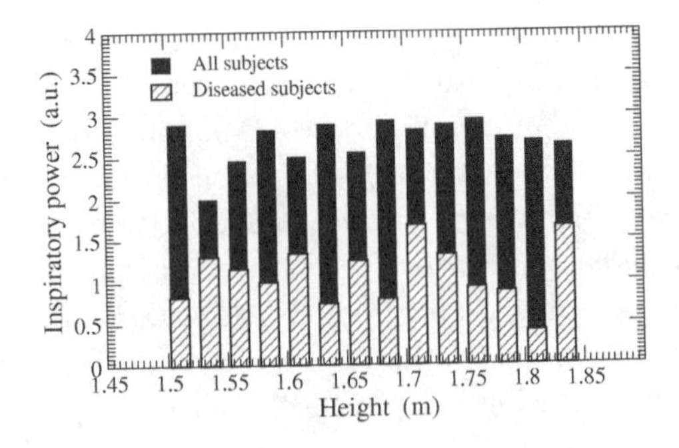

Figure 8.34 Inspiratory power by height in healthy and diseased male subjects (drawn from the data collected by Hutchinson, 1844).

leaks[85] but this is not necessarily the case.[86]

Even when inspiratory efforts correctly trigger pressure cycles, ventilation cycles are similar but not identical. Known for healthy subjects since Hutchinson's works, this is also the case for patient with chronic respiratory failure assisted by a mechanical ventilation, even if the mechanical ventilation tends to reduce it (Figure 8.35). Instead, there is a cycle-to-cycle variability in breathing period and airflow. Sometimes, the patient is not always able to trigger his ventilator, and there is some flow oscillations which are not associated with a pressure cycle (Figure 8.32(c)). These ineffective inspiratory efforts affect the quality of the mechanical ventilation.[87] This can lead to patient's unwillingness to be treated with noninvasive mechanical ventilation.

We showed that there is a variability of breathing rhythm in healthy as well as in diseased subjects. In the other hand, there is a inter-subject variability of ventilatory volumes at rest.[88] Such a variability is not purely random and may be explained either by a central neural mechanism or by instability in the chemical feedback loops,[89] and by the anatomic variability as first pointed out by Hutchinson. These different ventilatory profiles could depend on departures in size, weight, body

[85] C. Rabec, D. Rodenstein, P. Leger, S. Rouault, C. Perrin & J. Gonzalez-Bermejo, Ventilator modes and settings during non-invasive ventilation: effects on respiratory events and implications for their identification, *Thorax*, **66**, 170–178, 2011.

[86] R. Naeck, D. Bounoiare, U. S. Freitas, H. Rabarimanantsoa, A. Portmann, F. Portier, A. Cuvelier, J.-F. Muir & C. Letellier, Dynamics underlying patient-ventilator interactions during nocturnal noninvasive ventilation, *International Journal of Bifurcation & Chaos*, **22** (2), 1250030, 2012.

[87] L. Vignaux, F. Vargas, J. Roeseler, D. Tassaux, A. W. Thille, M. P. Kossowsky, L. Brochard & P. Jolliet, Patient-ventilator asynchrony during non-invasive ventilation for acute respiratory failure: a multicenter study, *Intensive Care Medicine*, **35** (5), 840–846, 2009.

[88] P. Dejours, Y. Bechtel-Labrousse, P. Monzein & J. Raynaud, Étude de la diversité des régimes ventilatoires chez l'homme, *Journal de Physiologie* (Paris), **53**, 320–321, 1961 — S. A. Shea, J. Walter, K. Murphy & A. Guz, Evidence for individuality of breathing patterns in resting healthy man, *Respiration Physiology*, **68** (3), 331–344, 1987.

[89] G. Benchetrit, Breathing pattern in humans: diversity and individuality, *Respiration Physiology*, **122**, (2–3), 123–129, 2000.

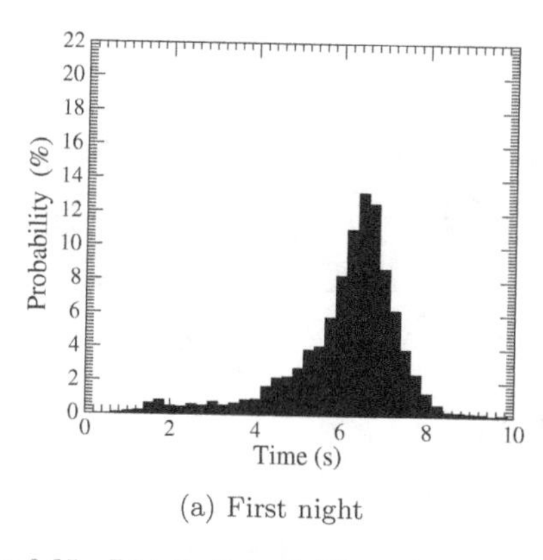

(a) First night

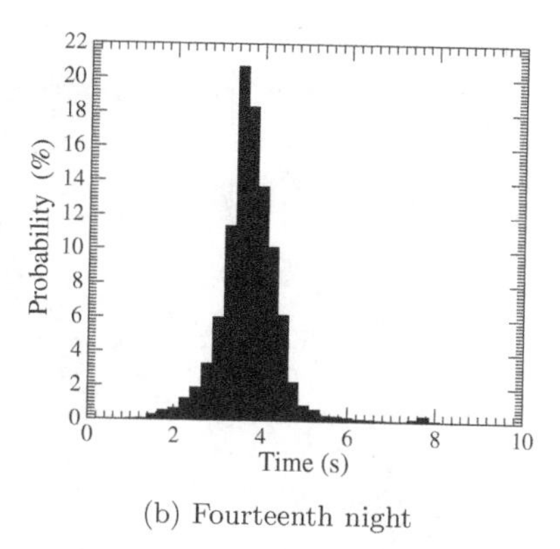

(b) Fourteenth night

Figure 8.35 Distribution of all breath-to-breath intervals for a patient with an amyotrophic lateral sclerosis assisted with a noninvasive mechanical ventilation. The large variability observed in a woman during the first night she was assisted with a noninvasive ventilation was significantly reduced after two weeks of treatment.

surface area, sex or smoking habits.[90] If mechanical ventilation can affect breathing patterns, it is doubtful that the diversity and individuality can be completely removed. Thus breathing patterns in patients placed in similar conditions (at rest, using the same ventilator and the same parameter settings) are quite different as revealed by the state portraits reconstructed from the airflow using delay coordinates (Figure 8.36).[91] These state portraits evidence a diversity which cannot be correlated to patients' disease and, consequently, which is more likely due to the individuality of patient's breathing patterns.

Patient-ventilator interactions in the data showed in Figure 8.36 were also investigated in terms of Shannon entropies computed from recurrences plots.[92] The complexity of the underlying dynamics was characterized using two different entropies. Entropy S_P was computed from the maximum of pressure reached during each breathing cycle. Nontriggered cycles automatically induce an increase of the variability and so of the entropy S_P. Nontriggered cycles were considered to have a non-significant impact on the comfort of patients when $S_P < 1$. A second entropy S_T was computed from the time duration of each cycle. It reflects patient's breath-to-breath variability (complexity) in rhythm: when $S_T < 1$, the patient was considered as breathing at a "regular" rhythm. Optimal patient-ventilator interactions were thus obtained when $S_P < 1$ and $S_T < 1$. Three other cases were also

[90]G. Benchetrit, P. Baconnier, J. Demongeot & T. Pham Dinh, Flow profile analysis of human breathing at rest, in *Concepts and Formalizations in the Control of Breathing* (G. Benchetrit, P. Baconnier & J. Demongeot, Eds.), Manchester University Press, pp. 207–213, 1987.
[91]From data initially investigated in L. Achour, C. Letellier, A. Cuvelier, E. Vérin, J.-F. Muir, Asynchrony and cyclic variability in pressure support noninvasive ventilation, *Computers in Biology and Medicine*, **37**, 1308–1320, 2007.
[92]C. Letellier, H. Rabarimanantsoa, L. Achour, A. Cuvelier & J.-F. Muir, Recurrence plots for dynamical analysis of non invasive mechanical ventilation, *Philosophical Transactions of the Royal Society of London A*, **366**, 621–634, 2008.

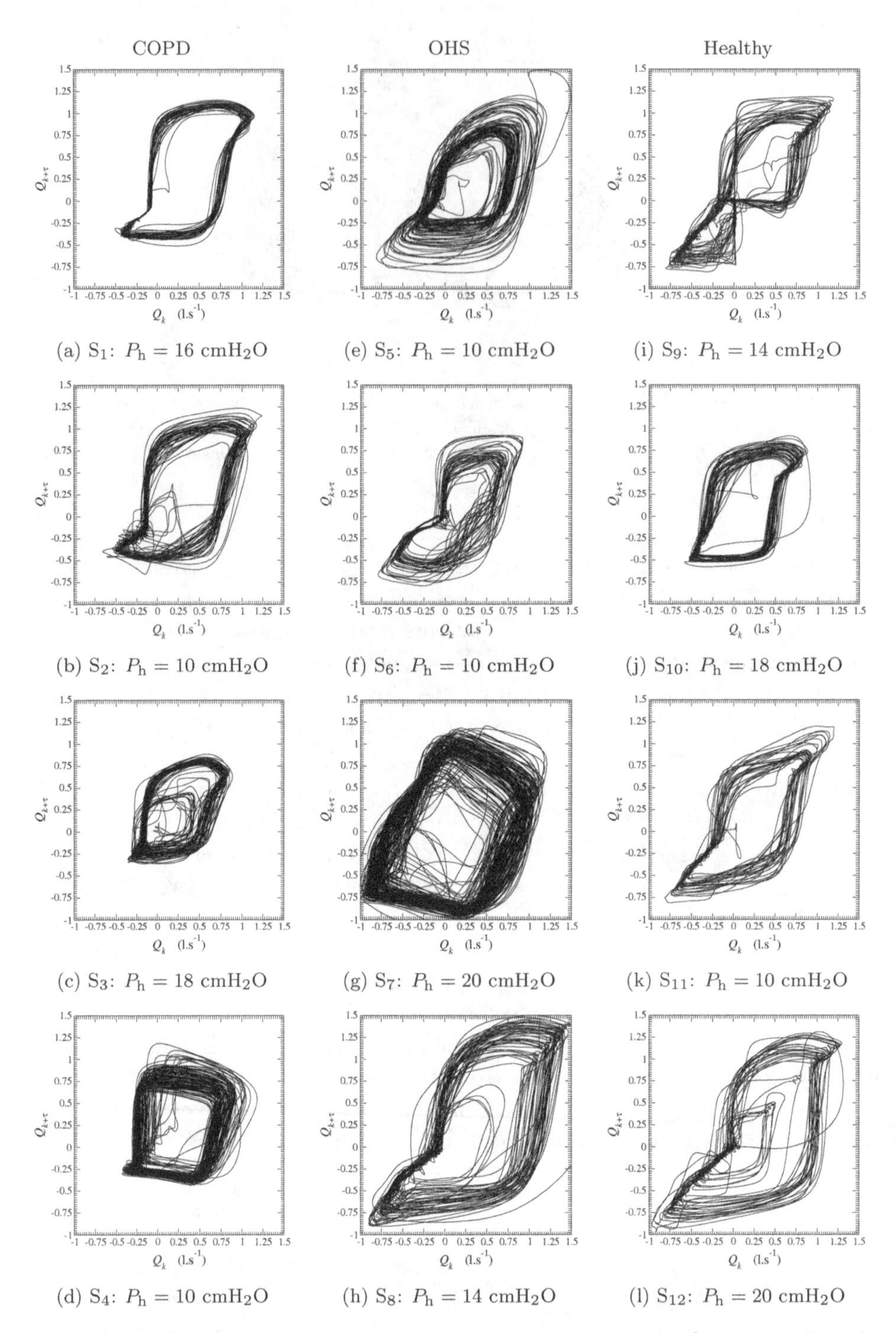

Figure 8.36 State portraits reconstructed delay coordinates with the airflow measured in the ventilatory circuit for 12 subjects assisted with noninvasive mechanical ventilation. The value of the inspiratory pressure was chosen to minimize the ineffective inspiratory efforts. The time delay is $\tau = 0.2$ s. COPD = Chronic Obstructive Pulmonary Disease, OHS = Obesity Hypoventilation Syndrome.

distinguished as follows.

(1) $S_P < 1$ and $S_T > 1$: irregular breathing without a significant amount of non-triggered cycles;
(2) $S_P > 1$ and $S_T < 1$: regular breathing with a significant amount of nontriggered cycles;
(3) $S_P > 1$ and $S_T > 1$: this is the worse situation for which the patient does not regularly breath and has many difficulties to produce effective inspiratory efforts.

The results obtained for these twelve subjects are plotted in Figure 8.37. Some subjects are correctly synchronized with their ventilators ($S_T < 1$ and $S_P < 1$); some others correctly trigger the pressure cycles but breath irregularly ($S_P < 1$ and $S_T > 1$). There are also subjects who do not trigger correctly the pressure cycles but breath regularly ($S_T < 1$ and $S_P > 1$): those patients are well trained to breath with a mechanical ventilation. Some subjects do not breath regularly nor trigger correctly the pressure cycle ($S_P > 1$ and $S_T > 1$); most likely, the quality of ventilation might be improved for these subjects, either by modifying ventilator settings or by better training them to breathe with their ventilators.

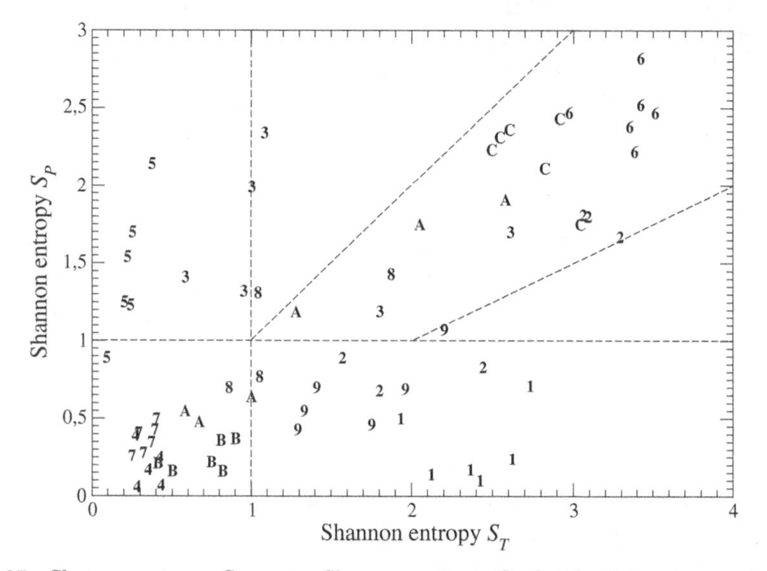

Figure 8.37 Shannon entropy S_P versus Shannon entropy S_T for the data sets recorded during the protocole. Integers i ($i \in [1\ ;9]$) designate subjects S_i for the six measurements at different P_h values. Letters A, B and C designate subjects S_{10}, S_{11} and S_{12}, respectively. Adapted from Rabarimantsoa *et al.*, 2007.

As we did for the time evolution of the copper electrodissolution (Section 5.3), and for the lynx population (Section 6.4), global models were attempted from the airflow and the pressure measured in the ventilation circuit. Our objective was to capture the deterministic component in the dynamics underlying patient-ventilator interaction and, possibly, to reveal a chaotic behavior. All the models we obtained were estimated from data set without nontriggered cycles.[93] This means that we did not obtain global model for patients who were ventilated with $S_P > 1$ and $S_T > 1$. We were only able to obtain global models for optimal patient-ventilator interaction ($S_P < 1$ and $S_T < 1$) or for patients with regular breathing but only with a moderate rate of nontriggered cycles ($S_T < 1$ and $S_P \approx 1$).

For a patient breathing quite regularly but with a significant rate of nontriggered cycles, the model produced the attractor shown in Figure 8.38(a). A first-return map to the Poincaré section presents six monotonic branches (Figure 8.38(b)). This map alternates increasing and decreasing branches separated by smooth extrema, as commonly observed in chaotic maps.

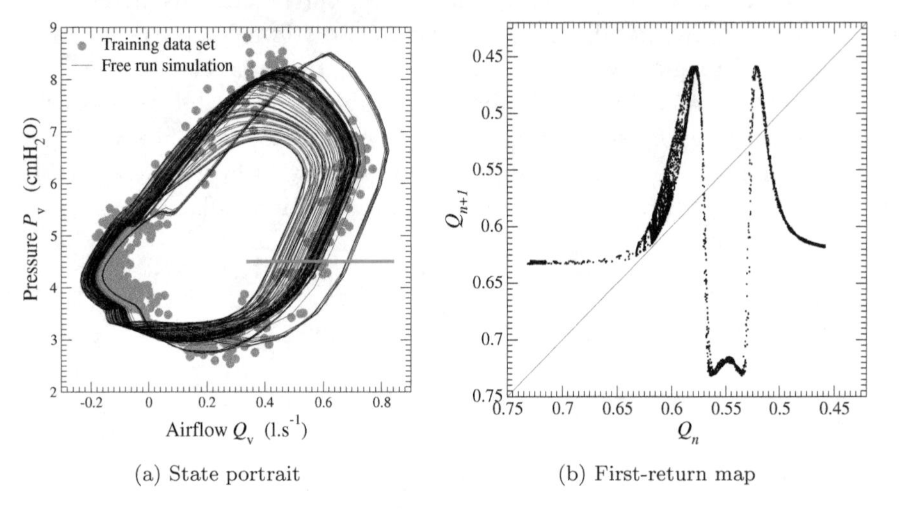

(a) State portrait

(b) First-return map

Figure 8.38 Chaotic behavior produced by the global model obtained from breathing data of subject S_3 with $P_h = 10$ cmH$_2$O. Data used for estimating the model (grey dots) and the Poincaré section — horizontal line in (a) — are also represented.

The model is stable enough to produce a bifurcation diagram (Figure 8.39) by varying some of its parameters. It reveals a period-doubling cascade as a route to chaos when the bifurcation parameter is decreased from 1.078. An inverse period-doubling cascade is also observed for parameter values around 1.075.

A topological analysis is performed for a chaotic attractor (Figure 8.40(a)) characterized by a smooth unimodal first-return map (Figure 8.40(b)). In fact, this map is slightly layered but we here neglected this. The map is thus considered as a unimodal map, as expected after a period-doubling cascade. According to this map, the attractor was split into two domains: one associated with the increasing

[93] C. Letellier, G. G. Rodrigues, J.-F. Muir & L. A. Aguirre, Individuality of breathing patterns in patients under noninvasive mechanical ventilation evidenced by chaotic global models, *Chaos*, **23** (1), 013137, 2013.

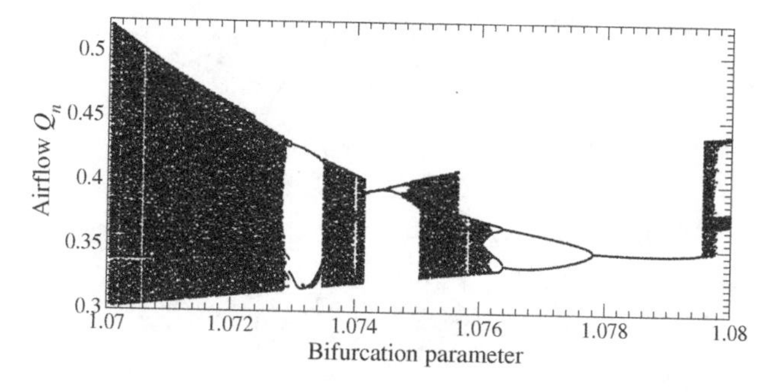

Figure 8.39 Bifurcation diagram produced by varying one of the parameters of the global model.

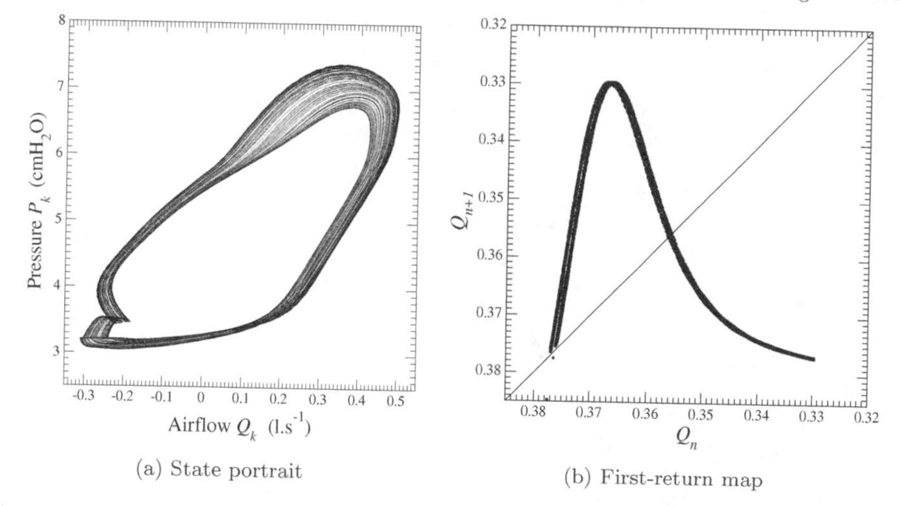

(a) State portrait

(b) First-return map

Figure 8.40 Unimodal chaotic attractor solution to the global model obtained from breathing data. Bifurcation parameter value: 1.0757.

branch (labelled "0") and one corresponding to the decreasing branch (labelled "1"). Branch 0 (1) is associated with an even (odd) number of half-twists (see Chapter 4 for details). The topology of this attractor is correctly sketched by the template shown in Figure 8.41. This chaotic behavior is thus quite close (from a topological point of view) to the Rössler attractor.

Another model was obtained from subject S_9 who was breathing with an irregular rhythm ($S_T = 1.23 > 1$) but who did not present difficulty in triggering her ventilator ($S_P = 0.43 < 1$). At first sight, the corresponding state portrait (Figure 8.42(a)) could be considered as a limit cycle, due to the small breath-to-breath variability. A Poincaré section (not a first-return map) reveals a layered toroidal structure (Figure 8.42(b)). The insert in Figure 8.42(b) evidences the existence of some foldings in the toroidal structure. According to Curry and Yorke scenario,[94] these foldings are responsible for the chaotic nature of such behavior.

[94] J. Curry & J. A. Yorke, A transition from Hopf bifurcation to chaos: computer experiments with maps on $\mathbb{R}^2$, *Lecture Notes in Mathematics*, **668**, 48–66, 1978.

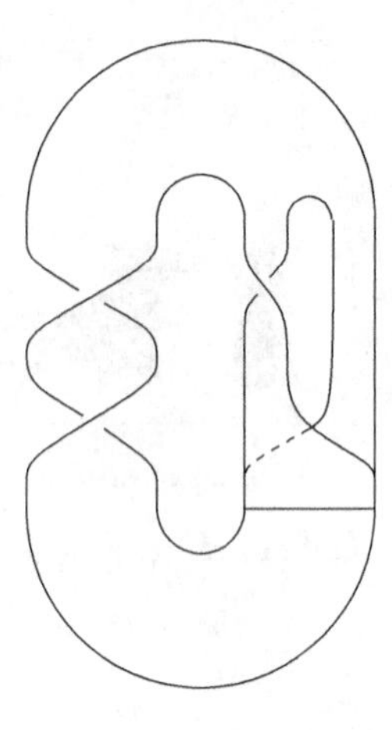

Figure 8.41 Template for the unimodal chaotic attractor produced by the global model obtained from measurements in the subject S_3.

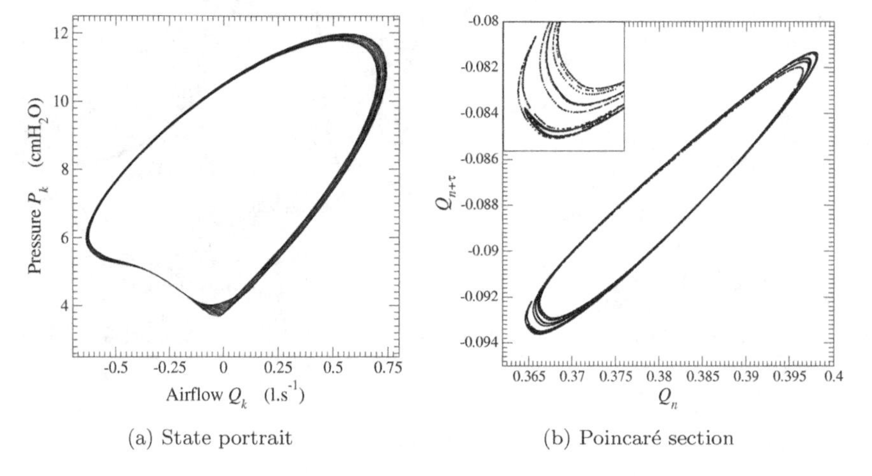

(a) State portrait (b) Poincaré section

Figure 8.42 Toroidal chaos for the breathing dynamics of subject S_9 who was ventilated with $P_{\text{h}} = 10$ cmH$_2$O.

Subject S_1 with a breathing dynamics characterized by $S_T = 2.42 > 1$ and $S_P = 0.1 < 1$ presents breathing patterns suggesting toroidal chaos. The breath-to-breath variability is slightly larger than in the previous case (Figure 8.43(a)) and, consequently, the layered structure of the torus is more developed (Figure 8.43(b)). Therefore two different subjects, a female — subject S_9 — without breathing pathology and a female — subject S_1 — with a chronic obstructive pulmonary disease, were breathing under mechanical ventilation with a variability governed by a toroidal chaos. It is interesting to point out that both were breathing regularly in spite of a certain lack of abilities for triggering the pressure cycles.

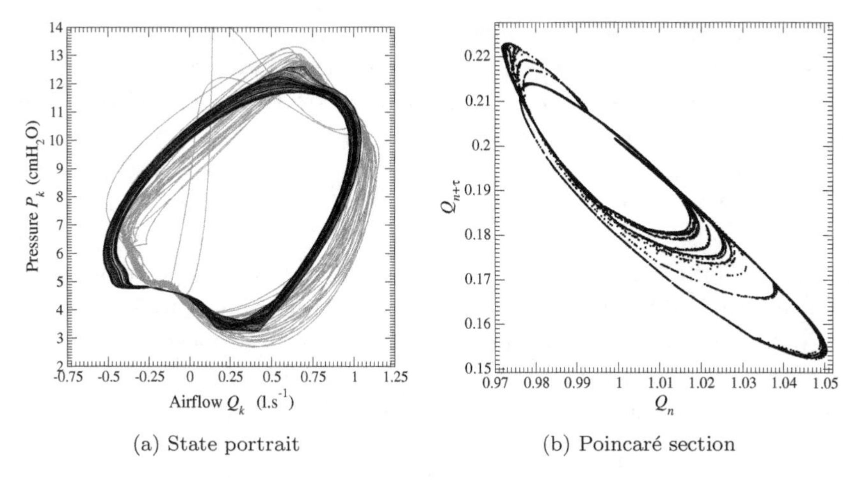

(a) State portrait (b) Poincaré section

Figure 8.43 Toroidal chaos observed in the breathing dynamics of subject S_1 who was ventilated with $P_h = 16$ cmH$_2$O.

These global models with different chaotic dynamics were thus obtained from data measured in patients under noninvasive mechanical ventilation. One of them produces chaotic attractors characterized by a horseshoe map, and two produce toroidal chaos. These departures in the intrinsic deterministic dynamics extracted from data represent another evidence for the individuality of breathing patterns. Moreover, the estimated models provide a strong piece of evidence that the dynamics underlying breathing patterns can be chaotic, indeed. Note that the morphology of the state portraits reconstructed from the airflow is still largely unexploited in the investigation of breathing patterns and the characterization of patients peculiarities.

8.5 Dynamics of Tumor Growth

In any mammals, tissues are naturally regenerated, that is, produce new cells to replace too old cells for keeping organs in good conditions. Such replacement may also be due to injury as a scar: regeneration is thus needed in some tissue. In adults, stem cells thus repair the body, replenishing tissues. Typically, a stem cell divides into one mother cell that is identical to the original one, and another daughter cell that is differentiated for reproducing a given tissue. During this replication process, some errors can randomly arise: in principle, the body is able to repair itself these errors but sometimes this process fails and a mutated cell is produced. Most of the time, the immune system and the environment jointly work for eradicating such a mutated cell, and these errors have no consequence. Nevertheless, sometimes it occurs that the environment of such a mutated cell is not sufficiently efficient to kill it, and mutated cells start to replicate. There are some very special cases for which this proliferation turns in a non-controlled way: a tumor thus occurs. In this case, the growing rate of tumor cells is larger than the renewing rate of host cells (the cells from the environment where the tumor is nested).

Without any treatment, the tumor invades the organ, triggers the production of neo-vessels for satisfying its demand in nutrients and oxygen carried by the blood: this is neo-angiogenesis.[95] Typically a tumor starts to be vascularized when its size reaches 2 mm, that is, when it reaches the level of resolution of a routine imaging: consequently, most of the detected tumor are already vascularized. This is an important step because these neo-vessels, directly connected to the tumor, allow tumor cells to circulate within the body, carried by the blood or the lymph. This is a required condition for the occurrence of metastases, but not a sufficient one. Indeed, tumor cells that evaded the primary tumor must find another tissue with suitable conditions for initiating a new tumor. In fact, most of the circulating tumor cells die before encountering a suitable location for proliferating. Typically, less than 0.01% of circulating tumor cells for 24 hours can produce metastasis.[96] Stephen Paget (1855–1926) was the first to suggest that the nesting tissue "*cannot be altogether passive or indifferent.*"[97] He followed Ernst Fuchs (1851–1931) in asserting that certain organs must be predisposed for triggering some pathologies.[98] By predisposition, Saget pushed the idea that it could mean *diminished resistance.*

Commonly cancer is considered from a genetic point of view: during the replication process, a mutated cell randomly occurs due to a damage in its DNA and starts to proliferate. In that case, if one considers that the occurrence of a tumor is only dependent on the probability to have a mutated cell during the replication process, cancer incidence would be directly related to the rate with which tissues are regenerated. Indeed, it is known that different "organs have different rates of regeneration."[99] For instance, bone tissues present a long remodelling period (roughly 10 years) and the liver has a high capacity for regeneration (few weeks). These differences could thus explain how cancer incidence depends strongly on the tissue considered, the occurrence of cancer only depending on random mutations arising during DNA replication in non-malignant (host) cells.[100] In this approach, any mutation of a normal cell into a malignant cell during one of the cell divisions has an equal probability to become a growing tumor detected regardless of its microenvironment.

---

[95] J. Folkman, Tumor angiogenesis: therapeutic implications, *New England Journal of Medicine*, **285** (21), 1182–1186, 1971.

[96] I. J. Fidler, Metastasis: quantitative analysis of distribution and fate of tumor embolilabeled with 125 I-5-iodo-2'-deoxyuridine, *Journal of the National Cancer Institute*, **45**, 773–782, 1970.

[97] S. Paget, The distribution of secondary growths in cancer of the breast, *The Lancet*, **133** (3421), 571–573, 1889.

[98] E. Fuchs, *Das Sarcom des Uvealtractus*, Wilhelm Braumüller (Vienna, Austria) 1882.

[99] A. Landahl, Tissue homeostasis, in *Tissue Engineering*, edited by J. De Boer, C. Van Blitterswijk, P. Thomsen, J. Hubbell, R. Cancedda, J. D. de Bruijn, A. Lindahl, J. Sohier and D. F. Williams (Academic Press), pp. 73–87, 2008.

[100] C. Tomasetti & B. Vogelstein, Variation in cancer risk among tissues can be explained by the number of stem cell divisions, *Science*, **347**, 78–81, 2015 — C. Tomasetti, L. Li & B. Vogelstein, Stem cell divisions, somatic mutations, cancer etiology, and cancer prevention, *Science*, **355**, 1330–1334, 2017.

A major objection to this approach is that, if one assumes that every cell with an equal chance for inducing mutant malignant cells during its division, not only large but also long-lived organisms should present an increased risk for developing a cancer compared to small organisms, a feature that is not observed in nature. For instance, bowhead whales have 1000 times more cells than humans but do not exhibit a larger lifetime cancer rate,[101] thus suggesting that they own natural mechanisms suppressing tumor cells with an efficiency more than 1000 times greater than the ones presented by humans. There is therefore no evidence for a correlation between the body size and the lifespan cancer rate.[102] Indeed, cancers have been very rarely recorded in blue whales[103] and, in general, whales have a very low lifespan cancer rate. In fact, the long lifespan expectancy for bowhead whales can be explained by an anti-oncogenic phenotype that they acquired by selection during millions of years, and which is not found in humans. The long lifespan expectancy of these bowhead whales is also due to a particular immune system.[104] Indeed, only a small fraction of tumor cells initiates a detectable tumor.[105] This is mainly due to the fact that tumors result from complex ecologies between numerous cell types[106] and that the microenvironment could revert the malignant phenotype to a non-proliferating one.[107]

The dynamics governing the interactions between various types of cells is indeed of primordial relevance for tumor growth because it is known that this dynamics is poorly affected by the personal and/or family history: since only less than 10% of cancers could be attributed to hereditary facts.[108] For instance, if some types of cancers (prostate, colorectal, breast...) can be associated with inheritable factors, there are others (pancreas, stomach, lung, uterus, ovary, bladder...) for which this is

[101] J. D. Nagy, E. M. Victor & J. H. Cropper, Why don't all whales have cancer? A novel hypothesis resolving Peto's paradox, *Integrative and Comparative Biology*, **47** (2), 317–328, 2007 — F. Denis & C. Letellier, Is high cancer rate in human due to a weakness in biology resulting from the rapid increase in lifetime expectancy?, *Bulletin du Cancer*, **103** (3), 224–226, 2016.

[102] R. B. Landy, in *Pathology of zoo animals*, edited by R. J. Montali & G. Migaki (Smithsonian Institution Press, Washington DC), 1980.

[103] A. F. Caulin & C. C. Maley, Peto's paradox: Evolution's prescription for cancer prevention, *Trends in Ecology & Evolution*, **26** (4), 175–182, 2011.

[104] M. Keane, J. Semeiks, B. Thomsen & J. P. de Magalhaes, Insights into the evolution of longevity from the bowhead whale genome, *Cell Reports*, **10**, 1–11, 2015.

[105] A. M. Soto & C. Sonnenschein, The somatic mutation theory of cancer: Growing problems with the paradigm?, *Bioessays*, **26** (10), 1097–1107, 2004 — T. Borovski, F. de Sousa E Melo, L. Vermeulen & J. P. Medema, Cancer stem cell niche: The place to be, *Cancer Research*, **71** (3), 634–639, 2011.

[106] H. Ducasse, A. Arnal, M. Vittecoq, S. P. Daoust, B. Ujvari, C. Jacqueline, T. Tissot, P. Ewald, R. A. Gatenby, K. C. King, F. Bonhomme, J. Brodeur, F. Renaud, E. Solary, B. Roche & F. Thomas, Cancer: An emergent property of disturbed resource-rich environments? Ecology meets personalized medicine, *Evolutionary Applications*, **8** (6), 527–540, 2015.

[107] P. A. Kenny & M. J. Bissell, Tumor reversion: Correction of malignant behavior by microenvironmental cues, *International Journal of Cancer*, **107** (5), 688–695, 2003 — J. A. Joyce & J. W. Pollard, Microenvironmental regulation of metastasis, *Nature Review Cancer*, **9** (4), 239–252, 2009.

[108] E. R. Fearon, Human cancer syndromes: Clues to the origin and nature of cancer, *Science*, **278**, 1043–1050, 1997.

significantly less relevant.[109] The genetic contribution is therefore only a small part of tumor growth. As we just briefly detailed, to proliferate mutated cells must find favorable conditions. This is then a balance between the immune system and the surrounding tissue, in one hand, and the tumor cells, in the other hand. Host and tumor cells are in competition for nutrients and oxygen. Tumor cells will therefore proliferate in an environment where host cells are not too competitive. It is now well accepted that the micro-environment of the tumor provides more or less strong barriers against tumor growth,[110] these barriers quantifying the competitivity of the environment. The proliferation of the tumor cells would directly result from the "*diminished resistance*" provided by these barriers.

8.5.1 *The Model*

Among the very rare models taking into account the environment in the interactions between different populations of cells at a tumor site, the model proposed by Lisette de Pillis and Ami Radunskaya[111] is particularly interesting because it is able to reproduce some relevant clinical features.[112] This model describes the interactions between host (normal), effector immune (natural killer) and tumor cells in a single tumor site. The host cells correspond to healthy cells which are structuring the considered organ. The effector immune cells are cytotoxic lymphocytes that can kill the tumor cells. The system is adimensionalized in such a way that all populations are within the unit interval (a population equal to 1 thus saturates the site at its carrying capacity). Without any interaction between them, the populations x of host cells and z of tumor cells are governed by logistic functions depending on the growth rates $\rho_{\rm h}$ and $\rho_{\rm t}$, respectively. Host and tumor cells are in competition for space, oxygen and nutrients, as evidenced by the negative coupling term $-\alpha_{\rm ht}$, where $\alpha_{\rm ht}$ is the death rate of host cells due to tumor cells reducing the population x and the negative coupling term $-\alpha_{\rm th}$, where $\alpha_{\rm th}$ is the death rate of tumor cells due to host cells reducing the population z. Similar terms are used between the population y of effector immune cells and the population z of tumor cells. From that point of view, these last two populations are also in competition. Nevertheless, the growth rate of effector immune cells is governed by a type-II Holling term $\frac{\rho_{\rm i} yz}{1+z}$; the proliferation of effector immune cells is therefore induced by the presence of tumor cells. The most important process quantified by parameter $\rho_{\rm i}$ is the growth rate of immune cells.

[109] P. Lichtenstein, N. V. Holm, P. K. Verkasalo, A. Iliadou, J. Kaprio, M. Koskenvuo, E. Pukkala, A. Skytthe & K. Hemminki, Environmental and heritable factors in the causation of cancer — Analyses of cohorts of twins from Sweden, Denmark, and Finland, *New England Journal of Medecine*, **343**, 78–85, 2000.
[110] M. J. Bissell & W. C. Hines, Why don't we get more cancer? A proposed role of the microenvironment in restraining cancer progression, *Nature Medicine*, **17**, (3), 320–329, 2011.
[111] L. G. De Pillis & A. Radunskaya, A mathematical tumor model with immune resistance and drug therapy: An optimal control approach, *Journal of Theoretical Medicine*, **3**, 79–100, 2001.
[112] C. Letellier, F. Denis & L. A. Aguirre, What can be learned from a chaotic cancer model?, *Journal of Theoretical Biology*, **322**, 7–16, 2013.

Depending on the parameter values $\rho_{\rm i}$ and $\alpha_{\rm it}$, the coupling between effector immune and tumor cells can be positive: in that case, the interactions between these two populations with one positive term ($\rho_{\rm i} \frac{yz}{1+z} - \alpha_{\rm it} yz$ with appropriate parameter values) and one negative term ($-\alpha_{\rm ti} zy$) correspond to contramensalism (two populations having opposite effects on each other).[113] Without tumor cells, the population y remains null. The natural death of effector immune cells is taken into account by the term $-\delta_{\rm i} y$. At the site S_{ij}, the three populations are thus governed by the three differential equations

$$\begin{cases} \dot{x}_{ij} = \rho_{\rm h} x_{ij} \left(1 - x_{ij}\right) - \alpha_{\rm ht}\, x_{ij}\, z_{ij} \\ \dot{y}_{ij} = \rho_{\rm i} \dfrac{y_{ij}\, z_{ij}}{1 + z_{ij}} - \alpha_{\rm it}\, y_{ij}\, z_{ij} - \delta_{\rm i} y_{ij} \\ \dot{z}_{ij} = \rho_{\rm t}\, z_{ij} \left(1 - z_{ij}\right) - \alpha_{\rm th}\, x_{ij}\, z_{ij} - \alpha_{\rm ti}\, y_{ij}\, z_{ij} - \nabla \cdot \left(\kappa \cdot \nabla z\right) \end{cases} \tag{8.5}$$

proposed by de Pillis and Radunskaya, and where $\nabla \cdot (\kappa \cdot \nabla z)$ is here added to describe the diffusion of tumor cells from one site to another when the corresponding population exceeds a given threshold value. Our tumor sites are located in a plane (two-dimensional space). Each site is a square whose edges have $\eta = 100$ μm in length. Our two-dimensional tissue is made of a lattice of 10×10 sites. The tissue is thus a square of 1 mm^2. Each site has eight neighboring sites whose location is designated according to N, S, W, E, NE, NW, SE, and SW, where N corresponds to North, S to South, W to West and E to East. For instance, the population of host cells within the site located at the North-East of site S_{ij} will be designated by $x_{ik}^{\rm NE}$, and so on.

The rate of diffusion is dependent on parameter κ. When homogeneous tumor in homogeneous tissue is considered, all sites are characterized by the same parameter values. The diffusion of tumor cells is governed by an isotropic Laplacian operator[114] which is discretized on the lattice according to

$$\nabla \cdot (\kappa \nabla z) = \mathcal{H}(z_{ij} - 0.99)\, \kappa \sum_k \left(\frac{z_{ij}^k - z_{ij}}{\beta_k\, \eta^2} \right) \tag{8.6}$$

where z_{ij}^k with $k = \{\mathrm{N, S, E, W, NE, NW, SE, SW}\}$ designates the tumor cell density at the kth sites around the site (i, j) and the coefficients $\beta_k = \{2, 2, 2, 2, 4, 4, 4, 4\}$. For instance, $z_{ij}^{\rm NE}$ corresponds to the tumor cell density at the site located at the North-East of the site (i, j), that is, at the site $(i+1, j+1)$. For all our simulations, we used $K = 10^{-10}$. Such a modelling allows to simulate a spatial tumor growth, taking into account the interaction with the micro-environment.

[113] S. Hodge & W. Arthur, Contramensal interactions between species, *Oikos*, **77** (2), 371–375, 1996.

[114] M. Patra & M. Karttunen, Stencils with isotropic discretization error for differential operators, *Numerical Methods for Partial Differential Equations*, **22** (4), 936–953, 2006 — A. H. Panaretos, J. T. Aberle & R. E. Diaz, The effect of the 2-D Laplacian operator approximation on the performance of finite-difference time-domain schemes for Maxwell's equations, *Journal of Computational Physics*, **227**, 513–536, 2007.

8.5.2 *The Dynamics within a Single Site*

Table 8.2 Parameters of the model (8.5) used for describing the interactions between the populations of host (x), effector immune (y) and tumor (z) cells. The values (or the interval over which they are varied) used in our simulations are also reported. Default values correspond to the chaotic attractor shown in Figure 8.44.

Symbol	Meaning	Range	Default
$\rho_{\rm h}$	growth rate of host cells	$[0;1]$	0.518
$\rho_{\rm i}$	growth rate of effector immune cells	$[0.1;6]$	4.5
$\rho_{\rm t}$	growth rate of tumor cells	$2\rho_{\rm h}$	1.0
$\alpha_{\rm ht}$	death rate of host cells by tumor cells	$[0.5;2]$	1.5
$\alpha_{\rm it}$	inhibition rate of effector immune cells by tumor cells	$[0.1;3.5]$	0.2
$\alpha_{\rm th}$	death rate of tumor cells by host cells	$[0.5;2]$	1.0
$\alpha_{\rm ti}$	death rate of tumor cells by effector immune cells	2.5	2.5
$\delta_{\rm i}$	natural death rate of effector immune cells	0.5	0.5

The default parameter values (reported in the last column of Table 8.2) correspond to the chaotic attractor shown in Figure 8.44. This chaotic regime corresponds to a slowly growing tumor, characterized by a layer of proliferating tumor cells which is rather heterogeneously populated.[115] Due to the impossibility to estimate all parameter values of such a model *in vivo* or *in vitro*, mostly due to the large differences observed between animal, culture or human models,[116] there are no serious possibilities to accurately assess parameter values for such a model. Since our objective is not to reproduce quantitatively the dynamics for a given patient but rather to browse qualitatively the different situations which can be observed, parameter values were chosen for browsing the different dynamics provided by our model.

The model (8.5) has four main singular points. Three of them have coordinates which are not dependent on the parameter values; they are

$$\mathrm{S}_0 = \left| \begin{array}{l} x_0 = 0 \\ y_0 = 0 \\ z_0 = 0 \end{array} \right. , \quad \mathrm{S}_\mathrm{H} = \left| \begin{array}{l} x_1 = 1 \\ y_1 = 0 \\ z_1 = 0 \end{array} \right. , \text{ and } \mathrm{S}_\mathrm{T} = \left| \begin{array}{l} x_2 = 0 \\ y_2 = 0 \\ z_2 = 1 \end{array} \right. .$$

When the first singular point is stable, the model describes a necrotic site, where all cells died. When the second one is stable, it is associated with a healthy tissue with strong barriers against tumor progression. The singular point S_T corresponds to a site inhabited by tumor cells, that is, typically a site located in the proliferating shell of a tumor. The fourth singular point S_HIT has nonzero and positive coordinates: the three populations of cells coexist in the site, as it could be at the boundary of a tumor. The first three points bound a domain $\mathcal{D}$ in which oscillatory behavior

[115] L. Viger, F. Denis, C. Draghi, T. Ménard & C. Letellier, Spatial avascular growth of tumor in a homogeneous environment, *Journal of Theoretical Biology*, **416**, 99–112, 2017.

[116] K.-S. Chan, C.-G. Koh & H.-Y. Li, Mitosis-targeted anti-cancer therapies: Where they stand, *Cell Death & Disease*, **3**, e411, 2012.

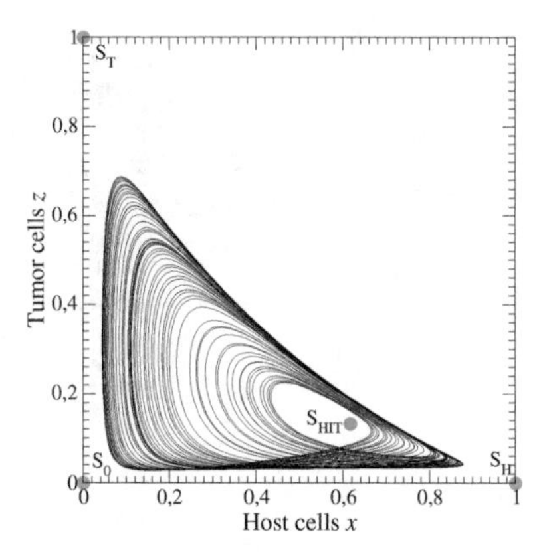

Figure 8.44 Chaotic attractor produced by the model (8.5) in a single site ($\kappa = 0$) and with the default parameter values as reported in Table 8.2. The singular points with positive coordinates are also shown.

can take place. The fourth singular point S_{HIT} is the point around which these oscillations are structured as shown in Figure 8.44 where the chaotic attractor is structured around the point S_{HIT} that is characterized by a rather large population of host cells and a quite small population of tumor cells; this explains why slowly expanding tumors are associated with chaotic dynamics.

In the model (8.5), the growth rate ρ_h of host cells is directly related to the number of stem cell divisions, that is, to the rate of regeneration of a tissue. As we already discussed, different "*organs have different rate of regeneration.*" Thus parameter ρ_h can be used for distinguishing organ tissues. The bifurcation diagram *versus* the growth rate of host cells ρ_h (Figure 8.45) is computed by retrieving minimal and maximal values of the population of tumor cells.[117] We also plotted points corresponding to stable singular points. The route to the chaotic attractor shown in Figure 8.44 is a period-doubling cascade. Some periodic windows are also identified as in any chaotic systems. For small values of the growth rate ($\rho_h < 0.38$), the trajectory converges to the singular point S_{IT} where the population of host cells is zero. For large values of ρ_h, the dynamics is more developed, that is, structured around a larger population of periodic orbits (see Chapter 4, p. 189), leading to a chaotic behavior.

For tissue with a low growth rate ρ_h of host cells, that is, tissue with a long regeneration period, the population of tumor cells remains at very low value ($z \approx 0.13$); the tumor starts to colonize the site only when there is a deficiency of the immune system (an episode of "weakness" as everyone may have in his life and during which $y(t) \approx 0$), and then it spatially expands. In the case of rather large value of the growth rate ρ_h, there is large amplitude oscillations and the population of tumor cells can take quite large value ($z \approx 0.7$) for short durations. Most

[117]C. Letellier, F. Denis & L. A. Aguirre, What can be learned from a chaotic cancer model?, *Journal of Theoretical Biology*, **322**, 7–16, 2013.

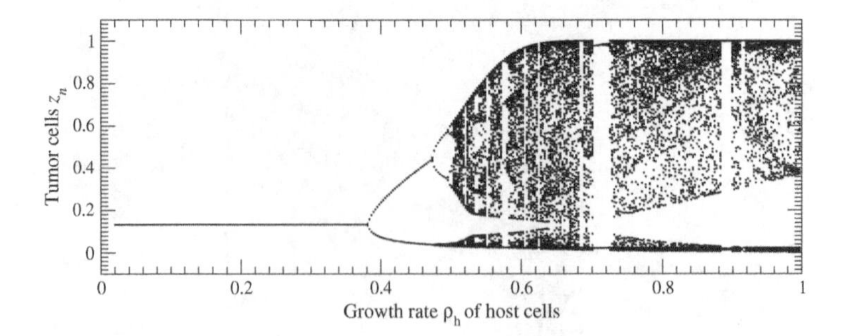

Figure 8.45 Bifurcation diagram *versus* the growth rate of host cells $\rho_{\rm h}$ when other parameters have the default values reported in Table 8.2.

often, this leads to slowly expanding tumor. Nevertheless, as observed for tissues with a slow regeneration, when the immune system presents a deficiency, there is a rapid saturation of the site by tumor cells and the tumor starts to expand. This feature explains how a temporary deficiency of the immune system can lead to tumor expansion as shown in Figure 8.46 where $y = 0$ for $160 < t < 200$ a.u.t. In this model, the process is reversible because the model (8.5) does not take into account the irreversible degradation of the tissue by the tumor progression and by the treatment.[118] The bifurcation diagram (Figure 8.45) shows that until the immune system is active, the faster the regeneration of the tissue (larger growth rate $\rho_{\rm h}$), the larger the population of tumor cells can be and, consequently, the faster the tumor progression is.

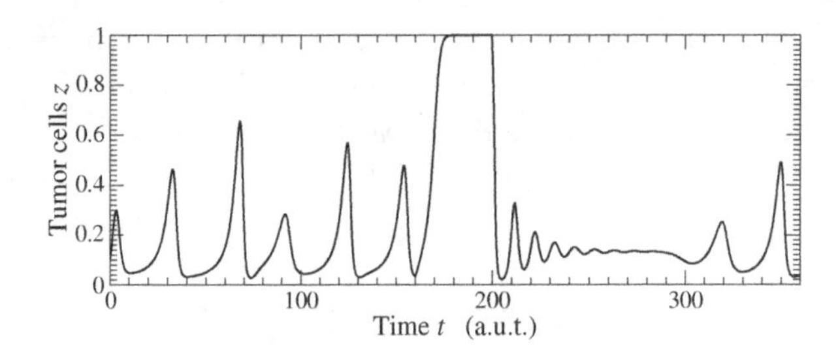

Figure 8.46 Time evolution of the population of tumor cells for a tissue with a moderate regeneration duration (moderate growth rate, $\rho_{\rm h} = 0.518$). Other parameters have the default values reported in Table 8.2. The deficiency of the immune system occurs at $t = 160$ a.u.t. ($y = 0$); its action is recovered at $t = 200$ a.u.t. ($y = 0.1$).

The growth rate $\rho_{\rm t}$ of tumor cells is related to the growth rate $\rho_{\rm h}$ since $\rho_{\rm t}$ is always greater than the growth rate $\rho_{\rm h}$ of cells from which they mutated.[119] It is

[118] C. Letellier, S. K. Sasmal, C. Draghi, F. Denis & D. Ghosh, A chemotherapy combined with an anti-angiogenic drug applied to a cancer model including angiogenesis, *Chaos, Solitons & Fractals*, **99**, 297–311, 2017.

[119] J. C. Mottram, On the correlation between malignancy and the rate of growth of tar warts in mice, *American Journal of Cancer Research*, **22**, 801–830, 1934 — G. M. Cooper, *The cell: A molecular approach*, 2nd ed. (Sinauer Associates, Sunderland MA), 2000.

therefore convenient to choose $\rho_t = 2\rho_h$ in the simulations. The bifurcation diagram *versus* ρ_t is shown in Figure 8.47(b). There is a threshold value for this growth rate ($\rho_t \approx 0.95$) under which the population of tumor cells remains to 0. There is a chaotic regime followed by a sequence of reverse bifurcations leading to an inverse cascade of period-doublings, and then the point S_{HIT} becomes a stable node-focus ($\rho_t \approx 1.25$).

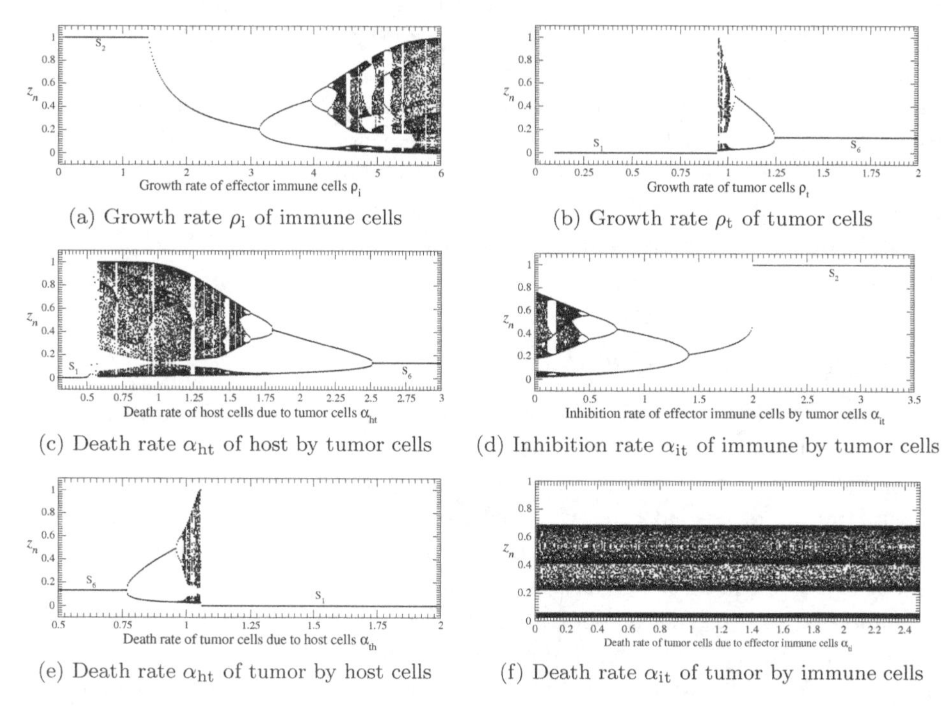

(a) Growth rate ρ_i of immune cells

(b) Growth rate ρ_t of tumor cells

(c) Death rate α_{ht} of host by tumor cells

(d) Inhibition rate α_{it} of immune by tumor cells

(e) Death rate α_{ht} of tumor by host cells

(f) Death rate α_{it} of tumor by immune cells

Figure 8.47 Bifurcation diagrams *versus* the different parameters of the cancer model (8.5) for an isolated site (the diffusion parameter κ is set to zero).

Among the six remaining parameters of model (8.5), the natural death rate of effector immune cells δ_i is commonly considered as being non patient dependent.[120] This parameter is therefore kept to its default value. The bifurcation diagrams *versus* each of the five free parameters are shown in Figure 8.47. No bifurcation is observed in the diagram versus the death rate of tumor cells by effector immune cells α_{it} (Figure 8.47(f)), meaning that the value of this parameter has no effect on the dynamics: this parameter is therefore kept to its default value. The four other parameters can be grouped into two classes. Increasing parameter ρ_i and α_{th} contribute to reduce the population of tumor cells; the former by increasing the efficiency of the immune system and the latter by increasing the barrier against

[120] J. Sprent & D. F. Tough, Lymphocyte life-span and memory, *Science*, **265**, 1395–1400, 1994 — D. F. Tough & J. Sprent, Life span of naive and memory T cells, *Stem Cells*, **13** (3), 242–249, 1995.

tumor progression provided by the nesting tissue. Parameters $\alpha_{\rm ht}$ and $\alpha_{\rm it}$ promote the proliferation of tumor cells, the former by inhibiting the immune system and the latter by reducing the barriers provided by host cells. Notice that what is important in these bifurcation diagrams is not how is developed the dynamics (the population of unstable periodic orbits) but rather the transition between the attractors located at the two ends of the diagram, which are most often stable singular points. For instance, promoting tumor cells is obtained by switching from point $S_{\rm H}$ to $S_{\rm HIT}$ or toward point $S_{\rm T}$. Reducing the proliferation of these cells is associated with the transition from point $S_{\rm T}$ to chaos (or point $S_{\rm H}$ if $\rho_{\rm i}$ is increased up to 7.0) or from $S_{\rm HIT}$ to $S_{\rm H}$. Tumors are therefore aggressive for low values of $\rho_{\rm i}$ and $\alpha_{\rm th}$, and large values of $\alpha_{\rm ht}$ and $\alpha_{\rm it}$. There are various configurations for which the tumor can remain under the clinical level of detection, can slowly grow (for instance when there is a chaotic regime) or can present a fast expansion. These four parameters are therefore useful for distinguishing how the tumor micro-environment provides barriers against tumor progression.

8.5.3 *Spatial Tumor Growth*

The spatial model (8.5) was used for investigating whether randomness in cancer occurrences is only apparent or could be casually explained with the quality of the surrounding tissue, a quality which would strongly depend on the way of life.[121] The growth rate $\rho_{\rm h}$ of normal cells was used as the parameter determining the organ tissue. For each type of tissue (organ), the selected parameter values were varied to take into account how a given type of tissue can be affected by external factors, thus allowing to construct a cohort of simulated patients with different qualities of tissue. It was thus possible to compute a probability for an expanding tumor *versus* the growth rate of host cells. Indeed, many genomic changes occur simply in a random way during DNA replication and the endogenous mutation rate of all types of human cells is nearly the same.[122] Nevertheless, the apparition of a malignant cell is considered as being sufficiently frequent that the key factor is not this mechanism but rather the occurrence of a nesting tissue in favor of an expanding colony of tumor cells, the tissue state being characterized by the parameter $\rho_{\rm i}$, $\alpha_{\rm ht}$, $\alpha_{\rm it}$, and $\alpha_{\rm th}$. Variations in the values of these four parameters allow to take into account how the spatial growth of the tumor mass mainly depends on carcinogenic factors as pesticides, benzene, light particles, tobacco, quality of the food, etc.[123] Typically,

[121] C. Draghi, L. Viger, F. Denis & C. Letellier, How the growth rate of host cells affects cancer risk in a deterministic way, *Chaos*, **27**, 093101, 2017.

[122] M. Lynch, Rate, molecular spectrum, and consequences of human mutation, *Proceedings of the National Academy of Sciences* (USA), **107** (3), 961–968, 2010 — C. Tomasetti, B. Vogelstein & G. Parmigiani, Half or more of the somatic mutations in cancers of self-renewing tissues originate prior to tumor initiation, *Proceedings of the National Academy of Sciences* (USA), **110** (6), 1999–2004, 2013.

[123] See `http://monographs.iarc.fr/ENG/Monographs/PDFs/index.php` for the IARC monograph on the evaluation of carcinogenic risks to humans — National Cancer Institute (NCI) and the National Institute of Environmental Health Sciences (NIEHS), *Cancer and the environment: What you need to know what you can do* (NIH Publication, 2003), No. 03-2039.

a set of parameter values providing a fast expanding tumor would correspond to a tissue which was degraded by carcinogenic factors.

The central site ($i = 5$ and $j = 5$) is such that, at time $t = 0$, it contains a small colony of tumor cells. This site is thus initialized with $x_{5,5}(0) = 0.6$, $y_{5,5}(0) = 0.1$, and $z_{5,5}(0) = 0.2$. In all other sites, at time $t = 0$, the population y_{ij} of effector immune cells is null since there is no tumor cells in them. These sites are thus considered to be only filled with host cells. Initial conditions for sites S_{ij} ($i \neq 5$ and $j \neq 5$) are therefore $x_{ij}(0) = 1$, $y_{ij}(0) = 0$, and $z_{ij}(0) = 0$. When some tumor cells diffuse at time $t > 0$ into one of these sites, the population y_{ij} of that site is set to a non-zero value ($y^k_{ij}(t) = 0.1$ for $k = \{$ N, S, W, E $\}$ and $y^k_{ij}(t) = 0.05$ for $k = \{$NE, NW, SE, SW$\}$).

Each of the four parameters α_{ht}, ρ_{i}, α_{it}, and α_{th} was varied by using ten values equidistributed over the intervals reported in Table 8.2. This was therefore 10^4 different sets of parameter values which were investigated for each value of the growth rate ρ_{h} of host cells. A given tissue (organ) was thus considered in 10,000 different states from the cell interaction point of view. Since each patient has a tissue in a particular state, each tissue state can be interpreted as representing a given patient. This is thus a cohort of 10,000 different simulated patients which was considered.

The simulations were performed for 50,000 time step ($\mathrm{d}t = 5 \cdot 10^{-2}$ arbitrary units of time). Such a duration is large enough to allow a significant spatial growth of the tumor mass, provided that a diffusion of tumor cells occurs. A spatial growth was confirmed at the end of each simulation when the population of tumor cells was such that $z_{8,5}(50,000) \neq 0$, that is, when tumor cells were detected at a distance greater than 300 μm from the initial location. With 10,000 different simulated patients in the investigated cohort, up to 10,000 expanding tumors were possible to detect for each ρ_{h}-value. The probability P_{gt} for a growing tumor is therefore the number of the sets of parameter values ($\alpha_{\mathrm{ht}}, \rho_{\mathrm{i}}, \alpha_{\mathrm{it}}, \alpha_{\mathrm{th}}$) leading to an expanding tumor divided by 10,000. This probability was thus computed for each value ρ_{h} (varied from 0 to 1 by a step $\mathrm{d}\rho_{\mathrm{h}} = 0.05$). By plotting the probability P_{gt} versus the growth rate ρ_{h} (Figure 8.48), the probability P_{gt} is found to be highly significantly correlated ($r = 0.99$, $p < 10^{-6}$) to the growth rate ρ_{h}. This curve shows that tissues with fast regeneration lead more often to an expanding tumor than those with slow regeneration. This is equivalent the relationship between the number of stem cell divisions in the lifetime in a given tissue and the lifetime risk of cancer in that tissue which was obtained by Tomasetti and Vogelstein.[124]

These results show that the lifetime risk is strongly correlated with the total number of divisions of the normal self-renewing cells. In this approach, the random mutations arising during DNA replication does not play any role since all "patients" were considered with an initial small population of tumor cells (a mutation occurred

[124]C. Tomasetti & B. Vogelstein, Variation in cancer risk among tissues can be explained by the number of stem cell divisions, *Science*, **347**, 78–81, 2015.

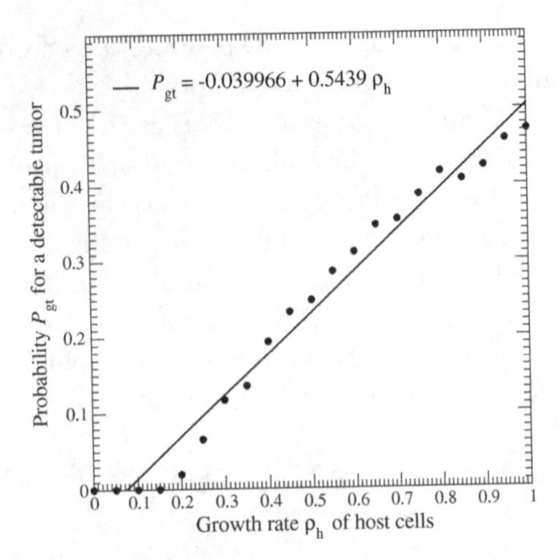

Figure 8.48 The relationship between the probability P_{gt} for detecting a growing tumor after 50,000 arbitrary units of time *versus* the growth rate ρ_h of host cells.

in each case). Thus, the correlation obtained between the probability for a growing tumor and the growth rate of host cells results from the variations in the parameter values of the model (8.5) describing the inter-patient variability related to the interactions tumor cells have with the surrounding micro-environment. For instance, the smallest growth rate ρ_h (0.15) of host cells for which the number of detected growing tumors is non-zero would correspond to *Pelvis osteocarcoma* as shown in the data provided by Tomasetti and Vogelstein[125] and the largest ($\rho_h = 1.0$) to the basal cell cancer. This shows that the variations in the probabilities for an expanding tumor is fully explained by the nesting tissue state mostly affected by the way of life and external factors. This explanation offers a fully deterministic relationship between the lifetime risks for cancer and the way of life.

These simulations clearly show that the state of the surrounding tumor tissue is preponderant in the evolution of a cancer. Since only in 10% of the cases, the state of the nesting tissue is related to the heredity,[126] this state necessarily results from the way of life and external factors as the quality of the air breathed, working conditions, sleep quality, exercise, etc. The optimal functioning of a given body with its genetic properties is mainly governed by the way of life. For instance, obesity induces high level of saturated fatty acids in blood which, in turns, promotes inflammation. Such a feature has a direct consequence on the parameter values governing interaction of immune and host cells with tumor ones. Obesity increases the rate of insulin growth factor that directly affects the growth rate of tumor cells.[127] The level of exercise

[125] Tomasetti & Vogelstein, 2015, *Ibid.*

[126] P. Anand, A. B. Kunnumakara, C. Sundaram, K. B. Harikumar, S. T. Tharakan, O. S. Lai, B. Sung & B. B. Aggarwal, Cancer is a preventable disease that requires major lifestyle changes, *Pharmaceutical Research*, **25** (9), 2097–2116, 2008.

[127] L. R. Howe, K. Subbaramaiah, C. A. Hudis & A. J. Dannenberg, Molecular pathways: Adipose inflammation as a mediator of obesity associated cancer, *Clinical Cancer Research*, **19** (22), 6074–6083, 2013.

performed by patients is known for improving the response of the immune system and for increasing the rate of intra-cellular glutathione.[128] Exercise therefore affects values of parameter $\rho_{\rm i}$, $\alpha_{\rm it}$ and $\alpha_{\rm ti}$. Smoking, alcohol drinking, and ingesting anti-oxidant agents also influence these parameter values. All of this would suggest that preserving the tissue, where mutations always occur, in good conditions, could be an efficient strategy to reduce cancer risks.

8.5.4 *Observability of Tumor Growth*

We saw that there is a powerful technique for evidencing a chaotic attractor from experimental data (see p. 251): it consists in plotting the measured time series $x(t)$ versus itself but shifted by a delay τ. The reconstructed space spanned by $x(t-\tau)$ and $x(t)$ thus provides a projection of the state portrait. In principle, any time series is convenient and there is a beautiful theorem due to Floris Takens that ensures that, if the measurement function is generic, it is sufficient to use a reconstructed space whose dimension is $2d_{\rm f}+1$ where $d_{\rm f}$ is the fractal dimension of the attractor to have a diffeomorphism between the original state portrait and the reconstructed one.[129] A diffeomorphism ensures not only that two different states in the original space are indeed distinguished in the reconstructed one, but also that the differential properties in the original space are preserved in the reconstructed one (a smooth curve cannot become a curve with a singularity). This is the most demanding property between two different representations of a given state portrait. It ensures that the determinism is preserved (the reconstructed trajectory cannot intersect itself) as well as most of the properties of the underlying dynamics. Due to this theorem, it was believed that any measured variable was suitable for getting a reliable reconstruction of the dynamics. Nevertheless, as any other, this theorem needs some conditions to be safely applied. In this case, the measurement function, that is, the map $h(\boldsymbol{x}) : \mathbb{R}^d \mapsto \mathbb{R}$ that selects one variable from the state vector $\boldsymbol{x}$ spanning the d-dimensional original state space has to be "generic". This means that the chosen measurement function must behave as "almost all" measurement functions. For a three-dimensional system, a generic measurement function could be such as

$$h(\boldsymbol{x}) = ax + by + cz \tag{8.7}$$

where x, y, and z are three components of the state vector $\boldsymbol{x}$ and a, b and c are nonzero parameter values. The main problem is that most often, and this is also true in experiments, the measurement function returns one of the variables spanning the state space, that is, x, y or z. By definition, such a measurement function has little chance to be generic and the condition under which the Takens theorem can

[128] A. Rundle, Molecular epidemiology of physical activity and cancer, *Cancer Epidemiology, Biomarkers & Prevention*, **14** (1), 227–236, 2005.

[129] F. Takens, Detecting strange attractors in turbulence, *Lecture Notes in Mathematics*, **898**, 366–381, 1981.

be applied does not hold. The choice of the measured variable is therefore a key step in the reconstruction procedure.

A reconstruction procedure is nothing else than a coordinate transformation. Rather than using the delay coordinates, it is possible to use derivative ones that present the advantage to allow easy analytical computations. There is a rotation and a rescaling between delay and derivative coordinates: these two sets of coordinates are therefore equivalent.[130] Thus, when a variable x is measured, the attractor can be reconstructed in the space spanned by the successive time derivatives of x (formally, these derivatives are the Lie derivatives). Takens wrote one version of its theorem for using derivative coordinates. If the coordinate transformation $\Phi : \boldsymbol{x} \mapsto \boldsymbol{X}$ between the original state space $\mathbb{R}^d(\boldsymbol{x})$ and the reconstructed one $\mathbb{R}^{d_r}(\boldsymbol{X})$ is such as it is one-to-one and the determinant $\text{Det}\mathcal{J}_\Phi$ of its Jacobian matrix never vanishes, then two distinct states $\boldsymbol{x}_1 \neq \boldsymbol{x}_2$ in the original state space are also distinguished in the reconstructed space, that is, $\boldsymbol{X}_1 \neq \boldsymbol{X}_2$. Contrary to this, when there is a subset $\mathcal{M}^{\text{obs}} \subset \mathbb{R}^d(\boldsymbol{x})$ for which the determinant $\text{Det}\mathcal{J}_\Phi = 0$, then any state in $\mathcal{M}^{\text{obs}}$ cannot be observed from the measurement of the variable x. This subset is called the *singular observability manifold.*[131] The more often this singular observability manifold is visited, the less observable through the measurements the dynamics is. The singular observability manifold is strongly dependent on the measured variable. The concept of observability was introduced by Rudolf Emil Kálmán (1930–2016).[132] Observability can be viewed as characterizing the quality of information carried by a variable. Kálmán also established that observability was the dual of controllability. The addressed question was "*What kind and how much information is needed to achieve a desired control?*" Observability deals with the ability to distinguish different states of the studied system, controllability with the ability to lead the system toward a targeted state.

The common approach in control theory for assessing observability is to determine whether the so-called *observability matrix*, that is, the jacobian matrix of the coordinate transformation,[133] is full rank or not: the original state space is thus fully observable or not. These concepts were extended to nonlinear systems by Robert Hermann and Arthur Krener.[134] In order to have a not so crisp classification in terms of observability, Bernard Friedland introduced an observability (controllability) index as a continuous function of the parameter of the system.[135] This concept

[130] J. F. Gibson, J. D. Farmer, M. Casdagli & S. Eubank, An analytic approach to practical state space reconstruction, *Physica D*, **57**, 1–30, 1992.

[131] M. Frunzete, J.-P. Barbot & C. Letellier, Influence of the singular manifold of nonobservable states in reconstructing chaotic attractors, *Physical Review E*, **86**, 026205, 2012.

[132] R. E. Kálmán, On the general theory of control systems, *Proceedings of the First IFAC Moscow Congress*, Butterworth Scientific Publications, pp. 481–492, 1960.

[133] C. Letellier, L. A. Aguirre & J. Maquet, Relation between observability and differential embeddings for nonlinear dynamics, *Physical Review E*, **71**, 066213, 2005.

[134] R. Hermann & A. J. Krener, Nonlinear controllability and observability, *IEEE Transactions on Automatic Control*, **22** (5), 728–740, 1977.

[135] B. Friedland, Controllability index based on conditioning number, *Journal of Dynamic Systems, Measurement, and Control*, **97** (4), 444–445, 1975.

that allows to distinguish between more and less observable scenarios was then extended by Luis A. Aguirre for ranking the variables of a given system according to the observability of the corresponding state space they provide.[136] The observability coefficients, initially derived from the linear theory,[137] were then extended to nonlinear systems.[138] The problem with these numerical observability coefficients was that they were not normalized and it was not possible to compare results among different dynamical systems. In order to overcome this weakness, symbolic observability coefficients were developed.[139] Within the unit interval $[0;1]$, these coefficients $\eta_{\boldsymbol{X}}$ allow to determine whether the observability provided by some measured variable is either full ($\eta_{\boldsymbol{X}} = 1$), good ($1 > \eta_{\boldsymbol{X}} > 0.75$), or poor otherwise.[140]

The symbolic observability coefficients were computed for the cancer model (8.5) when isolated in a single site ($\kappa = 0$). Surprisingly, it occurred that measuring the population of host cells provides a better observability ($\eta_{x,\dot{x},\ddot{x}} = 0.56$) of the dynamics than measuring the population of tumor cells ($\eta_{z,\dot{z},\ddot{z}} = 0.30$).[141] This results led to reconsider how patients should be followed after a treatment for a primary tumor. Indeed, the observability analysis of the cancer model (8.5) suggests that to investigate the dynamics underlying the tumor growth, it was more reliable to monitor the micro-environment of the tumor than the tumor itself. With Fabrice Denis (an oncologist working at the Centre Jean Bernard, Le Mans, France), we choose the symptomatic lung cancer and started to design a follow-up easy to use in routine clinics.[142] Using the experience gained in investigating chaotic dynamics, it was clear that for monitoring dynamical changes, it was necessary to have higher sampling rate than the 3 or 6 months commonly used in routine follow-up based on imaging: to keep reasonable the cost of such a procedure and to ensure a good compliance by the patients, the single possibility was to ask the patients to assess themselves their symptoms at home, and to send the weekly filled form by a web-application. The lung cancer being symptomatic, the relevant symptoms were

[136] L. A. Aguirre, Controllability and observability of linear systems: some noninvariant aspects, *IEEE Transactions on Education*, **38**, 33–39, 1995.

[137] C. Letellier, J. Maquet, L. Le Sceller, G. Gouesbet & L. A. Aguirre, On the non-equivalence of observables in phase space reconstructions from recorded time series, *Journal of Physics A*, **31**, 7913–7927, 1998.

[138] C. Letellier, L. A. Aguirre & J. Maquet, How the choice of the observable may influence the analysis of non linear dynamical systems, *Communications in Nonlinear Science and Numerical Simulation*, **11** (5), 555–576, 2006.

[139] C. Letellier & L. A. Aguirre, Symbolic observability coefficients for univariate and multivariate analysis, *Physical Review E*, **79**, 066210, 2009 — E. Bianco-Martinez, M. S. Baptista & C. Letellier, Symbolic computations of nonlinear observability, *Physical Review E*, **91**, 062912, 2015.

[140] I. Sendiña-Nadal, S. Boccaletti & C. Letellier, Observability coefficients for predicting the class of synchronizability from the algebraic structure of the local oscillators, *Physical Review E*, **94**, 042205, 2016.

[141] Initially the numerical observability were computed — see C. Letellier, F. Denis & L. A. Aguirre, What can be learned from a chaotic cancer model?, *Journal of Theoretical Biology*, **322**, 7–16, 2013 — and the symbolic ones were computed by Bianco-Martinez *et al.*, 2015, *Ibid.*

[142] F. Denis, L. Viger, A. Charron, E. Voog & C. Letellier, Detecting lung cancer relapse using self-evaluation forms weekly filled at home: the sentinel follow-up, *Supportive Care in Cancer*, **22** (1), 79–85, 2013.

progressively selected: weight, appetite loss, weakness, pain, cough, breathlessness, depression, fever, face swelling (to detect superior cave syndrome), lump under skin (to detect sub-cutaneous metastasis), voice changing (to detect potential mediastinal involvement), and blood in sputum.[143] The patient score his[144] symptoms using the scale as follows.

$$\begin{vmatrix} 0 & & \text{no problem} \\ 1 & \text{if} & \text{mild problem} \\ 2 & & \text{medium problem} \\ 3 & & \text{important problem.} \end{vmatrix}$$

The patient reports these 12 markers via a web-application.[145] A Patient self-Reported Outcome score — the so-called PRO-score — is then constructed by taking the sum of these 12 numbers. When the PRO-score exceeds the threshold value of 7 during two consecutive weeks, one should consider that there is a clinically significant degradation of the general health status, that is, the environment gives way under the strain of the tumor.[146] In such a case, an automatically triggered alert is sent to the oncologist by e-mail. The oncologist then calls the patient to confirm that there is no input error and to assess clinical symptoms accuracy. Visit and imaging are brought forward when relapse is suspected.

An example of the graph provided to the clinician is shown in Figure 8.49.[147] The patient, a man born in 1949, had a left pneumonectomy in 2005 for a T_3 squamous cell — that form the lining of the lungs — carcinoma (see Table 8.3 for the tumor staging[148]). A trifocal relapse occurred in his right lung 6 years later and the patient was treated by a stereotactic surgery. Another relapse occurred in this right lung nearly three years later: the patient received a chemotherapy combining two drugs (paclitaxel and carboplatin) for 6 successive cycles of 21 days. Maintenance with erlotinib (a drug designed to block tumor cell growth by targeting

[143] F. Denis, L. Viger, A. Charron, E. Voog, O. Dupuis, Y. Pointreau & C. Letellier, Detection of lung cancer relapse using self-reported symptoms transmitted via an Internet Web-application : pilot study of the sentinel follow-up, *Support Care Cancer*, **22** (6), 1467–1473, 2014.

[144] I am not sexist in writing "his" but I dislike the inclusive way of writing that is inserting an instability in the mind, and since I am a man... I indeed suggest to women to write "her", and men to write "his" when the two genders can be used... this would be easier and less disturbing while reading. The key solution would be to introduce a neutral pronoun or to use "its", but I leave that to linguists...

[145] MOOVECARE™ is now a class I medical device CE marked developed by SIVAN INNOVATION: `http://www.sivan-innovation.com/moovcare`.

[146] F. Denis, S. Yossi, Senna, A.-L. Septans, A. Charron, E. Voog, O. Dupuis, G. Ganem, Y. Pointreau & C. Letellier, Improving survival in patients treated for a lung cancer using self-evaluated symptoms reported through a web application, *American Journal of Clinical Oncology*, **40** (5), 464–469, 2017.

[147] F. Denis, B. Koontz & C. Letellier, Apparent progression on imaging of a lung tumor in a patient treated by nivolumab correctly assessed by self-reported outcomes, *Case Report on Oncology*, accepted on October 26, 2018.

[148] F. U. Kay, A. Kandathil, K. Batra, S. S. Saboo, S. Abbara & P. Rajiah, Revisions to the Tumor, Node, Metastasis staging of lung cancer (8th edition): Rationale, radiologic findings and clinical implications, *World Journal of Radiology*, **9** (6), 269–279, 2017.

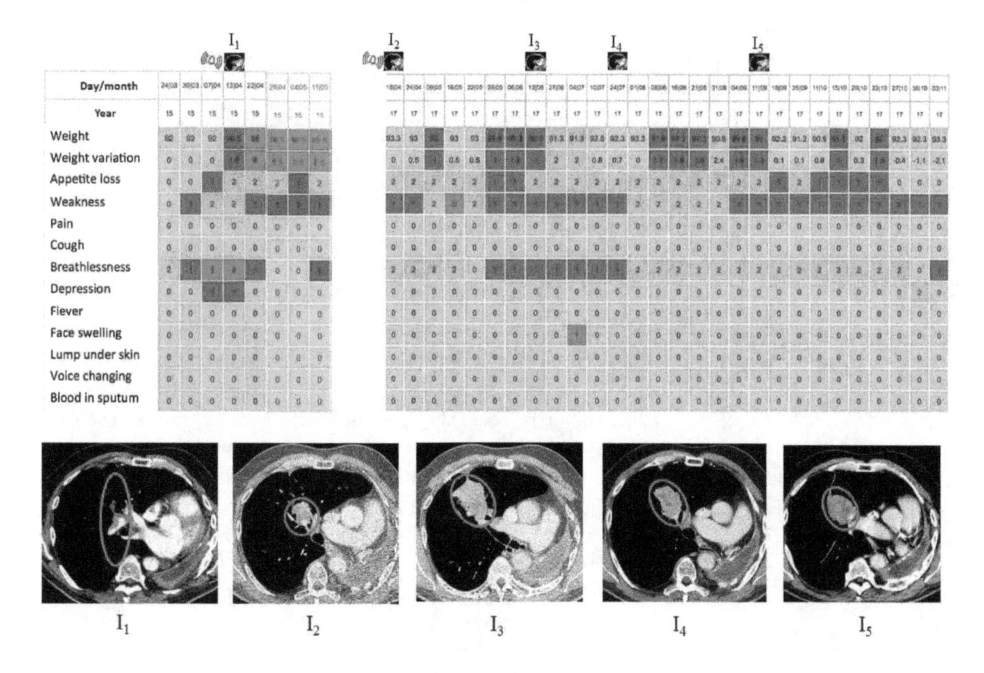

Figure 8.49 Screenshots of the synthetic representation (not provided to the patient) of the time evolution of patient's symptoms from his weekly completed forms. Scores are converted into a color scale as follows. $0 \equiv$ light green, $1 \equiv$ dark green, $2 \equiv$ yellow, and $3 \equiv$ red.

a protein epidermal growth factor receptor present on the surface of some cancer cells and some normal cells) was also used after a partial response to chemotherapy (adding this drug to chemotherapy improves the overall survival by 19% and the progression-free survival by 29% when compared to chemotherapy alone[149]). A web-mediated follow-up of this patient was initiated in a phase III randomized trial performed for assessing the relevance of weekly reported symptoms to the medical team.[150]

[149] F. Cappuzzo, T. Ciuleanu, L. Stelmakh, S. Cicenas, A. Szczesna, E. Juhasz, E. Esteban Gonzalez, O. Molinier, G. Klingelschmitt & G. Giaccone, SATURN: A double-blind, randomized, phase III study of maintenance erlotinib versus placebo following nonprogression with first-line platinum-based chemotherapy in patients with advanced NSCLC, *Journal of Clinical Oncology*, **27** (15), 8001–8001, 2009.

[150] F. Denis, C. Lethrosne, N. Pourel, O. Molinier, Y. Pointreau, J. Domont, H. Bourgeois, H. Senellart, P. Trémolières, T. Lizée, J. Bennouna, T. Urban, C. El Khouri, A. Charron, A.-L. Septans, M. Balavoine, S. Landry, P. Solal-Céligny & C. Letellier, Randomized trial comparing a web-mediated follow-up with routine surveillance in lung cancer patients, *Journal of the National Cancer Institute*, **109** (9), djx029, 2017.

Table 8.3 Lung cancer staging of the primary tumor. The size S of the primary tumor is reported but it should be clear that this is not necessarily the most important characteristics that determine the pronostic: it characterizes the tumor, not the micro-environment.

Stage	Size S	Description
T_x		The tumor cannot be characterized
T_0		No evidence for a tumor
T_{is}		Carcinoma *in situ*: there are abnormal cells that grow in their normal place (*in situ*) and that usually not form a tumor
T_1	$T_{1a} : S \leq 1$ cm $T_{1b} : 1 < S \leq 2$ cm $T_{1c} : 2 < S \leq 3$ cm	The tumor is surrounded by the lung or the visceral pleura and does not involve the main bronchus
T_2	$T_{2a} : 3 < S \leq 4$ cm $T_{2b} : 4 < S \leq 5$ cm	The tumor involves the main bronchus without carina (the ridge of cartilage in the trachea that occurs between the division of the two main bronchi) involvement or visceral pleural invasion
T_3	$5 < S \leq 7$ cm	There is a separate tumor in the same lobe or a direct invasion of the chest wall (including the parietal pleura and either the superior sulcus, the parietal pericardium or the phrenic nerve)
T_4	$S > 7$ cm	There is a separate tumor in the different lobe of ipsilateral lung or an invasion of either the heart, the great vessels, the diaphragm, the mediastinum, the trachea, the carina, the esophagus, the recurrent laryngeal nerve or the vertebral body.

In the present case (Figure 8.49), the medical staff received an automatic alert sent by the web-application (see the red signal) subsequently to an important dyspnea that occurred at the end of the tenth year after the treatment of patient's primary tumor. A phone call confirmed the symptoms and an anticipated computerized tomography scan (imaging I_1) was performed the same day, and revealed a massive pulmonary embolism. Treatment was quickly initiated and clinical improvement was reported (breathlessness and weakness returned to light and dark green, respectively after 2-weeks with anti-coagulant drug). Two-years later, an alarm (see the red signal) triggered an imaging (I_2) which revealed a relapse; and a chemotherapy (nivolumab) blocking a negative regulator of T-lymphocyte activation and response, thus allowing the immune system to attack the tumor, was initiated. An apparent increase of the tumor size was detected by the imaging (I_3 in Figure 8.49) but it was associated with a contradictory good response to treatment as indicated by the color map. The next imaging (I_4) showed a partial response (decrease in the tumor size) and clinical benefit was maintained as reported by the color map after that imaging. All this improvements were later confirmed (I_5). The patient did not present any further complications...

The phase III study showed that the median overall survival was 19 months in the experimental group and 12 months in the control group ($p = 0.001$). The patient status at the first relapse was 0 to 1 in 75.9% of the patients in the experimental group and 32.5% of those in the control group ($p < 0.001$), leading to optimal treatment in 72.4% of the patients from the experimental group and in 32.5% from the control group ($p < 0.001$). The rate of imaging was reduced by 49% per patient per year compared with the control group. More patients attended unscheduled visits in the experimental group (58.3%) than in the control group (24.6%, $p = 0.008$).

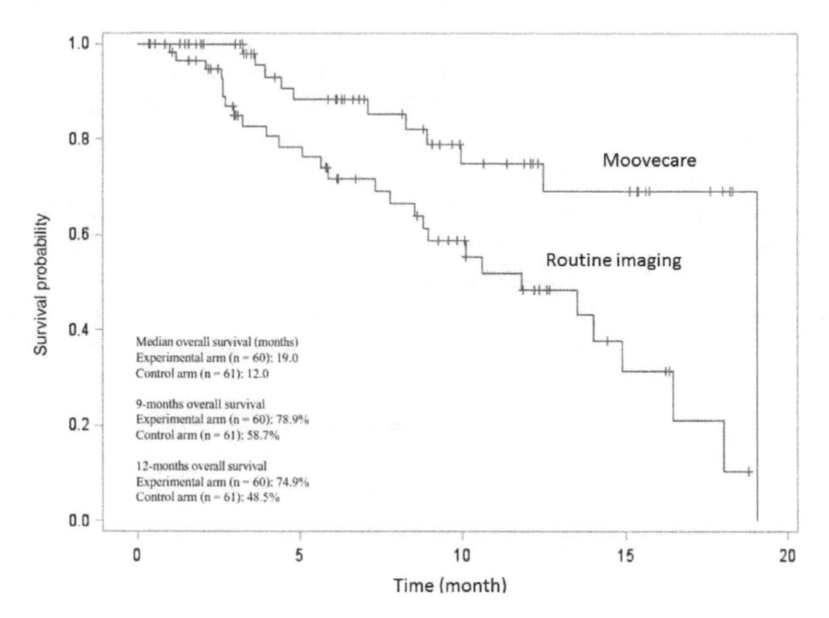

Figure 8.50 Kaplan-Meier estimates for the survival between the initiation and the end of the trial. Adapted from Denis *et al.*, 2017.

There is thus a better survival in patients using the web-application than in patients with control follow-up including serial imaging. The web-mediated follow-up also allowed a decrease in the number of imaging tests. The survival benefit observed in most of patients could be explained by earlier relapse detection at which patients have a better performance status, thus allowing optimal salvage treatment. Optimal treatments are indeed reserved for patients with a good global status, presenting better abilities to manage drug toxicities; indeed, there is a lack of a survival benefit in patients with a poorer global status.[151] Moreover, other dangerous medical conditions (one pulmonary embolism, two pneumonia, one severe bronchitis, one pericarditis, and one deep venous thrombosis) were also detected and treated earlier in the web-mediated follow-up group, leading to a reduction in mortality. A better quality of life was observed for patients in the experimental group at six months: such a feature could favor a better survival and progression-free survival: early management of physical and depressive symptoms as well as

[151]N. Hanna, D. Johnson, S. Temin & G. Masters, Systemic therapy for stage IV non-small-cell lung cancer: American Society of Clinical Oncology clinical practice guideline update summary, *Journal of Oncology Practice*, **13** (12), 832–837, 2017.

iatrogenic events may delay patient degradation, while these symptoms may be not necessarily managed as quickly with a routine follow-up. Investigating a simple cancer model thus helped to develop an efficient and innovative follow-up for patients treated for a lung cancer.

8.6 Conclusion

Using tools drawn from chaos theory, we have not really shown that cardiac dynamics or tumor growth is chaotic: this question remains open in view of the difficulty for getting reliable recordings, that is, recordings without real-world influences. In some specific cases, we were even able to show that the breathing dynamics in patients under noninvasive mechanical ventilation may be actually chaotic. In all these cases, investigating the measured dynamics using techniques borrowed from chaos theory allows to provide useful answers to physicians, particularly when we do not forget the question that can be posed by them: we were not too concerned by showing whether the underlying dynamics is chaotic or not.

Chapter 9

Epilogue

While there is a firm foundation for the laws of chaos when a system has low dimension and is governed by highly dissipative dynamics, "chaoticians" do not always have a good understanding when behavior is governed by systems with low dissipation[1] and/or high dimension (that is, dimension greater than 3). Very many difficulties are encountered for such systems, and so far it has not been possible to understand chaos in situations more complicated than those encountered in previous chapters.

9.1 The Fourth Dimension

In the plane, that is, in a two-dimensional space, the possible dynamical behavior is very simple as a result of the Poincaré-Bendixon theorem which guarantees that only singular points and limit cycles can occur. In three dimensions things are more complicated because chaotic behavior can be seen, but we are very often able to gain an understanding of how these structures are organized (Part II, Chapter 4). By contrast, when the state space dimension is four,[2] things become enormously more complicated because of our inability to visualize things in such a space, as hinted at in Figure 9.1. This comes from the fact that we really cannot visualize things in spaces except when we can move around in these spaces. Poincaré believed that *anyone who devoted his existence to it perhaps might be able to understand the fourth dimension.*[3]

To gain an insight about the difficulty of understanding the structure of objects embedded in spaces of dimension greater than three, we consider how many different ways it is possible to pairwise glue together the edges of a rectangle. The first case is the simplest: the parallel pairs of edges are glued together pairwise to construct a torus (Figure 9.1(a)). This object, more prosaically called a tire tube, can be imagined without difficulty in our ordinary three-dimensional space.

[1]The weakly dissipative systems are systems which have a small rate of energy dissipation under the form of heat, by friction for instance.

[2]Four axes are thus required to define an appropriate space and four coordinates are needed to define a point in this space.

[3]H. Poincaré, *La Science et l'hypothèse*, Flammarion, p. 68, 1902.

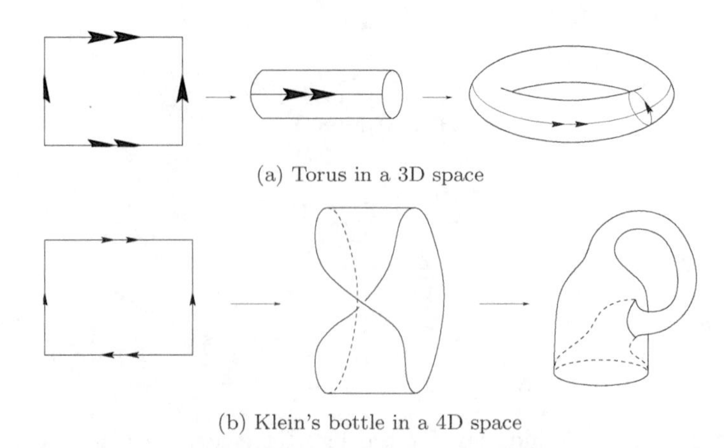

(a) Torus in a 3D space

(b) Klein's bottle in a 4D space

Figure 9.1 Evidence of the complexity of objects in spaces of dimension greater than three: begin with a rectangle where the opposite edges are glued together pairwise. If no half-turns are introduced, one constructs a torus (tire tube) which can physically exist in a three-dimensional space. If a half-turn is introduced before the opposite edges are glued together, one constructs a "Klein bottle" which can only be represented without self-intersections in a four-dimensional space.

We point out that the surface defined in this way has two sides and no boundary. If the initial rectangle is now glued together after two opposite sides have been given a half-twist, one obtains a somewhat bizarre surface, called a *Klein bottle*, discovered by Felix Klein (1849–1925) in 1882.[4] This somewhat peculiar bottle has its neck glued to its interior bottom side. In our usual three-dimensional space this surface intersects itself (Figure 9.1(b)). It is necessary to use a four-dimensional space to represent this surface in such a way that it does not exhibit self intersections. We ought to confess that it is absolutely not trivial to represent this surface in a four-dimensional space. This surface also has no boundary, and it has only one side in four dimensions.

We point out that some of the difficulties in describing chaotic behaviors in spaces of dimension greater than three come from the difficulties in representing objects in such higher-dimensional spaces. This is closely related to the fact that, if there are many topological results available for three-dimensional spaces, there are far fewer available for four-dimensional spaces. In fact, this branch of mathematics, where intuition and drawings play a very large role, currently suffers from our inability to understand the fourth dimension, which hides its secrets in abstractions.

[4]F. Klein, *Uber Riemann's Theorie der algebraischen Functionen und ihrer integrale*, B. G. Teunbner, 1882.

9.2 A Weakly Dissipative System

Another property of dynamical systems can complicate the analysis of chaotic behavior: a weak energy dissipation can impede the rapid relaxation of trajectories to a band whose thickness can be neglected (as occurs for the Rössler system). In this case, extracting a branched manifold from the data is not an easy task and an analysis using symbolic dynamics can be astonishingly complicated because of the difficulty of defining a good partition for the attractor. Edward Lorenz has proposed an example of this, as usual, in the field of meteorology. In 1984 this pioneer proposed the three-dimensional model

$$\begin{cases} \dot{x} = -y^2 - z^2 - ax + aF \\ \dot{y} = xy - bxz - y + G \\ \dot{z} = bxy + xz - z \end{cases}$$

that could claim to be the simplest model for global atmospheric circulation.[5] This system produces a fairly complicated toroidal chaos (Figure 9.2(a)). A Poincaré section reveals the complexity of this model (Figure 9.2(b)).

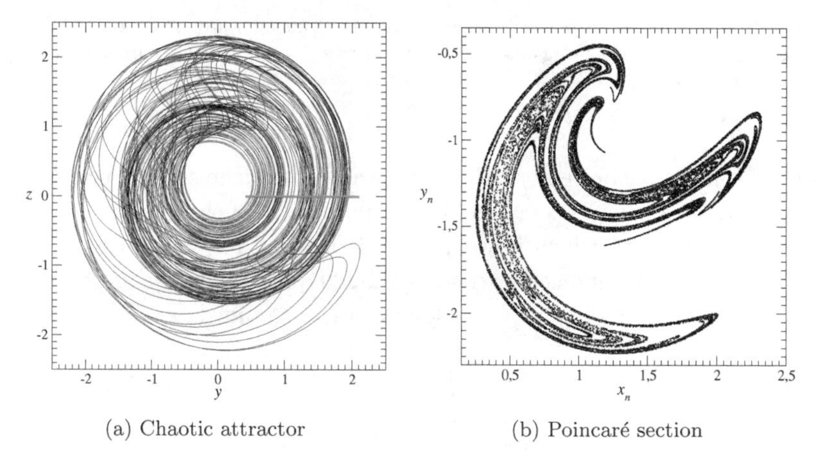

(a) Chaotic attractor (b) Poincaré section

Figure 9.2 Chaotic behavior of a geophysical model proposed by Lorenz. The foliation occurring in the Poincaré section (b) combined with the toroidal structure does not allow a characterization as easy as those that can be provided for highly dissipative dynamical systems. The 25,000 points shown in the Poincaré section correspond to a duration of about 2,500 years. Parameter values: $a = 0.25$, $b = 4$, $F = 8$, and $G = 1$.

The Poincaré section is foliated, a property that is responsible for the difficulties encountered in describing the structure of this attractor. One of the difficulties resides in the absence of simple criteria for constructing a partition for toroidal attractor and, as a result, for constructing a good symbolic dynamics. In fact, periodic

[5]E. N. Lorenz, Irregularity: a fundamental property of the atmosphere, *Tellus A*, **36**, 98–110, 1984.

orbits cannot be identified and it is not easy to propose a branched manifold. An interesting attempt was provided by Sylvain Mangiarotti and coworkers.[6] At present we are faced with the impossibility of describing weakly dissipative phenomena in terms of stripes that are stretched and folded on themselves.

9.3 Another Toroidal Chaos

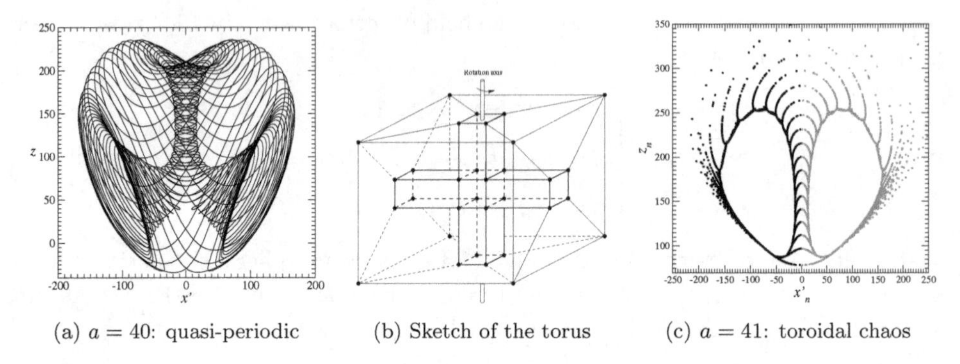

(a) $a = 40$: quasi-periodic (b) Sketch of the torus (c) $a = 41$: toroidal chaos

Figure 9.3 Toroïdal chaos produced by the Li system. Organized around a nontrivial torus (b), this attractor presents a quite large number of foldings as shown by the Poincaré section (c). Other parameter values: $c = 11/6$, $d = 0.16$, $e = 0.65$, $k = 55$ and $f = 20$.

Most of the behaviors embedded within a three-dimensional space have been well described by a branched manifold (template), with few exceptions as the geophysical Lorenz system which is weakly dissipative. This class of attractors still resists to a topological characterization. Although quite rarely encountered in three-dimensional space, toroidal chaos was found in the modified Lorenz system

$$\begin{cases} \dot{x} = a(y - x) + dxz \\ \dot{y} = kx + fy - xz \\ \dot{z} = cz + xy - ex^2 \end{cases} \tag{9.1}$$

by Dequan Li.[7] The attractor, in fact a long limit cycle that is replaced with the chaotic regime under a light change in the parameter values (Figure 9.3(a)), is organized around a non trivial torus that is sketched in Figure 9.3(b).[8] Its chaotic nature is revealed by the numerous foldings observed in a Poincaré section computed for the chaotic regime (Figure 9.3(b)). The main difficulty arises from the fact that it is not obvious to identify some stripes within such attractor.

[6]S. Mangiarotti, M. Peyre & M. Huc, A chaotic model for the epidemic of Ebola virus disease in West Africa (2013–2016), *Chaos*, **26**, 113112, 2016.

[7]D. Li, A three-scroll chaotic attractor, *Physics Letters A*, **372** (4), 387–393, 2008.

[8]C. Letellier & R. Gilmore, Poincaré sections for a new three-dimensional toroïdal attractor, *Journal of Physics A*, **42**, 015101, 2009.

9.4 Hyperchaotic Behavior

Most of the studied chaotic behaviors are associated with a single stretching direction combined with a single squeezing direction, such as that shown schematically in Figure 5.10 (p. 59). When the evolution of a system occurs in a four-dimensional space, a second stretching direction can appear (Figure 9.4).

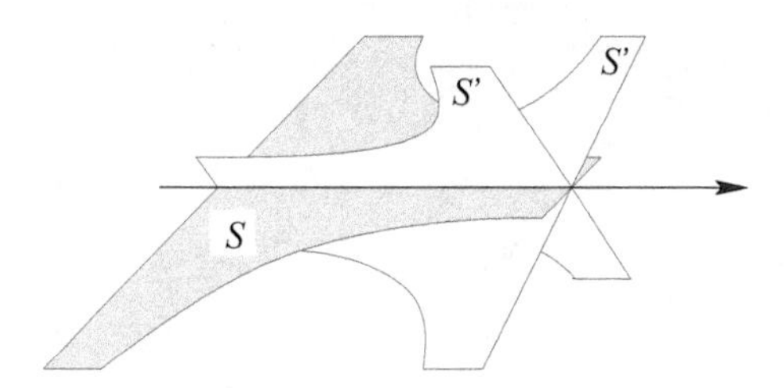

Figure 9.4 Sketch of hyperchaotic trajectory located at the intersection of two expanding directions S' and one contracting surface S. A double difficulty is encountered when a description is attempted: one is related to the state space which has four dimensions and another results from the layered structure due to the combination of the two stretching directions.

In 1979 Otto Rössler proposed the set of equations[9]

$$\begin{cases} \dot{x} = -y - z \\ \dot{y} = x + 0.25y + w \\ \dot{z} = 3.0 + xz \\ \dot{w} = -0.5z + 0.05w \end{cases} \tag{9.2}$$

that produces such dynamics. Without the third variable z, the trajectory produced by this system is ejected to infinity. Variable z acts as a retroaction beyond a given threshold and ensures the folding sending the trajectory back to the center of the attractor (Figure 9.5). He called this behavior *hyperchaotic.* This model is not particularly complicated, other than for the fact that the associated state space is four-dimensional. The two stretching directions produce a first-return map without any very clear structure; this does not permit a partition to be constructed for this attractor (Figure 9.5). Because of the thickness of the first-return map it is quite unthinkable that a branched manifold can correctly describe the structure of this attractor. The topological description of such a structure is currently an open question...

9.5 Simple Models and Complex Behaviors

Towards the middle of the 1970s the adjective *chaotic* entered the common vocabulary. The term *chaos* appeared for the second time in a scientific context in an article prepared in 1975 by Tien-Yien Li and James Yorke,[10] who studied solutions

[9]O. E. Rössler, An equation for hyperchaos, *Physics Letters A*, **71**, 155–157, 1979.

[10]T.-Y. Li and J. A. Yorke, Period three implies chaos, *American Mathematical Monthly, 82*, 985–992, 1975.

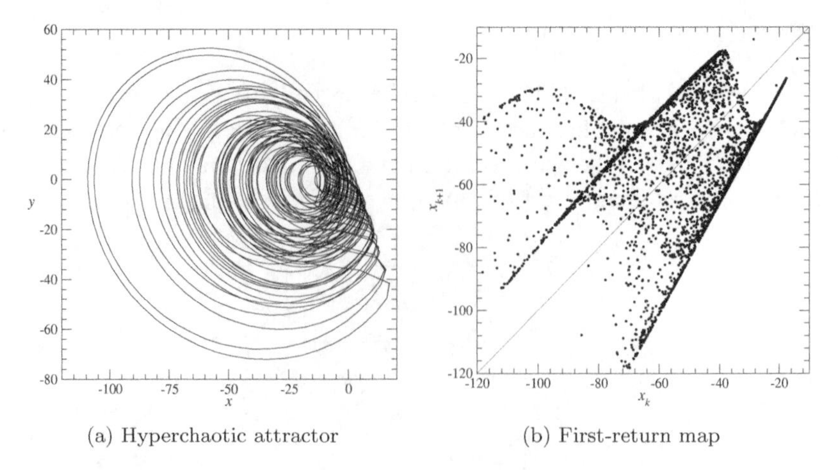

(a) Hyperchaotic attractor (b) First-return map

Figure 9.5 Hyperchaotic behavior produced by the four-dimensional model (9.2) proposed by Rössler. The union of two expanding directions forbids a description using a simple thin stripe. This complicates the problem of finding a good partition for this attractor. It is doubtful that this object can be described by a branched manifold.

to the simple logistic map $x_{n+1} = \mu x_n(1-x_n)$ (a second-order recurrence equation). The set of values $\{x_n\}$ represents a trajectory in the dynamical system so defined. The central result of Li and Yorke was that under the recurrence $x_{n+1} = f(x_n)$, with $f(x)$ a quadratic polynomial, if there is a period-three orbit, that is, points x_n that satisfy $x_{n+3} = x_n$, then there is also an infinite number of aperiodic solutions. These are solutions with $n_{n+p} = x_n$ no matter what value p assumes. Aside from the title *Period three implies chaos*, Li and Yorke used the word *chaos* only once, to designate "the aperiodic solutions *that could be called chaotic.*" A year later, in 1976, a small note entitled *A precise definition of chaos* appeared in the review *Nature.*[11] There chaos was defined as aperiodic solutions by mathematicians. In the same year Otto E. Rössler published "*A continuous equation for chaos*", this being an even simpler model than that proposed by Edward Lorenz. At that time three different communities spoke of the same concept using three different words: mathematicians spoke of *aperiodic solutions*; hydrodynamicists spoke of *turbulence*; and a group of young scientists, midway between mathematicians and physicists who used computers as their preferred mathematical tool, designated the complicated solutions that they had computed using the term *chaos.*

The first to systematically use this term was most probably Rössler, who peppered his articles with this word. In the United States it was used systematically by the entire group at the University of California at Santa Cruz starting in the 1980s. Lorenz did not use this word until 1983. From that time on the three communities converged on this one word. We point out that mathematicians did not characterize chaotic trajectories as such; rather they used the periodic orbits in chaotic

[11]P. Kloeden, M. A. B. Deckin & A. Z. Trikel, A Precise definition of chaos, *Nature*, **264**, 295, 1976.

attractors as advocated by Poincaré. Hydrodynamicists and numerical integrators turned themselves inside out trying to characterize these behaviors which seemed to resist every possible attempt to describe them. As a result, they settled on this terminology, *chaos*, a term traditionally applied to the indescribable.

Chaotic behavior is deterministic behavior, for instance governed by differential equations, for which long term prediction is not possible. The term *chaos* currently incorporates both senses — of determinism and of long term unpredictability. But pay attention!! chaotic behavior is structured by underlying determinism, and unpredictable does not mean random.

A number of different types of chaotic behavior have already been correctly described. They are solutions, for the most part, of dissipative three-dimensional systems. Their global structure is described in terms of a branched manifold, periodic orbits, symbolic dynamics, and one now understands that the rigid organization of periodic orbits is governed by strict laws. In fact, chaotic behavior can certainly not be associated with motions that are *without form or regularity*. This type of motion does not deserve the qualifier "*chaotic*." At this point we are confronted with an epistemological problem related to the choice of words. It cannot be denied that the complexity (apparent?) touches one of the most sensitive scientific nerves: the ability to predict the future based on the laws that govern motion. This idea of determinism, which seems inseparable from that of prediction, so forcefully presented by Laplace, can no longer symbolize the power of scientific thought. With nonlinear systems, we must humbly back off from this ambitious view and confess that deterministic systems might not allow long term predictions.

The term *chaos* is probably used because it describes very complicated behavior arising from very simple equations. Rather than admit to defeat in the face of such complicated behavior, scientists voluntarily adopted a mythical and ambiguous term to describe the complicated behavior hidden behind simple origins. From there, it is a small step to reintroduce the term *random* into deterministic systems.

The inadequacy of these terms becomes clear when we look at three dimensional dissipative dynamical systems, and when we drop the idea of quantitative predictability. It must then be admitted that the fluctuations of an aperiodic trajectory on an attractor do not conform to the idea of predictability and that it is possible to avoid this trap... By contrast, if one approaches this problem from a global level, that is, from a qualitative rather than a quantitative approach, one sees a well-defined structure — the architecture of the attractor that can be described. According to Aristotle, what can be described is atemporal. This is what provides the state portrait: a representation of the dynamics without any explicit occurrence of the time. In fact, scientists do not completely forgot prediction; what is predicted is no longer the quantitative temporal evolution of a single solution but rather the large-scale relative organization of an entire set of solutions. What is time-invariant, and can be described, is not a particular (periodic) solution but the relative organization of an entire set of solutions... One always falls back on the approach of Poincaré whose objective was to study the organization of an ensemble of trajectories in the state space: and it is there that the organized structure appears. Paraphrasing René Thom, one is able to explain but not predict... All our understanding extends to a global scale, at which we can describe the structure following deterministic ideas.

Is there a firm foundation for "chaos"? From the examples presented in this Epilogue, it appears that certain classes of dynamical behavior still escape our analyses... A statistical description is still in place because the global description, essentially based on topological arguments that exist for three-dimensional spaces but hardly for higher-dimensional spaces, do not allow us to construct an architecture of higher-dimensional attractors. "Law and order" cannot currently be applied to the behavior for which the current description is *beyond grasp*. To be specific, the systems of Lorenz (1984) and Rössler (1979) are sufficient to humble us. To use the term "chaos" seems in part to justify our inability to describe such states. Whatever these structures, we hope they are robust and hope for understanding in the future.

Rightly or wrongly, when we talk about chaos, one may keep in mind what follows.

(1) One cannot contradict the fundamental truths that Nature provides us in any scientific discipline;
(2) That scientists are not allowed to make hypotheses, except in those cases for which Physics does not make precise statements;
(3) That as a result one would be wrong, as several zealots recently have, to blame for desertion a physicist who outrageously worships chance.
(4) That Physics was made not to teach us about the great determinism of the Grand Book of Nature, but about its phenomena; there is thus no danger to be indulgent in regards to the probabilist approach, particularly when one does not argue against those phenomena;
(5) That if several scientists have believed, and still believe, that in place of ordered and deterministic phenomena, one needs to think of them as disordered and probabilistic, this idea is not at all heterodox because a large number of them resist a deterministic description and believe that only a probabilistic approach offers understanding;
(6) Following the preceding precautions, one can talk about *chaos* all he wants!

General Index

Author Index

CPSIA information can be obtained
at www.ICGtesting.com
Printed in the USA
BVHW012119090519
546820BV00010B/3/P

9 789811 201196